INSTRUCTOR'S SOLUTIONS MANUAL
to accompany

CALCULUS

Deborah Hughes-Hallett
Harvard University

Andrew M. Gleason
Harvard University

et al.

Prepared By: Duff G. Campbell
Kenny Ching
Eric Connally
Adrian Iovita
Alex Kasman
Stephen A. Mallozzi
Michael Mitzenmacher
Alice H. Wang

John Wiley & Sons, Inc.
New York • Chichester • Brisbane • Toronto • Singapore

ISBN 0-471-01039-1

Printed in the United States of America

10 9 8 7 6 5 4

CONTENTS

CHAPTER ONE

1.1 SOLUTIONS

1. **(I)** The first graph does not match any of the given stories. In this picture, the person keeps going away from home, but his speed decreases as time passes. So a story for this might be: *I started walking to school at a good pace, but since I stayed up all night studying calculus, I got more and more tired the farther I walked.*
   (II) This graph matches (b), the flat tire story. Note the long period of time during which the distance from home did not change (the horizontal part).
   (III) This one matches (c), in which the person started calmly but sped up.
   (IV) This one is (a), in which the person forgot her books and had to return home.

2.

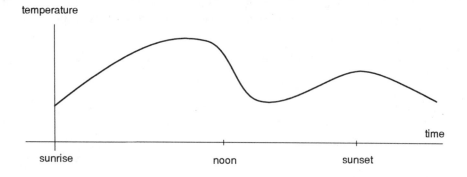

3.

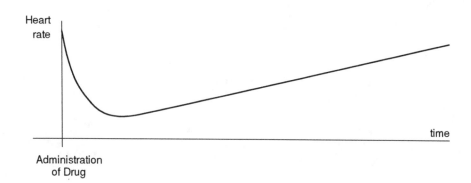

4.

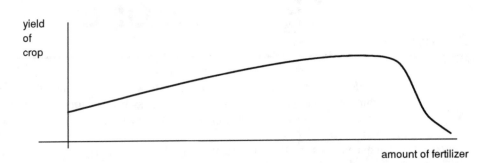

5. At first, as the number of workers increases, productivity also increases. As a result, the graph of the curve goes up initially. After a certain point the curve goes downward; in other words, as the number of workers increases beyond that point, productivity decreases. This might be due either to the inefficiency inherent in large organizations or simply to workers getting in each other's way as too many are crammed on the same line.

6.

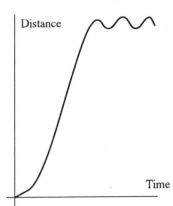

7.

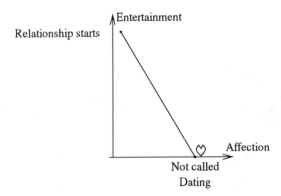

8. Generally manufacturers will produce more when prices are higher. Therefore, the first curve is a supply curve. Consumers consume less when prices are higher. Therefore, the second curve is a demand curve.

9. The price p_1 represents the maximum price any consumer would pay for the good. The quantity q_1 is the quantity of the good that could be given away if the item were free.

10. Domain: $-1 \leq x \leq 1.5$ Range: $-1.5 \leq y \leq 0$

11. (a) $-5 \leq p \leq 0$, $2 \leq p < 6$
    (b) $r \geq 0$
    (c) $0 \leq r < 2$ and $r > 5$

12. There is no real $g(y)$ when $y^2 - y = 0$ so $y = 0, 1$.
    Solving

    $$g(y) = \frac{1}{y^2 - y} = \frac{1}{2}$$

    gives

    $$2 = y^2 - y$$
    $$y^2 - y - 2 = 0$$
    $$(y - 2)(y + 1) = 0$$

    so $y = -1$ or 2.

13. The values $x \geq 2$ and $x \leq -2$ do not determine real values for f, because at those points either the denominator is zero or the square root is of a negative number.
    If $f(x) = 5$ then $\frac{1}{\sqrt{4-x^2}} = 5$, or $\sqrt{4 - x^2} = \frac{1}{5}$. Solving for x, we have

    $$x = \pm\sqrt{\frac{99}{25}} = \pm\frac{3}{5}\sqrt{11}.$$

14. Looking at the given data, it seems that Galileo's hypothesis was incorrect. The first table suggests that velocity is not a linear function of distance, since the increases in velocity for each foot of distance are themselves getting smaller. Moreover, the second table suggests that velocity is instead proportional to *time*, since for each second of time, the velocity increases by 32 ft/sec.

1.2 SOLUTIONS

1. Rewriting the equation as $y = -\frac{5}{2}x + 4$ shows that the slope is $-\frac{5}{2}$ and the vertical intercept is 4.

2. Slope $= \frac{6-0}{2-(-1)} = 2$ so the equation is $y - 6 = 2(x - 2)$ or $y = 2x + 2$.

3. $y - c = m(x - a)$

4. $y = 5x - 3$. Since the slope of of the line is 5, we want a line with slope $-\frac{1}{5}$ passing through the point $(2, 1)$. The equation is $(y - 1) = -\frac{1}{5}(x - 2)$, or $y = -\frac{1}{5}x + \frac{7}{5}$.

5. The line $y + 4x = 7$ has slope -4. Therefore the parallel line has slope -4 and equation $y - 5 = -4(x - 1)$ or $y = -4x + 9$. The perpendicular line has slope $\frac{-1}{(-4)} = \frac{1}{4}$ and equation $y - 5 = \frac{1}{4}(x - 1)$ or $y = 0.25x + 4.75$.

6. The intercepts appear to be $(0,3)$ and $(7.5,0)$, giving

$$\text{Slope} = \frac{-3}{7.5} = -\frac{6}{15} = -\frac{2}{5}.$$

    The y-intercept is at $(0,3)$, so

$$y = -\frac{2}{5}x + 3$$

    is a possible equation for the line (answers may vary).

7. (a) (V)
    (b) (IV)
    (c) (I)
    (d) (VI)
    (e) (II)
    (f) (III)

8. (a) is (V), because slope is negative, y intercept is 0
    (b) is (VI), because slope and y intercept both positive
    (c) is (I), because slope is negative, y intercept is positive
    (d) is (IV), because slope is positive, y intercept is negative
    (e) is (III), because slope and y intercept are both negative
    (f) is (II), because slope is positive, y intercept is 0

9. (a) Finding slope (-50) and intercept gives $q = 1000 - 50p$.
    (b) Solving for p gives $p = 20 - 0.02q$.

10. Given that the equation is linear, choose any two points, e.g. $(5.2, 27.8)$ and $(5.3, 29.2)$. Then

$$\text{Slope} = \frac{29.2 - 27.8}{5.3 - 5.2} = \frac{1.4}{0.1} = 14$$

    Using the point-slope formula, with the point $(5.2, 27.8)$, we get the equation

$$y - 27.8 = 14(x - 5.2)$$

    which is equivalent to

$$y = 14x - 45.$$

11. For the line $3x + 4y = -12$, the x-intercept is $(-4, 0)$ and the y-intercept is $(0, -3)$. The distance between these two points is

$$d = \sqrt{(-4 - 0)^2 + (0 - (-3))^2} = \sqrt{16 + 9} = \sqrt{25} = 5.$$

12. (a) The first company's price for a day's rental with m miles on it is $C_1(m) = 40 + 0.15m$. Its competitor's price for a day's rental with m miles on it is $C_2(m) = 50 + 0.10m$.

    (b)

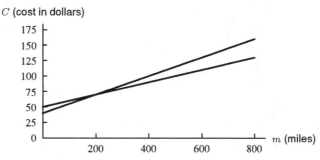

    (c) If you are going more than 200 miles, the competitor is cheaper. If you are going less than 200 miles, the first company is cheaper.

13. (a) Given the two points $(0, 32)$ and $(100, 212)$, and assuming the graph is a line,

$$\text{Slope} = \frac{212 - 32}{100} = \frac{180}{100} = 1.8.$$

    (b) The F-intercept is $(0, 32)$, so

$$^\circ\text{Fahrenheit} = 1.8(^\circ\text{Celsius}) + 32.$$

    (c) If the temperature is 20°Celsius, then

$$^\circ\text{Fahrenheit} = 1.8(20) + 32 = 68^\circ\text{Fahrenheit}.$$

    (d) If $^\circ$Fahrenheit $= {}^\circ$Celsius then

$$^\circ\text{Celsius} = 1.8^\circ\text{Celsius} + 32$$
$$-32 = 0.8^\circ\text{Celsius}$$
$$^\circ\text{Celsius} = -40^\circ = {}^\circ\text{Fahrenheit}$$

14. (a) The variable costs for x acres are $\$200x$, or $0.2x$ thousand dollars. The total cost, C (again in thousands of dollars), of planting x acres is:

$$C = f(x) = 10 + 0.2x.$$

This is a linear function. See Figure 1.1. Since $C = f(x)$ increases with x, f is an increasing function of x. Look at the values of C shown in the table; you will see that each time x increases by 1, C increases by 0.2. Because C increases at a constant rate as x increases, the graph of C against x is a line.

(b)

Cost of Planting Seed

x	C
0	10
2	10.4
3	10.6
4	10.8
5	11
6	11.2

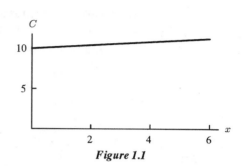

Figure 1.1

(c)   What does the 0.2 tell us? It reflects the variable costs, telling us that for every additional acre planted, the costs go up by 0.2 thousand dollars. The rate at which the cost is increasing is 0.2 thousand dollars per acre. Thus the variable costs are represented by the slope of the line $f(x) = 10 + 0.2x$.

What does the 10 tell us? For $C = f(x) = 10 + 0.2x$, the intercept on the vertical axis is 10 because $C = f(0) = 10 + 0.2(0) = 10$. Since 10 is the value of C when $x = 0$, we recognize it as the initial outlay for equipment, or the fixed cost.

15.

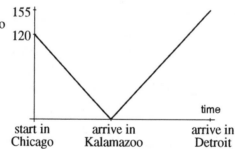

16.   (a)   Let

$$I = \text{number of Indian peppers}$$
$$M = \text{number of Mexican peppers}.$$

Then (from the given information)

$$1{,}200I + 900M = 14{,}000$$

is the Scoville constraint.

(b)   Solving for I yields

$$I = \frac{14{,}000 - 900M}{1{,}200}$$
$$= \frac{35}{3} - \frac{3}{4}M.$$

17. (a) $k = p_1 s + p_2 l$ where $s = $ # of liters of soda and $l = $ # of liters of oil.

(b) If $s = 0$, then $l = \frac{k}{p_2}$. Similarly, if $l = 0$, then $s = \frac{k}{p_1}$. These two points give you enough information to draw a line containing the points which satisfy the equation.

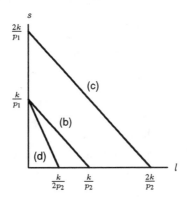

(c) If the budget is doubled, we have the constraint: $2k = p_1 s + p_2 l$. We find the intercepts as before. If $s = 0$, then $l = \frac{2k}{p_2}$; if $l = 0$, then $s = \frac{2k}{p_1}$. The intercepts are both twice what they were before.

(d) If the price of oil doubles, our constraint is $k = p_1 s + 2p_2 l$. Then, calculating the intercepts gives that the s intercept remains the same, but the l intercept gets cut in half. $s = 0$ means $l = \frac{k}{2p_2} = \frac{1}{2}\frac{k}{p_2}$. Therefore the maximum amount of oil you can buy is half of what it was previously.

18. (a) Since the population center is moving west at 50 miles per 10 years, or 5 miles per year, if we start in 1990, when the center is in De Soto, its distance d west of Steelville t years after 1990 is given by

$$d = 5t.$$

(b) It moved 700 miles over the 200 years from 1790 to 1990, so its average speed was $\frac{700}{200} = 3.5$ miles/year, somewhat slower than its present rate.

(c) According to the function in (a), after 300 years the population center would be 1500 miles west of Steelville, in Baja, California, which seems rather unlikely.

19. Given $l - l_0 = al_0(t - t_0)$ with l_0, t_0 and a all constant,

(a) We have $l = al_0(t - t_0) + l_0 = al_0 t - al_0 t_0 + l_0$, which is a linear function of t with slope al_0 and y-intercept at $(0, -al_0 t_0 + l_0)$.

(b) If $l_0 = 100, t_0 = 60°F$ and $a = 10^{-5}$, then

$$l = 10^{-5}(100)t - 10^{-5}(100)(60) + 100 = 10^{-3}t + 99.94$$
$$= 0.001t + 99.94$$

(c) If the slope is positive, (as in (b)), then as the temperature rises, the length of the metal increases: it expands. If the slope were negative, then the metal would contract as the temperature rises.

20. (a) $R = k(350 - H)$, where k is a positive constant.

    If H is greater than $350°$, the rate is negative, indicating that a very hot yam will cool down toward the temperature of the oven.

    (b) Letting H_0 equal the initial temperature of the yam, the graph of R against H looks like:

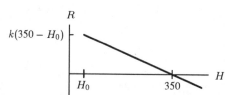

    Note that by the temperature of the yam, we mean the average temperature of the yam, since the yam's surface will be hotter than its center.

21. (a) $R = k(20 - H)$, where k is a positive constant. For $H > 20$, R is negative, indicating that the coffee is cooling.

    (b)

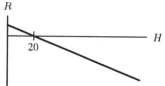

22. (a) Assembling the given information, we have

$$F = ma = F_g - F_r = (mg - kv)$$

where k is the constant that relates velocity to air resistance (which depends on the shape of the object).

    (b) Solving the above equation for a, we have

$$a = g - \frac{k}{m}v$$

    (c)

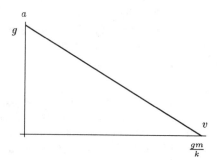

1.3 SOLUTIONS

1.

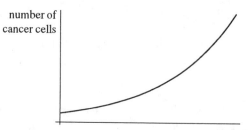

2.

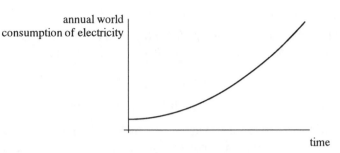

3.

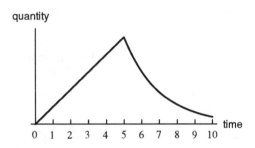

4.

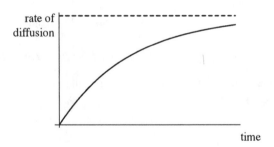

5. (a) This is the graph of a linear function, which increases at a constant rate, and thus corresponds to $k(t)$, which increases by 0.3 over each interval of 1.
    (b) This graph is concave down, so it corresponds to a function whose increases are getting smaller, as is the case with $h(t)$, whose increases are 10, 9, 8, 7, and 6.
    (c) This graph is concave up, so it corresponds to a function whose increases are getting bigger, as is the case with $g(t)$, whose increases are 1, 2, 3, 4, and 5.

6. (a) This is a linear function, corresponding to $g(x)$, whose rate of decrease is constant.
    (b) This graph is concave down, so it corresponds to a function whose rate of decrease is increasing, like $h(x)$.
    (c) This graph is concave up, so it corresponds to a function whose rate of decrease is decreasing, like $f(x)$.

7. $f(s) = 2(1.1)^s$, $g(s) = 3(1.05)^s$, and $h(s) = (1.03)^s$.

8. The values of $f(x)$ given seem to increase by a factor of 1.4 for each increase of 1 in x, so we expect an exponential function with base 1.4. To assure that $f(0) = 4.30$, we multiply by the constant, obtaining

    $$f(x) = 4.30(1.4)^x.$$

9. Each increase of 1 in t seems to cause $g(t)$ to decrease by a factor of 0.8, so we expect an exponential function with base 0.8. To make our solution agree with the data at $t = 0$, we need a coefficient of 5.50, so our completed equation is

    $$g(t) = 5.50(0.8)^t.$$

10. We look for an equation of the form $y = y_0 a^x$ since the graph looks exponential. The points $(0, 3)$ and $(2, 12)$ are on the graph, so

    $$3 = y_0 a^0 = y_0$$

    and

    $$12 = y_0 \cdot a^2 = 3 \cdot a^2, \quad \text{giving} \quad a = \pm 2.$$

    Since $a > 0$, our equation is $y = 3(2^x)$.

11. We look for an equation of the form $y = y_0 a^x$ since the graph looks exponential. The points $(1, 6)$ and $(2, 18)$ are on the graph, so

    $$6 = y_0 a^1 \quad \text{and} \quad 18 = y_0 a^2$$

    Therefore $\dfrac{18}{6} = \dfrac{y_0 a^2}{y_0 a} = a$, and so $6 = y_0 a = y_0 \cdot 3$, so $y_0 = 2$. Hence $y = 2(3^x)$.

12. We look for an equation of the form $y = y_0 a^x$ since the graph looks exponential. The points $(-1, 8)$ and $(1, 2)$ are on the graph, so

    $$8 = y_0 a^{-1} \quad \text{and} \quad 2 = y_0 a^1$$

    Therefore $\dfrac{8}{2} = \dfrac{y_0 a^{-1}}{y_0 a} = \dfrac{1}{a^2}$, giving $a = \frac{1}{2}$, and so $2 = y_0 a^1 = y_0 \cdot \frac{1}{2}$, so $y_0 = 4$.
    Hence $y = 4\left(\frac{1}{2}\right)^x = 4(2^{-x})$.

13. The difference, D, between the horizontal asymptote and the graph appears to decrease exponentially, so we look for an equation of the form

    $$D = D_0 a^x$$

    where $D_0 = 4 =$ difference when $x = 0$. Since $D = 4 - y$, we have

    $$4 - y = 4a^x \quad \text{or} \quad y = 4 - 4a^x = 4(1 - a^x)$$

    The point $(1, 2)$ is on the graph, so $2 = 4(1 - a^1)$, giving $a = \frac{1}{2}$.
    Therefore $y = 4(1 - (\frac{1}{2})^x) = 4(1 - 2^{-x})$.

14. (a) The formula is $Q = Q_0 \left(\frac{1}{2}\right)^{(t/1620)}$.
     (b) The percentage left after 500 years is

$$\frac{Q_0\left(\frac{1}{2}\right)^{(500/1620)}}{Q_0}.$$

The Q_0's cancel giving

$$\left(\frac{1}{2}\right)^{(500/1620)} \approx 0.807,$$

so 80.7% is left.

15. Let Q_0 be the initial quantity absorbed in 1960. Then the quantity, Q of strontium-90 left after t years is

$$Q = Q_0 \left(\frac{1}{2}\right)^{(t/29)}.$$

Since $1990 - 1960 = 30$ years elapsed, the fraction of strontium-90 left in 1990 is

$$Q = \frac{Q_0 \left(\frac{1}{2}\right)^{(30/29)}}{Q_0} = \left(\frac{1}{2}\right)^{(30/29)} \approx .488 = 48.8\%.$$

16. If the pressure at sea level is P_0, the pressure P at altitude h is given by

$$P = P_0 \left(1 - \frac{0.4}{100}\right)^{\frac{h}{30}},$$

since we want the pressure to be multiplied by a factor of $(1 - \frac{0.4}{100}) = 0.996$ for each 100 feet we go up to make it decrease by 0.4% over that interval. At Mexico City $h = 2237$, so the pressure is

$$P = P_0(0.996)^{\frac{7340}{100}} \approx 0.745 P_0.$$

So the pressure is reduced from P_0 to approximately $0.745 P_0$, a decrease of 25.5%.

17. The doubling time is approximately 2.3. For example, the population is 20,000 at time 3.7, 40,000 at time 6, and 80,000 at time 8.3.

18. The doubling time t depends only on the growth rate; it is the solution to

$$2 = (1.02)^t,$$

since 1.02^t represents the factor by which the population has grown after time t. Trial and error shows that $(1.02)^{35} \approx 1.9999$ and $(1.02)^{36} \approx 2.0399$, so that the doubling time is about 35 years.

19. The quantity Q of the substance at time t can be represented by an equation of the form

$$Q = Q_0 a^t.$$

We are given $Q = 0.70Q_0$ when $t = 10$, so we have

$$0.70Q_0 = Q_0 a^{10}$$
$$0.70 = a^{10}$$
$$a = (0.70)^{\frac{1}{10}}$$
$$a \approx 0.965.$$

Thus $Q = Q_0(0.70)^{\frac{1}{10}t}$, or $Q \approx Q_0(0.965)^t$.

In 50 years, $Q \approx Q_0(0.965)^{50} \approx 0.168Q - 0$, so about 17% of the original quantity is left. To find the half life, we want to find t such that

$$0.5Q_0 = Q_0(0.965)^t$$
$$0.5 = (0.965)^t.$$

Trying different values for t, we find

$$(0.965)^{19} \approx 0.51$$
$$(0.965)^{20} \approx 0.49,$$

so the half life is about 19.5 years.
20% will be left if

$$0.20Q_0 = Q_0(0.965)^t$$
$$0.20 = (0.965)^t.$$

Again, trying different values for t we find

$$(0.965)^{45.2} \approx 0.20,$$

so 20% will be left after 45.2 years.

We could solve for when there is 10% remaining as above. Instead, however, we could note that since 10% is half of 20%, it should take about 19.5 years for 20% to decay to 10%. Thus the time to decay to 10% of the original amount is about $45.2 + 19.5 = 64.7$ years.

20. (a) The slope is given by
$$m = \frac{P - P_1}{t - t_1} = \frac{100 - 50}{20 - 0} = \frac{50}{20} = 2.5,$$

so the equation is

$$P - P_1 = m(t - t_1)$$
$$P - 50 = 2.5(t - 0)$$
$$P = 2.5t + 50.$$

(b)   Given $P = P_0 a^t$ and $P = 50$ when $t = 0$,

$$50 = P_0 a^0 \text{, so } P_0 = 50.$$

Then, using $P = 100$ when $t = 20$

$$100 = 50a^{20}$$
$$2 = a^{20}$$
$$a = (2)^{\frac{1}{20}} = 1.035.$$

And so we have

$$P = 50(1.035)^t.$$

The completed table is then

TABLE 1.1   *The cost of a home*

	a) Linear Growth	b) Exponential Growth
t	Price in 1000's of $	Price in 1000's of $
0	50	50
10	75	70.71
20	100	100
30	125	141.42
40	150	200

(c)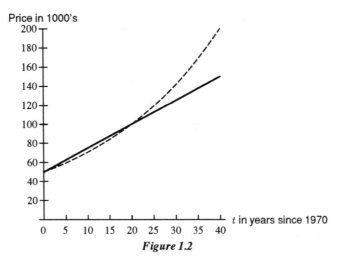

Figure 1.2

21. (a) Compounding 33% interest 12 times should be the same as compounding the yearly rate R once, so we get

$$\left(1 + \frac{R}{100}\right)^1 = \left(1 + \frac{33}{100}\right)^{12}$$

Solving for R, we obtain $R = 2963.51$. The yearly rate, R, is 2963.51%.

(b) The monthly rate r satisfies

$$\left(1 + \frac{4.6}{100}\right)^1 = \left(1 + \frac{r}{100}\right)^{12}$$

$$1.046^{\frac{1}{12}} = 1 + \frac{r}{100}$$

$$r = 100(1.046^{\frac{1}{12}} - 1) = 0.3755.$$

The monthly rate is 0.3755%.

22. (a) Its cost in 1989 would be $1000 + \frac{1290}{100} \cdot 1000 = 13900$ cruzados.

(b) The monthly inflation rate r solves

$$\left(1 + \frac{1290}{100}\right)^1 = \left(1 + \frac{r}{100}\right)^{12},$$

since we compound the monthly inflation 12 times to get the yearly inflation. Solving for r, we get $r = 24.52\%$. Notice that this is much different than $\frac{1290}{12} = 107.5\%$.

1.4 SOLUTIONS

1. (a) $8^{2/3} = (8^{1/3})^2 = 2^2 = 4$.

(b) $9^{-(3/2)} = (9^{1/2})^{(-3)} = 3^{(-3)} = \frac{1}{3^3} = \frac{1}{27}$.

2. $y = x^{2/3}$ is larger as $x \to \infty$.

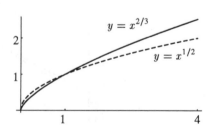

3. $y = x^4$ goes to positive infinity in both cases.

4. $y = -x^7$ goes to negative infinity as $x \to \infty$, and goes to positive infinity as $x \to -\infty$.

5.

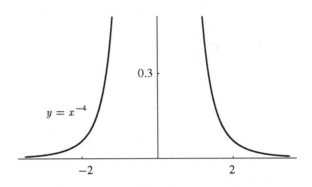

$$y = x^{-4}$$

6.   The odd powers are increasing everywhere, whereas the even powers are U-shaped. For $x > 0$, the highest powers are largest for big x, and the smallest are largest for x near 0. This is as expected from the graphs in the text.

(a)

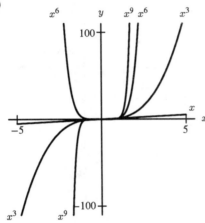

(b)

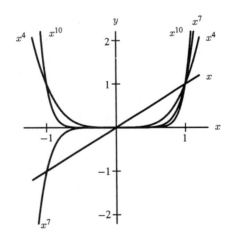

7. When $x = \frac{1}{2} = 0.5$,

$$\left(\frac{1}{2}\right)^{(1/2)} \approx 0.71, \quad \text{and} \quad \left(\frac{1}{2}\right)^{(1/3)} \approx 0.79,$$

so

$$\left(\frac{1}{2}\right) < \left(\frac{1}{2}\right)^{(1/2)} < \left(\frac{1}{2}\right)^{(1/3)}.$$

Thus at $x = \frac{1}{2}$, we have $x < x^{(1/2)} < x^{(1/3)}$.

8. (a) $-0.00001 \le y \le 0.00001$ (b) $-10^7 < y < 10^7$

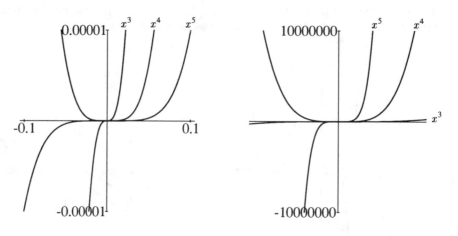

9.

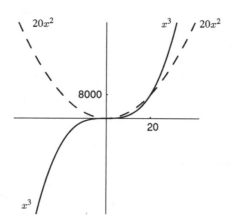

$f(x) = x^3$ is larger as $x \to \infty$.

10. As $x \to \infty$, $f(x) = x^5$ has the largest positive values. As $x \to -\infty$, $g(x) = -x^3$ has the largest positive values.

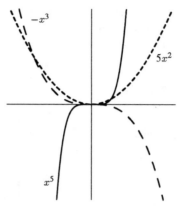

11. Since $2^{9.935} \approx 978.9$ and $9.935^3 \approx 980.6$, whereas $2^{9.94} \approx 982.3$ and $9.94^3 \approx 982.1$, we know that $9.935 < x < 9.94$. Thus $x \approx 9.94$.

12.

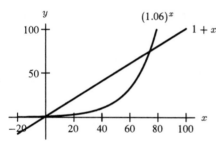
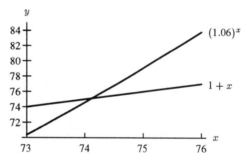

    Looking at the large-scale graph on the left, we see that the functions intersect at $x = 0$ and near $x = 75$, at about 74.1, as we see by zooming in with the graph on the right.

13. They are clearly equal at $x = 4$, and for all $x > 4$ the exponential function is greater. For very negative values of x, the power function is quite large, while the exponential is going to zero. The more difficult region is $-2 < x < 4$. For this region, we take a closer look at the two functions. See Figure 1.3. In this close up, it is easier to see that the exponential is greater between about -0.7 and 2. As we saw above, the exponential is also greater for $x > 4$.

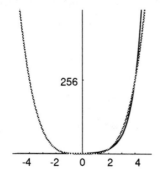
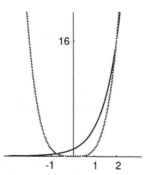

Figure 1.3: The close-up

14. 3^x is always positive while x^3 is negative for $x < 0$, so we know that $3^x > x^3$ for $x < 0$. Looking at the large-scale graph, we see that for $x > 4$, 3^x is also clearly bigger than x^3. We zoom in on the interval $(0, 4)$ to see the behavior there, shown by the graph on the right. We see that the graphs approach very close to each other near $x = 3$ (where the values are equal), but elsewhere, $3^x > x^3$. To figure out what is going on near $x = 3$, we zoom in again, and notice that on the interval from about 2.5 to 3, $x^3 > 3^x$. Thus $3^x > x^3$ if $x < 2.5$ (approximately) or $x > 3$.

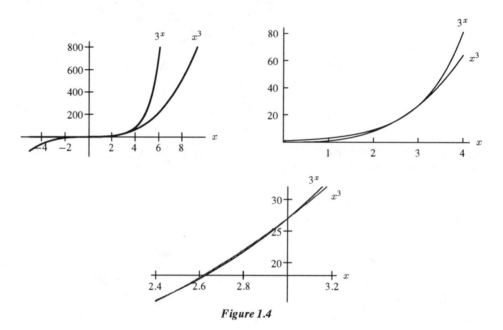

Figure 1.4

Alternatively, graph $f(x) = 3^x - x^3$ for $0 \le x \le 3.5$ and $-2 \le y \le 4$. This shows $3^x > x^3$ for $x > 3$ and $x < 2.48$.

15.   Let $D(v)$ be the stopping distance required by an Alpha Romeo as a function of its velocity. The assumption that stopping distance is proportional to the square of velocity is equivalent to the equation

$$D(v) = kv^2$$

where k is a constant of proportionality. To determine the value of k, we use the fact that $D(70) = 177$.

$$D(70) = k(70)^2 = 177.$$

Thus,

$$k = \frac{177}{70^2} \approx 0.361$$

It follows that

$$D(56) = \left(\frac{177}{70^2}\right)(56)^2 = \frac{177}{4} = 44.25 \text{ ft}$$

and

$$D(224) = \left(\frac{177}{70^2}\right)(224)^2 = 708 \text{ ft}.$$

Thus at half the speed it requires one fourth the distance, whereas at twice the speed it requires four times the distance, as we would expect from the equation. (We could in fact have figured it out that way, without solving for k explicitly.)

16. (a)   Since the rate R varies directly with the fourth power of the radius r, we have the formula

$$R = kr^4$$

where k is a constant.

(b)   Given $R = 400$ for $r = 3$, we can determine the constant k.

$$400 = k(3)^4$$
$$400 = k(81)$$
$$k = \frac{400}{81} \approx 4.938.$$

So the formula is

$$R = 4.938r^4$$

(c)   Evaluating the formula above at $r = 5$ yields

$$R = 4.928(5)^4 = 3086.42\frac{\text{cm}^3}{\text{sec}}.$$

17. $h(t)$ cannot be of the form at^2 or bt^3 since $h(0.0) = 2.04$. Therefore $h(t)$ must be the exponential, and we see that the ratio of successive values of h is approximately 1.5. Therefore $h(t) = 2.04(1.05)^t$. If $g(t) = at^2$, then $a = 3$ since $g(1.0) = 3.00$. However, $g(2.0) = 24.00 \neq 3 \cdot 2^2$. Therefore $g(t) = bt^3$, and using $g(1.0) = 3.00$, we obtain $g(t) = 3t^3$. Thus $f(t) = at^2$, and since $f(2.0) = 4.40$, we have $f(t) = 1.1t^2$.

18.   Looking at g, we see that the ratio of the values is:

$$\frac{3.12}{3.74} \approx \frac{3.74}{4.49} \approx \frac{4.49}{5.39} \approx \frac{5.39}{6.47} \approx \frac{6.47}{7.76} \approx 0.83.$$

Thus g is an exponential function, and so f and k are the power functions. Each is of the form ax^2 or ax^3, and since $k(1.0) = 9.01$ we see that for k, the constant coefficient is 9.01. Trial and error gives

$$k(x) = 9.01x^2,$$

since $k(2.2) = 43.61 \approx 9.01(4.84) = 9.01(2.2)^2$. Thus $f(x) = ax^3$ and we find a by noting that $f(9) = 7.29 = a(9^3)$ so

$$a = \frac{7.29}{9^3} = 0.01$$

and $f(x) = 0.01x^3$.

19.   (a)   The differences in production, p, over the 5-year intervals are 0.55, 0.59, 0.56, and 0.59. That these differences are almost constant suggests that a linear function will fit the data well. The average of the increases in p over an interval is 0.5725, and the interval is 5 years long. Thus we try a slope of

$$m = \frac{0.5725}{5} = 0.1145.$$

Using this and the point $(0, 5.35)$ with the point-slope formula, we get

$$p - p_1 = m(t - t_1)$$
$$p - 5.35 = 0.1145(t - 0)$$
$$p = 0.1145t + 5.35$$

where t is the number of years since 1970.

If we try to fit an exponential to the production data, we calculate the ratios of successive terms, giving 1.10, 1.100, 1.086, and 1.084. The fact that these ratios are not constant suggests that an exponential will not fit well.

For the population data, if we try to fit a linear function, we calculate the increases in population P over the 5-year intervals, giving 3.7, 4, 4.3, and 4.5. Since these differences vary very widely, a linear function will not fit the population data.

To fit an exponential to the population data, we look at the ratios of successive terms, which are 1.070, 1.070, 1.071, 1.069. Since these values are pretty close, the population appears to be growing exponentially by a factor of about 1.07 every 5 years. Thus we expect to be able to fit the formula

$$P = P_0 a^t.$$

We will let $P_0 = 53.2$, and then use the fact that $P = 56.9$ when $t = 5$ to solve for a:

$$56.9 = 53.2a^5.$$

Solving gives

$$a^5 = \frac{56.9}{53.2} = 1.070 \quad \text{so} \quad a = (1.070)^{1/5} = 1.0136.$$

Thus, if t is the number of years since 1970,

$$P = 53.2(1.0136)^t.$$

(b)   Since the region had neither surpluses nor shortages in 1970 (it was exactly self-supporting), we can assume that the amount of grain needed per person per year is given by

$$\frac{5.35 \text{ million tons}}{53.2 \text{ million people}} = 0.1005639 \text{ tons/person.}$$

From 1975 to 1990, the ratios were

$$1975: \frac{5.90}{56.9} = 0.1036907 \text{ tons/person}$$

$$1980: \frac{6.49}{60.9} = 0.1065681 \text{ tons/person}$$

$$1985: \frac{7.05}{65.2} = 0.1081288 \text{ tons/person}$$

$$1990: \frac{7.64}{69.7} = 0.1096126 \text{ tons/person}$$

so the region was not only self-supporting, it had an increasing surplus.

(c) If the population continues to grow like an exponential function while production only grows like a linear function, eventually the population will get too big for the production and there will be shortages.

20.
(a)
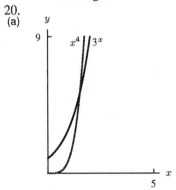
(b)
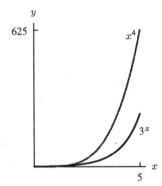
(c)
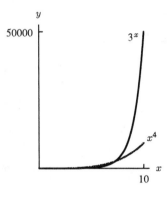

Figure 1.5

1.5 SOLUTIONS

1. $f^{-1}(75)$ is the length of the column of mercury in the thermometer when the temperature is 75°F.

2. f is an increasing function since the amount of fuel used increases as flight time increases. Therefore f is invertible.

3. Not invertible. Given a certain number of customers, say $f(t) = 1500$, there could be many times, t, during the day at which that many people were in the store. So we don't know which time instant is the right one.

4. Invertible. Since at 4°C, 1 liter of water weighs 1 kilogram, x liters of water weigh x kilograms. So $f(x) = x$ and therefore, $f^{-1}(x) = x$.

5. Not invertible, since it costs the same to mail a 50-gram letter as it does to mail a 51-gram letter.

6. Probably not invertible. Since your calculus class probably has less than 363 students, there will be at least two days in the year, say a and b, with $f(a) = f(b) = 0$. Hence we don't know what to choose for $f^{-1}(0)$.

7.

x	3	-7	19	4	178	2	1
$f^{-1}(x)$	1	2	3	4	5	6	7

The domain of f^{-1} is the set consisting of the integers $\{3, -7, 19, 4, 178, 2, 1\}$.

8. Graphing $f(x)$ (on a graphing calculator), we get the following:

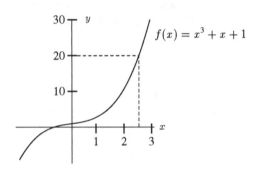

From the graph we can get an approximate value for $f^{-1}(20) = 2.5$.

9.

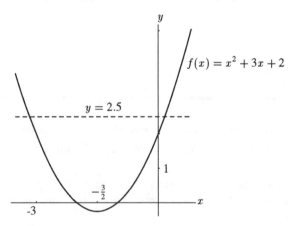

Since a horizontal line cuts the graph of $f(x) = x^2 + 3x + 2$ two times, f is not invertible.

10.

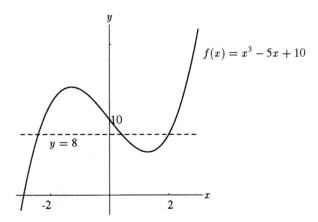

Since a horizontal line cuts the graph of $f(x) = x^3 - 5x + 10$ three times, f is not invertible.

11.

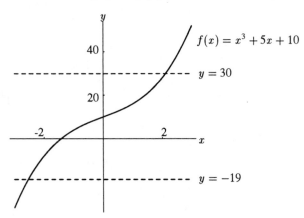

Since any horizontal line cuts the graph once, f is invertible.

12. (a) The function f tells us C in terms of q. To get its inverse, we want q in terms of C, which we find by solving for q:

$$C = 100 + 2q,$$
$$C - 100 = 2q,$$
$$q = \frac{C - 100}{2} = f^{-1}(C).$$

(b) The inverse function tells us the number of articles that can be produced for a given cost.

13. (a) For each 2.2 pounds of weight the object has, it has 1 kilogram of mass, so the conversion formula is

$$k = f(p) = \frac{1}{2.2}p.$$

(b)   The inverse function is

$$p = 2.2k,$$

and it gives the weight of an object in pounds as a function of its mass in kilograms.

14.   Since f is increasing, we have $f(x_2) > f(x_1)$ for all $x_2 > x_1$. Therefore, the inverse function must also be increasing, as if $f(x_2) > f(x_1)$ (in the domain of f^{-1}), we have $x_2 > x_1$ (in the range of f^{-1}).

15.   One cannot be sure of the concavity of the inverse unless one also knows whether f is increasing or decreasing.

For example, $y = x^2$ is increasing on the interval $x \geq 0$. It is concave up but its inverse, $y = \sqrt{x}$, is concave down. However, $y = \frac{1}{x}$ is decreasing on the interval $x > 0$, and it is its own inverse, so both $y = \frac{1}{x}$ and its inverse are concave up.

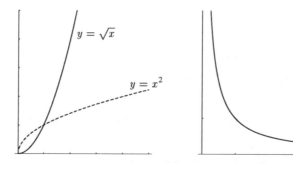

16.   (a)   Yes, f is invertible, since f is increasing.

(b) $f^{-1}(400)$ is the year in which 400 million motor vehicles were registered in the world. From the picture, we see that $f^{-1}(400)$ is around 1979.

(c)   Since the graph of f^{-1} is the reflection of the graph of f over the line $y = x$, we get Figure 1.6.

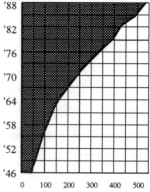

Figure 1.6: The Graph of f^{-1}

1.6 SOLUTIONS

1.

TABLE 1.2

x	1	2	3	4	5	6	7	8	9	10
$f(x)$	0	0.30	0.48	0.60	0.70	0.78	0.85	0.90	0.95	1.00
$g(x)$	1.00	1.41	1.73	2.00	2.24	2.45	2.65	2.83	3.00	3.16

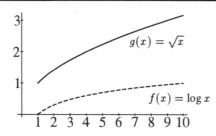

2. $y = \log 10^x$ is a straight line with slope 1, passing through the origin. This is so because $y = \log 10^x = x \log 10 = x \cdot 1 = x$. So, this function is really $y = x$ in disguise.

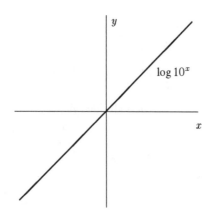

3. Since $10^{\log x} = x$ for $x > 0$, this equation is $y = x$ for $x > 0$. Its graph is therefore a straight line, with slope 1, to the right of the origin.

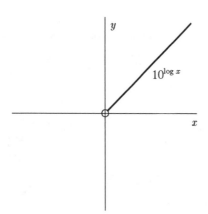

4. Taking logs of both sides yields $t \log 5 = \log 7$, so $t = \dfrac{\log 7}{\log 5} \approx 1.209$.

5. $t = \dfrac{\log 2}{\log 1.02} \approx 35.003$.

6. Collecting similar factors yields $\left(\frac{3}{2}\right)^t = \frac{5}{7}$, so

$$t = \frac{\log\left(\frac{5}{7}\right)}{\log\left(\frac{3}{2}\right)} \approx -0.830.$$

7. Collecting similar terms yields

$$\left(\frac{a}{b}\right)^t = \frac{Q_0}{P_0}.$$

Hence

$$t = \frac{\log\left(\frac{Q_0}{P_0}\right)}{\log\left(\frac{a}{b}\right)}.$$

8. $t = \dfrac{\log a}{\log b}$.

9. $t = \dfrac{\log\left(\frac{P}{P_0}\right)}{\log a} = \dfrac{\log P - \log P_0}{\log a}$.

10. Taking logs of both sides yields

$$nt = \frac{\log\left(\frac{Q}{Q_0}\right)}{\log a}.$$

Hence

$$t = \frac{\log\left(\frac{Q}{Q_0}\right)}{n \log a} = \frac{\log Q - \log Q_0}{n \log a}.$$

11. Collecting similar factors yields $\left(\frac{1.04}{1.03}\right)^t = \frac{12.01}{5.02}$. Solving for t yields

$$t = \frac{\log\left(\frac{12.01}{5.02}\right)}{\log\left(\frac{1.04}{1.03}\right)} \approx 90.283.$$

12. $\log A^2 + \log B - \log A - \log B^2 = 2\log A + \log B - \log A - 2\log B$
$$= \log A - \log B$$
$$= \log \frac{A}{B}.$$

13. $\log(10^{x+7}) = x + 7$.

14. $10^{\log A^2} = A^2$.

15. $10^{2\log Q} = 10^{\log Q^2} = Q^2$.

16. $10^{-\log P} = \dfrac{1}{10^{\log P}} = \dfrac{1}{P}$.   Alternatively, $10^{-\log P} = 10^{\log \frac{1}{P}} = \dfrac{1}{P}$.

17. $10^{-(\log B)/2} = \left[10^{\log B}\right]^{-\frac{1}{2}} = \dfrac{1}{\sqrt{B}}$.

18. $\dfrac{\log A^2 - \log A}{\log B - \frac{1}{2}\log B} = \dfrac{2\log A - \log A}{\frac{1}{2}\log B} = \dfrac{\log A}{\log \sqrt{B}}$.

19. $2\log \alpha - 3\log B - \dfrac{\log \alpha}{2} = \dfrac{3}{2}\log \alpha - 3\log B = 3\log \dfrac{\sqrt{\alpha}}{B} = \dfrac{3}{2}\log \dfrac{\alpha}{B^2}$.

20. We know that the y-intercept of the line is at $(0,1)$, so we need one other point to determine the equation of the line. We observe that it intersects the graph of $f(x) = 10^x$ at the point $x = \log 2$. The y-coordinate of this point is then

$$y = 10^x = 10^{\log 2} = 2,$$

so $(\log 2, 2)$ is the point of intersection. We can now find the slope of the line:

$$m = \frac{2-1}{\log 2 - 0} = \frac{1}{\log 2}.$$

Plugging this into the point-slope formula for a line, we have

$$y - y_1 = m(x - x_1)$$
$$y - 1 = \frac{1}{\log 2}(x - 0)$$
$$y = \frac{1}{\log 2}x + 1 \approx 3.3219x + 1.$$

21. If $p(t) = (1.04)^t$, then, for p^{-1} the inverse of p, we should have

$$(1.04)^{p^{-1}(t)} = t,$$
$$p^{-1}(t)\log(1.04) = \log t,$$
$$p^{-1}(t) = \frac{\log t}{\log(1.04)} \approx 58.708\log t.$$

22. Since the factor by which the prices have increased after time t is given by $(1.05)^t$, the time after which the prices have doubled solves

$$2 = (1.05)^t$$
$$\log 2 = \log(1.05^t) = t\log(1.05)$$
$$t = \frac{\log 2}{\log 1.05} \approx 14.21 \text{ years.}$$

23. Let t = number of years since 1980. Then the number of vehicles, V, in millions, at time t is given by

$$V = 170(1.04)^t$$

and the number of people, P, in millions, at time t is given by

$$P = 227(1.01)^t.$$

There is an average of one vehicle per person when $\dfrac{V}{P} = 1$, or $V = P$. Thus, we must solve for t the equation:

$$170(1.04)^t = 227(1.01)^t,$$

which implies

$$\left(\frac{1.04}{1.01}\right)^t = \frac{(1.04)^t}{(1.01)^t} = \frac{227}{170}$$

Taking logs on both sides,

$$t \log \frac{1.04}{1.01} = \log \frac{227}{170}.$$

Therefore,

$$t = \frac{\log\left(\frac{227}{170}\right)}{\log\left(\frac{1.04}{1.01}\right)} \approx 9.9 \text{ years.}$$

So there was, according to this model, about one vehicle per person in 1990.

24. The population has increased by a factor of $\frac{56000000}{40000000} = 1.4$ in 10 years. Thus we have the formula

$$P = 40{,}000{,}000(1.4)^{\frac{t}{10}},$$

thus $\frac{t}{10}$ gives the number of 10-year periods that have passed since 1980.

In 1980, $\frac{t}{10} = 0$, so we have $P = 40{,}000{,}000$.

In 1990, $\frac{t}{10} = 1$, so $P = 40{,}000{,}000(1.4) = 56{,}000{,}000$.

In 2000, $\frac{t}{10} = 2$, so $P = 40{,}000{,}000(1.4)^2 = 78{,}400{,}000$.

To find the doubling time, solve $80{,}000{,}000 = 40{,}000{,}000(1.4)^{\frac{t}{10}}$, to get $t \approx 20.6$ years.

25. (a) Let r be the interest rate expressed as a decimal, so $r = i/100$. Then $2 = (1 + r)^D$ so $\log 2 = \log[(1 + r)^D] = D \log(1 + r)$ so

$$D = \frac{\log 2}{\log(1 + r)}$$

For $r = 0.02$, $\quad D = 35.0$ years
For $r = 0.03$, $\quad D = 23.4$ years
For $r = 0.04$, $\quad D = 17.7$ years
For $r = 0.05$, $\quad D = 14.2$ years

(b) If $D = 70/i$, then $70/2 = 35.0$, $70/3 = 23.3$, $70/4 = 17.5$, and $70/5 = 14.0$, showing pretty good agreement.

26. (a) Using the formula for exponential decay, $A = A_0 e^{-kt}$, we plug in $A = 10.32$ when $t = 0$. Since $e^0 = 1$, $A_0 = 10.32$

    Since the half-life is 12 days, when $t = 12$, $A = \frac{10.32}{2} = 5.16$. Plugging this into the formula, we have

    $$5.16 = 10.32 e^{-12k},$$
    $$0.5 = e^{-12k}, \quad \text{and, taking ln of both sides,}$$
    $$\ln 0.5 = -12k,$$
    $$k = -\frac{\ln(0.5)}{12} \approx 0.057762.$$

    The full equation is

    $$A = 10.32 e^{-0.057762t}.$$

    (b) We want to solve for t when $A = 1$. Plugging into the equation from (a) yields

    $$1 = 10.32 e^{-0.057762t},$$
    $$\frac{1}{10.32} = 0.096899 = e^{-0.057762t},$$
    $$\ln 0.096899 = -0.057762t,$$
    $$t = \frac{-2.33408}{-0.057762} = 40.41 \text{ days.}$$

27. Let n be the infant mortality of Senegal. As a function of time t, n is given by

    $$n = n_0 (0.90)^t.$$

    To find when $n = 0.50 n_0$ (so the number of cases has been reduced by 50%), we solve

    $$0.50 = (0.90)^t,$$
    $$\log(0.50) = t \log(0.90),$$
    $$t = \frac{\log(0.50)}{\log(0.90)} \approx 6.58 \text{ years.}$$

28. Assuming a rate of inflation of 4.6% a year, prices increase from one year to the next by a factor of 1.046. Letting t be time in years from 1990, the price P of a stamp in dollars is given, in our model, by the equation

    $$P(t) = 0.29(1.046)^t,$$

    where the 0.29 comes from the condition that $P(t) = 29¢$ at $t = 0$. To find the time when it will cost a dollar to mail a letter, we solve

    $$0.29(1.046)^t = 1,$$
    $$\log 0.29(1.046)^t = \log 1,$$
    $$\log 0.29 + t \log 1.046 = 0,$$
    $$t = -\frac{\log 0.29}{\log 1.046} \approx 27.52.$$

    So a stamp should cost \$1 by the middle of the year $1990 + 27.52 = 2017$.

1.7 SOLUTIONS

1.
   TABLE 1.3

x	1	2	3	4	5	6	7	8	9	10
$f(x)$	0	0.30	0.48	0.60	0.70	0.78	0.85	0.90	0.95	1.00
$g(x)$	0	0.69	1.10	1.39	1.61	1.79	1.95	2.08	2.20	2.30

   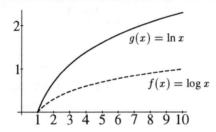

2. $3(1) + (-1) = 2$

3. $2\ln e + e^{-1} = 2 + e^{-1}$

4. $3\ln(e) + \ln 1 = 3 + 0 = 3$

5. $e^{\ln(1/\sqrt{e})} = \dfrac{1}{\sqrt{e}}$

6. $\ln(A^2) - \ln(B^3) + \ln AB = \ln\left(\dfrac{A^2 \cdot AB}{B^3}\right) = \ln\left(\dfrac{A^3}{B^2}\right)$

7. $e^{\ln A^2 - \ln \sqrt{B}} = e^{\ln(A^2/\sqrt{B})} = A^2/\sqrt{B}$

8. $\ln(x \cdot \frac{1}{x}) = \ln(1) = 0$

9. $\ln(e^2 \ln e) = \ln(e^2) = 2$

10. $\ln(2^x) = \ln(e^{x+1})$
    $x\ln 2 = (x+1)\ln e$
    $x\ln 2 = x + 1$
    $0.693x = x + 1$
    $$x = \frac{1}{0.693 - 1} = -3.26$$

11. $\ln(2e^{3x}) = \ln(4e^{5x})$
    $\ln 2 + \ln(e^{3x}) = \ln 4 + \ln(e^{5x})$
    $0.693 + 3x = 1.386 + 5x$
    $x = -0.347$

12. $4e^{2x-3} = e + 5$
    $\ln 4 + \ln(e^{2x-3}) = \ln(e + 5)$
    $1.386 + 2x - 3 = 2.044$
    $x = 1.83$

13. $\ln(10^{x+3}) = \ln(5e^{7-x})$
        $(x+3)\ln 10 = \ln 5 + (7-x)\ln e$
        $2.303(x+3) = 1.609 + (7-x)$
        $3.303x = 1.609 + 7 - 2.303(3)$
        $x = 0.515$

14. $P = P_0(e^{0.2})^t = P_0(1.2214)^t$. Exponential growth because $0.2 > 0$ or $1.2214 > 1$.

15. $P = 10(e^{0.917})^t = 10(2.5)^t$. Exponential growth because $0.917 > 0$ or $2.5 > 1$.

16. $P = P_0(e^{-0.73})^t = P_0(0.4819)^t$. Exponential decay since $-0.73 < 0$ or $0.4819 < 1$.

17. $P = 79(e^{-2.5})^t = 79(0.0821)^t$. Exponential decay because $-2.5 < 0$ or $0.0821 < 1$.

18. $P = 7(e^{-\pi})^t = 7(0.0432)^t$. Exponential decay because $-\pi < 0$ or $0.0432 < 1$.

19.   We want $2^t = e^{kt}$ so $2 = e^k$ and $k = \ln 2 = 0.693$. Thus $P = P_0 e^{0.693t}$.

20.   We want $1.7^t = e^{kt}$ so $1.7 = e^k$ and $k = \ln 1.7 = 0.5306$. Thus $P = 10e^{0.5306t}$.

21.   We want $0.2^t = e^{kt}$ so $0.2 = e^k$ and $k = \ln 0.2 = -1.6094$. Thus $P = 5.23e^{-1.6094t}$.

22.   We want $0.9^t = e^{kt}$ so $0.9 = e^k$ and $k = \ln 0.9 = -0.1054$. Thus $P = 174e^{-0.1054t}$.

23. $y = \ln e^x$ is a straight line with slope 1, passing through the origin. This is so because $y = \ln e^x = x \ln e = x \cdot 1 = x$. So this function is really $y = x$ in disguise.

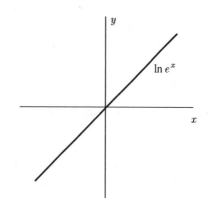

24.   Since $e^{\ln x} = x$ for $x > 0$, this equation is $y = x$ for $x > 0$. Its graph is therefore a straight line, with slope 1, to the right of the origin.

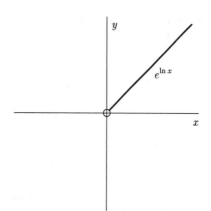

25. (a) The quantity $\dfrac{\ln x}{\log x}$ remains constant, about $\ln 10 \approx 2.30$.

(b) You see a horizontal line, $y \approx 2.30$, for $x > 0$. The line does not extend left of the y-axis. Thus, the function is constant for positive values of x.

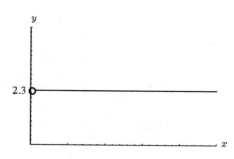

26. $t = \ln \frac{a}{b}$

27. $\ln \frac{P}{P_0} = kt$, so $t = \frac{\ln \frac{P}{P_0}}{k}$.

28. $\ln a + kt = bt$, so $t = \dfrac{\ln a}{b - k}$, since $k \neq b$.

29.
$$\frac{c}{b} = e^{(-\gamma t/n) + \alpha t} = e^{t\left(\alpha - \frac{\gamma}{n}\right)}$$
$$\ln \frac{c}{b} = t\left(\alpha - \frac{\gamma}{n}\right)$$
$$t = \frac{\ln \frac{c}{b}}{\alpha - \frac{\gamma}{n}}, \quad \text{since } \alpha \neq \frac{\gamma}{n}.$$

30. Since f is increasing, f has an inverse. To find the inverse of $f(t) = 50e^{0.1t}$, we replace t with $f^{-1}(t)$, and, since $f(f^{-1}(t)) = t$, we have
$$t = 50e^{0.1f^{-1}(t)}.$$

We then solve for $f^{-1}(t)$:

$$t = 50e^{0.1f^{-1}(t)}$$
$$\frac{t}{50} = e^{0.1f^{-1}(t)}$$
$$\ln\left(\frac{t}{50}\right) = 0.1f^{-1}(t)$$
$$f^{-1}(t) = \frac{1}{0.1}\ln\left(\frac{t}{50}\right) = 10\ln\left(\frac{t}{50}\right).$$

31. (a) As x gets larger, e^{-x} gets smaller, so $1 + e^{-x}$ gets smaller, but $\frac{1}{1+e^{-x}}$ gets *larger*. Therefore, the function is increasing.

(b) Since f is increasing, its graph intersects any horizontal line at most once. Therefore, f has an inverse. We can find that inverse by expressing x in terms of y, i.e., $x = f^{-1}(y)$.

$$y = \frac{1}{1 + e^{-x}}$$

$$1 + e^{-x} = \frac{1}{y}$$

$$e^{-x} = \frac{1}{y} - 1 = \frac{1 - y}{y}$$

$$e^x = \frac{y}{1 - y}$$

$$\ln e^x = \ln\left(\frac{y}{1 - y}\right)$$

$$x = \ln\left(\frac{y}{1 - y}\right)$$

$$f^{-1}(y) = \ln\left(\frac{y}{1 - y}\right),$$

or, by switching the variables y and x,

$$f^{-1}(x) = \ln\left(\frac{x}{1 - x}\right).$$

(c) The domain of f^{-1} is the same as the range of f, which is all numbers between 0 and 1 not including the endpoints. The domain of f^{-1} is therefore $0 < x < 1$. On this domain, $\dfrac{x}{1 - x}$ is positive and hence $\ln\left(\dfrac{x}{1 - x}\right)$ makes sense.

(d) The graph of f^{-1} is the reflection of the graph of f across the line $y = x$. This is because if a point (a, b) is on the graph of f, then the point (b, a) is on the graph of f^{-1}. [For example, the point $(0, \frac{1}{2})$ is on the graph of f, so the point $(\frac{1}{2}, 0)$ must be on the graph of f^{-1}.] Note that the graph of f is asymptotic to the lines $y = 1$ and $y = 0$, and the graph of f^{-1} is asymptotic to the lines $x = 1$ and $x = 0$.

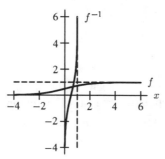

32. (a) We have $P_0 = 1$ million, and $k = 0.02$, so $P(t) = (1,000,000)(e^{0.02t})$.
    (b)

P

1,000,000

P

Figure 1.7

33. (a) The pressure P at 6,198 meters is given in terms of the pressure P_0 at sea level to be

$$P = P_0 e^{-1.2 \times 10^{-4} h}$$
$$= P_0 e^{(-1.2 \times 10^{-4})6198}$$
$$= P_0 e^{-0.74376}$$
$$= 0.47532 P_0 \quad \text{or about 47.5\% of sea level pressure.}$$

(b) At $h = 12,000$ meters, we have

$$P = P_0 e^{-1.2 \times 10^{-4} h}$$
$$= P_0 e^{(-1.2 \times 10^{-4})12,000}$$
$$= P_0 e^{-1.44}$$
$$= 0.2369 P_0 \quad \text{or about 24\% of sea level pressure.}$$

34. (a)

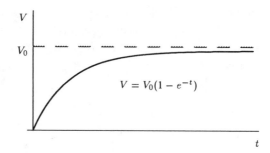

V

V_0

$$V = V_0(1 - e^{-t})$$

t

(b) V_0 represents the terminal velocity of the raindrop or the maximum speed it can attain as it falls (although a raindrop starting at rest will never quite reach V_0 exactly).

35. (a) We know the decay follows the equation

$$P = P_0 e^{-kt},$$

and that 10% of the pollution is removed after 5 hours (meaning that 90% is left). Therefore,

$$0.90 P_0 = P_0 e^{-5k}$$
$$k = -\frac{1}{5} \ln(0.90)$$

So, after 10 hours:

$$P = P_0 e^{-10(-\frac{1}{5} \ln 0.90)}$$
$$P = P_0 (0.9)^2 = 0.81 P_0$$

so 81% of the original amount is left.

(b)   We want to solve for the time when $P = 0.50 P_0$:

$$0.50 P_0 = P_0 e^{t(\frac{1}{5} \ln 0.90)}$$
$$0.50 = e^{\ln(0.90^{\frac{t}{5}})}$$
$$0.50 = 0.90^{\frac{t}{5}}$$
$$t = \frac{5 \ln(0.50)}{\ln(0.90)} \approx 32.9 \text{ hours.}$$

(c)

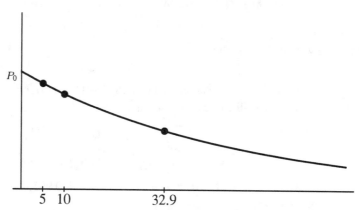

(d)   When highly polluted air is filtered, there is more pollutant per liter of air to remove. If a fixed amount of air is cleaned every day, there is a higher amount of pollutant removed earlier in the process.

36.   (a) $P = 3.6(1.034)^t$

(b) $P = 3.6 e^{kt} = 3.6(1.034)^t$

so

$$e^{kt} = (1.034)^t$$
$$kt = t \ln(1.034)$$
$$k = 0.0334$$

so

$$P = 3.6 e^{0.0334t}.$$

(c)   Annual growth rate $= 3.4\%$

Continuous growth rate $= 3.3\%$

Thus the growth rates are not equal, though for small growth rates (such as these), they are close. The annual growth rate is larger.

37.   If Q is the amount of strontium-90 which remains at time t, and Q_0 is the original amount, then

$$Q = Q_0 e^{-0.0247t}.$$

So after 100 years,

$$Q = Q_0 e^{-0.0247 \cdot 100}$$

and

$$\frac{Q}{Q_0} = e^{-2.47} \approx 0.0846$$

so about 8.46% of the strontium-90 would remain.

Note: If you assume that 2.47% is the *annual* rate, rather than the continuous rate, the answer is not very different:

$$Q = Q_0(1 - 0.0247)^{100} \quad \text{giving} \quad \frac{Q}{Q_0} \approx 0.082 \quad \text{or} \quad 8.2\%.$$

38.   (a)   We want to find t such that

$$0.15Q_0 = Q_0 e^{-0.000121t},$$

so $0.15 = e^{-0.000121t}$, meaning that $\ln 0.15 = -0.000121t$, or $t = \frac{\ln 0.15}{-0.000121} \approx 15{,}678.7$ years.

      (b)   Let T be the half-life of carbon-14. Then

$$0.5Q_0 = Q_0 e^{-0.000121T},$$

so $0.5 = e^{-0.000121T}$, or $T = \frac{\ln 0.5}{-0.000121} \approx 5{,}728.5$ years.

39. $e^{-k(5730)} = 0.5$ so $k = 1.21 \cdot 10^{-4}$. Thus, $e^{-1.21 \cdot 10^{-4}t} = 0.995$, so $t = \frac{\ln 0.995}{-1.21 \cdot 10^{-4}} = 41.43$ years, so the painting is a fake.

40.   (a) $P = P_0 \left(\frac{1}{2}\right)^{t/(1.28 \cdot 10^9)}$, since the quantity is reduced by a factor of 1/2 every $1.28 \cdot 10^9$ years.

      (b)   We know that for some constant k,

$$P = P_0 e^{kt}.$$

It suffices to find k. We use the relation $P = \frac{P_0}{2}$, where T is the half-life. So

$$\frac{P_0}{2} = P_0 e^{kT};$$

canceling P_0 and taking natural logs,

$$\ln\left(\frac{1}{2}\right) = kT.$$

Since we know that $T = 1.28 \cdot 10^9$ years,

$$-0.6931 = 1.28 \cdot 10^9 k,$$

or

$$k \approx -5.42 \cdot 10^{-10}.$$

Thus our formula is

$$P(t) = P_0 e^{-5.42 \cdot 10^{-10} t}.$$

1.8 SOLUTIONS

1. For $20 \leq x \leq 100$, $0 \leq y \leq 1.2$, this function looks like a horizontal line at $y = 1.0725\ldots$ (In fact, the graph approaches this line from below.) Now, $e^{0.07} \approx 1.0725$, which strongly suggests that, as we already know, As $x \to \infty$, $\left(1 + \frac{0.07}{x}\right)^x \to e^{0.07}$.

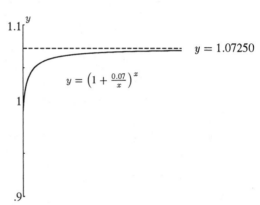

2. We use the equation $B = Pe^{rt}$, where P is the initial principal, t is the time in years the deposit is in the account, r is the annual interest and B is the balance. After $t = 5$ years, we will have

$$B = (10{,}000)e^{(0.08)5} = (10{,}000)e^{0.4} \approx \$14{,}918.25.$$

3. (a) (i)

$$\left(1 + \frac{0.05}{1000}\right)^{1000} = 1.05126978\ldots,$$

so the effective annual yield is $5.126978\ldots\%$.

(ii)

$$\left(1 + \frac{0.05}{10000}\right)^{10000} = 1.05127096\ldots,$$

so the effective annual yield is $5.127096\ldots\%$.

(iii)

$$\left(1 + \frac{0.05}{100000}\right)^{100000} = 1.05127108\ldots,$$

so the effective annual yield is $5.127108\ldots\%$.

(b)   The effective annual rates in part (a) are closing in on 5.127%, so this is the effective annual yield for a 5% annual rate compounded continuously.

(c) $e^{0.05} = 1.05127109\ldots$. Since continuous compounding is equivalent to multiplying by $e^{0.05}$, the effective annual yield for continuous compounding is $0.05127109\ldots \approx 5.127\%$.

4.   (a)

$$\left(1 + \frac{0.04}{10000}\right)^{10000} \approx 1.0408107$$

$$\left(1 + \frac{0.04}{100000}\right)^{100000} \approx 1.0408108$$

$$\left(1 + \frac{0.04}{1000000}\right)^{1000000} \approx 1.0408108$$

Effective annual yield:
4.08108%

(b) $e^{0.04} = 1.048108$ as expected.

5. $e^{0.06} = 1.0618365$, so the effective annual rate $\approx 6.18365\%$.

6.   (a) $e^{0.06} = 1.0618365$ which means the bank balance has increased by approximately 6.18%.

(b) $e^{0.06t} = 2$, so $t = \frac{\ln 2}{0.06} = 11.55$ years.

(c) $e^{it} = 2$ so $t = \frac{\ln 2}{i}$.

7.   (a)   Since we have 6% annual interest compounded continuously,

$$P = P_0 e^{0.06t}$$
$$2000 = 1000 e^{0.06t}$$
$$2 = e^{0.06t}$$
$$0.06t = \ln 2$$
$$t = \frac{\ln 2}{0.06} = 11.55 \text{ years.}$$

(b)   The investment doubles approximately every 11.55 years, so

$$P = P_0(2)^{t/11.55}.$$

8. $e^{0.12} = 1.1274969$, so the effective annual yield$\approx 12.74969\%$.

9.   (a)   Using the formula $A = A_0(1 + \frac{r}{n})^{nt}$, we have $A = 10^6(1 + \frac{1}{12})^{12} \approx 10^6(2.61303529) \approx 2,613,035$ zaïre after one year.

(b)   (i)   Compounding daily, $A = 10^6(1 + \frac{1}{365})^{365} \approx 10^6(2.714567) \approx 2,714,567$ zaïre

(ii)   Compounding hourly, $A = 10^6(1 + \frac{1}{8760})^{8760} \approx 10^6(2.7181267) \approx 2,718,127$ zaïre

(iii)   Compounding each minute, $A = 10^6(1 + \frac{1}{525600})^{525600} \approx 10^6(2.718280) \approx 2,718,280$ zaïre

(c)   The amount does not seem to be increasing without bound, but rather it seems to level off at a value just over 2,718,000 zaïre. A close upper limit might be 2,718,300 (amounts may vary). In fact, the limit is $(e \times 10^6)$ zaïre.

10. We know that for a given annual rate, the higher the frequency of compounding, the higher the effective annual yield. So the effective yield of (a) will be greater than that of (c) which is greater than that of (b). Also, the effective annual yield of (e) will be greater than that of (d). Now the effective annual yield of (e) will be less than the effective annual yield of 5.5% annual rate, compounded twice a year, and the latter will be less than the yield from (b). Thus $d < e < b < c < a$. Matching these up with our choices, we get

    (d) I, (e) II, (b) III, (c) IV, (a) V.

11. (a) At the end of the year, the landlord's investment amounts to $\$1000e^{0.06} = \$1061.83$, and so has earned $\$61.83$ in interest. Each year, the landlord pays the tenant $\$1000(0.05) = \$50$. Therefore the landlord made $\$11.83$ in interest.

    (b) At the end of the year, the landlord's investment amounts to $\$1000e^{0.04} = \$1040.81$, and so has earned $\$40.81$ in interest. By paying the tenant $\$50$, the landlord loses $\$9.19$.

12. We use the formula $A = A_0(1 + \frac{r}{n})^{nt}$, where t is in years, r is annual rate of interest and n is number of times interest is compounded per year.

    (a) Compounding daily,

    $$A = 450,000 \left(1 + \frac{0.06}{365}\right)^{(213)(365)}$$
    $$= 450,000 \, (1.00016438)^{77745}$$
    $$\approx \$1.59602561 \times 10^{11}$$

    This amounts to approximately $\$160$ billion.

    (b) Compounding yearly,

    $$A = 450,000 \, (1 + 0.06)^{213}$$
    $$= 450,000(1.06)^{213} = 450,000(245555.29)$$
    $$= \$1.10499882 \times 10^{11}$$

    This is only $\$110.5$ billion.

    (c) We first wish to find the interest that will accrue during 1990. For 1990, the principal is $\$1.105 \times 10^{11}$. At 6% annual interest, during 1990 the money will earn

    $$0.06 \times \$1.105 \times 10^{11} = \$6.63 \times 10^9.$$

    The number of seconds in a year is

    $$\left(365 \frac{\text{day}}{\text{year}}\right) \left(24 \frac{\text{hr}}{\text{day}}\right) \left(60 \frac{\text{min}}{\text{hr}}\right) \left(60 \frac{\text{sec}}{\text{min}}\right) = 31536000 \text{ sec.}$$

    Thus, over 1990, interest is accumulating at the rate of

    $$\frac{\$6.63 \times 10^9}{31536000 \text{ sec}} \approx \$210.24 \text{ /sec.}$$

1.9   SOLUTIONS

1.   (a)   The equation is $y = 2x^2 + 1$. Note that its graph is narrower than the graph of $y = x^2$ which appears in grey.

(b) $y = 2(x^2 + 1)$ moves the graph up one unit and *then* stretches it by a factor of two.

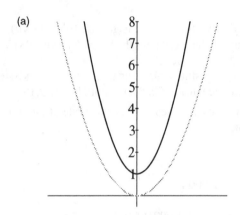

(a)

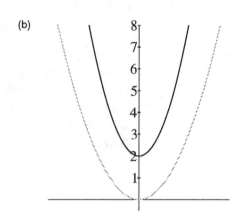

(b)

(c)   No, the graphs are not the same. Note that stretching vertically leaves any point whose y-value is zero in the same place but moves any other point. This is the source of the difference because if you stretch it first, its lowest point stays at the origin. Then you shift it up by one and its lowest point is $(0, 1)$. Alternatively, if you shift it first, its lowest point is $(0, 1)$ which, when stretched by 2, becomes $(0, 2)$.

2.   (a) $g\left(f(x)\right) = g(2x + 3) = \log(2x + 3)$
     (b) $f\left(g(x)\right) = f(\log x) = 2\log x + 3$
     (c) $f\left(f(x)\right) = f(2x + 3) = 2(2x + 3) + 3 = 4x + 6 + 3 = 4x + 9$

3. $\ln(\ln(x))$ means take the $\ln$ of the value of the function $\ln x$. On the other hand, $\ln^2(x)$ means take the function $\ln x$ and square it. For example, consider each of these functions evaluated at e. Since $\ln e = 1$, $\ln^2 e = 1^2 = 1$, but $\ln(\ln(e)) = \ln(1) = 0$. See the graphs below. (Note that $\ln(\ln(x))$ is only defined for $x > 1$.)

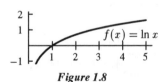

Figure 1.8

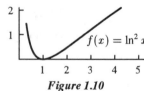

Figure 1.9

Figure 1.10

4. (a) $g(h(x)) = g(x^3 + 1) = \sqrt{x^3 + 1}$
   (b) $h(g(x)) = h(\sqrt{x}) = (\sqrt{x})^3 + 1 = x^{3/2} + 1$
   (c) $h(h(x)) = h(x^3 + 1) = (x^3 + 1)^3 + 1$
   (d) $g(x) + 1 = \sqrt{x} + 1$
   (e) $g(x + 1) = \sqrt{x + 1}$

5. (a) $f(g(t)) = f\left(\dfrac{1}{t+1}\right) = \left(\dfrac{1}{t+1} + 7\right)^2$
   (b) $g(f(t)) = g((t+7)^2) = \dfrac{1}{(t+7)^2 + 1}$
   (c) $f(t^2) = (t^2 + 7)^2$
   (d) $g(t - 1) = \dfrac{1}{(t-1)+1} = \dfrac{1}{t}$

6. (a) $f(g(100)) = f(\log 100) = f(2) = 10^2 = 100$
   (b) $g(f(3)) = g(10^3) = g(1000) = \log(1000) = 3$
   (c) $f(g(x)) = 10^{\log x} = x$
   (d) $g(f(x)) = \log(10^x) = x$

7. $m(z + 1) - m(z) = (z + 1)^2 - z^2 = 2z + 1.$

8. $m(z + h) - m(z) = (z + h)^2 - z^2 = 2zh + h^2.$

9. $m(z) - m(z - h) = z^2 - (z - h)^2 = 2zh - h^2.$

10. $m(z + h) - m(z - h) = (z + h)^2 - (z - h)^2 = z^2 + 2hz + h^2 - (z^2 - 2hz + h^2) = 4hz.$

11. $f(x) = x + 1, \quad g(x) = x^3.$

12. $f(x) = x^3, \quad g(x) = x + 1.$

13. $f(x) = x^3, \quad g(x) = \ln x.$

14. $f(x) = \ln x, \quad g(x) = x^3.$ (Another possibility: $f(x) = 3x, \quad g(x) = \ln x.$)

15.

(a)
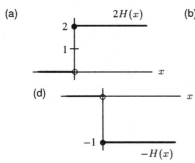

(b)
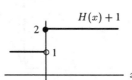

(c)
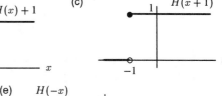

(d)

(e)
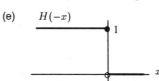

16. Here are the graphs.

(a)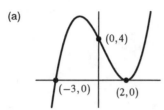

Figure 1.11: $y = 2f(x)$

(b)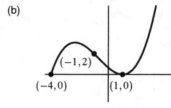

Figure 1.12: $y = f(x+1)$

(c)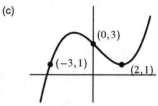

Figure 1.13: $y = f(x) + 1$

17. (a)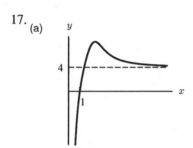

Figure 1.14: $y = 2f(x)$

(b)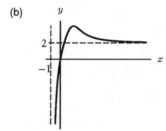

Figure 1.15: $y = f(x+1)$

(c)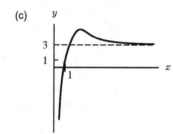

Figure 1.16: $y = f(x) + 1$

18. The graph of an even function is symmetric about the y-axis. The graph of an odd function is symmetric about the origin.

19. $1/x$ is odd; $\ln(x^2)$ is even; e^x is neither.

20.

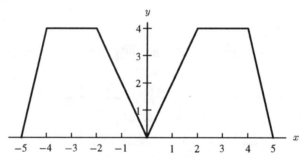

21.

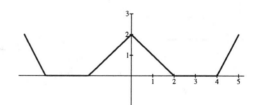

22.

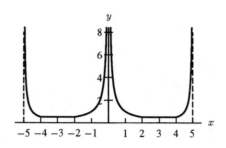

23. $f(g(1)) = f(2) = 0.4$.

24. $g(f(2)) = g(0.4) = 1.1$.

25. $f(f(1)) = f(-0.4) \approx -0.9$.

26. Computing $f(g(x))$ as in Problem 23, we get the following table. From it we graph $f(g(x))$.

TABLE 1.4

x	$g(x)$	$f(g(x))$
−3	0.6	−0.5
−2.5	−1.1	−1.3
−2	−1.9	−1.2
−1.5	−1.9	−1.2
−1	−1.4	−1.3
−0.5	−0.5	−1
0	0.5	−0.6
0.5	1.4	−0.2
1	2	0.4
1.5	2.2	0.5
2	1.6	0
2.5	0.1	−0.7
3	−2.5	0.1

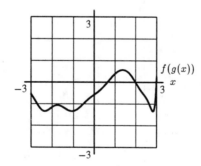

27.   Using the same way to compute $g(f(x))$ as in Problem 24, we get the following table. Then we can plot the graph of $g(f(x))$.

TABLE 1.5

x	$f(x)$	$g(f(x))$
−3	3	−2.6
−2.5	0.1	0.8
−2	−1	−1.4
−1.5	−1.3	−1.8
−1	−1.2	−1.7
−0.5	−1	−1.4
0	−0.8	−1
0.5	−0.6	−0.6
1	−0.4	−0.3
1.5	−0.1	0.3
2	0.3	1.1
2.5	0.9	2
3	1.6	2.2

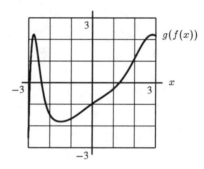

28.   Using the same way to compute $f(f(x))$ as in Problem 25, we get the following table. Then we can plot the graph of $f(f(x))$.

TABLE 1.6

x	$f(x)$	$f(f(x))$
−3	3	1.6
−2.5	0.1	−0.7
−2	−1	−1.2
−1.5	−1.3	−1.3
−1	−1.2	−1.3
−0.5	−1	−1.2
0	−0.8	−1.1
0.5	−0.6	−1
1	−0.4	−0.9
1.5	−0.1	−0.8
2	0.3	−0.6
2.5	0.9	−0.4
3	1.6	0

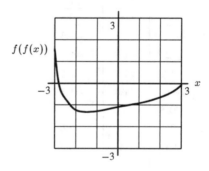

29.

TABLE 1.7

x	$f(x)$	$g(x)$	$h(x)$
-3	0	0	0
-2	2	2	-2
-1	2	2	-2
0	0	0	0
1	2	-2	-2
2	2	-2	-2
3	0	0	0

30.

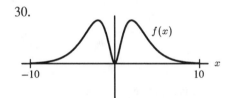

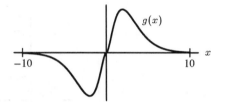

1.10   SOLUTIONS

1.

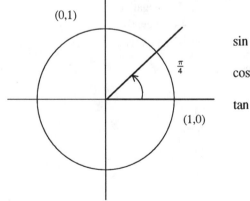

$\sin \frac{\pi}{4}$ is positive

$\cos \frac{\pi}{4}$ is positive

$\tan \frac{\pi}{4}$ is positive

2.

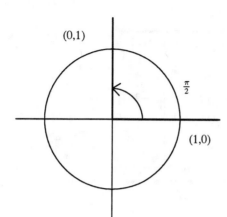

$\sin \frac{\pi}{2} = 1$ is positive

$\cos \frac{\pi}{2} = 0$

$\tan \frac{\pi}{2} = \dfrac{\sin \frac{\pi}{2}}{\cos \frac{\pi}{2}}$ is undefined

3.

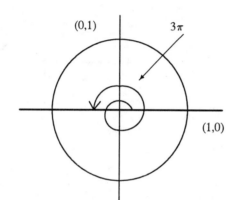

$\sin 3\pi = 0$

$\cos 3\pi = -1$ is negative

$\tan 3\pi = 0$

4.

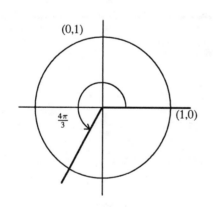

$\sin \frac{4\pi}{3}$ is negative
$\cos \frac{4\pi}{3}$ is negative
$\tan \frac{4\pi}{3}$ is positive

5.

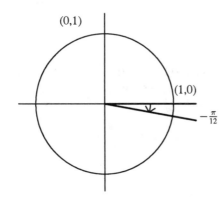

$\sin\left(-\frac{\pi}{12}\right)$ is negative
$\cos\left(-\frac{\pi}{12}\right)$ is positive
$\tan\left(-\frac{\pi}{12}\right)$ is negative

6.

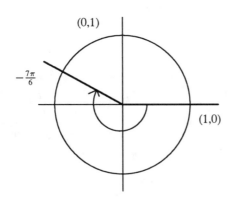

$\sin\left(-\frac{7\pi}{6}\right)$ is positive
$\cos\left(-\frac{7\pi}{6}\right)$ is negative
$\tan\left(-\frac{7\pi}{6}\right)$ is negative

7. $4 \text{ radians} \cdot \dfrac{180°}{\pi \text{ radians}} = \left(\dfrac{720}{\pi}\right)° \approx 240°$

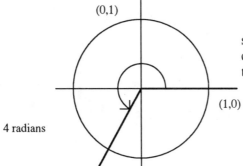

$\sin 4$ is negative
$\cos 4$ is negative
$\tan 4$ is positive

8. $-1 \text{ radian} \cdot \dfrac{180°}{\pi \text{ radians}} = -\left(\dfrac{180°}{\pi}\right) \approx -60°$

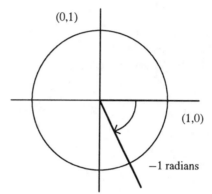

$\sin(-1)$ is negative
$\cos(-1)$ is positive
$\tan(-1)$ is negative

9.

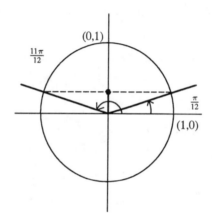

$\sin \dfrac{11\pi}{12} = \sin\left(\pi - \dfrac{\pi}{12}\right)$

$\qquad\quad = \sin \dfrac{\pi}{12}$ (by picture)

$\qquad\quad = 0.258.$

10.

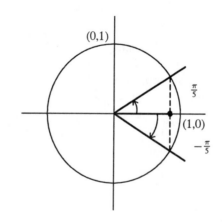

$\cos\left(-\dfrac{\pi}{5}\right) = \cos\dfrac{\pi}{5}$ (by picture)

$\qquad\qquad = 0.809.$

11.

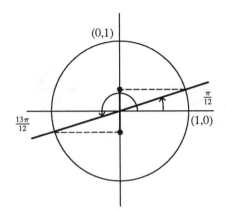

$$\sin \frac{13\pi}{12} = \sin\left(\pi + \frac{\pi}{12}\right)$$
$$= -\sin\frac{\pi}{12} \quad \text{(by picture)}$$
$$= -0.258.$$

12.

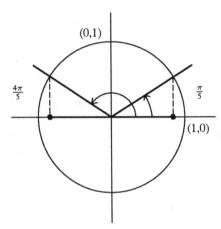

$$\cos\frac{4\pi}{5} = \cos\left(\pi - \frac{\pi}{5}\right)$$
$$= -\cos\frac{\pi}{5} \quad \text{(by picture)}$$
$$= -0.809.$$

13.

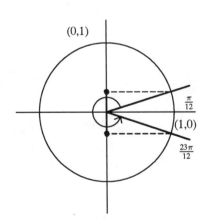

$$\sin\frac{23\pi}{12} = \sin\left(2\pi - \frac{\pi}{12}\right)$$
$$= -\sin\frac{\pi}{12} \quad \text{(by picture)}$$
$$= -0.258.$$

14.

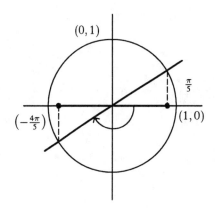

$$\cos\left(-\frac{4\pi}{5}\right) = \cos\left(-\pi + \frac{\pi}{5}\right)$$
$$= -\cos\frac{\pi}{5}$$
$$= -0.809.$$

15.

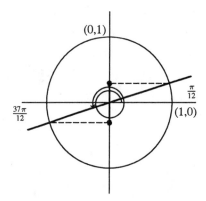

$$\sin\frac{37\pi}{12} = \sin\left(3\pi + \frac{\pi}{12}\right)$$
$$= -\sin\frac{\pi}{12} \quad \text{(by picture)}$$
$$= -0.258.$$

16.

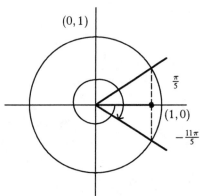

$$\cos\left(-\frac{11\pi}{5}\right) = \cos\left(-2\pi - \frac{\pi}{5}\right)$$
$$= \cos\frac{\pi}{5} \quad \text{(by picture)}$$
$$= 0.809.$$

17.

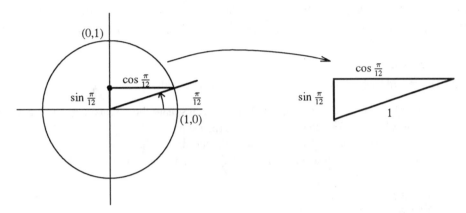

By the Pythagorean Theorem, $(\cos\frac{\pi}{12})^2 + (\sin\frac{\pi}{12})^2 = 1^2$; so $(\cos\frac{\pi}{12})^2 = 1 - (\sin\frac{\pi}{12})^2$ and $\cos\frac{\pi}{12} = \sqrt{1 - (\sin\frac{\pi}{12})^2} = \sqrt{1 - (0.258)^2} \approx 0.966$.

We take the positive square root since by the picture we know that $\cos\frac{\pi}{12}$ is positive.

18.

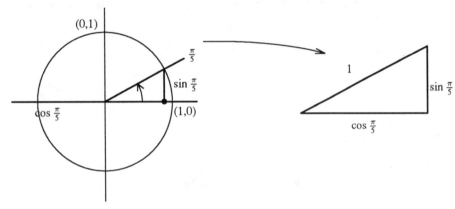

By the Pythagorean Theorem, $(\cos\frac{\pi}{5})^2 + (\sin\frac{\pi}{5})^2 = 1^2$;

so $(\sin\frac{\pi}{5})^2 = 1 - (\cos\frac{\pi}{5})^2$, and $\sin\frac{\pi}{5} = \sqrt{1 - (\cos\frac{\pi}{5})^2} = \sqrt{1 - (0.809)^2} \approx 0.588$.

We take the positive square root since by the picture we know that $\sin\frac{\pi}{5}$ is positive.

19.   From the example, we know that $h = 5 + 4.9\cos(\frac{\pi}{6}t)$, where t represents hours after midnight and h represents the height of the water.

$$\text{At 3:00 am, } t = 3 \text{ so } h = 5 + 4.9\cos\left(\frac{\pi}{6} \cdot 3\right) = 5 + 4.9(0) = 5 \text{ feet}$$

$$\text{At 4:00 am, } t = 4 \text{ so } h = 5 + 4.9\cos\left(\frac{\pi}{6} \cdot 4\right) = 5 + 4.9(-0.5) = 2.55 \text{ feet}$$

$$\text{At 5:00 pm, } t = 17 \text{ so } h = 5 + 4.9\cos\left(\frac{\pi}{6} \cdot 17\right) \approx 5 + 4.9(-0.866) \approx 0.76 \text{ feet}$$

20. The earth makes one revolution around the sun in one year, so its period is one year.

21. The moon makes one revolution around the earth in about 27.3 days, so its period is 27.3 days ≈ one month.

22. One hour.

23. The record's period is $\frac{1}{33\frac{1}{3}} = \frac{3}{100}$ minute, or 1.8 seconds.

24. $\sin x^2$ is by convention $\sin(x^2)$, which means you square the x first and then take the sine.
$\sin^2 x = (\sin x)^2$ means find $\sin x$ and then square it.
$\sin(\sin x)$ means find $\sin x$ and then take the sine of that.
Expressing each as a composition: If $f(x) = \sin x$ and $g(x) = x^2$, then
$\sin x^2 = f(g(x))$
$\sin^2 x = g(f(x))$
$\sin(\sin x) = f(f(x))$.

25. (a) $f(t) = -0.5 + \sin t,$ $g(t) = 1.5 + \sin t,$ $h(t) = -1.5 + \sin t,$ $k(t) = 0.5 + \sin t.$
 (b) $g(t) = 1 + k(t);$ $g(t) = 1.5 + \sin t = 1 + 0.5 + \sin t = 1 + k(t).$
 (c) Since $-1 \le \sin t \le 1$, adding 1.5 everywhere we get $0.5 \le 1.5 + \sin t \le 2.5$ and since $1.5 + \sin t = g(t)$, we get $0.5 \le g(t) \le 2.5$. Similarly, $-2.5 \le -1.5 + \sin t = h(t) \le -0.5$.

26.

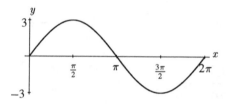

The amplitude is 3; the period is 2π.

27.

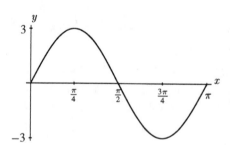

The amplitude is 3; the period is π.

28.

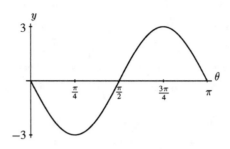

The amplitude is 3; the period is π.

29.

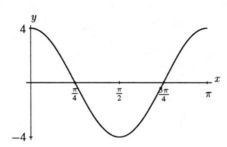

The amplitude is 4; the period is π.

30.

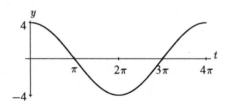

The amplitude is 4; the period is 4π.

31.

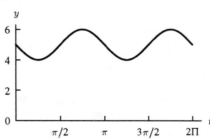

The amplitude is 1; the period is π.

32.   (a) $h(t) = 2\cos(t - \pi/2)$
      (b) $f(t) = 2\cos t$
      (c) $g(t) = 2\cos(t + \pi/2)$

33.   This graph is a sine curve with period 8π and amplitude 2, so it is given by $f(x) = 2\sin(\frac{x}{4})$.

34.   This graph is the same as in Problem 33 but shifted up by 2, so it is given by $f(x) = 2\sin(\frac{x}{4}) + 2$.

35.   This graph is a cosine curve with period 6π and amplitude 5, so it is given by $f(x) = 5\cos(\frac{x}{3})$.

36.   This graph is an inverted sine curve with amplitude 4 and period π, so it is given by $f(x) = -4\sin(2x)$.

37.   This graph is an inverted cosine curve with amplitude 8 and period 20π, so it is given by $f(x) = -8\cos(\frac{x}{10})$.

38.   This can be represented by a sine function of amplitude 3 and period 18. Thus, $y = A\sin(Bx)$ with $A = 3$ and $B = 2\pi/18 = \pi/9$, so $y = 3\sin(\pi x/9)$.

39.   This can be represented by a sine function of amplitude 3 and period 18, shifted 1 to the right. Therefore $A = 3$ and $B = 2\pi/18 = \pi/9$, and x is replaced by $(x - 1)$, giving $y = 3\sin[\pi(x - 1)/9]$.

40.   This can be represented by a sine function of amplitude 3 and period 18, shifted 2 to the left. Therefore $A = 3$ and $B = 2\pi/18 = \pi/9$, and x is replaced by $(x + 2)$, giving $y = 3\sin[\pi(x + 2)/9]$.

41.   (a)

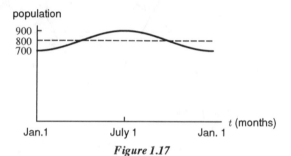

Figure 1.17

    (b)   Average value of population $= \frac{700+900}{2} = 800$, amplitude $= \frac{900-700}{2} = 100$, and period $= 12$ months, so $B = 2\pi/12 = \pi/6$. Since the population is at its minimum when $t = 0$, we use a negative cosine:

$$P = 800 - 100\cos\left(\frac{\pi t}{6}\right).$$

42.   (a) $y_0 =$ the average depth of the water.
    (b) $A =$ the amplitude $= 15/2 = 7.5$.
    (c)   Period $= 12.5$ hours. Thus $B(12.5) = 2\pi$ so $B = 2\pi/12.5 \approx 0.503$.
    (d) t_0 is the time of a high tide.

43.   Over the one-year period, the average value is about $75°$ and the amplitude of the variation is about $\frac{90-60}{2} = 15°$. The function assumes its minimum value right at the beginning of the year, so we want a negative cosine function. Thus, for t in years, we have the function

$$f(t) = 75 - 15\cos\left(\frac{2\pi}{12}t\right).$$

(Many other answers are possible, depending on how you read the chart.)

44. (a) Beginning at time $t = 0$, the voltage will have oscillated through a complete cycle when $\cos(120\pi t) = \cos(2\pi)$, hence when $t = \frac{1}{60}$ second. The period is $\frac{1}{60}$ second.

(b) V_0 represents the amplitude of the oscillation.

(c)

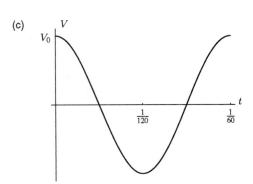

45. (a)

x	-1	-0.8	-0.6	-0.4	-0.2	0	0.2	0.4	0.6	0.8	1
arcsin x	-1.57	-0.93	-0.64	-0.41	-0.20	0	0.20	0.41	0.64	0.93	1.57

(b) The domain is $-1 \leq x \leq 1$.
The range is $-\frac{\pi}{2} \leq x \leq \frac{\pi}{2}$.

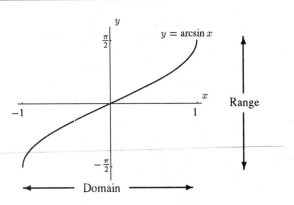

46. (a)

x	-1	-0.8	-0.6	-0.4	-0.2	0	0.2	0.4	0.6	0.8	1
arccos x	3.14	2.50	2.21	1.98	1.77	1.57	1.37	1.16	0.93	0.64	0

(b)

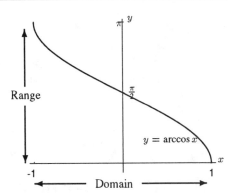

(c) Domain is $-1 \leq x \leq 1$. Range is $0 \leq y \leq \pi$.

(d) The domain of arccos and arcsin are the same, $-1 \leq x \leq 1$, since their inverses (sine and cosine) only take on values in this range.

(e) The domain of the original sine function was restricted to the the interval $[-\frac{\pi}{2}, \frac{\pi}{2}]$ to construct the arcsine function. Hence, the range of arcsine is also $[-\frac{\pi}{2}, \frac{\pi}{2}]$.

Now, if we restrict the domain of cosine in the same way, we obtain an arccosine curve which is not a function:

For example, for $x = 0$, $y = \arccos x$ will have two values, $-\frac{\pi}{2}$, and $\frac{\pi}{2}$. Also, it gives no values for $x < 0$, so it is not very useful.

The domain of cosine should instead be restricted to $[0, \pi]$, so that $y = \arccos x$ gives a unique y for each value of x.

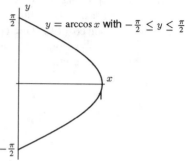

47. Notice that whenever x increases by 0.5, $f(x)$ increases by 1, indicating that $f(x)$ is linear. By inspection, we see that $f(x) = 2x$.

Similarly, $g(x)$ decreases by 1 each time x increases by 0.5. We know, therefore, that $g(x)$ is a linear function with slope $\frac{-1}{0.5} = -2$. The y-intercept is 10, so $g(x) = 10 - 2x$.

$h(x)$ is an even function which is always positive. Comparing the values of x and $h(x)$, it appears that $h(x) = x^2$.

$F(x)$ is an odd function that seems to vary between -1 and 1. We guess that $F(x) = \sin x$ and check with a calculator.

$G(x)$ is also an odd function that varies between -1 and 1. Notice that $G(x) = F(2x)$, and thus $G(x) = \sin 2x$.

Notice also that $H(x)$ is exactly 2 more than $F(x)$ for all x, so $H(x) = 2 + \sin x$.

48. From a plot of the two functions, we can see that there are three obvious points of intersection in the domain $|x| \leq 2$. There is one at $(0,0)$, another at about $(1.31, 2.29)$ and another at about $(-1.31, -2.29)$. Now we show that there are no points of intersection for these graphs, provided that $|x| > 2$.

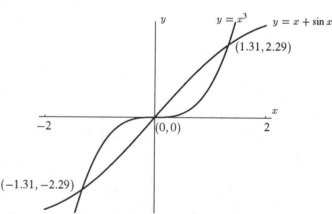

We know that $x + \sin x$ will never exceed $x + 1$, since $\sin x$ is never greater than 1. Now, for $x > 2$,

$$x + 1 < 2x < x^2 < x^3.$$

So,

$$x + \sin x \leq x + 1 < x^3.$$

Therefore, the curves cannot intersect when $x > 2$. A similar argument applies when $x < -2$.

49. (a) Yes, they must intersect at $3.64 - \pi \approx 0.5$.
    (b) They also intersect at $3.64 + \pi \approx 6.78$.
    (c) $3.64 - 2\pi \approx -2.64$.

50. (a) The period is 2π.
    (b) The period of $\sin 3t$ is $\dfrac{2}{3}\pi$. Period of $\cos t$ is 2π.
    (c) The combined function repeats when each part repeats separately—although $\sin 3t$ repeats every $\dfrac{2}{3}\pi$, the combined function must "wait" until $\cos t$ repeats for it to return to its original value.

1.11   SOLUTIONS

1. (I) Degree ≥ 3, leading coefficient negative.
   (II) Degree ≥ 4, leading coefficient positive.
   (III) Degree ≥ 4, leading coefficient negative.
   (IV) Degree ≥ 5, leading coefficient negative.
   (V) Degree ≥ 5, leading coefficient positive.

2. (a) As $x \to +\infty$, $f(x) \to -\infty$; as $x \to -\infty$, $f(x) \to +\infty$. f has odd degree and negative leading coefficient.
   (b) As $x \to +\infty$, $f(x) \to +\infty$; as $x \to -\infty$, $f(x) \to +\infty$. f has even degree and positive leading coefficient.
   (c) As $x \to +\infty$, $f(x) \to -\infty$; as $x \to -\infty$, $f(x) \to -\infty$. f has even degree and negative leading coefficient.
   (d) As $x \to +\infty$, $f(x) \to +\infty$; as $x \to -\infty$, $f(x) \to -\infty$. f has odd degree and positive leading coefficient.
   (e) As $x \to +\infty$, $f(x) \to -\infty$; as $x \to -\infty$, $f(x) \to -\infty$. f has even degree and negative leading coefficient.

3.

4.

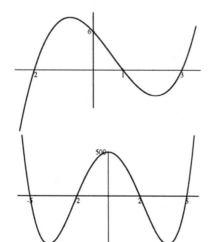

5.

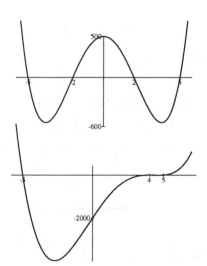

6.

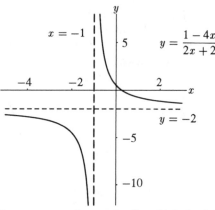

7. To find vertical asymptote(s), look at the behavior of y as x approaches a value for which the denominator is 0.

$$2x + 2 = 0 \quad \text{when} \quad x = -1.$$

If we plug in values for x near -1, we will see that y goes to $+\infty$ as x approaches -1 from the right, but y goes to $-\infty$ as x approaches -1 from the left. Clearly, $x = -1$ is a vertical asymptote.

To find horizontal asymptote(s), look at the behavior of y as x goes to $+\infty$ and as x goes to $-\infty$. Note that as $x \to \pm\infty$, only the highest power of x matters, so that the 1 and the 2 become insignificant compared to x for large values of x. Thus,

$$y = \frac{1 - 4x}{2x + 2} \approx \frac{-4x}{2x} = -2.$$

Clearly, $y = -2$ is a horizontal asymptote.

8. To find vertical asymptote(s), look at the behavior of y as x approaches a value for which the denominator is 0.

$$x^3 + 8 = 0 \quad \text{when} \quad x = -2.$$

If we plug in values for x near -2, we will see that $y \to -\infty$ as $x \to -2$ from the right, but $y \to +\infty$ as $x \to -2$ from the left. Clearly, $x = -2$ is a vertical asymptote.

To find horizontal asymptote(s), look at the behavior of y as x goes to $+\infty$ and as x goes to $-\infty$. Note that as $x \to \pm\infty$, only the highest power of x matters, so that the $2x^2$, the -11, and the 8 become insignificant compared to the x^3 terms for large values of x. Thus,

$$y = \frac{3x^3 + 2x^2 - 11}{x^3 + 8} \approx \frac{3x^3}{x^3} = 3$$

Clearly, $y = 3$ is a horizontal asymptote.

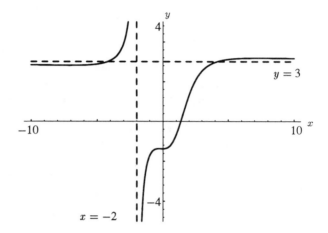

9.   To find vertical asymptote(s), look at the behavior of y as x approaches a value for which the denominator is 0.

$$x^2 - 4 = 0 \quad \text{when} \quad x = \pm 2.$$

If we plug in values for x near -2 and near $+2$, we will see that

$$y \to +\infty \text{ as } x \to 2^+$$
$$y \to -\infty \text{ as } x \to 2^-$$
$$y \to -\infty \text{ as } x \to -2^+$$
$$y \to +\infty \text{ as } x \to -2^-$$

Clearly, $x = -2$ and $x = 2$ are vertical asymptotes.

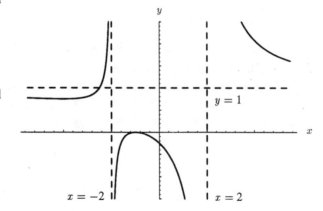

To find horizontal asymptote(s), look at the behavior of y as x goes to $+\infty$ and as x goes to $-\infty$. Note that as $x \to \pm\infty$, only the highest power of x matters, so that the $2x$, the 1, and the -4 become insignificant compared to the x^2 terms for large values of x. Thus,

$$y = \frac{x^2 + 2x + 1}{x^2 - 4} \approx \frac{x^2}{x^2} = 1$$

Clearly, $y = 1$ is a horizontal asymptote.

10. To find vertical asymptote(s), look at the behavior of y as x approaches a value for which the denominator is 0.

$$x - 2 = 0 \quad \text{when} \quad x = 2.$$

If we plug in values for x near 2, we will see that $y \to -\infty$ as $x \to 2$ from the right, but $y \to +\infty$ as $x \to 2$ from the left. Clearly, $x = 2$ is a vertical asymptote. $y(x)$ has no horizontal asymptote because, for large x,

$$y = \frac{1 - x^2}{x - 2} \approx \frac{-x^2}{x} = -x,$$

and so

$$y \to -\infty \quad \text{as} \quad x \to +\infty,$$
$$y \to +\infty \quad \text{as} \quad x \to -\infty.$$

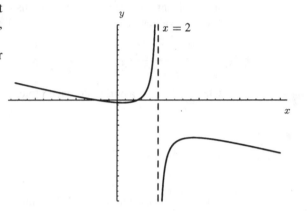

(Also, if $|x|$ is big enough, $\dfrac{1 - x^2}{x - 2} \approx -x$, and the straight line $y = -x$ is an asymptote for the graph.)

11. $f(x) = x^n$ is even for n an even integer, and odd for n an odd integer.

12. All polynomials whose terms are only of even degree are even. For example, $f(x) = x^8 + 4x^6 - 5x^2 + 9$ is even. All polynomials whose terms are only of odd degree are odd. For example, $g(x) = x^{11} + 11x^9 - 3x^3$ is odd. There are polynomials which are neither. For example, $h(x) = x^{13} + 13x^8 - 5x^7$ is neither.

13. (a) If $(1, 1)$ is on the graph, we know that

$$1 = a(1)^2 + b(1) + c = a + b + c.$$

(b) If $(1, 1)$ is the vertex, then the axis of symmetry is $x = 1$, so

$$-\frac{b}{2a} = 1,$$

and thus

$$a = -\frac{b}{2}, \text{ so } b = -2a.$$

But to be the vertex, $(1, 1)$ must also be on the graph, so we know that $a + b + c = 1$. Substituting $b = -2a$, we get $-a + c = 1$, which we can rewrite as $a = c - 1$, or $c = 1 + a$.

(c) For $(0, 6)$ to be on the graph, we must have $f(0) = 6$. But $f(0) = a(0^2) + b(0) + c = c$, so $c = 6$.

(d) To satisfy all the conditions, we must first, from (c), have $c = 6$. From (b), $a = c - 1$ so $a = 5$. Also from (b), $b = -2a$, so $b = -10$. Thus the completed equation is

$$y = f(x) = 5x^2 - 10x + 6,$$

which satisfies all the given conditions.

14. The pomegranate is at ground level when $f(t) = -16t^2 + 64t = -16t(t - 4) = 0$, so when $t = 0$ or $t = 4$. At time $t = 0$ it is thrown, so it must hit the ground at $t = 4$ seconds. The symmetry of its path with respect to time may convince you that it reaches its maximum height after 2 seconds. Alternatively, we can think of the graph of $f(t) = -16t^2 + 64t = -16(t - 2)^2 + 64$, which is a downward parabola with vertex (i.e., highest point) at $(2, 64)$. The maximum height is $f(2) = 64\,feet$.

15. (a) The object starts at $t = 0$, when $s = v_0(0) - g(0)^2/2 = 0$. Thus it starts on the ground, with zero height.
    (b) The object hits the ground when $s = 0$. This is satisfied at $t = 0$, before it has left the ground, and at some later time t that we must solve for.

    $$0 = v_0 t - gt^2/2 = t\left(v_0 - gt/2\right)$$

    Thus $s = 0$ when $t = 0$ and when $v_0 - gt/2 = 0$, i.e., when $t = 2v_0/g$. The starting time is $t = 0$, so it must hit the ground at time $t = 2v_0/g$.
    (c) The object reaches its maximum height halfway between when it is released and when it hits the ground, or at

    $$t = (2v_0/g)/2 = v_0/g.$$

    (d) Since we know the time at which the object reaches its maximum height, to find the height it actually reaches we just use the given formula, which tells us s at any given t. Plugging in $t = \frac{v_0}{g}$,

    $$s = v_0\left(\frac{v_0}{g}\right) - \frac{1}{2}g\left(\frac{v_0^2}{g^2}\right) = \frac{v_0^2}{g} - \frac{v_0^2}{2g}$$
    $$= \frac{2v_0^2 - v_0^2}{2g} = \frac{v_0^2}{2g}.$$

16. (a) $f(x) = k(x + 3)(x - 1)(x - 4) = k(x^3 - 2x^2 - 11x + 12)$, where $k < 0$. ($k \approx -\frac{1}{6}$ if the horizontal and vertical scales are equal; otherwise one can't tell how large k is.)
    (b) This function appears to be increasing for $-1.5 < x < 3$, decreasing for $x < -1.5$ and for $x > 3$.

17. (a) $f(x) = kx(x + 3)(x - 4) = k(x^3 - x^2 - 12x)$, where $k < 0$. ($k \approx -\frac{2}{9}$ if the horizontal and vertical scales are equal; otherwise one can't tell how large k is.)
    (b) This function appears to be increasing for $-1.5 < x < 2.5$, decreasing for $x < -1.5$ and for $x > 2.5$.

18. (a) $f(x) = k(x + 2)(x - 1)(x - 3)(x - 5) = k(x^4 - 7x^3 + 5x^2 + 31x - 30)$, where $k > 0$. ($k \approx \frac{1}{15}$ if the horizontal and vertical scales are equal; otherwise one can't tell how large k is.)
    (b) This function appears to be increasing for $-1 < x < 2$ and for $x > 4.3$, decreasing for $x < -1$ and for $2 < x < 4.3$.

19. (a) $f(x) = k(x+2)(x-2)^2(x-5) = k(x^4 - 7x^3 + 6x^2 + 28x - 40)$, where $k < 0$. ($k \approx -\frac{1}{15}$ if the scales are equal; otherwise one can't tell how large k is.)

    (b) This function is increasing for $x < -1$ and for $2 < x < 4$, decreasing for $-1 < x < 2$ and for $4 < x$.

20. (a) From the x-intercepts, we know the equation has the form

$$y = k(x+2)(x-1)(x-5).$$

Since $y = 2$ when $x = 0$,

$$2 = k(2)(-1)(-5) = k \cdot 10$$
$$k = \frac{1}{5}.$$

Thus we have

$$y = \frac{1}{5}(x+2)(x-1)(x-5).$$

21. (a) Because our cubic has a root at 2 and a double root at -2, it has the form

$$y = k(x+2)(x+2)(x-2).$$

Since $y = 4$ when $x = 0$,

$$4 = k(2)(2)(-2) = -8k,$$
$$k = -\frac{1}{2}.$$

Thus our equation is

$$y = -\frac{1}{2}(x+2)^2(x-2).$$

22. From the figure it appears that the "seat" of the graph $y = x^3$ has been moved to the left and up by 1, to the point $(-1, 1)$. Since translation to the right by h is achieved by replacing x with $(x - h)$ and translation up by k is achieved by replacing y with $(y - k)$, the equation of our translated graph appears to be

$$y - 1 = (x - (-1))^3$$

or

$$y = (x+1)^3 + 1.$$

Since the picture *suggests* that the graph of $y = x^3$ has been moved over and up by 1 (but does not show this explicitly), we will confirm that our equation is correct by checking the x and y intercepts (which are shown explicitly in the picture). The desired y-intercept is 2, and substituting $x = 0$ into the equation gives

$$y = (0+1)^3 + 1 = 2.$$

In addition, the desired x-intercept is -2, and substituting $y = 0$ into the equation gives

$$0 = (x+1)^3 + 1$$

so

$$(x+1)^3 = -1$$
$$x+1 = \sqrt[3]{-1} = -1$$
$$x = -2.$$

Thus our equation does have the graph shown.

We could also have solved this problem, with less guessing and more algebra, by finding a translation of x^3 which has the given x- and y-intercepts. Let h be the horizontal, and k the vertical translation; then the formula for the translated function is

$$f(x) = (x-h)^3 + k.$$

The y-intercept of f is $f(0) = 2$, so

$$f(0) = (0-h)^3 + k = -h^3 + k = 2.$$

Therefore $k = 2 + h^3$ and we have $f(x) = (x-h)^3 + (2+h^3)$. The x-intercept, -2, is the x-value for which $f(x) = 0$, so

$$0 = f(-2) = (-2-h)^3 + (2+h^3)$$
$$= -6h^2 - 12h - 6$$
$$= -6(h+1)^2$$

Therefore $h = -1$ and $k = 2 + h^3 = 1$.

23. $g(x) = 2x^2$, $h(x) = x^2 + k$ for any $k > 0$. Notice that the graph is symmetric about the y-axis and $\lim_{x \to \infty} f(x) = 2$.

24. (a) $a(v) = \frac{1}{m}(\text{ENGINE} - \text{WIND}) = \frac{1}{m}(F_E - kv^2)$, where k is a positive constant.
    (b)

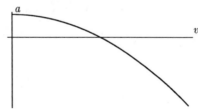

25. (a) $R(P) = kP(L - P)$, where k is a positive constant.
    (b)

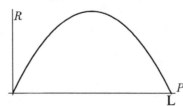

SOLUTIONS TO REVIEW PROBLEMS FOR CHAPTER ONE

1.

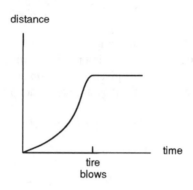

2.

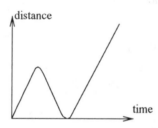

3. There are three peaks in the curve, each one of which occurs around one of the three meal times. The first peak is about 7 am, the next one right before noon and the third one around 6 pm. From the relative magnitudes of the peaks, more gas is used to cook dinner than lunch, and more gas is used to cook lunch than breakfast.

4. One possibility is $f(x) = -x^3$; see figure.

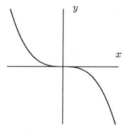

5. (a)   Four zeros, at approximately $x = -4.6, 1.2, 2.7$, and 4.1.
  (b) $f(2)$ is the y-value corresponding to $x = 2$, so $f(2)$ is about -1. Likewise, $f(4)$ is about 0.4.
  (c)   Decreasing near $x = -1$, increasing near $x = 3$.
  (d)   Concave up near $x = 2$, concave down near $x = -4$.
  (e)   Increasing on $x < -1.5$ and on $2 < x < 3.5$.

6. (a)   It was decreasing from March 2 to March 5 and increasing from March 5 to March 9.
  (b)   From March 5 to 8, the average temperature increased, but the rate of increase went down, from $12°$ between March 5 and 6 to $4°$ between March 6 and 7 to $2°$ between March 7 and 8.
        From March 7 to 9, the average temperature increased, and the rate of increase went up, from $2°$ between March 7 and 8 to $9°$ between March 8 and 9.

7.   We are looking for a linear function $y = f(x)$ that, given a time x in years, gives a value y in dollars for the value of the refrigerator. We know that when $x = 0$, that is, when the refrigerator is new, $y = 950$, and when $x = 7$, the refrigerator is worthless, so $y = 0$. Thus $(0,950)$ and $(7,0)$ are on the line that we are looking for. The slope is then given by

$$m = \frac{950}{-7}$$

It is negative, indicating that the value decreases as time passes. Having found the slope, we can take the point $(7,0)$ and use the point-slope formula:

$$y - y_1 = m(x - x_1).$$

So,

$$y - 0 = -\frac{950}{7}(x - 7)$$
$$= -\frac{950}{7}x + 950$$

8.   We will let

$$T = \text{amount of fuel for take-off}$$
$$L = \text{amount of fuel for landing}$$
$$P = \text{amount of fuel per mile in the air}$$
$$m = \text{the length of the trip in miles}$$

Then Q, the total amount of fuel needed, is given by

$$Q(m) = T + L + Pm$$

9. (a) Advertising is generally cheaper in bulk; spending more money will give better and better marginal results initially. (Spending \$5,000 could give you a big newspaper ad reaching 200,000 people; spending \$100,000 could give you a series of TV spots reaching 50,000,000 people.)

    (b) The temperature of a hot object decreases at a rate proportional to the difference between its temperature and the temperature of the air around it. Thus, the temperature of a very hot object decreases more quickly than a cooler object. The graph is decreasing and concave up. (We are assuming that the coffee is all at the same temperature.)

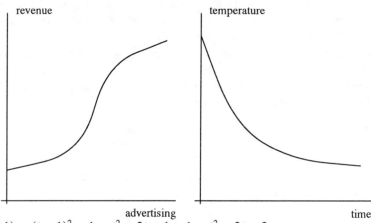

10. (a) $f(t+1) = (t+1)^2 + 1 = t^2 + 2t + 1 + 1 = t^2 + 2t + 2.$
     (b) $f(t^2+1) = (t^2+1)^2 + 1 = t^4 + 2t^2 + 1 + 1 = t^4 + 2t^2 + 2.$
     (c) $f(2) = 2^2 + 1 = 5.$
     (d) $2f(t) = 2(t^2 + 1) = 2t^2 + 2.$
     (e) $\left(f(t)\right)^2 + 1 = \left(t^2 + 1\right)^2 + 1 = t^4 + 2t^2 + 1 + 1 = t^4 + 2t^2 + 2.$

11. (a) $g(2+h) = (2+h)^2 + 2(2+h) + 3 = 4 + 4h + h^2 + 4 + 2h + 3 = h^2 + 6h + 11.$
     (b) $g(2) = 2^2 + 2(2) + 3 = 4 + 4 + 3 = 11$, which agrees with what we get by substituting $h = 0$ into (a).
     (c) $g(2+h) - g(2) = (h^2 + 6h + 11) - (11) = h^2 + 6h.$

12. (a) $f(n) + g(n) = (3n^2 - 2) + (n + 1) = 3n^2 + n - 1.$
     (b) $f(n)g(n) = (3n^2 - 2)(n + 1) = 3n^3 + 3n^2 - 2n - 2.$
     (c) the domain of $\frac{f(n)}{g(n)}$ is defined everywhere where $g(n) \neq 0$, i.e. for all $n \neq -1.$
     (d) $f(g(n)) = 3(n + 1)^2 - 2 = 3n^2 + 6n + 1.$
     (e) $g(f(n)) = (3n^2 - 2) + 1 = 3n^2 - 1.$

13. One possible graph is given below.

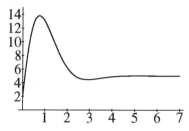

14. "The rate at which new people try it" is the rate of change of the total number of people who have tried the product. Thus the statement of the problem is telling you that the graph is concave down — the slope is positive but decreasing, as the graph shows.

15. $P = 2.91(e^{0.55})^t = 2.91(1.733)^t$

16. $P = (5 \cdot 10^{-3})(e^{-1.9 \cdot 10^{-2}})^t = (5 \cdot 10^{-3})(0.9812)^t$

17. (a) Since $Q = 25$ at $t = 0$, we have $Q_0 = 25$ (since $e^0 = 1$). We then plug the value at $t = 1$ into the equation

$$Q = 25e^{rt}$$

to find r. Doing so, we get

$$43 = 25e^{r(1)}$$
$$\frac{43}{25} = 1.72 = e^r$$
$$\ln 1.72 = r$$
$$0.5423 \approx r.$$

And so the equation is

$$Q = 25e^{0.5423t}.$$

(b) At the time t when the population has doubled,

$$2 = e^{0.5423t}$$
$$\ln 2 = 0.5423t$$
$$t = \frac{\ln 2}{0.5423} \approx 1.3 \text{ months.}$$

(c) At the time t when the population is 1000 rabbits,

$$1000 = 25e^{0.5423t}$$
$$40 = e^{0.5423t}$$
$$\ln 40 = 0.5423t$$
$$t = \frac{\ln 40}{0.5423} \approx 6.8 \text{ months.}$$

18. We use the equation $B = Pe^{rt}$. We want to have a balance of $B = \$20,000$ in $t = 6$ years, with an annual interest rate of 10%.

$$20,000 = Pe^{(0.1)6}$$
$$P = 20,000e^{-0.6}$$
$$\approx \$10,976.23.$$

19. $e^r = 1.05$ so $r = \ln(1.05) = 0.0488$ or 4.88%.

20. $e^{0.08} = 1.0833$ so the effective annual yield$= 8.33\%$.

21. To find a half-life, we want to find at what t value $Q = \frac{1}{2}Q_0$. Plugging this into the equation of the decay of plutonium-240, we have

$$\frac{1}{2} = e^{-0.00011t}$$
$$t = \frac{\ln\frac{1}{2}}{-0.00011} \approx 6{,}301 \text{ years.}$$

The only difference in the case of plutonium-242 is that the constant -0.00011 in the exponent is now -0.0000018. Thus, following the same procedure, the solution for t is

$$t = \frac{\ln\frac{1}{2}}{-0.0000018} \approx 385{,}000 \text{ years.}$$

22. If C is the amount of carbon-14 originally present in the skull, then after 5730 years, $\frac{1}{2}C$ is left. Hence,

$$\frac{1}{2}C = Ce^{-k\cdot 5730}$$
$$\frac{1}{2} = e^{-k\cdot 5730}$$
$$\ln\left(\frac{1}{2}\right) = -k \cdot 5730$$
$$k = \frac{-\ln\frac{1}{2}}{5730} = \frac{\ln 2}{5730}.$$

The question asks how long it took for the skull to lose 80% of its carbon-14. In other words, when will the remaining carbon-14$= \frac{1}{5}C$?

$$\text{Remaining carbon-14} = \frac{1}{5}C = Ce^{-\frac{\ln 2}{5730}\cdot t}$$
$$\frac{1}{5} = e^{-\frac{\ln 2}{5730}\cdot t}$$
$$\ln\left(\frac{1}{5}\right) = -\frac{\ln 2}{5730}t.$$

Since $\ln \frac{1}{5} = -\ln 5$, we have

$$t = \frac{\ln 5}{\ln 2}(5730) \approx 13,300 \text{ years},$$

the approximate age of the skull.

23. (a) Each day prices are multiplied by 1.001, so after 365 days prices are $(1.001)^{365} \approx 1.44$ what they were originally. Therefore, they increase by about 44% a year.

    (b) Guess about two years, since $1.44^2 \approx 2$. $(1.001)^{2(365)} = (1.001)^{730} \approx 2.074$, so it's a good guess.

24. If r was the average yearly inflation rate, in decimals, then $\frac{1}{4}(1+r)^3 = 2,400,000$, so $r = 211.53$, i.e. $r = 21,153\%$.

25. The period T_E of the earth is (by definition!) one year or about 365.24 days (don't forget leap-years). Since the semimajor axis of the earth is 150 million km, we can use Kepler's Law to derive the constant of proportionality, k.

$$T_E = k(S_E)^{\frac{3}{2}}$$

where S_E is the earth's semimajor axis, or 150 million km.

$$365.24 = k(150)^{\frac{3}{2}}$$

$$k = \frac{365.24}{(150)^{\frac{3}{2}}} \approx 0.198.$$

Now that we know the constant of proportionality, we can use it to derive the periods of Mercury and Pluto. For Mercury,

$$T_M = (0.198)(58)^{\frac{3}{2}} \approx 87.818 \text{ days}.$$

For Pluto,

$$T_P = (0.198)(6000)^{\frac{3}{2}} \approx 92,400 \text{ days},$$

or (converting Pluto's period to years),

$$\frac{(0.198)(6000)^{\frac{3}{2}}}{365.24} \approx 253 \text{ years}.$$

26. (a) goes with VIII, (b) goes with V, (c) goes with VII, (d) goes with I, (e) goes with III, (f) goes with VI, (g) goes with II, (h) goes with IV, and (i) goes with IX.

27. (a) The line given by $(0,2)$ and $(1,1)$ has slope $m = \frac{2-1}{-1} = -1$ and y-intercept 2, so its equation is

$$y = -x + 2.$$

The point of intersection of this line with the parabola $y = x^2$ is given by

$$x^2 = -x + 2$$
$$x^2 + x - 2 = 0$$
$$(x+2)(x-1) = 0.$$

The solution $x = 1$ corresponds to the point we are already given, so the other solution, $x = -2$, gives the x-coordinate of C. When we substitute back into either equation to get y, we get the coordinates for C, $(-2, 4)$.

(b) The line given by $(0, b)$ and $(1, 1)$ has slope $m = \frac{b-1}{-1} = 1 - b$, and y-intercept at $(0, b)$, so we can write the equation for the line as we did in part (a):

$$y = (1 - b)x + b$$

We then solve for the point of intersection with $y = x^2$ the same way:

$$x^2 = (1 - b)x + b$$
$$x^2 - (1 - b)x - b = 0$$
$$x^2 + (b - 1)x - b = 0$$
$$(x + b)(x - 1) = 0$$

Again, we have the solution at the given point $(1, 1)$, and a new solution at $x = -b$, corresponding to the other point of intersection C. Substituting back into either equation, we can find the y-coordinate for C, b^2 and thus C is given by $(-b, b^2)$. This result agrees with the particular case of part (a) where $b = 2$.

28. Starting with the general exponential equation $y = Ae^{kx}$, we first find that for $(0, 1)$ to be on the graph, we must have $A = 1$. Then to make $(3, 4)$ lie on the graph, we require

$$4 = e^{3k}$$
$$\ln 4 = 3k$$
$$k = \frac{\ln 4}{3} \approx 0.4621.$$

Thus the equation is

$$y = e^{0.4621x}.$$

29. Since this function has a y-intercept at $(0, 2)$, we expect it to have the form $y = 2e^{kx}$. Again, we find k by forcing the other point to lie on the graph:

$$1 = 2e^{2k}$$
$$\frac{1}{2} = e^{2k}$$
$$\ln\left(\frac{1}{2}\right) = 2k$$
$$k = \frac{\ln(\frac{1}{2})}{2} \approx -0.34657.$$

This value is negative, which makes sense since the graph shows exponential decay. The final equation, then, is

$$y = 2e^{-0.34657x}.$$

30. There are many solutions for a graph like this one. The simplest is $y = 1 - e^{-x}$, which gives the graph of $y = e^x$, flipped over the x-axis and moved up by 1. The resulting graph passes through the origin and approaches $y = 1$ as an upper bound, the two features of the given graph.

31. $y = -kx(x + 5) = -k(x^2 + 5x)$, where $k > 0$ is any constant.

32. $y = k(x + 2)(x + 1)(x - 1) = k(x^3 + 2x^2 - x - 2)$, where $k > 0$ is any constant.

33. $x = ky(y - 4) = k(y^2 - 4y)$, where $k > 0$ is any constant.

34. $y = 5 \sin\left(\frac{\pi t}{20}\right)$

35. This is an exponential decay curve reflected in the t-axis. $y = -2\left(\frac{1}{4}\right)^t = -2\left(4^{-t}\right)$

36. $z = 1 - \cos \theta$

37. (a) There are at least 3 roots in the interval: one between $x = 1$ and $x = 2$, one between $x = 2$ and $x = 3$, and one between $x = 3$ and $x = 4$.

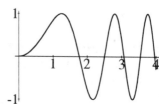

  (b) The picture of the graph to the right shows that there are a total of five roots: there are *three*, not just one, between $x = 3$ and $x = 4$.

  (c) In order, the roots are approximately $1.8, 2.5, 3.1, 3.5$, and 4.0.

  (d) $\sin x = 0$ only when x is an integer multiple of π, so $\sin\left(x^2\right) = 0$ only when t^2 is a multiple of π, say $k\pi$ where k is an integer. Thus the positive roots of $\sin\left(t^2\right)$ are $\sqrt{\pi}, \sqrt{2\pi}, \sqrt{3\pi}$, etc. The smallest positive root is therefore $\sqrt{\pi}$.

  (e) $\sqrt{\pi} \approx 1.8, \sqrt{2\pi} \approx 2.5, \sqrt{3\pi} \approx 3.1, \sqrt{4\pi} \approx 3.5, \sqrt{5\pi} \approx 4.0$.

38. (a) $\arcsin x =$ the angle between $-\frac{\pi}{2}$ and $\frac{\pi}{2}$ whose sine is x

  (b) $\arcsin(\sin 1) = 1$
  $\arcsin(\sin 2) = 1.1416$
  $\sin(\arcsin 1) = 1$
  $\sin(\arcsin 2)$ is undefined.

  (c) $\arcsin(\sin 1) =$ the angle between $-\frac{\pi}{2}$ and $\frac{\pi}{2}$ whose sine is $\sin 1$.
  $\arcsin(\sin 2) = \arcsin(0.9093) = 1.14$ since $\sin(1.1416) = 0.9093$
  $\sin(\arcsin 1) = \sin\left(\frac{\pi}{2}\right) = 1$
  $\arcsin 2$ is undefined.

39. (a) Two solutions: 0.4 and 2.7.

  (b) $\arcsin(0.4)$ is the first solution approximated above; the second is an approximation to $\pi - \arcsin(0.4)$.

  (c) By symmetry, there are two solutions: -0.4 and -2.7.

  (d) $-0.4 \approx -\arcsin(0.4)$ and $-2.7 \approx -(\pi - \arcsin(0.4)) = \arcsin(0.4) - \pi$.

40. Depth $= d = 7 + 1.5 \sin\left(\frac{\pi}{3}t\right)$

41. (a) From the graph the period appears to be about 3:

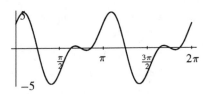

(b) Since we are dealing with trigonometric functions, it makes sense that the actual period is π.

(c) $\cos 2x$ is periodic with period π. $\sin 4x$ is periodic with period $\frac{\pi}{2}$, so it is also periodic with period π, since if it repeats itself after $\frac{\pi}{2}$, it will repeat itself again after π. Sums and multiples of periodic functions that have the same period are also periodic with that period, so the composition function has period π.

42. (a) is $g(x)$ since it is linear. (b) is $f(x)$ since it has decreasing slope; the slope starts out about 1 and then decreases to about $\frac{1}{10}$. (c) is $h(x)$ since it has increasing slope; the slope starts out about $\frac{1}{10}$ and then increases to about 1.

43. (a) (i) The inverse function is

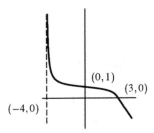

(ii) The reciprocal function is

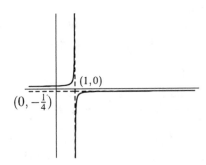

(b) The horizontal asymptote at $y = -4$ in the original function becomes a vertical asymptote at $x = -4$ in the inverse function.

44. (a) This moves the graph one unit to the left.

(b) A non-constant polynomial tends toward $+\infty$ or $-\infty$ as $x \to \infty$. This polynomial p does not. Therefore p must be a constant function, i.e. its graph is a horizontal line.

45. (a) $p(x) = ax^2 + c$ for any a and any c.

(b) $p(x) = bx$ for any b.

46. (a) $r(p) = kp(A - p)$, where $k > 0$ is a constant.

(b) $p = A/2$.

47. (a) The rate R is the difference of the rate at which the glucose is being injected, which is given to be constant, and the rate at which the glucose is being broken down, which is given to be proportional to the amount of glucose present. Thus we have the formula

$$R = k_1 - k_2 G$$

where k_1 is the rate that the glucose is being injected, k_2 is the constant relating the rate that it is broken down to the amount present, and G is the amount present.

(b)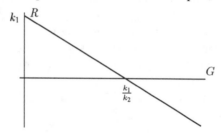

48. (a) The rate of change of the fish population is the difference between the rate they are reproducing, and the rate they are being caught. We are given that they are reproducing at a rate of 5% of P where P is their population, and being caught at a constant rate Y. Thus the net rate of change R (in fish per year) is given by

$$R = (0.05)P - Y$$

(b)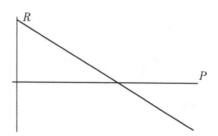

49. (a) $S(0) = 12$ since the days are always 12 hours long at the equator.

(b) Since $S(0) = 12$ from part (a) and the formula gives $S(0) = a$, we have $a = 12$. Since $S(x)$ must be continuous at $x = x_0$, and the formula gives $S(x_0) = a + b\arcsin(1) = 12 + b\left(\frac{\pi}{2}\right)$ and also $S(x_0) = 24$, we must have $12 + b\left(\frac{\pi}{2}\right) = 24$ so $b\left(\frac{\pi}{2}\right) = 12$ and $b = \frac{24}{\pi} \approx 7.64$.

(c) $S(32°13') \approx 14.12$ and $S(46°4') \approx 15.58$.

(d)   As the graph to the right shows, $S(x)$ is not smooth. This is because above the Arctic Circle, there cannot be more than 24 hours of sunlight in a day.

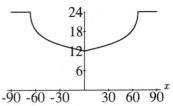

50. (a)   The graph shows that $f(15)$ is approximately 48. So, the place to find find 15 million-year-old rock is about 48 meters below the Atlantic sea floor.

(b)   Since f is increasing (not decreasing, since the depth axis is reversed!), f is invertible. One can see this also by noting that the graph of f is cut by a horizontal line at most once.

(c)   Look at where the horizontal line through 120 intersects the graph of f and read downwards: $f^{-1}(120)$ is about 35. In practical terms, this means that at a depth of 120 meters down, the rock is 35 million years old.

(d)   First, we normalize the graph of f so that time and depth are increasing from left to right and bottom to top. Points (t, d) on the graph of f correspond to points (d, t) on the graph of f^{-1}. So one could graph f^{-1} by taking points from the original graph of f reversing their coordinates, and connecting them up. However, an easier way is to change the graph of f so that the t and d axes are exchanged. (This amounts to the same thing.) When this is done, the graph of f will be flipped over a line bisecting the 90° angle at the origin. The resulting graph (Figure 1.18) is the graph of f^{-1}.

   (One cannot find the graph of f^{-1} by flipping along the line $t = d$ in this instance because t and d are in different scales.)

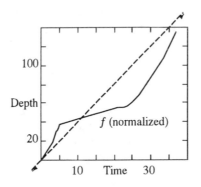
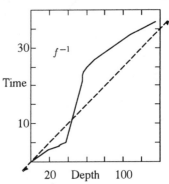

Figure 1.18: Graph of f, reflected to give that of f^{-1}.

CHAPTER TWO

2.1 SOLUTIONS

1.

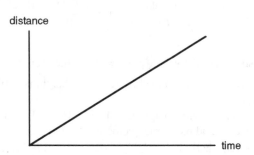

2.

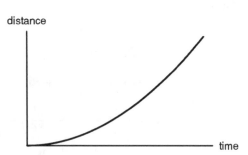

3.

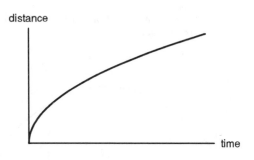

4.

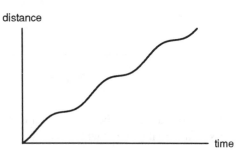

5.

$$\left(\begin{array}{c} \text{Average velocity} \\ 0 < t < 0.2 \end{array} \right) = \frac{s(0.2) - s(0)}{0.2 - 0} = \frac{0.5}{0.2} = 2.5 \text{ ft/sec.}$$

$$\left(\begin{array}{c} \text{Average velocity} \\ 0.2 < t < 0.4 \end{array} \right) = \frac{s(0.4) - s(0.2)}{0.4 - 0.2} = \frac{1.3}{0.2} = 6.5 \text{ ft/sec.}$$

A reasonable estimate of the velocity at $t = 0.2$ is the average: $\frac{1}{2}(6.5 + 2.5) = 4.5$ ft/sec.

6. (a) When $t = 0$, the ball is on the bridge and its height is $f(0) = 36$, so the bridge is 36 feet above the ground.
    (b) After 1 second, the ball's height is $f(1) = -16 + 50 + 36 = 70$ feet, so it traveled $70 - 36 = 34$ feet in 1 second, and its average velocity was 34 ft/sec.
    (c) At $t = 1.001$, the ball's height is $f(1.001) \approx 70.017984$ feet, and its velocity about $\frac{70.017984 - 70}{1.0001 - 1} = 17.984 \approx 18$ ft/sec.
    (d) We complete the square:

$$\begin{aligned} f(t) &= -16t^2 + 50t + 36 \\ &= -16\left(t^2 - \frac{25}{8}t\right) + 36 \\ &= -16\left(t^2 - \frac{25}{8}t + \frac{625}{256}\right) + 36 + 16\left(\frac{625}{256}\right) \\ &= -16(t - 1\tfrac{9}{16})^2 + 75\tfrac{1}{16} \end{aligned}$$

so the graph of f is a downward parabola with vertex at the point $(1\tfrac{9}{16}, 75\tfrac{1}{16}) = (1.5625, 75.0625)$.

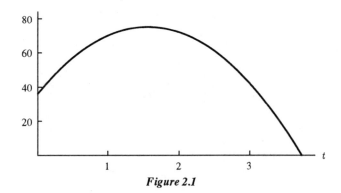

Figure 2.1

The velocity of the ball should be zero when it is at the peak.
    (e) The ball reaches its maximum height when $t = 1\tfrac{9}{16} = 1.5625$.

7.

TABLE 2.1

slope	point
-3	F
-1	C
0	E
$\frac{1}{2}$	A
1	B
2	D

8. The slope is positive at A and D; negative at C and F. The slope is most positive at A; most negative at F.

9. $0 <$ slope at $C <$ slope at $B <$ slope of $AB < 1 <$ slope at A.

10. One possibility is:

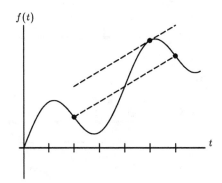

11.

$$\frac{(3+0.1)^2 - 9}{0.1} = 6.1$$

$$\frac{(3+0.01)^2 - 9}{0.01} = 6.01$$

$$\frac{(3+0.001)^2 - 9}{0.001} = 6.001$$

These calculations suggest that $\lim_{h \to 0} \dfrac{(3+h)^2 - 9}{h} = 6.0$

12.

$$\frac{7^{0.1} - 1}{0.1} = 2.148$$

$$\frac{7^{0.01} - 1}{0.01} = 1.965$$

$$\frac{7^{0.001} - 1}{0.001} = 1.948$$

$$\frac{7^{0.0001} - 1}{0.0001} = 1.946$$

This suggests that $\displaystyle\lim_{h \to 0} \frac{7^h - 1}{h} \approx 1.9 \ldots$

13.

TABLE 2.2

h	$(\cos h - 1)/h$
0.01	−0.005
0.001	−0.0005
0.0001	−0.00005

$$\lim_{h \to 0} \frac{\cos h - 1}{h} = 0$$

14.

TABLE 2.3

h	$(e^{1+h} - e)/h$
0.01	2.7319
0.001	2.7196
0.0001	2.7184

$$\lim_{h \to 0} \frac{e^{1+h} - e}{h} = 2.7 \ldots$$

In fact, this limit is e.

2.2 SOLUTIONS

1. (a)

TABLE 2.4

x	1	1.5	2	2.5	3
$\log x$	0	0.18	0.30	0.40	0.48

(b)   The average rate of change of $f(x) = \log x$ between $x = 1$ and $x = 3$ is

$$\frac{f(3) - f(1)}{3 - 1} = \frac{\log 3 - \log 1}{3 - 1} \approx \frac{0.48 - 0}{2} = 0.24$$

(c)   First we find the average rates of change of $f(x) = \log x$ between $x = 1.5$ and $x = 2$, and between $x = 2$ and $x = 2.5$.

$$\frac{\log 2 - \log 1.5}{2 - 1.5} = \frac{0.30 - 0.18}{0.5} \approx 0.24$$

$$\frac{\log 2.5 - \log 2}{2.5 - 2} = \frac{0.40 - 0.30}{0.5} \approx 0.20$$

Now we approximate the instantaneous rate of change at $x = 2$ by finding the average of the above rates, i.e.

$$\left(\begin{matrix} \text{the instantaneous rate of change} \\ \text{of } f(x) = \log x \text{ at } x = 2 \end{matrix} \right) \approx \frac{0.24 + 0.20}{2} = 0.22.$$

2.

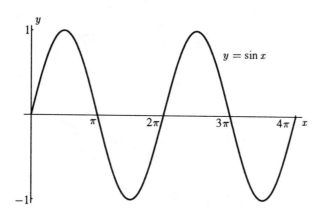

Since $\sin x$ is decreasing for values near $x = 3\pi$, its derivative at $x = 3\pi$ is negative.

3.

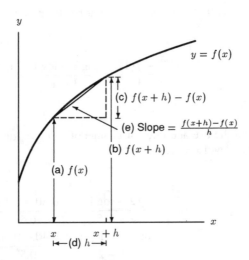

4.

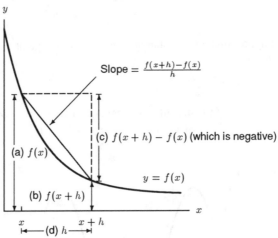

5.

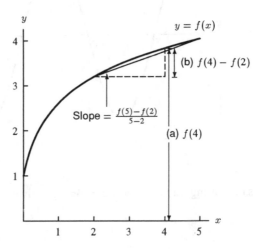

6.

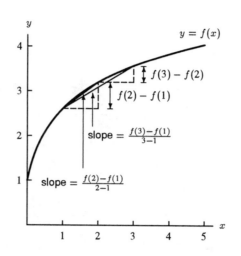

(a) $f(4) > f(3)$ since f is increasing.
(b)   From the figure, it appears that $f(2) - f(1) > f(3) - f(2)$.
(c) $\dfrac{f(2) - f(1)}{2 - 1}$ represents the slope of the secant line connecting the graph at $x = 1$ and $x = 2$.
    This is greater than the slope of the secant line connecting the graph at $x = 1$ and $x = 3$ which is
    $\dfrac{f(3) - f(1)}{3 - 1}$.

7.   (a) $f(4)/4$ is the slope of the line connecting $(0,0)$ to $(4, f(4))$. (See Figure 2.2.)
    (b)   It is clear from the picture for part (a) that $f(3)/3 > f(4)/4$.

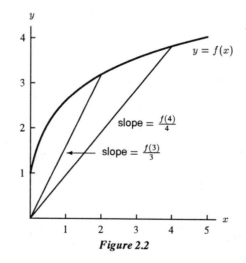

Figure 2.2

8.

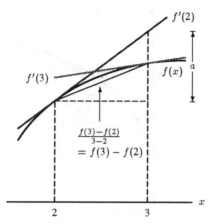

The quantities $f'(2)$, $f'(3)$ and $f(3) - f(2)$ have the following interpretations:

$f'(2)$ = slope of the tangent line at $x = 2$

$f'(3)$ = slope of the tangent line at $x = 3$

$f(3) - f(2) = \frac{f(3)-f(2)}{3-2}$ = slope of the secant line from $f(2)$ to $f(3)$.

From the figure, it is clear that $0 < f(3) - f(2) < f'(2)$. By extending the secant line past the point $(3, f(3))$, we can see that it lies above the tangent line at $x = 3$. Thus $0 < f'(3) < f(3) - f(2) < f'(2)$. From the figure, the height a appears less than 1, so $f'(2) = \frac{a}{3-2} = \frac{a}{1} < 1$.

Thus

$$0 < f'(3) < f(3) - f(2) < f'(2) < 1.$$

9. (a) C and D.

    (b) B and C.

    (c) A and B, and C and D.

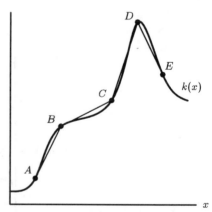

Figure 2.3

10.

$$f'(1) = \lim_{h \to 0} \frac{f(1 + h) - f(1)}{h} = \lim_{h \to 0} \frac{((1 + h)^3 + 5) - (1^3 + 5)}{h}$$

$$= \lim_{h \to 0} \frac{1 + 3h + 3h^2 + h^3 + 5 - 1 - 5}{h} = \lim_{h \to 0} \frac{3h + 3h^2 + h^3}{h}$$

$$= \lim_{h \to 0} (3 + 3h + h^2) = 3.$$

11.

$$g'(2) = \lim_{h \to 0} \frac{g(2 + h) - g(2)}{h} = \lim_{h \to 0} \frac{\frac{1}{2+h} - \frac{1}{2}}{h}$$

$$= \lim_{h \to 0} \frac{2 - (2 + h)}{h(2 + h)2} = \lim_{h \to 0} \frac{-h}{h(2 + h)2}$$

$$= \lim_{h \to 0} \frac{-1}{(2 + h)2} = -\frac{1}{4}$$

12.

$$g'(-1) = \lim_{h \to 0} \frac{g(-1 + h) - g(-1)}{h} = \lim_{h \to 0} \frac{(3(-1 + h)^2 + 5(-1 + h)) - (3(-1)^2 + 5(-1))}{h}$$

$$= \lim_{h \to 0} \frac{(3(1 - 2h + h^2) - 5 + 5h) - (-2)}{h} = \lim_{h \to 0} \frac{3 - 6h + 3h^2 - 3 + 5h}{h}$$

$$= \lim_{h \to 0} \frac{(-h + 3h2)}{h} = \lim_{h \to 0} (-1 + 3h) = -1.$$

13.

$$g'(2) = \lim_{h \to 0} \frac{g(2 + h) - g(2)}{h} = \lim_{h \to 0} \frac{\frac{1}{(2+h)^2} - \frac{1}{2^2}}{h}$$

$$= \lim_{h \to 0} \frac{2^2 - (2 + h)^2}{2^2(2 + h)^2 h} = \lim_{h \to 0} \frac{4 - 4 - 4h - h^2}{4h(2 + h)^2}$$

$$= \lim_{h \to 0} \frac{-4h - h^2}{4h(2 + h)^2} = \lim_{h \to 0} \frac{-4 - h}{4(2 + h)^2} =$$

$$= \frac{04}{4(2)^2} = -\frac{1}{4}.$$

14.

$$f'(3) = \lim_{h \to 0} \frac{f(3 + h) - f(3)}{h} = \lim_{h \to 0} \frac{(3 + h)^2 + 3 + h - (3^2 + 3)}{h}$$

$$= \lim_{h \to 0} \frac{9 + 6h + h^2 + 3 + h - 9 - 3}{h} = \lim_{h \to 0} \frac{7h + h^2}{h} = \lim_{h \to 0} (7 + h) = 7.$$

Thus the slope of the tangent line is 7. Since $f(3) = 3^2 + 3 = 12$, the line goes through the point $(3, 12)$, and therefore its equation is

$$y - 12 = 7(x - 3) \quad \text{or} \quad y = 7x - 9.$$

The graph is in Figure 2.4.

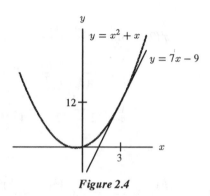

Figure 2.4

15.   First find the derivative of $f(x) = 1/x^2$ at $x = 1$.

$$\begin{aligned}
f'(1) &= \lim_{h \to 0} \frac{f(1 + h) - f(1)}{h} = \lim_{h \to 0} \frac{\frac{1}{(1+h)^2} - \frac{1}{1^2}}{h} \\
&= \lim_{h \to 0} \frac{1^2 - (1 + h)^2}{h(1 + h)^2} = \lim_{h \to 0} \frac{1 - (1 + 2h + h^2)}{h(1 + h)^2} \\
&= \lim_{h \to 0} \frac{-2h - h^2}{h(1 + h)^2} = \lim_{h \to 0} \frac{-2 - h}{(1 + h)^2} = -2
\end{aligned}$$

Thus the tangent line has a slope of -2 and goes through the point $(1, 1)$, and so its equation is

$$y - 1 = -2(x - 1) \quad \text{or} \quad y = -2x + 3.$$

16.   (a)

$$f'(0) = \lim_{h \to 0} \frac{\overbrace{\sin h}^{h \text{ in degrees}} - \overbrace{\sin 0}^{0}}{h} = \frac{\sin h}{h}.$$

To four decimal places,

$$\frac{\sin 0.2}{0.2} \approx \frac{\sin 0.1}{0.1} \approx \frac{\sin 0.01}{0.01} \approx \frac{\sin 0.001}{0.001} \approx 0.01745$$

so $f'(0) \approx 0.01745$.

(b) Consider the ratio $\frac{\sin h}{h}$. As we approach 0, the numerator, $\sin h$, will be much smaller in magnitude if h is in degrees than it would be if h were in radians. For example, if $h = 1°$ radian, $\sin h = 0.8415$, but if $h = 1$ degree, $\sin h = 0.01745$. Thus, since the numerator is smaller for h measured in degrees while the denominator is the same, we expect the ratio $\frac{\sin h}{h}$ to be smaller.

17.

TABLE 2.5

x	2.998	2.999	3.000	3.001	3.002
$x^3 + 4x$	38.938	38.969	39.000	39.031	39.062

We see that each x increase of 0.001 leads to an increase in $f(x)$ by about 0.031, so $f'(3) \approx \frac{0.031}{0.001} = 31$.

18.

TABLE 2.6

x	1.998	1.999	2.000	2.001	2.002
$g(x)$	31.8403	31.9201	32.0000	32.0801	32.1603

TABLE 2.7

x	−2.002	−2.001	−2.000	−1.999	−1.998
$g(x)$	−31.8403	−31.9201	−32.0000	−32.0801	−32.1603

Looking at the first table, we'd estimate $g'(2) = \frac{0.0800}{0.001} = 80$. From the second table, we have $g'(-2) = \frac{-0.0800}{-0.001} = 80$, so $g'(2) = g'(-2)$. This is what we'd expect from an odd function; because it is symmetric around the origin, tangent lines at corresponding points have the same slope.

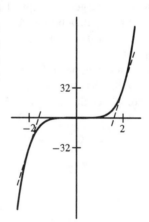

19. We want $f'(2)$. The exact answer is

$$f'(2) = \lim_{h \to 0} \frac{f(2 + h) - f(2)}{h} = \lim_{h \to 0} \frac{(2 + h)^{2+h} - 4}{h},$$

but we can approximate this by using, say, $h = 0.0001$. Then

$$f'(2) \approx \frac{(2.0001)^{2.0001} - 4}{0.0001} \approx 6.773.$$

20.

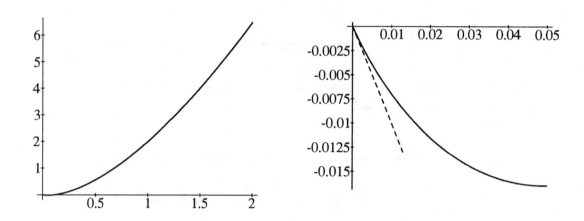

Notice that we can't get all the information we want just from the graph of f for $0 \leq x \leq 2$, shown above to the left. Looking at this graph, it looks as if the slope at $x = 0$ is 0. But if we zoom in on the graph near $x = 0$, we get the graph of f for $0 \leq x \leq 0.05$, shown above on the upper right. We see that f does dip down quite a bit between $x = 0$ and $x \approx 0.11$. In fact, it now looks like $f'(0)$ is around -1. Note that since $f(x)$ is undefined for $x < 0$, this derivative only makes sense as we approach zero from the right.

We zoom in on the graph of f near $x = 1$ to get a more accurate picture to estimate $f'(1)$. A graph of f for $0.7 \leq x \leq 1.3$ is shown below. [Keep in mind that the axes shown in this graph don't cross at the origin!] Here we see that $f'(1) \approx 3.5$.

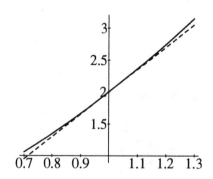

21. (a)

TABLE 2.8

x	$\frac{\sinh(x+0.001)-\sinh(x)}{0.001}$	$\frac{\sinh(x+0.0001)-\sinh(x)}{0.0001}$	so $f'(0) \approx$	$\cosh(x)$
0	1.00000	1.00000	1.00000	1.00000
0.3	1.04549	1.04535	1.04535	1.04534
0.7	1.25555	1.25521	1.25521	1.25517
1	1.54367	1.54314	1.54314	1.54308

(b) It seems that they are approximately the same, i.e. the derivative of $\sinh(x) = \cosh(x)$ for $x = 0, 0.3, 0.7$, and 1.

22.

$$f'(1) = \lim_{h \to 0} \frac{f(1+h) - f(1)}{h} = \lim_{h \to 0} \frac{\ln(\cos(1+h)) - \ln(\cos 1)}{h}$$

For $h = 0.001$, the difference quotient $= -1.55912$; for $h = 0.0001$, the difference quotient $= -1.55758$.

The instantaneous rate of change of f therefore appears to be about -1.558 at $x = 1$.
At $x = \frac{\pi}{4}$, if we try $h = 0.0001$, then

$$\text{difference quotient} = \frac{\ln[\cos(\frac{\pi}{4} + 0.0001)] - \ln(\cos \frac{\pi}{4})}{0.0001} \approx -1.0001.$$

The instantaneous rate of change of f appears to be about -1 at $x = \frac{\pi}{4}$.

23. We want to approximate $P'(0)$ and $P'(2)$. Since for small h

$$P'(0) \approx \frac{P(h) - P(0)}{h},$$

if we take $h = 0.01$, we get

$$P'(0) \approx \frac{1.15(1.014)^{0.01} - 1.15}{0.01} = 0.01599 \, \text{billion/year} = 16.0 \, \text{million people/year}$$

$$P'(2) \approx \frac{1.15(1.014)^{2.01} - 1.15(1.014)^2}{0.01} = 0.0164 \, \text{billion/year} = 16.4 \, \text{million people/year}$$

24.

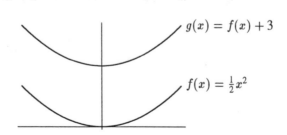

(a)   From the figure above, it appears that the slopes of the tangent lines to the two graphs are the same at each x. For $x = 0$, the slopes of the tangents to the graphs of $f(x)$ and $g(x)$ at 0 are

$$f'(0) = \lim_{h \to 0} \frac{f(0 + h) - f(0)}{h}$$

$$= \lim_{h \to 0} \frac{f(h) - 0}{h}$$

$$= \lim_{h \to 0} \frac{\frac{1}{2}h^2}{h}$$

$$= \lim_{h \to 0} \frac{1}{2}h$$

$$= 0,$$

$$g'(0) = \lim_{h \to 0} \frac{g(0 + h) - g(0)}{h}$$

$$= \lim_{h \to 0} \frac{g(h) - g(0)}{h}$$

$$= \lim_{h \to 0} \frac{\frac{1}{2}h^2 + 3 - 3}{h}$$

$$= \lim_{h \to 0} \frac{\frac{1}{2}h^2}{h}$$

$$= \lim_{h \to 0} \frac{1}{2}h$$

$$= 0.$$

For $x = 2$, the slopes of the tangents to the graphs of $f(x)$ and $g(x)$ are

$$f'(2) = \lim_{h \to 0} \frac{f(2 + h) - f(2)}{h}$$

$$= \lim_{h \to 0} \frac{\frac{1}{2}(2 + h)^2 - \frac{1}{2}(2)^2}{h}$$

$$= \lim_{h \to 0} \frac{\frac{1}{2}(4 + 4h + h^2) - 2}{h}$$

$$= \lim_{h \to 0} \frac{2 + 2h + \frac{1}{2}h^2 - 2}{h}$$

$$= \lim_{h \to 0} \frac{2h + \frac{1}{2}h^2}{h}$$

$$= \lim_{h \to 0} \left(2 + \frac{1}{2}h\right)$$

$$= 2,$$

$$g'(2) = \lim_{h \to 0} \frac{g(2 + h) - g(2)}{h}$$

$$= \lim_{h \to 0} \frac{\frac{1}{2}(2 + h)^2 + 3 - (\frac{1}{2}(2)^2 + 3)}{h}$$

$$= \lim_{h \to 0} \frac{\frac{1}{2}(2 + h)^2 - \frac{1}{2}(2)^2}{h}$$

$$= \lim_{h \to 0} \frac{\frac{1}{2}(4 + 4h + h^2) - 2}{h}$$

$$= \lim_{h \to 0} \frac{2 + 2h + \frac{1}{2}(h^2) - 2}{h}$$

$$= \lim_{h \to 0} \frac{2h + \frac{1}{2}(h^2)}{h}$$

$$= \lim_{h \to 0} \left(2 + \frac{1}{2}h\right)$$

$$= 2.$$

For $x = x_0$, the slopes of the tangents to the graphs of $f(x)$ and $g(x)$ are

$$f'(x_0) = \lim_{h \to 0} \frac{f(x_0 + h) - f(x_0)}{h}$$

$$= \lim_{h \to 0} \frac{\frac{1}{2}(x_0 + h)^2 - \frac{1}{2}x_0^2}{h}$$

$$= \lim_{h \to 0} \frac{\frac{1}{2}(x_0^2 + 2x_0h + h^2) - \frac{1}{2}x_0^2}{h}$$

$$= \lim_{h \to 0} \frac{x_0 h + \frac{1}{2}h^2}{h}$$

$$= \lim_{h \to 0} \left(x_0 + \frac{1}{2}h \right)$$

$$= x_0,$$

$$g'(x_0) = \lim_{h \to 0} \frac{g(x_0 + h) - g(x_0)}{h}$$

$$= \lim_{h \to 0} \frac{\frac{1}{2}(x_0 + h)^2 + 3 - (\frac{1}{2}(x_0)^2 + 3)}{h}$$

$$= \lim_{h \to 0} \frac{\frac{1}{2}(x_0 + h)^2 - \frac{1}{2}(x_0)^2}{h}$$

$$= \lim_{h \to 0} \frac{\frac{1}{2}(x_0^2 + 2x_0h + h^2) - \frac{1}{2}x_0^2}{h}$$

$$= \lim_{h \to 0} \frac{x_0 h + \frac{1}{2}h^2}{h}$$

$$= \lim_{h \to 0} \left(x_0 + \frac{1}{2}h \right)$$

$$= x_0.$$

(b)

$$g'(x) = \lim_{h \to 0} \frac{g(x + h) - g(x)}{h}$$

$$= \lim_{h \to 0} \frac{f(x + h) + C - (f(x) + C)}{h}$$

$$= \lim_{h \to 0} \frac{f(x + h) - f(x)}{h}$$

$$= f'(x).$$

25. As h gets smaller, round-off error becomes important. When $h = 10^{-12}$, the quantity $2^h - 1$ is so close to 0 that the calculator rounds off the difference to 0, making the difference quotient 0. The same thing will happen when $h = 10^{-20}$.

2.3 SOLUTIONS

1. The graph is that of the line $y = -2x + 2$. Its derivative is -2.

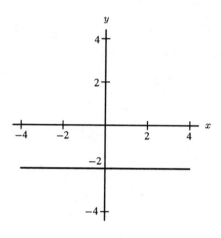

2.

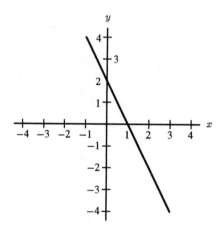

3. Note: This graph should start at $x = -4$, $y = -1$, intersect the x-axis around -2.5, the y-axis around 1, then the x-axis again around 1.5, and end around $(4, -1)$.

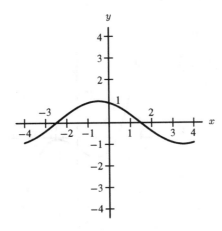

4.

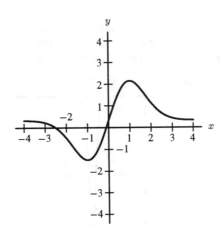

5.

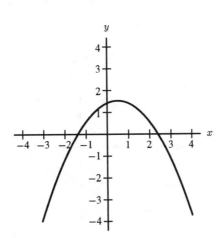

6.

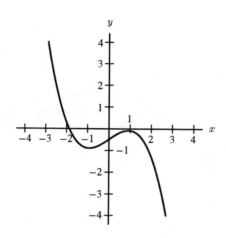

7. A possible graph for g' is shown in the figure to the right. On intervals where $g(t)$ is constant (i.e. flat), $g' = 0$. The small interval where g decreases very quickly corresponds to the downwards spike on the graph of g'. At the point where g' hits the bottom of its spike, the rate of decrease of $g(t)$ is greatest.

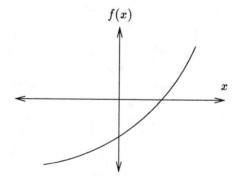

Figure 2.5

8. (a)

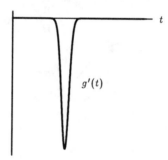

(b)

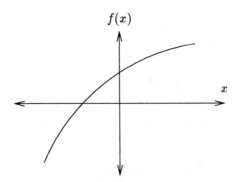

(c)

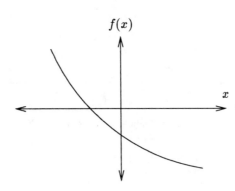

(d)

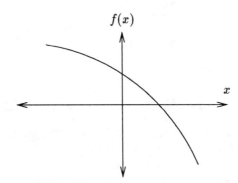

9. We know that $f'(x) \approx \dfrac{f(x+h) - f(x)}{h}$. For this problem, we'll take the average of the values obtained for $h = 1$ and $h = -1$; that's the average of $f(x+1) - f(x)$ and $f(x) - f(x-1)$ which equals $\dfrac{f(x+1) - f(x-1)}{2}$. Thus, $f'(0) \approx f(1) - f(0) = 13 - 18 = -5$.

$f'(1) \approx [f(2) - f(0)]/2 = [10 - 18]/2 = -4.$
$f'(2) \approx [f(3) - f(1)]/2 = [9 - 13]/2 = -2.$
$f'(3) \approx [f(4) - f(2)]/2 = [9 - 10]/2 = -0.5.$
$f'(4) \approx [f(5) - f(3)]/2 = [11 - 9]/2 = 1.$
$f'(5) \approx [f(6) - f(4)]/2 = [15 - 9]/2 = 3.$
$f'(6) \approx [f(7) - f(5)]/2 = [21 - 11]/2 = 5.$
$f'(7) \approx [f(8) - f(6)]/2 = [30 - 15]/2 = 7.5.$
$f'(8) \approx f(8) - f(7) = 30 - 21 = 9.$

The rate of change of $f(x)$ is positive for $4 \leq x \leq 8$, negative for $0 \leq x \leq 3$. The rate of change is greatest at about $x = 8$.

10.

TABLE 2.9

x	$f(x)$	x	$f(x)$	x	$f(x)$
1.998	2.6587	2.998	8.9820	3.998	21.3013
1.999	2.6627	2.999	8.9910	3.999	21.3173
2.000	2.6667	3.000	9.0000	4.000	21.3333
2.001	2.6707	3.001	9.0090	4.001	21.3493
2.002	2.6747	3.002	9.0180	4.002	21.3653

Near 2, the values of $f(x)$ seem to be increasing by 0.004 for each increase of 0.001 in x, so the derivative appears to be $\frac{0.004}{0.001} = 4$. Near 3, the values of $f(x)$ are increasing by 0.009 for each step of 0.001, so the derivative appears to be 9. Near 4, $f(x)$ increases by 0.016 for each step of 0.001, so the derivative appears to be 16. The pattern seems to be, then, that at a point x, the derivative of $f(x) = \frac{1}{3}x^3$ is x^2.

11.

TABLE 2.10

t	$g(t)$	t	$g(t)$	t	$g(t)$
0.998	1.994	1.998	5.990	2.998	11.986
0.999	1.997	1.999	5.995	2.999	11.993
1.000	2.000	2.000	6.000	3.000	12.000
1.001	2.003	2.001	6.005	3.001	12.007
1.002	2.006	2.002	6.010	3.002	12.014

Near 1, the values of $g(t)$ increase by 0.003 for each t increase of 0.001, so the derivative appears to be 3. Near 2, the increase is 0.005 for each step of 0.001, so the derivative appears to be 5. Near 3, the increase is 0.007 for each step of 0.001, so the derivative appears to be 7. These values seem to be increasing in a linear manner as we go to higher and higher t values, so we'll guess that the formula is $2t + 1$.

12.

$$f'(x) = \lim_{h \to 0} \frac{f(x + h) - f(x)}{h} = \lim_{h \to 0} \frac{(x + h)^3 - x^3}{h}$$

$$= \lim_{h \to 0} \frac{x^3 + 3x^2h + 3xh^2 + h^3 - x^3}{h} = \lim_{h \to 0} \frac{3x^2h + 3xh^2 + h^3}{h}$$

$$= \lim_{h \to 0} (3x^2 + 3xh + h^2) = 3x^2.$$

13.

$$g'(x) = \lim_{h \to 0} \frac{g(x + h) - g(x)}{h} = \lim_{h \to 0} \frac{2(x + h)^2 - 3 - (2x^2 - 3)}{h}$$

$$= \lim_{h \to 0} \frac{2(x^2 + 2xh + h^2) - 3 - 2x^2 + 3}{h} = \lim_{h \to 0} \frac{4xh + 2h^2}{h}$$

$$= \lim_{h \to 0} (4x + 2h) = 4x$$

14.

$$k'(x) = \lim_{h \to 0} \frac{k(x + h) - k(x)}{h} = \lim_{h \to 0} \frac{\frac{1}{x+h} - \frac{1}{x}}{h} = \lim_{h \to 0} \frac{x - (x + h)}{h(x + h)x}$$

$$= \lim_{h \to 0} \frac{-h}{h(x + h)x} = \lim_{h \to 0} \frac{-1}{(x + h)x} = -\frac{1}{x^2}.$$

15.

$$l'(x) = \lim_{h \to 0} \frac{\frac{1}{(x+h)^2} - \frac{1}{x^2}}{h} = \lim_{h \to 0} \frac{x^2 - (x + h)^2}{h(x + h)^2x^2}$$

$$= \lim_{h \to 0} \frac{x^2 - (x^2 + 2xh + h^2)}{h(x + h)^2x^2} = \lim_{h \to 0} \frac{-2xh - h^2}{h(x + h)^2x^2}$$

$$= \lim_{h \to 0} \frac{-2x - h}{(x + h)^2x^2} = \frac{-2x}{x^2x^2} = -\frac{2}{x^3}$$

16. Since $f'(x) > 0$ for $1 < x < 3$, $f(x)$ is increasing on this interval.
Since $f'(x) < 0$ for $x < 1$ or $x > 3$, $f(x)$ is decreasing on this interval.
Since $f'(x) = 0$ for $x = 1$ and $x = 3$, the tangent to $f(x)$ will be horizontal at these x's.
One of many possible shapes of $y = f(x)$ is shown to the right.

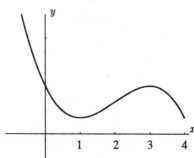

17. Since $f'(x) > 0$ for $x < -1$, $f(x)$ is increasing on this interval.
Since $f'(x) < 0$ for $x > -1$, $f(x)$ is decreasing on this interval.

Since $f'(x) = 0$ at $x = -1$, the tangent to $f(x)$ is horizontal at $x = -1$.
One of many possible shapes of $y = f(x)$ is shown in Figure 2.6.

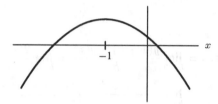

Figure 2.6

18.   (a) x_3 (b) x_4 (c) x_5 (d) x_3

19.   Note that f' and g' are periodic, with the same period as f and g respectively. Since g oscillates between 1 and -1 more quickly, its values change faster and therefore we would expect its derivative to reach larger values (both positive and negative); g' has a larger amplitude than f'.

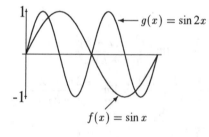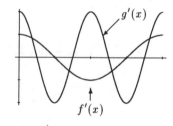

20.

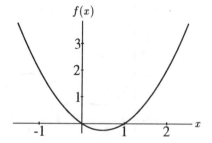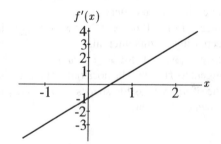

21.

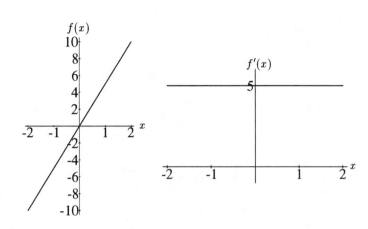

22.

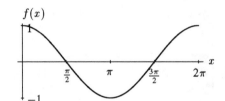
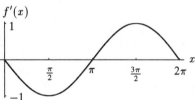

23.   The graph of $f(x)$ and its derivative look the same, like the graph below:

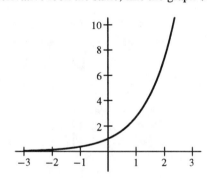

24.

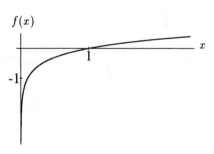

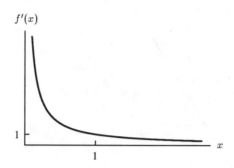

25.

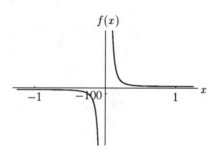

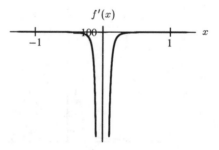

26.

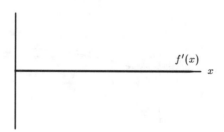

27.

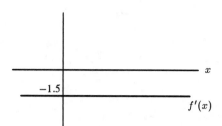

28.

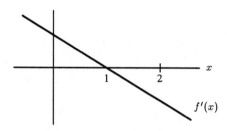

29.

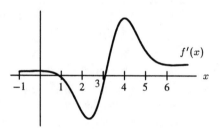

30.

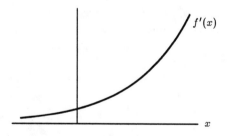

31.

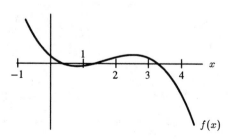

32. (a) The population varies periodically with a period of 1 year.

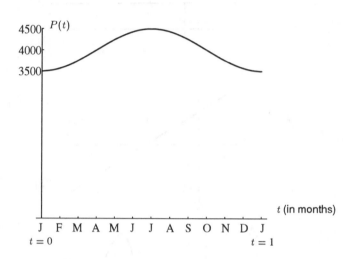

(b) The population is at a maximum on July 1st. At this time $\sin(2\pi t - \frac{\pi}{2}) = 1$, so the actual maximum population is $4000 + 500(1) = 4500$. Similarly, the population is at a minimum on January 1st. At this time, $\sin(2\pi t - \frac{\pi}{2}) = -1$, so the minimum population is $4000 + 500(-1) = 3500$.

(c) The rate of change is most positive about April 1st and most negative around October 1st.

(d) Since the population is at its maximum around July 1st, its rate of change is about 0 then.

33. If $f(x)$ is even, its graph is symmetric about the y-axis. So the tangent line to f at $x = x_0$ is the same as that at $x = -x_0$ reflected about the y-axis.

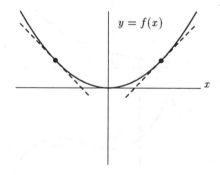

So the slopes of these two tangent lines are opposite in sign, so $f'(x_0) = -f'(-x_0)$, and f' is odd.

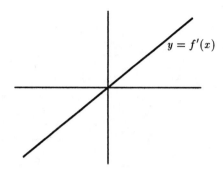

34. If $g(x)$ is odd, its graph remains the same if you rotate it 180° about the origin. So the tangent line to g at $x = x_0$ is the tangent line to g at $x = -x_0$, rotated 180°.

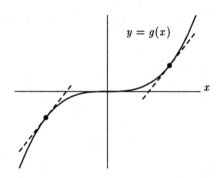

But the slope of a line stays constant if you rotate it 180°. So $g'(x_0) = g'(-x_0)$; g' is even.

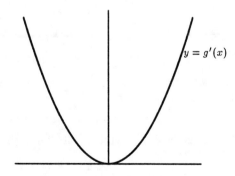

35. (a)

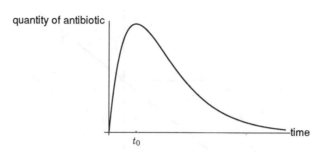

(b) The injection puts a reservoir of antibiotics in the muscle which begins to diffuse into the blood. As the antibiotic diffuses into the bloodstream, it begins to leave the blood either through normal metabolic action or absorption by some other organ. For a while the antibiotic diffuses into the blood faster than it is lost and its concentration rises, but as the reservoir in the muscle is drawn down, the diffusion rate into the blood decreases and eventually becomes less than the loss rate. After that, the concentration in the blood goes down. But the rate of decrease in concentration gets smaller as we approach the time when all the antibiotic is lost. This is shown in the graph below.

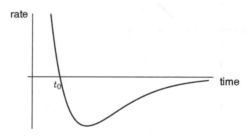

2.4 SOLUTIONS

1. (a) Velocity is zero at points A, C, F, and H.
   (b) These are points where the acceleration is zero, and hence where the particle switches from speeding up to slowing down or vice versa.
2. If $\lim_{x \to \infty} f(x) = 50$ and $f'(x)$ is positive for all x, then $f(x)$ increases to 50, but never rises above it. A possible graph of $f(x)$ is shown in Figure 2.7. If $\lim_{x \to \infty} f'(x)$ exists, it must surely be zero, since f looks more and more like a horizontal line. If $f'(x)$ approached another positive value c, then f would look more and more like a line with positive slope c, which would eventually go above $y = 50$.

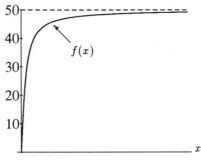

Figure 2.7

3. The units of $f'(x)$ are feet/mile. The derivative, $f'(x)$, represents the rate of change of elevation with distance from the source, so if the river is flowing downhill everywhere, the elevation is always decreasing and $f'(x)$ is always negative. (In fact, there may be some stretches where the elevation is more or less constant, so $f'(x) = 0$.)

4. The units of $g'(t)$ are inches/year. The quantity $g'(10)$ represents how fast Amelia Earhart was growing at age 10, so $g'(10) > 0$. The quantity $g'(30)$ represents how fast she was growing at age 30, so $g'(30) = 0$ because she was probably not growing at that age.

5. Units of $C'(r)$ are dollars/percent. Approximately, $C'(r)$ means the additional amount needed to pay off the loan when the interest rate is increased by 1%. The sign of $C'(r)$ is positive, because increasing the interest rate will increase the amount it costs to pay off a loan.

6. Units of $P'(t)$ are dollars/year. The practical meaning of $P'(t)$ is the rate at which the monthly payments change as the duration of the mortgage increases. Approximately, $P'(t)$ represents the change in the monthly payment if the duration is increased by one year. $P'(t)$ is negative because increasing the duration of a mortgage decreases the monthly payments.

7. Since B is measured in dollars and t is measured in years, $\frac{dB}{dt}$ is measured in dollars per year. We can interpret dB as the extra money added to your balance in dt years. Therefore $\frac{dB}{dt}$ represents how fast your balance is growing, in units of dollars/year.

8. $f(10) = 240{,}000$ means that if the commodity costs \$10, then 240,000 units of it will be sold. $f'(10) = -29{,}000$ means that if the commodity costs \$10 now, each \$1 increase in price will cause a decline in sales of 29,000 units.

9. (Note that we are considering the average temperature of the yam, since its temperature is different at different points inside it.)

    (a) It is positive, because the temperature of the yam increases the longer it sits in the oven.

    (b) The units of $f'(20)$ are °F/min. $f'(20) = 2$ means that at time $t = 20$ minutes, the temperature T increases by approximately 2°F for each additional minute in the oven.

10. (a) This means that investing the \$1000 at 5% would yield \$1649 after 10 years.

    (b) Writing $g'(r)$ as $\frac{dB}{dt}$, we see that the units of $\frac{dB}{dt}$ are dollars per percent (interest). We can interpret dB as the extra money earned if interest rate is increased by dr percent. Therefore $g'(5) = \frac{dB}{dr}\big|_{r=5} \approx 165$ means that the balance, at 5% interest, would increase by about \$165 if interest was increased by 1%. In other words, $g(6) \approx g(5) + 165 = 1649 + 165 = 1814$.

11. Units of $g'(55)$ are mpg/mph = hr/gal. $g'(55) = -0.54$ means that at 55 miles per hour the fuel efficiency (in miles per gallon, or mpg) of a car decreases as the velocity increases at a rate of approximately one half mpg for an increase of one mph.

12. Units of dP/dt are barrels/year. dP/dt is the change in quantity of petroleum per change in time (a year). This is negative. We could estimate it by finding the amount of petroleum used worldwide over a short period of time.

13. (a)

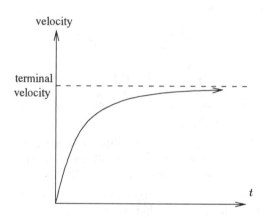

  (b) The graphs should be concave down because wind resistance decreases your acceleration as you speed up, and so the slope of the graph of velocity is decreasing.
  (c) The slope represents the acceleration due to gravity.

14. (a) The company hopes that increased advertising always brings in more customers instead of turning them away. Therefore, it hopes $f'(a)$ is always positive.
  (b) If $f'(100) = 2$, it means that if the advertising budget is $100,000, each extra dollar spent on advertising will bring in $2 worth of sales. If $f'(100) = 0.5$, each dollar above $100 thousand spent on advertising will bring in $0.50 worth of sales.
  (c) If $f'(100) = 2$, then as we saw in part (b), spending slightly more than $100,000 will increase revenue by an amount greater than the additional expense, and thus more should be spent on advertising. If $f'(100) = 0.5$, then the increase in revenue is less than the additional expense, hence too much is being spent on advertising. The optimum amount to spend is an amount that makes $f'(a) = 1$. At this point, the increases in advertising expenditures just pay for themselves. If $f'(a) < 1$, too much is being spent; if $f'(a) > 1$, more should be spent.

15. Since $\frac{P(67)-P(66)}{67-66}$ is an estimate of $P'(66)$, we may think of $P'(66)$ as an estimate of $P(67) - P(66)$, and the latter is the number of people between 66 and 67 inches tall. Alternatively, since $\frac{P(66.5)-P(65.5)}{66.5-65.5}$ is a better estimate of $P'(66)$, we may regard $P'(66)$ as an estimate of the number of people of height between 65.5 and 66.5 inches. The units for $P'(x)$ are people per inch.

   Since there were 250 million people at the 1990 census, we might guess that there are about 200 million full-grown persons in the US whose heights are distributed between $60''(5')$ and $75''(6'3'')$.

There are probably quite a few people of height 66″–perhaps $1\frac{1}{2}$ what you'd expect from an even, or uniform, distribution–because it's nearly average. An even distribution would yield $P'(66) = \frac{200 \text{ million}}{15''} = 13.4$ million per inch–so we can expect $P'(66)$ to be perhaps $13.4 \cdot 1.5 = 20.1$.

$P'(x)$ is never negative because $P(x)$ is never decreasing. To see this, let's look at an example involving a particular value of x, say $x = 70$. The value $P(70)$ represents the number of people whose height is less than 70 inches, and $P(71)$ represents the number of people whose height is less than 71 inches. Since everyone shorter than 70 inches is also shorter than 71 inches, $P(70) \leq P(71)$. In general, $P(x)$ is 0 for small x, and increases as x increases, and is eventually constant (for large enough x).

16. (a) $f^{-1}(100)$ is the point in time when the population of the US was 100 million people (somewhere between 1910 and 1920).

(b) The derivative of $f^{-1}(P)$ at $P = 100$ represents the ratio of change in time to change in population, and its units are years per million people. In other words, this derivative represents how long it took, around 1916, for the population to increase by 1 million.

(c) Since the population increased by $105.7 - 92.0 = 13.7$ million people in 10 years, the average rate of increase is 1.37 million people per year. If the rate is fairly constant in that period, the amount of time it would take for an increase of 8 million people (100 million − 92.0 million) would be

$$\frac{8 \text{ million people}}{1.37 \text{ million people/year}} \approx 5.8 \text{ years} \approx 6 \text{ years}$$

Adding this to our starting point of 1910, we estimate that the population of the US reached 100 million around 1916, i.e. $f^{-1}(100) \approx 1916$.

(d) Since it took 10 years between 1910 and 1920 for the population to increase by $105.7 - 92.0 = 13.7$ million people, the derivative of $f^{-1}(P)$ at $P = 100$ is approximately

$$\frac{10 \text{ years}}{13.7 \text{ million people}} = 0.73 \text{ years/million people}$$

17. (a) Estimating derivatives using difference quotients (but other answers are possible):

$$P'(1900) \approx \frac{P(1910) - P(1900)}{10} = \frac{92.0 - 76.0}{10} = 1.6 \text{ million people per year}$$

$$P'(1945) \approx \frac{P(1950) - P(1940)}{10} = \frac{150.7 - 131.7}{10} = 1.9 \text{ million people per year}$$

$$P'(1990) \approx \frac{P(1990) - P(1980)}{10} = \frac{248.7 - 226.5}{10} = 2.22 \text{ million people per year}$$

(b) The population growth was maximal somewhere between 1950 and 1960.

(c) $P'(1950) \approx \frac{P(1960) - P(1950)}{10} = \frac{179.0 - 150.7}{10} = 2.83$ million people per year, so $P(1956) \approx P(1950) + P'(1950)(1956 - 1950) = 150.7 + 2.83(6) \approx 167.7$ million people.

(d) If the growth rate between 1990 and 2000 was the same as the growth rate from 1980 to 1990, then the total population should be about 271 million people in 2000.

18. (a) Clearly the population of the US at any instant is an integer that varies up and down every few seconds as a child is born, a person dies, or a new immigrant arrives. Since these events cannot

usually be assigned to an exact instant, the population of the US at any given moment might actually be indeterminate. If we count in units of a thousand, however, the population appears to be a smooth function that has been rounded to the nearest thousand.

　　　Major land acquisitions such as the Louisiana Purchase caused larger jumps in the population, but since the census is taken only every ten years and the territories acquired were rather sparsely populated, we cannot see these jumps in the census data.

(b)　We can regard rate of change of the population for a particular time t as representing an estimate of how much the population will increase during the year after time t.

(c)　Many economic indicators are treated as smooth, such as the Gross National Product, the Dow Jones Industrial Average, volumes of trading, and the price of commodities like gold. But these figures only change in increments, and not continuously.

2.5　SOLUTIONS

1.　(a)　increasing, concave up.
　　(b)　decreasing, concave down
2.　(a)

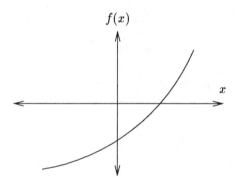

(b)

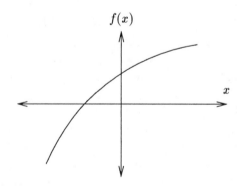

(c)

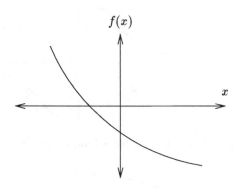

(d)

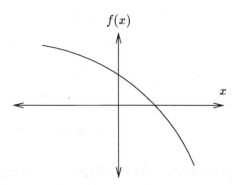

3. (a) Such a graph is shown below. The change takes place at the origin.

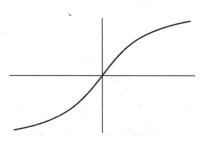

(b)

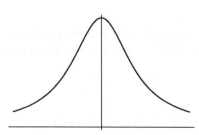

(c)

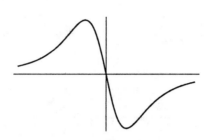

4. (a)

$N(t) =$ Number of people below poverty line

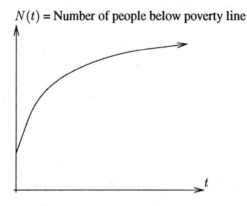

Figure 2.8

(b) $\frac{dN}{dt}$ is positive, since people are still slipping below the poverty line. $\frac{d^2N}{dt^2}$ is negative, since the rate at which people are slipping below the poverty line, $\frac{dN}{dt}$, is decreasing.

5. (a)

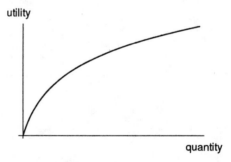

(b)   As a function of quantity, utility is increasing but at a decreasing rate; the graph is increasing but concave down. So the derivative of utility is positive, but the second derivative of utility is negative.

6. (a) $\frac{dP}{dt} > 0$ and $\frac{d^2P}{dt^2} > 0$.

(b) $\frac{dP}{dt} < 0$ and $\frac{d^2P}{dt^2} > 0$ (but $\frac{dP}{dt}$ is close to zero).

7. Since all advertising campaigns are assumed to produce an increase in sales, a graph of sales against time would be expected to have a positive slope.

    A positive second derivative means the rate at which sales are increasing is increasing. If a positive second derivative is observed during a new campaign, it is reasonable to conclude that this increase in the rate sales are increasing is caused by the new campaign–which is therefore judged a success. A negative second derivative means a decrease in the rate at which sales are increasing, and therefore suggests the new campaign is a failure.

8. (a)

$$f'(0.6) \approx \frac{f(0.8) - f(0.6)}{0.8 - 0.6} = \frac{4.0 - 3.9}{0.2} = 0.5.$$

$$f'(0.5) \approx \frac{f(0.6) - f(0.4)}{0.6 - 0.4} = \frac{0.4}{0.2} = 2$$

.

(b) Using the values of f' from part (a), we get $f''(0.6) \approx \frac{f'(0.6) - f'(0.5)}{0.6 - 0.5} = \frac{0.5 - 2}{0.2} = \frac{-1.5}{0.2} = -7.5$, where $f'(0.7) \approx \frac{f(0.8) - f(0.6)}{0.8 - 0.6} = \frac{4.0 - 3.9}{0.2} = \frac{0.1}{0.2} = 0.5$.

(c) The maximum value of f is probably near $x = 0.8$. The minimum value of f is probably near $x = 0.3$.

9. (a) The EPA will say that the rate of discharge is still rising. The industry will say that the rate of discharge is increasing less quickly, and may soon level off or even start to fall.

(b) The EPA will say that the rate at which pollutants are being discharged is levelling off, but not to zero — so pollutants will continue to be dumped in the lake. The industry will say that the rate of discharge has decreased significantly.

10. Since f' is everywhere positive, f is everywhere increasing. Hence the greatest value of f is at x_6 and the least value of f is at x_1. Directly from the graph, we see that f' is greatest at x_3 and least at x_2. Since f'' gives the slope of the graph of f', f'' is greatest where f' is rising most rapidly, namely at x_6, and f'' is least where f' is falling most rapidly, namely at x_1.

11. (a) B and E

(b) A and D

2.6 SOLUTIONS

1. The tangent line has slope $1/4$ and goes through the point $(4, 2)$. Its equation is

$$y - 2 = \frac{1}{4}(x - 4) \qquad y = \frac{1}{4}x + 1.$$

Thus when $x = 4.007$, we have $y = \frac{1}{4}(4.007) + 1 = 2.00175$. Since 2.0017496 rounds to 2.00175, the point $(4.007, 2.0017496) \approx (4.007, 2.00175)$ lies on the tangent line.

2. Each time x changes by 0.001, the value of x^3 changes by approximately $12(0.001) = 0.012$. So the missing values are approximately 8.036, 8.048, 8.060, as shown in the filled-in table below.

x	2.000	2.001	2.002	2.003	2.004	2.005
x^3	8.000	8.012	8.024	8.036	8.048	8.060

3.

x	tan x	x	tan x
0.80	1.030	0.86	1.162
0.81	1.050	0.87	1.185
0.82	1.072	0.88	1.210
0.83	1.093	0.89	1.235
0.84	1.116	0.90	1.260
0.85	1.138		

The value of tan x increases by about 0.023 for each increase of 0.01 in x. The table is approximately linear.

4. (a) $f'(0.6) \approx \frac{f(0.8)-f(0.4)}{0.8-0.4} = \frac{0.5}{0.4} = 1.25$.

Using $x = 0.6$, $y = 3.9$, $y - 3.9 = 1.25(x - 0.6)$ so $y = 1.25x + 3.15$.

(b) Using the equation from part (a) yields

$$f(0.7) \approx 1.25(0.7) + 3.15 = 4.025$$
$$f(1.2) \approx 1.25(1.2) + 3.15 = 4.65$$
$$f(1.4) \approx 1.25(1.4) + 3.15 = 4.9$$

It's OK to be confident about $f(0.7)$ as 0.7 is close to 0.6 (and $f(0.8) = 4$, not too far off). However, $f(1.2)$ is likely to be less than $f(1.0) = 3.9$ as f is decreasing from $0.8 < x < 1.0$. The estimate for $f(1.4)$ could be even further off.

5. (a) $f'(6.75) \approx \frac{f(7.0)-f(6.5)}{7.0-6.5} = \frac{8.2-10.3}{0.5} = -4.2$.

$f'(7.0) \approx \frac{f(7.5)-f(6.5)}{7.5-6.5} = \frac{6.5-10.3}{1.0} = -3.8$.

$f'(8.5) \approx \frac{f(9.0)-f(8.0)}{9.0-8.0} = \frac{3.2-5.2}{1.0} = -2.0$.

(b) To estimate f'' at 7, we should have values for f' at points near 7. We know from (a) that $f'(6.75) \approx -4.2$. Next, estimate $f'(7.25) \approx \frac{6.5-8.2}{0.5} = -3.4$. Then $f''(7) \approx \frac{f'(7.25)-f'(6.75)}{0.5} \approx \frac{-3.4-(-4.2)}{0.5} = 1.6$.

(c) $y - 8.2 = -3.8(x - 7)$ or $y = -3.8x + 34.8$.

(d) We may use the tangent line from (c) to approximate $f(6.8)$. In this case we get

$$y \approx -3.8x + 34.8 = 8.96.$$

[We may also estimate $f(6.8)$ by assuming that the graph of f is straight between the given points $(6.5, 10.3)$ and $(7.0, 8.2)$. This line has the equation $y = -4.2(x - 6.5) + 10.3$ and passes through $(6.8, 9.04)$, so we may estimate $f(6.8) \approx 9.04$. Here, we approximate using the secant line rather than the tangent line.]

As we can see, the two estimates are fairly close.

6. The derivative at $x = 6$ is

$$\lim_{h \to 0} \frac{f(6 + h) - f(6)}{h} = \lim_{h \to 0} \frac{\sqrt{100 - (6 + h)^2} - \sqrt{64}}{h}$$

when $h = 0.001$, the difference quotient $= -0.7500977 \approx -0.75$, which we use as the slope of the tangent line. Since $(6, 8)$ is on the line,

$$y - 8 = -0.75(x - 6)$$
$$y = -0.75x + 12.5.$$

We can see that the slope of the tangent is exactly $\frac{3}{4}$ because we know that the tangent to a circle is perpendicular to the radius drawn to the point of tangency. In this case the radius has slope $\frac{4}{3}$, so the tangent has slope $-\frac{3}{4}$.

7. At $(0, 0)$: $f'(0) = 0$, so the tangent line has slope 0 and equation $y = 0$.
   At $(1, 1)$:

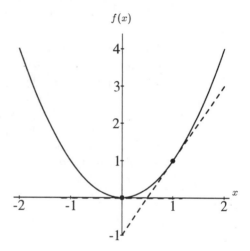

$$f'(1) = \lim_{h \to 0} \frac{f(1 + h) - f(1)}{h}$$
$$= \lim_{h \to 0} \frac{(1 + h)^2 - (1)^2}{h}$$
$$= \lim_{h \to 0} (2 + h) = 2,$$

so the tangent line has slope 2 and equation $y - 1 = 2x - 2$, or $y = 2x - 1$.

8. (a) We will assume that the per capita health cost grows exponentially, i.e. that it is given by ae^{bt}, where we need to determine the constants a and b, and where t is time in years since 1985.

   Using the data from Table 2.17, we can write

   $$f(0) = a \cdot e^{b \cdot 0} = a = 1596, \text{ so}$$
   $$f(t) = 1596 \cdot e^{bt}.$$

   Also,

   $$f(2) = 1596e^{2b} = 1987$$
   $$e^{2b} = \frac{1987}{1596} \approx 1.24$$
   $$2b = \ln 1.24 \approx 0.22$$
   $$b = 0.11,$$

giving us

$$f(t) = 1596 \cdot e^{0.11t}.$$

To find predictions for 1988 and 1995, we compute $f(3)$ and $f(10)$ respectively:

$$f(3) = 1596 \cdot e^{0.11(3)} \approx \$2220$$

$$f(10) = 1596 \cdot e^{0.11(10)} \approx \$4795$$

(b) From Example 6, page 134, we know that a linear model predicts the expenditures of \$2182.50 and \$3551 for the years 1988 and 1995 respectively, so the exponential model gives higher estimates for both years. It is to be expected that the exponential model will continue to produce higher estimates than the linear model. This follows from the fact that the graph of the exponential function is already above the graph of the linear one at $t = 3$, and will grow at a faster rate thereafter.

9. (a) The graph is a sine curve. It looks straight because the graph shows only a small part of the curve magnified greatly. The period of the sine curve is $\frac{2\pi}{0.0172} \approx 365$ (the number of days in a year).

   (b) The month is March: We see that about the 21ˢᵗ of the month there are twelve hours of daylight and hence twelve hours of night. This phenomenon (the length of the day equaling the length of the night) occurs at the equinox, midway between winter and summer. Since the length of the days is increasing, and Madrid is in the northern hemisphere, we are looking at March, not September.

   (c) The slope of the curve is found either from the graph or the formula to be about 0.04 (the rise is about 0.8 hours in 20 days or 0.04 hours/day). This means that the amount of daylight is increasing by about 0.04 hours (about $2\frac{1}{2}$ minutes) per calendar day, or that each day is $2\frac{1}{2}$ minutes longer than its predecessor.

10.

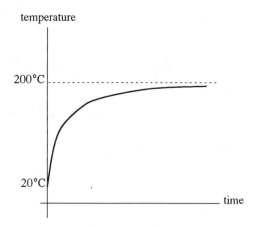

(a) At first, the yam heats up very quickly, since the difference in temperature between it and its surroundings is so large. As time goes by, the yam gets hotter and hotter, its rate of temperature increase slows down, and its temperature approaches the temperature of the oven as an asymptote.

The graph is thus concave down. (We are considering the average temperature of the yam, since the temperature in its center and on its surface will vary in different ways.)

(b) If the temperature increase were to remain 2°/min, in ten minutes the yam's temperature would increase 20°, from 120° to 140°. Since we know the graph is not linear, but concave down, the actual temperature is a little less, perhaps about 135°.

(c) In 30 minutes, we know the yam increases in temperature by 45°. Since the graph is concave down, from $t = 30$ to $t = 40$ the increase is more than one-third of that, namely more than 15°; from $t = 40$ to $t = 50$ the increase is perhaps 15°; and from $t = 50$ to $t = 60$ the increase is less than 15°. So we estimate the temperature at $t = 40$ to be perhaps 138°.

(d) By the reasoning above, at $t = 50$ the temperature should be about 153°, so the temperature is about 150° at about $t = 48$.

2.7 SOLUTIONS

1. The limit appears to be 1; a graph and table of values is shown below.

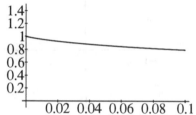

x	x^x
0.1	0.7943
0.01	0.9550
0.001	0.9931
0.0001	0.9990
0.00001	0.9999

2. For $-0.5 \le \theta \le 0.5$, $0 \le y \le 3$, the graph of $y = \dfrac{\sin 2\theta}{\theta}$ is shown to the right. Therefore,

$$\lim_{\theta \to 0} \frac{\sin 2\theta}{\theta} = 2.$$

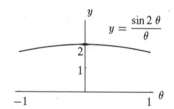

3. For $-1 \le \theta \le 1$, $-1 \le y \le 1$, the graph of $y = \dfrac{\cos \theta - 1}{\theta}$ is shown to the right. Therefore,

$$\lim_{\theta \to 0} \frac{\cos \theta - 1}{\theta} = 0.$$

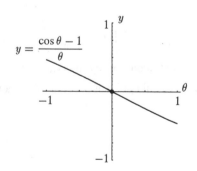

4. For $-90° \leq \theta \leq 90°$, $0 \leq y \leq 0.02$, the graph of $y = \dfrac{\sin\theta}{\theta}$ is shown to the right. Therefore, by tracing along the curve, we see that in degrees,

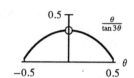

$$\lim_{\theta \to 0} \frac{\sin\theta}{\theta} = 0.01745\ldots.$$

5. For $-0.5 \leq \theta \leq 0.5$, $0 \leq y \leq 0.5$, the graph of $y = \dfrac{\theta}{\tan 3\theta}$ is shown to the right. Therefore, by tracing along the curve, we see that

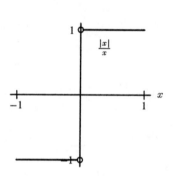

$$\lim_{\theta \to 0} \frac{\theta}{\tan 3\theta} = 0.3333\ldots.$$

6. $\lim_{x \to 0} \dfrac{|x|}{x}$ doesn't exist.

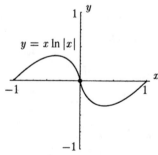

7. For $-1 \leq x \leq 1$, $-1 \leq y \leq 1$, the graph of $y = x \ln|x|$ is shown to the right. Therefore,

$$\lim_{x \to 0} x \ln|x| = 0.$$

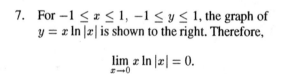

8. Since $\lim_{x \to 0^+} \dfrac{|x|}{x} = 1$ and $\lim_{x \to 0^-} \dfrac{|x|}{x} = -1$, we say that $\lim_{x \to 0} \dfrac{|x|}{x}$ doesn't exist. Therefore, $f(x)$ is not continuous on any interval containing 0.

9. The only point at which g might not be continuous is at $\theta = 0$. A graph shows that

$$\lim_{\theta \to 0} \frac{\sin\theta}{\theta} = 1.$$

However

$$\lim_{\theta \to 0} \frac{\sin \theta}{\theta} = 1 \neq g(0),$$

so $g(\theta)$ is not continuous on any interval containing 0.

10. The answer (see the graph to the right) appears to be about 2.7; if we zoom in further, it appears to be about 2.72, which is close to the value of $e \approx 2.71828$.

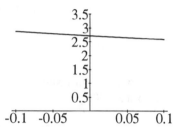

11. Looking at the graph below (which is centered at $y = 7$, not $y = 0$), the value appears to be about 7.4, which is close to the value of $e^2 \approx 7.38906$.

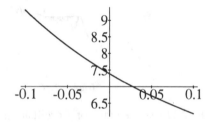

12. When $x = 0.1$, $xe^{1/x} \approx 2203$. When $x = 0.01$, $xe^{1/x} \approx 3 \times 10^{41}$. When $x = 0.001$, $xe^{1/x}$ is too big for a calculator to compute. Therefore, we say that $\lim_{x \to 0^+} xe^{1/x}$ does not exist.

2.8 SOLUTIONS

1. Yes, f is differentiable at $x = 0$ (see Figure 2.9).

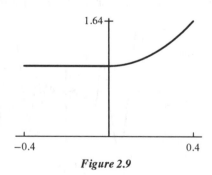

Figure 2.9

2. As we can see in Figure 2.10, f oscillates infinitely often between the x-axis and the line $y = x$ near the origin. Thus the secant line from $(0,0)$ to $(h, f(h))$ alternates between slope 0 (when $f(h) = 0$) and slope 1 (when $f(h) = h$) infinitely often as h tends to zero. Therefore, there is no limit of the slope of the secant as h tends to zero, and thus there is no derivative at the origin. In other words,

    $$\lim_{h \to 0} \frac{f(h) - f(0)}{h} = \lim_{h \to 0} \frac{h \sin(\frac{1}{h}) + h}{h}$$

    $$= \lim_{h \to 0} \sin\left(\frac{1}{h}\right) + 1$$

    does not exist, since $\sin(\frac{1}{h})$ does not converge to any point as h tends to zero. Thus, f is not differentiable at $x = 0$.

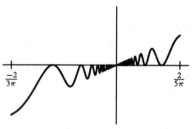

Figure 2.10

3. We can see from Figure 2.11 that the graph of f oscillates infinitely often between the curves $y = x^2$ and $y = -x^2$ near the origin. Thus the slope of the secant line from $(0,0)$ to $(h, f(h))$ oscillates between h and $-h$ as h tends to zero. So, the limit of the slope as h tends to zero is 0, which is the derivative of f at the origin. In other words,

    $$\lim_{h \to 0} \frac{f(h) - f(0)}{h} = \lim_{h \to 0} \frac{h^2 \sin(\frac{1}{h})}{h}$$

    $$= \lim_{h \to 0} h \sin(\frac{1}{h})$$

    $$= 0,$$

    since $\lim_{h \to 0} h = 0$ and $-1 \le \sin(\frac{1}{h}) \le 1$ for any h. Thus f is differentiable at $x = 0$, and $f'(0) = 0$.

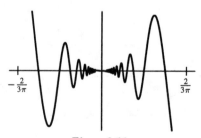

Figure 2.11

4. (a) Using the second formula with $r = R$ gives

$$g = \frac{GM}{R^2}.$$

Then, using the first formula with r approaching R from below, we see that as we get close to the surface of the earth

$$g \approx \frac{GMR}{R^3} = \frac{GM}{R^2}.$$

Since we get the same value for g from both formulas, g is continuous.

(b)

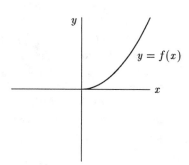

(c) For $r < R$, the graph of g is a line with positive slope (slope $= \dfrac{GM}{R^3}$). For $r > R$, the graph of g looks like $\frac{1}{x^2}$, and so has a negative slope. Therefore the graph has a "corner" at $r = R$ and so is not differentiable there.

5. (a) The graph of

$$f(x) = \begin{cases} 0 & \text{if } x < 0. \\ x^2 & \text{if } x \geq 0. \end{cases}$$

is shown to the right. The graph is continuous and has no vertical segments or corners, so $f(x)$ is differentiable everywhere.

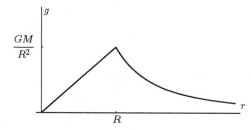

By Example 4 on page 115,

$$f'(x) = \begin{cases} 0 & \text{if } x < 0 \\ 2x & \text{if } x \geq 0 \end{cases}$$

So its graph is shown to the right.

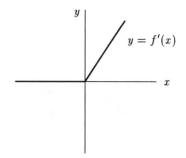

(b) The graph of the derivative has a corner at $x = 0$ so $f'(x)$ is not differentiable at $x = 0$. The graph of

$$f''(x) = \begin{cases} 0 & \text{if } x < 0 \\ 2 & \text{if } x > 0 \end{cases}$$

looks like:

The second derivative is not defined at $x = 0$. So it is certainly neither differentiable nor continuous at $x = 0$.

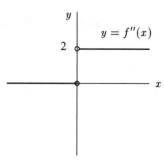

6.

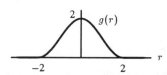

(a) The graph of $g(r)$ does not have a break or jump at $r = 2$, and so $g(r)$ is continuous there. This is confirmed by the fact that

$$g(2) = 1 + \cos(\pi 2/2) = 1 + (-1) = 0$$

so the value of $g(r)$ as you approach $r = 2$ from the left is the same as the value when you approach $r = 2$ from the right.

(b) The graph of $g(r)$ does not have a corner at $r = 2$, even after zooming in, so $g(r)$ appears to be differentiable at $r = 0$. This is confirmed by the fact that $\cos(\pi r/2)$ is at the bottom of a trough at $r = 2$, and so its slope is 0 there. Thus the slope to the left of $r = 2$ is the same as the slope to the right of $r = 2$.

7. (a) The graph of Q against t does not have a break at $t = 0$, so Q appears to be continuous at $t = 0$. See Figure 2.12.

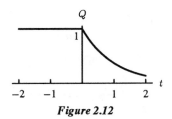

Figure 2.12

(b)   The slope dQ/dt is zero for $t < 0$, and negative for all $t > 0$. At $t = 0$, there appears to be a corner, which does not disappear as you zoom in, suggesting that I is defined for all times t except $t = 0$.

8.   (a)   The graph of ϕ does not have a break at $y = 0$, and so ϕ appears to be continuous there. See Figure 2.13.

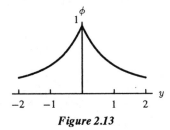

Figure 2.13

(b)   The graph of ϕ has a corner at $y = 0$ which does not disappear as you zoom in. Therefore ϕ appears not be differentiable at $y = 0$.

SOLUTIONS TO REVIEW PROBLEMS FOR CHAPTER TWO

1.

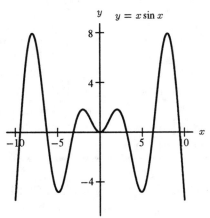

Figure 2.14

(a) Seven. $x \sin x = 0$ at $x = 0, \pm\pi, \pm2\pi, \pm3\pi$.

(b) $x \sin x$ is increasing at $x = 1$, decreasing at $x = 4$.

(c) $$\frac{f(2) - f(0)}{(2 - 0)} = \frac{2 \sin 2 - 0}{2} = \sin 2 \approx 0.91$$

$$\frac{f(8) - f(6)}{(8 - 6)} = \frac{8 \sin 8 - 6 \sin 6}{2} \approx 4.80. \text{ So the average rate of change over } 6 \leq x \leq 8 \text{ is greater.}$$

(d) It's greater at $x = -9$.

2. $f'(1) = \displaystyle\lim_{h \to 0} \frac{\log(1 + h) - \log 1}{h} = \lim_{h \to 0} \frac{\log(1 + h)}{h}$

Evaluating $\frac{\log(1+h)}{h}$ for $h = 0.01, 0.001,$ and 0.0001, we get $0.43214, 0.43408, 0.43427,$ so $f'(1) \approx 0.43427$. The corresponding secant lines are getting steeper, because the graph of $\log x$ is concave down. We thus expect the limit to be more than 0.43427. If we consider negative values of h, the estimates are too large. We can also see this from the graph below:

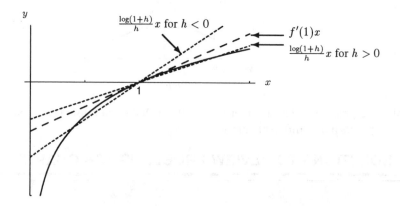

3.

TABLE 2.11

x	x^2	x	x^2	x	x^2
0.98	0.960	−1.02	1.040	4.98	24.800
0.99	0.980	−1.01	1.020	4.99	24.900
1.00	1.000	−1.00	1.000	5.00	25.000
1.01	1.020	−0.99	0.980	5.01	25.100
1.02	1.040	−0.98	0.960	5.02	25.200

At $x = 1$, the function seems to be increasing by 0.02 for each increase of 0.01 that we take, so the derivative appears to be $\frac{0.02}{0.01} = 2$. At $x = -1$, the function appears to be decreasing by 0.02 for each increase of 0.01 in x, so the derivative there appears to be $\frac{-0.02}{0.01} = -2$. At $x = 5$, the function is increasing by 0.1 for each step of 0.01 we take, so the derivative appears to be $\frac{0.1}{0.01} = 10$. If we make a table of x values and their corresponding derivatives:

TABLE 2.12

x	$f'(x)$
1	2
−1	−2
5	10

It appears that at a point x, the derivative of $f(x)$ is $2x$.

4.

TABLE 2.13

x	x^3	x	x^3	x	x^3
0.998	0.9940	2.998	26.946	4.998	124.850
0.999	0.9970	2.999	26.973	4.999	124.925
1.000	1.0000	3.000	27.000	5.000	125.000
1.001	1.0030	3.001	27.027	5.001	125.075
1.002	1.0060	3.002	27.054	5.002	125.150

At $x = 1$, the values of x^3 are increasing by about 0.0030 for each increase of 0.001 in x, so the derivative appears to be $\frac{0.0030}{0.001} = 3$. At $x = 3$, the values increase by 0.027 over an x increase of 0.001, so the value appears to be 27. At $x = 5$, the values increase by 0.075 for a change in x of 0.001, so the derivative appears to be 75. The function $3x^2$ fits these data, so it is a good candidate for the derivative function (although it is not immediately obvious just from these calculations).

5.

TABLE 2.14

x	$\ln x$	x	$\ln x$	x	$\ln x$	x	$\ln x$
0.998	−0.0020	1.998	0.6921	4.998	1.6090	9.998	2.3024
0.999	−0.0010	1.999	0.6926	4.999	1.6092	9.999	2.3025
1.000	0.0000	2.000	0.6931	5.000	1.6094	10.000	2.3026
1.001	0.0010	2.001	0.6936	5.001	1.6096	10.001	2.3027
1.002	0.0020	2.002	0.6941	5.002	1.6098	10.002	2.3028

At $x = 1$, the values of $\ln x$ are increasing by 0.001 for each increase in x of 0.001, so the derivative appears to be 1. At $x = 2$, the increase is 0.0005 for each increase of 0.001, so the derivative appears to be 0.5. At $x = 5$, $\ln x$ increases by 0.0002 for each increase of 0.001 in x, so the derivative appears to be 0.2. And at $x = 10$, the increase is 0.0001 over intervals of 0.001, so the derivative appears to be 0.1. These values suggest an inverse relationship between x and $f'(x)$, namely $f'(x) = \frac{1}{x}$.

6.   A graph of one such f is shown below:

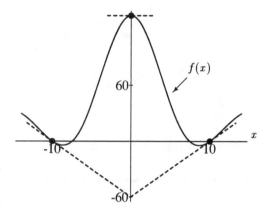

(a)   From the graph above, we can see that since f is symmetric about the y-axis, the tangent line at $x = -10$ is just the tangent line at $x = 10$ flipped about the y-axis, and so the slope of one tangent is the negative of that of the other. Therefore, $f'(-10) = -f'(10) = -6$.

(b)   From part (a) we can see that if f is even, then for any x, $f'(-x) = -f'(x)$. Thus $f'(-0) = -f'(0)$, but since $0 = -0, 2f'(0) = 0$, so $f'(0) = 0$.

7.   A graph of one such f is shown below:

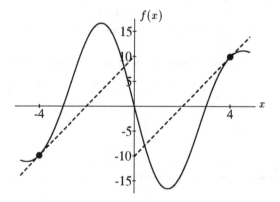

From the graph above, we can see that since f is symmetric about the origin, its tangent line at $x = -4$ is just the tangent line at $x = 4$ flipped about the origin, and so they have the same slope. Thus, $g'(-4) = 5$.

8.

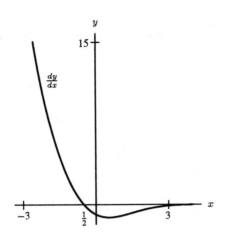

9.

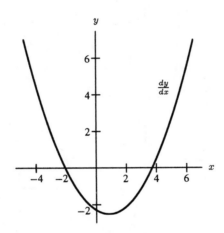

10.

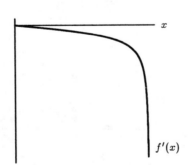

11.

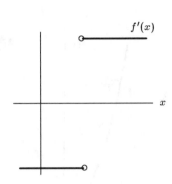

12.

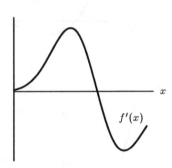

13.

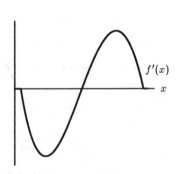

14.

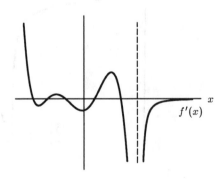

15. For $x < -2$, f is increasing and concave up.
For $-2 < x < 1$, f is increasing and concave down.
At $x = 1$, f has a local maximum.
For $x > 1$, f is decreasing and concave down.
One such possible f is shown to the right.

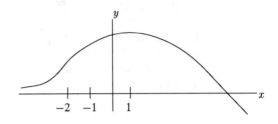

16. (a)

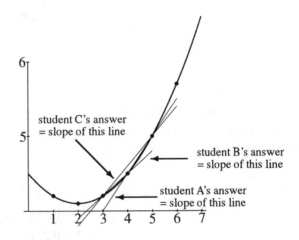

(b) The slope of f appears to be somewhere between student A's answer and student B's, so student C's answer, halfway in between, is probably the most accurate.

(c) Student A's estimate is $f'(x) \approx \frac{f(x+h)-f(x)}{h}$.
Student B's estimate is $f'(x) \approx \frac{f(x)-f(x-h)}{h}$.
Student C's estimate is the average of these two, or

$$f'(x) \approx \frac{1}{2}\left[\frac{f(x+h)-f(x)}{h} + \frac{f(x)-f(x-h)}{h}\right] = \frac{f(x+h)-f(x-h)}{2h}.$$

This estimate is the slope of the chord connecting $(x - h, f(x - h))$ to $(x + h, f(x + h))$.

Thus we estimate that the tangent to a curve is nearly parallel to a chord connecting points h units to the right and left.

17. (a) IV, (b) III, (c) II, (d) I, (e) IV, (f) II

18. (a) Slope of tangent line $= \lim_{h \to 0} \frac{\sqrt{4+h} - \sqrt{4}}{h}$. Using $h = 0.001$, $\frac{\sqrt{4.001} - \sqrt{4}}{0.001} = 0.249984$. Hence the slope of the tangent line is about 0.25.

(b)

$$y - y_1 = m(x - x_1)$$
$$y - 2 = 0.25(x - 4)$$
$$y - 2 = 0.25x - 1$$
$$y = 0.25x + 1$$

(c) $f(x) = kx^2$

If $(4, 2)$ is on the graph of f, then $f(4) = 2$, so $k \cdot 4^2 = 2$. Thus $k = \frac{1}{8}$, and $f(x) = \frac{1}{8}x^2$.

(d) To find where the graph of f crosses then line $y = 0.25x + 1$, we solve:

$$\frac{1}{8}x^2 = 0.25x + 1$$
$$x^2 = 2x + 8$$
$$x^2 - 2x - 8 = 0$$
$$(x - 4)(x + 2) = 0$$
$$x = 4 \text{ or } x = -2$$
$$f(-2) = \frac{1}{8}(4) = 0.5$$

Therefore, $(-2, 0.5)$ is the other point of intersection. (Of course, $(4, 2)$ is a point of intersection; we know that from the start.)

19. (a)   The slope of the tangent line at $(0, \sqrt{19})$ is zero: it is horizontal.
The slope of the tangent line at $(\sqrt{19}, 0)$ is undefined: it is vertical.

(b)   The slope appears to be about $\frac{1}{2}$. (Note that when x is 2, y is about -4, but when x is 4, y is approximately -3.)

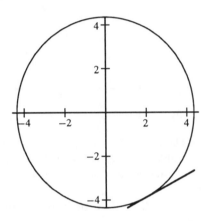

(c)   Using symmetry we can determine: Slope at $(-2, \sqrt{15})$: about $\frac{1}{2}$. Slope at $(-2, -\sqrt{15})$: about $-\frac{1}{2}$. Slope at $(2, \sqrt{15})$: about $-\frac{1}{2}$.

20. (a)   See (b).
(b)

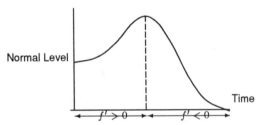

(c) f' is the rate at which the concentration is increasing or decreasing. f' is positive at the start of the disease and negative toward the end. In practice, of course, one cannot measure f' directly. Checking the value of C in blood samples taken on consecutive days would tell us

$$\frac{f(t+1) - f(t)}{(t+1) - t},$$

which is our estimate of $f'(t)$.

21. (a)   The population varies periodically with a period of 12 months (i.e. one year).

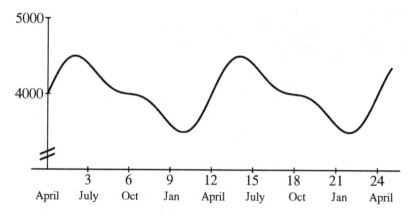

(b)   The herd is largest about June 1st when there are about 4500 deer.

(c)   The herd is smallest about February 1st when there are about 3500 deer.

(d)   The herd grows the fastest about April 1st. The herd shrinks the fastest about July 20 and again about November 15.

(e)   It grows the fastest about April 1st when the rate of growth is about 400 deer/month, i.e about 13 new fawns per day.

22.   (a)

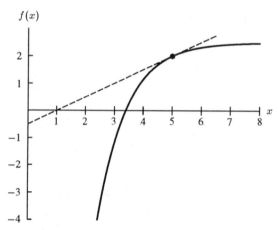

(b)   Exactly one. There can't be more than one zero because f is increasing everywhere. There does have to be one zero because f stays below its tangent line (dotted line in above graph), and therefore f must cross the x-axis.

(c)   The equation of the (dotted) tangent line is $y = \frac{1}{2}x - \frac{1}{2}$, and so it crosses the x-axis at $x = 1$. Therefore the zero of f must be between $x = 1$ and $x = 5$.

(d) $\lim\limits_{x \to -\infty} f(x) = -\infty$, because f is increasing and concave down. Thus, as $x \to -\infty$, $f(x)$ decreases, at a faster and faster rate.

(e)   Yes.

(f)   No. The slope is decreasing since f is concave down, so $f'(1) > f'(5)$, i.e. $f'(1) > \frac{1}{2}$.

23.

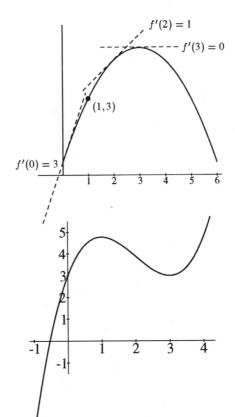

24.

CHAPTER THREE

3.1 SOLUTIONS

1. (a) Lower estimate $= 60+40+25+10+0 = 135$ feet. Upper estimate $= 88+60+40+25+10 = 223$ feet.
   (b)

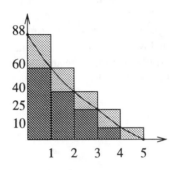

2. (a) Note that 15 minutes equals 0.25 hours. Lower estimate $= 11(0.25) + 10(0.25) = 5.25$ miles. Upper estimate $= 12(0.25) + 11(0.25) = 5.75$ miles.
   (b) Lower estimate $= 11(0.25) + 10(0.25) + 10(0.25) + 8(0.25) + 7(0.25) + 0(0.25) = 11.5$ miles. Upper estimate $= 12(0.25) + 11(0.25) + 10(0.25) + 10(0.25) + 8(0.25) + 7(0.25) = 14.5$ miles.
   (c) The difference between Roger's pace at the beginning and the end of his run is 12 mph. If the time between the measurements is h, then the difference between the upper and lower estimates is $12h$. We want $12h < 0.1$, so

$$h < \frac{0.1}{12} \approx 0.0083 \text{ hours} = 30 \text{ seconds}$$

Thus Jeff would have to measure Roger's pace every 30 seconds.

3. (a) An overestimate is 7 tons. An underestimate is 5 tons.
   (b) An overestimate is $7+8+10+13+16+20 = 74$ tons. An underestimate is $5+7+8+10+13+16 = 59$ tons.
   (c) If measurements are made every Δt months, then the error is $|f(6) - f(0)| \cdot \Delta t$. So for this to be less than 1 ton, we need $(20 - 5) \cdot \Delta t < 1$, or $\Delta t < 1/15$. So measurements every 2 days or so will guarantee an error in over- and underestimates of less than 1 ton.

4. Using whole grid squares, we can overestimate the area as $3 + 3 + 3 + 3 + 2 + 1 = 15$, and we can underestimate the area as $1 + 2 + 2 + 1 + 0 + 0 = 6$. Using triangles as in Figure 3.1, we can overestimate the area as $2 + 2\frac{7}{8} + 3 + 2\frac{1}{2} + 1\frac{1}{2} + \frac{3}{4} = 12\frac{5}{8}$ and we can underestimate the area as $1\frac{1}{2} + 2\frac{1}{4} + 2\frac{1}{2} + 2 + 1 + \frac{1}{4} = 9\frac{1}{2}$. It also appears from the graph that our upper estimate is closer than the lower estimate to the actual area, so we can further estimate the area to be a little greater than $\frac{1}{2}(9\frac{1}{2} + 12\frac{5}{8}) = 11\frac{1}{16}$.

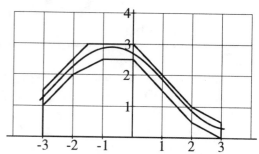

Figure 3.1: Estimating the Area

5. (a) We want the error to be less than 0.1, so take Δx such that $|f(1) - f(0)|\Delta x < 0.1$, giving

$$\Delta x < \frac{0.1}{|e^{-\frac{1}{2}} - 1|} \approx 0.25$$

so take $\Delta x = 0.25$ or $n = 4$. Then the left sum = 0.9016, and the right sum = 0.8033, so a reasonable estimate for the area is $\frac{0.9016+0.8033}{2} = 0.8525$. Certainly 0.85 is within 0.1 of the actual answer.

(b) Take Δx smaller. To have an error of at most E, you need Δx such that

$$|f(1) - f(0)|\Delta x < E$$

This means

$$\Delta x < \frac{E}{|e^{-\frac{1}{2}} - 1|} \approx \frac{E}{0.39}.$$

Using n equal subdivisions, we have

$$\Delta x = \frac{b - a}{n} = \frac{1 - 0}{n} = \frac{1}{n}.$$

Thus, to approximate the shaded area with an error $< E$ requires $n > \frac{0.39}{E}$ subdivisions.

6. Just counting the squares (each of which has area 10, in units of meters), and allowing for the broken squares, we can see that the area under the curve from 0 to 6 is between 140 and 150. Hence the distance traveled is between 140 and 150 meters.

7. First, note that, for $0 \le t \le 1.1$, $v(t)$ is an increasing function. The difference between the values of the function at the endpoints of the interval $[0,1.1]$ is $(\sin 1.21 - \sin 0) \approx 0.936$. If we approximate the area under the curve by rectangles above and below the curve of base h, then the difference between upper and lower estimates of the area $\approx 0.936h$. For one decimal place accuracy, we want $0.936h < 0.1$, so $h < 0.107$. This is the same as saying that we must have more than $\frac{1.1}{0.107} \approx 10.3$ rectangles for this degree of accuracy. With 11 rectangles, our underestimate is ≈ 0.353 and the overestimate is ≈ 0.447. Hence the value of the integral is 0.400 to one decimal place accuracy.

8. We'll use left and right hand sums to estimate the distance that the bug crawls. We can use the fact that v is monotonic to ensure that our answer will be off by no more than 0.1 meters. Since the difference in the velocity between $t = 0$ and $t = 1$ is 0.5, then the difference between our lower and upper estimate will be $0.5h$, where h is our interval of measurement. We want

$$0.5h \leq 0.1,$$

which gives $h \leq 0.2$. Choosing $h = 0.2$, our upper estimate is

$$\frac{1}{1+0}(0.2) + \frac{1}{1+0.2}(0.2) + \frac{1}{1+0.4}(0.2) + \frac{1}{1+0.6}(0.2) + \frac{1}{1+0.8}(0.2) \approx 0.75.$$

Our lower estimate is

$$\frac{1}{1+0.2}(0.2) + \frac{1}{1+0.4}(0.2) + \frac{1}{1+0.6}(0.2) + \frac{1}{1+0.8}(0.2) + \frac{1}{1+1.0}(0.2) \approx 0.65.$$

So the bug has crawled more than 0.65 meters, but less than 0.75 meters.

9. (a) An upper estimate is $9.81 + 8.03 + 6.53 + 5.38 + 4.41 = 34.16$ m/sec. A lower estimate is $8.03 + 6.53 + 5.38 + 4.41 + 3.61 = 27.96$ m/sec.

    (b) The average is $\frac{1}{2}(34.16 + 27.96) = 31.06$ m/sec. Because the graph of acceleration is concave up, this estimate is too high, as can be seen in the figure to the right. The area of the shaded region is the average of the areas of the rectangles $ABFE$ and $CDFE$.

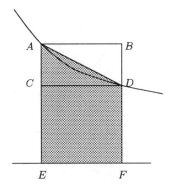

10. Since acceleration is the derivative of velocity $(a(t) = v'(t))$, and $a(t)$ is a constant, $v(t)$ must be a linear function. Its v-intercept is 0 since the object has zero initial velocity. Thus the graph of v is a line through the origin with slope 32: $v(t) = 32t$ ft/sec. Using $\Delta t = 1$, the right sum, $32 + 64 + 96 + 128 = 320$ feet, is an upper bound on the distance traveled. The left sum, $0 + 32 + 64 + 96 = 192$ feet, is a lower bound.

    To find the actual distance, we find the area of the region below that linear function exactly—it's just a triangle with height $32 \cdot 4 = 128$ and base 4, so its area is 256.

3.2 SOLUTIONS

1.

TABLE 3.1

n	2	10	50	250
Left-hand Sum	0.0625	0.2025	0.2401	0.248004
Right-hand Sum	0.5625	0.3025	0.2601	0.252004

The sums seem to be converging to $\frac{1}{4}$. Since x^3 is monotone on $[0, 1]$, the true value is between 0.248004 and 0.252004 .

2.

TABLE 3.2

n	2	10	50	250
Left-hand Sum	1.34076	1.07648	1.01563	1.00314
Right-hand Sum	0.55536	0.91940	0.98421	0.99686

The sums seem to be converging to 1. Since $\cos x$ is monotone on $[0, \pi/2]$, the true value is between 1.00314 and .99686 .

3.

TABLE 3.3

n	2	10	50	250
Left-hand Sum	1.14201	1.38126	1.44565	1.45922
Right-hand Sum	2.00115	1.55309	1.48002	1.46610

There is no obvious guess as to what the limiting sum is. We can only observe that since e^{t^2} is monotonic on $[0, 1]$, the true value is between 1.45922 and 1.46610 .

4.

TABLE 3.4

n	2	10	50	250
Left-hand Sum	1.41856	1.90525	2.02064	2.04445
Right-hand Sum	2.91856	2.20525	2.08064	2.05645

There is no obvious guess as to what the limiting sum is. We can only observe that since x^x is monotonic on $[1, 2]$, the true value is between 2.04445 and 2.05645 .

5.

TABLE 3.5

n	2	10	50	250
Left-hand Sum	-0.394991	-0.0920539	-0.0429983	-0.0335556
Right-hand Sum	0.189470	0.0248382	-0.0196199	-0.0288799

There is no obvious guess as to what the limiting sum is. Moreover, since $\sin(t^2)$ is *not* monotonic on $[2, 3]$, we cannot be sure that the true value is between -0.0335556 and -0.0288799.

6.

TABLE 3.6

n	2	10	50	250
Left-hand Sum	-0.52336	1.31159	1.49798	1.52526
Right-hand Sum	1.27721	1.6717	1.57000	1.53966

There is no obvious guess as to what the limiting sum is. Moreover, since $\sin(1/x)$ is *not* monotonic on $[0.2, 3]$, we cannot be sure that the true value is between 1.52526 and 1.53966.

7. For $n = 1300$, LHS ≈ 41.618 (rounding down) and RHS ≈ 41.715 (rounding up). Since the left and right sums differ by 0.097, their average must be within 0.0485 of the true value, so $\int_0^5 x^2 \, dx = 41.667$ to one decimal place.

8. For $n = 20$, LHS ≈ 1.249 (rounding up) and RHS ≈ 1.179 (rounding down). Since the left and right sums differ by 0.07, their average value must be within 0.035 of the true value, so $\int_1^4 \frac{1}{\sqrt{1+x^2}} \, dx = 1.214$ to one decimal place.

9. For $n = 10$, LHS ≈ 0.465 (rounding down) and RHS ≈ 0.474 (rounding up). Since the left and right sums differ by 0.009, their average must be within 0.0045 of the true value, so $\int_1^{1.5} \sin x \, dx = 0.470$ to one decimal place.

10. For $n = 10$, LHS ≈ 0.865 (rounding down) and RHS ≈ 0.899 (rounding up). Since the left and right sums differ by 0.034, their average must be within 0.017 of the true value, so $\int_0^{\frac{\pi}{4}} \frac{d\theta}{\cos \theta} = 0.882$ to one decimal place.

11. For $n = 110$, LHS ≈ 4.810 (rounding down) and RHS ≈ 4.905 (rounding up). Since the left and right sums differ by 0.095, their average must be within 0.0475 of the true value, so $\int_1^5 (\ln x)^2 \, dx = 4.858$ to one decimal place.

12. For $n = 20$, LHS ≈ 0.825 (rounding down) and RHS ≈ 0.905 (rounding up). Since the left and right sums differ by 0.08, their average must be within 0.04 of the true value, so $\int_{1.1}^{1.7} e^t \ln t \, dt = 0.865$ to one decimal place.

13. For $n = 30$, LHS ≈ 2.852 (rounding down) and RHS ≈ 2.919 (rounding up). Since the left and right sums differ by 0.067, their average must be within 0.0335 of the true value, so $\int_1^2 2^x \, dx = 2.886$ to one decimal place.

14. For $n = 5$, LHS ≈ 1.042 (rounding down) and RHS ≈ 1.049 (rounding up). Since the left and right sums differ by 0.007, their average must be within 0.0035 of the true value, so $\int_1^2 (1.03)^t \, dt = 1.046$ to one decimal place.

15. For $n = 10$, LHS ≈ 0.0045 (rounding down) and RHS ≈ 0.0276 (rounding up). Since the left and right sums differ by 0.0231, their average must be within 0.01155 of the true value, so $\int_{-2}^{-1} \cos^3 y \, dy = 0.016$ to one decimal place.

16. For $n = 50$, LHS ≈ 0.383 (rounding down) and RHS ≈ 0.415 (rounding up). Since the left and right sums differ by 0.032, their average must be within 0.016 of the true value, so $\int_0^1 \tan(z^2) \, dz = 0.399$ to one decimal place.

17. Since e^{-t^2} is an even function, $\int_{-3}^3 e^{-t^2} \, dt = 2 \int_0^3 e^{-t^2} \, dt$. This is because the integrand is symmetrical about the y-axis, and by symmetry, $\int_{-3}^0 e^{-t^2} \, dt = \int_0^3 e^{-t^2} \, dt$. Since e^{-t^2} is decreasing monotonically on the interval $0 < t < 3$, we can use our error estimation techniques to approximate $\int_0^3 e^{-t^2} \, dt$. Since we want our error to be less than 0.05 for the interval $-3 < t < 3$, we want our error to be less than $\frac{1}{2}(0.05) = 0.025$ for the interval $0 < t < 3$. For $n = 70$, LHS ≈ 0.908 (rounding up) and RHS ≈ 0.864 (rounding down). Since the left and right sums differ by 0.044, their average must be within

0.022 of the true value, so $\int_{-3}^{3} e^{-t^2}\, dt = 2\int_{0}^{3} e^{-t^2}\, dt = 2(0.886) = 1.772$, to one decimal place.

18. Instead of finding n by trial and error, as in the text, you can also start by calculating the value of n. Since the interval $1 \le t \le 3$ is of length 2, the length of one subdivision is $\Delta t = \frac{2}{n}$. If we choose n so that the difference between the left- and right-hand sums is less than 0.1, our result about errors tells us that

$$\text{Error} < |f(1) - f(3)| \cdot \Delta t < 0.1.$$

Therefore we should pick n so that

$$|f(3) - f(1)|\frac{2}{n} < 0.1$$

$$(9 - 1)\frac{2}{n} < 0.1$$

$$\text{so} \quad n > 160.$$

19. As in Figure 3.2, the left- and right-hand sums are both equal to $(4\pi) \cdot 3 = 12\pi$, while the integral is smaller. Thus we have:

$$\int_{0}^{4\pi} (2 + \cos x)\, dx < \text{left-hand sum} = \text{right-hand sum}.$$

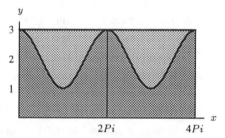

Figure 3.2: Integral vs. Left- and Right-Hand Sums

20.

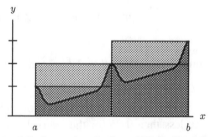

Figure 3.3: Integral vs. Left- and Right-Hand Sums

3.3 SOLUTIONS

1. The units of measurement are foot-pounds (which are units of work).

2. The units of measurement are meters per second (which are units of velocity).

3. The units of measurement are dollars.

4. For any t, consider the interval $[t, t + dt]$. During this interval, oil is leaking out at an approximately constant rate of $f(t)$ gallons/minute. Thus, the amount of oil which has leaked out during this interval can be expressed as

$$\text{Amount of oil leaked} = \text{Rate} \times \text{Time} = f(t)\, dt$$

and the units of $f(t)\, dt$ are gallons/minute $\times$ minutes $=$ gallons. The total amount of oil leaked is obtained by adding all these amounts between $t = 0$ and $t = 60$. (An hour is 60 minutes.) The sum of all these infinitesimal amounts is the integral

$$\begin{array}{c}\text{Total amount of} \\ \text{oil leaked, in gallons}\end{array} = \int_0^{60} f(t)\, dt.$$

5. Since x intercepts are $x = 0, \pi, 2\pi, \ldots$,

$$\text{Area} = \int_0^\pi \sin x \, dx = 2.00.$$

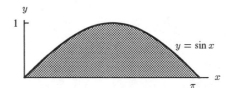

6. Since the θ intercepts of $y = \sin \theta$ are $\theta = 0, \pi, 2\pi, \ldots$,

$$\text{Area} = \int_0^\pi 1 \, d\theta - \int_0^\pi \sin \theta \, d\theta = \pi - 2 \approx 1.14.$$

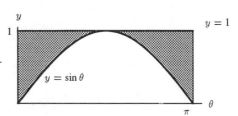

7. The x intercepts of $y = 4 - x^2$ are $x = -2$ and $x = 2$, and the graph is above the x-axis on the interval $[-2, 2]$.

$$\text{Area} = \int_{-2}^2 (4 - x^2) \, dx = 10.67.$$

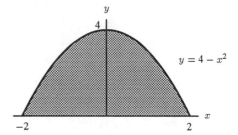

8. The x intercepts of $y = x^2 - 9$ are $x = -3$
    and $x = 3$, and since the graph is below the x
    axis on the interval $[-3, 3]$.

    $$\text{Area} = -\int_{-3}^{3} (x^2 - 9)\, dx = 36.00.$$

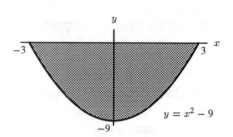

9. (a)

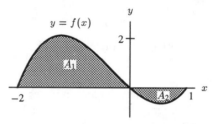

    (b) $A_1 = \int_{-2}^{0} f(x)\, dx = 2.667.$

    $A_2 = -\int_{0}^{1} f(x)\, dx = 0.417.$

    So Total area $= A_1 + A_2 = 3.08.$

    (c) $\int_{-2}^{1} f(x)\, dx = A_1 - A_2 = 2.50.$

10. Area $= \int_{0}^{2} \cos\sqrt{x}\, dx = 1.1$

11. $\int_{0}^{4} \cos\sqrt{x}\, dx = 0.80 = \text{Area } A_1 - \text{Area } A_2$

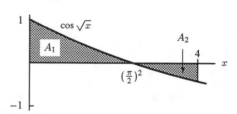

12. (a) Clearly, the points where $x = \sqrt{\pi}, \sqrt{2\pi}, \sqrt{3\pi}, \sqrt{4\pi}$ are where the graph intersects the x-axis
     because $f(x) = \sin(x^2) = 0$ where x is the square root of some multiple of π.

(b) Let $f(x) = \sin(x^2)$, and let A, B, C, and D be the areas of the regions indicated in the figure to the right. Then we see that $A > B > C > D$.

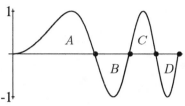

Note that

$$\int_0^{\sqrt{\pi}} f(x)\, dx = A, \quad \int_0^{\sqrt{2\pi}} f(x)\, dx = A - B,$$

$$\int_0^{\sqrt{3\pi}} f(x)\, dx = A - B + C, \quad \text{and} \quad \int_0^{\sqrt{4\pi}} f(x)\, dx = A - B + C - D.$$

It follows that

$$\int_0^{\sqrt{\pi}} f(x)\, dx = A > \int_0^{\sqrt{3\pi}} f(x)\, dx = A - (B - C) = A - B + C >$$

$$\int_0^{\sqrt{4\pi}} f(x)\, dx = A - B + C - D > \int_0^{\sqrt{2\pi}} f(x)\, dx = (A - B) > 0.$$

And thus the ordering is $n = 1$, $n = 3$, $n = 4$, and $n = 2$ from largest to smallest. All the numbers are positive.

13. Average value $= \dfrac{1}{2-0} \displaystyle\int_0^2 (1+t)\, dt = \dfrac{1}{2}(4) = 2.$

14. Average value $= \dfrac{1}{10-0} \displaystyle\int_0^{10} e^t\, dt = \dfrac{1}{10}(22025) = 2202.5$

15.

$$\text{Average value} = \frac{1}{b-a} \int_a^b f(x)\, dx$$

$$= \frac{1}{b-a} \int_a^b 2\, dx = \frac{1}{b-a} \cdot \left(\begin{array}{c} \text{Area of rectangle} \\ \text{of height 2 and base } b - a \end{array} \right)$$

$$= \frac{1}{b-a} \left[2(b-a)\right] = 2.$$

16. (a) Average value $= \displaystyle\int_0^1 \sqrt{1 - x^2}\, dx = 0.79$

(b) The area between the graph of $y = 1 - x$ and the x-axis is 0.5. Because the graph of $y = \sqrt{1 - x^2}$ is concave down, it lies above the line $y = 1 - x$, so its average value is above 0.5.

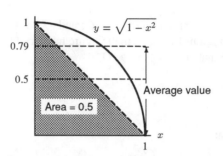

17. (a) Since $f(x) = \sin x$ over $[0, \pi]$ is between 0 and 1, the average of $f(x)$ must itself be between 0 and 1. Furthermore, since the graph of $f(x)$ is concave down on this interval, the average value must be greater than the average height of the triangle shown in the figure, namely, 0.5.

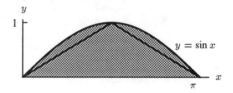

   (b) Average $= \dfrac{1}{\pi - 0} \displaystyle\int_0^{\pi} \sin x \, dx = \dfrac{2}{\pi} = 0.64$.

18. Since $t = 0$ in 1965 and $t = 35$ in 2000, we want:

$$\text{AverageValue} = \frac{1}{35 - 0} \int_0^{35} 225(1.15)^t dt$$

$$= \frac{1}{35}(212{,}787) = \$6080.$$

19. (a) Since $t = 0$ to $t = 31$ covers January:

$$\begin{pmatrix} \text{Average number of} \\ \text{daylight hours in January} \end{pmatrix} = \frac{1}{31} \int_0^{31} \left[12 + 2.4 \sin(0.0172(t - 80)) \right] \, dt.$$

Using left and right sums with $n = 100$ gives

$$\text{Average} \approx \frac{306}{31} \approx 9.9 \text{ hours.}$$

   (b) Assuming it is not a leap year, the last day of May is $t = 151 (= 31 + 28 + 31 + 30 + 31)$ and the last day of June is $t = 181 (= 151 + 30)$. Again finding the integral numerically:

$$\begin{pmatrix} \text{Average number of} \\ \text{daylight hours in June} \end{pmatrix} = \frac{1}{30} \int_{151}^{181} \left[12 + 2.4 \sin(0.0172(t - 80)) \right] \, dt$$

$$\approx \frac{431}{30} \approx 14.4 \text{ hours.}$$

(c)

$$\text{(Average for whole year)} = \frac{1}{365} \int_0^{365} \left[12 + 2.4 \sin(0.0172(t - 80)) \right] \, dt$$

$$\approx \frac{4381}{365} \approx 12.0 \text{ hours.}$$

(d) The average over the whole year should be 12 hours, as computed in (c). Since Madrid is in the northern hemisphere, the average for a winter month, such as January, should be less than 12 hours (it is 9.9 hours) and the average for a summer month, such as June, should be more than 12 hours (it is 14.4 hours).

20. (a) At the end of one hour $t = 60$, and $H = 22°$C.

   (b)

$$\text{Average temperature} = \frac{1}{60} \int_0^{60} (20 + 980e^{-0.1t}) dt$$

$$= \frac{1}{60}(10976) = 183°\text{C}.$$

   (c) Average temperature at beginning and end of hour $= (1000 + 22)/2 = 511°$C. The average found in part (b) is smaller than the average of these two temperatures because the bar cools quickly at first and so spends less time at high temperatures. Alternatively, the graph of H against t is concave up.

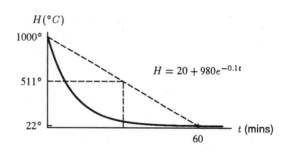

21. (a) For $-2 \leq x \leq 2$, f is symmetrical about the y-axis, so $\int_{-2}^0 f(x)\,dx = \int_0^2 f(x)\,dx$ and $\int_{-2}^2 f(x)\,dx = 2\int_0^2 f(x)\,dx$.

   (b) For any function f, $\int_0^2 f(x)\,dx = \int_0^5 f(x)\,dx - \int_2^5 f(x)\,dx$.

   (c) Note that $\int_{-2}^0 f(x)\,dx = \frac{1}{2}\int_{-2}^2 f(x)\,dx$, so $\int_0^5 f(x)\,dx = \int_{-2}^5 f(x)\,dx - \int_{-2}^0 f(x)\,dx = \int_{-2}^5 f(x)\,dx - \frac{1}{2}\int_{-2}^2 f(x)\,dx$.

22. (a) We know that $\int_2^5 f(x)\,dx = \int_0^5 f(x)\,dx - \int_0^2 f(x)\,dx$. By symmetry, $\int_0^2 f(x)\,dx = \frac{1}{2}\int_{-2}^2 f(x)\,dx$, so $\int_2^5 f(x)\,dx = \int_0^5 f(x)\,dx - \frac{1}{2}\int_{-2}^2 f(x)\,dx$.

   (b) $\int_2^5 f(x)\,dx = \int_{-2}^5 f(x)\,dx - \int_{-2}^2 f(x)\,dx = \int_{-2}^5 f(x)\,dx - 2\int_{-2}^0 f(x)\,dx$.

   (c) Using symmetry again, $\int_0^2 f(x)\,dx = \frac{1}{2}(\int_{-2}^5 f(x)\,dx - \int_2^5 f(x)\,dx)$.

23. (a) Average value of $f = \frac{1}{5}\int_0^5 f(x)\,dx$.

   (b) Average value of $|f| = \frac{1}{5}\int_0^5 |f(x)|\,dx = \frac{1}{5}(\int_0^2 f(x)\,dx - \int_2^5 f(x)\,dx)$.

24. We'll show that in terms of the average value of f,

$$I > II = IV > III$$

Using Problem 21a,

$$\text{Average value of } f \text{ on II} = \frac{\int_0^2 f(x)\,dx}{2} = \frac{\frac{1}{2}\int_{-2}^2 f(x)\,dx}{2}$$

$$= \frac{\int_{-2}^2 f(x)\,dx}{4}$$

$$= \text{Average value of } f \text{ on IV.}$$

Since f is decreasing on $[0, 5]$, the average value of f on the interval $[0, c]$ is decreasing as a function of c. The larger the interval the more low values of f are included. Hence

$$\begin{array}{ccc} \text{Average value of } f & > & \text{Average value of } f & > & \text{Average value of } f \\ \text{on } [0, 1] & & \text{on } [0, 2] & & \text{on } [0, 5] \end{array}$$

3.4 SOLUTIONS

1. Since $F(0) = 0$, $F(b) = \int_0^b f(t)\,dt$. For each b we determine $F(b)$ graphically as follows:
   $F(0) = 0$
   $F(1) = F(0) + \text{Area of } 1 \times 1 \text{ rectangle} = 0 + 1 = 1$
   $F(2) = F(1) + \text{Area of triangle } (\frac{1}{2} \cdot 1 \cdot 1) = 1 + 0.5 = 1.5$
   $F(3) = F(2) + \text{Negative of area of triangle} = 1.5 - 0.5 = 1$
   $F(4) = F(3) + \text{Negative of area of rectangle} = 1 - 1 = 0$
   $F(5) = F(4) + \text{Negative of area of rectangle} = 0 - 1 = -1$
   $F(6) = F(5) + \text{Negative of area of triangle} = -1 - 0.5 = -1.5$
   The graph of $F(t)$, for $0 \le t \le 6$, is shown in Figure 3.4.

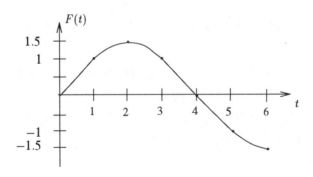

Figure 3.4

2. (a) $\displaystyle\int_{-3}^{0} f(x)\,dx = -2$

    (b) $\displaystyle\int_{-3}^{4} f(x)\,dx = \int_{-3}^{0} f(x)\,dx + \int_{0}^{3} f(x)\,dx + \int_{3}^{4} f(x)\,dx = -2 + 2 - \frac{A}{2} = -\frac{A}{2}$

3. By the Fundamental Theorem of Calculus,

$$F(b) - F(0) = \int_{0}^{b} f(\theta)\,d\theta = \int_{0}^{b} \sin(\theta^2)\,d\theta.$$

Since $F(0) = 0$, we have

$$F(b) = \int_{0}^{b} \sin(\theta^2)\,d\theta.$$

Using left Riemann sums on a calculator, with $n = 100$, we get

$$F(0) = 0$$
$$F(0.5) = 0.041$$
$$F(1) = 0.308$$
$$F(1.5) = 0.776$$
$$F(2) = 0.807$$
$$F(2.5) = 0.431.$$

4. The graph of $f(\theta) = F'(\theta) = \sin(\theta^2)$ is in Figure 3.5.

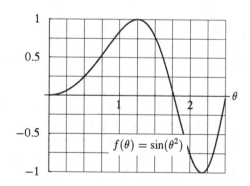

Figure 3.5

F is increasing where $F'(\theta) = f(\theta) > 0$, i.e. for $0 < \theta < \sqrt{\pi} \approx 1.77$. F is decreasing where $F'(\theta) = f(\theta) < 0$, i.e. for $1.77 < \theta \le 2.5$.

5. Using the solution to Problem 4, we see that F is increasing for $\theta < 1.77$ and F is decreasing for $\theta > 1.77$. Thus F has its maximum value when $\theta = 1.77$, and then by the Fundamental Theorem of Calculus,

$$F(1.77) - F(0) = \int_0^{1.77} f(\theta)\, d\theta = \int_0^{1.77} \sin(\theta^2)\, d\theta.$$

Since $F(0) = 0$, using Riemann sums we get

$$F(1.77) = \int_0^{1.77} \sin(\theta^2)\, d\theta = 0.89.$$

6. (a) For $n = 10$ subdivisions, the left sum ≈ 4.77 (rounding down) and the right sum ≈ 4.82 (rounding up). Since $\ln t$ is monotone on $[10,12]$, the actual value is between the sums. Since the left and right sums differ by 0.05, their average must be within 0.025 of the true value, so 4.795 is correct to one decimal place.

    (b) The Fundamental Theorem of Calculus tells us that we can get the exact answer by looking at $F(12) - F(10) = (12\ln 12 - 12) - (10\ln 10 - 10) \approx 4.79303.$

7. (a) Looking at Figure 3.6 we take note of places on the curve $F(x) = \sin x$ where the slope is zero. At the points $x = \frac{\pi}{2}, \frac{3\pi}{2}, \frac{5\pi}{2}, \ldots$ a tangent line to $\sin x$ is horizontal, so $F'(x) = 0$. We then notice that, for all x, at each point where the derivative is 0, the value of $\cos x$ is also 0. Thus it seems plausible that $F'(x) = \cos x$.

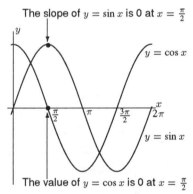

The slope of $y = \sin x$ is 0 at $x = \frac{\pi}{2}$

The value of $y = \cos x$ is 0 at $x = \frac{\pi}{2}$

Figure 3.6: Graph of $y = \sin x$ and $y = \cos x$

    (b) (i) For $n = 20$ subdivisions, the left sum ≈ 1.039 (rounding up), and the right sum ≈ 0.960 (rounding down). Since $\cos x$ is monotone over $[0, \frac{\pi}{2}]$, the actual value is between the sums. Since the left and right sums differ by 0.079, their average must be within 0.0395, so 0.9995 is correct to one decimal place.

        (ii) The Fundamental Theorem of Calculus says that we can find $\int_0^{\frac{\pi}{2}} \cos x\, dx = \int_0^{\frac{\pi}{2}} F'(x)\, dx$ by evaluating $F(x)$ at 0 and $\frac{\pi}{2}$. The integral is equal to $F(\frac{\pi}{2}) - F(0) = \sin(\frac{\pi}{2}) - \sin(0) = 1.$

8. By the Fundamental Theorem

$$f(1) - f(0) = \int_0^1 f'(x)\, dx.$$

Since $f'(x)$ is negative for $0 \le x \le 1$, this integral must be negative and so $f(1) < f(0)$.

9. First rewrite each of the quantities in terms of f', since we have the graph of f'. If A_1 and A_2 are the positive areas shown in Figure 3.7:

$$f(3) - f(2) = \int_2^3 f'(t)\, dt = -A_1$$

$$f(4) - f(3) = \int_3^4 f'(t)\, dt = -A_2$$

$$\frac{f(4) - f(2)}{2} = \frac{1}{2}\int_2^4 f'(t)\, dt = -\frac{A_1 + A_2}{2}$$

Since Area $A_1 >$ Area A_2,

$$A_2 < \frac{A_1 + A_2}{2} < A_1$$

so

$$-A_1 < -\frac{A_1 + A_2}{2} < -A_2$$

and therefore

$$f(3) - f(2) < \frac{f(4) - f(2)}{2} < f(4) - f(3).$$

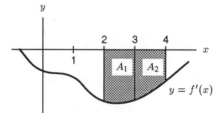

Figure 3.7

10. Change in income $= \int_0^{12} r(t)\, dt = \int_0^{12} 40(1.002)^t\, dt = \$485.80$

11. If $H(t)$ is the temperature of the coffee at time t, by the Fundamental Theorem of Calculus

$$\text{Change in temperature} = H(10) - H(0) = \int_0^{10} H'(t)\, dt = \int_0^{10} -7e^{-0.1t}\, dt.$$

Therefore,

$$H(10) = H(0) + \int_0^{10} -7e^{-0.1t}\, dt \approx 90 - 44.2 = 45.8°C.$$

12. (a) The amount leaked between $t = 0$ and $t = 2$ is $\int_0^2 R(t)\, dt$.
     (b)

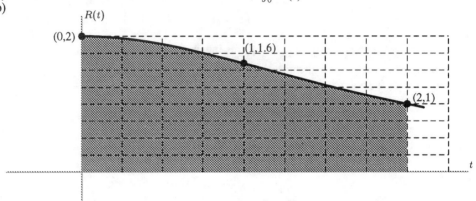

$R(t)$

(0,2)

(1,1.6)

(2,1)

t

(c) The rectangular boxes on the diagram each have area $\frac{1}{16}$. Of these 45 are wholly beneath the curve, hence the area under the curve is certainly more than $\frac{45}{16} = 2\frac{13}{16} > 2.81$. There are 10 more partially beneath the curve, and so the desired area is completely covered by 55 boxes. Therefore the area is less than $\frac{55}{16} = 3\frac{7}{16} < 3.44$.

These are very safe estimates but far apart. We can do much better by estimating what fractions of the broken boxes are beneath the curve. Using this method, we can estimate the area to be about 3.2, which corresponds to 3.2 gallons leaking over two hours.

13. (a) Quantity used $= \int_0^5 f(t)\, dt$.
     (b) Using a left sum, our approximation is

$$32e^{0.05(0)} + 32e^{0.05(1)} + 32e^{0.05(2)} + 32e^{0.05(3)} + 32e^{0.05(4)} = 177.27.$$

Since f is an increasing function, this represents an underestimate.
     (c) Each term is a lower estimate of one year's consumption of oil.

14. Notice that the area of a square on the graph represents $\frac{10}{6}$ miles. At $t = 1/3$ hours, $v = 0$. The area between the curve v and the t-axis over the interval $0 \le t \le 1/3$ is $-\int_0^{1/3} v\, dt \approx \frac{5}{3}$. v is negative here, so she is moving toward the lake. At $t = \frac{1}{3}$, she is about $5 - \frac{5}{3} = \frac{10}{3}$ miles from the lake. Then, as she moves away from the lake, v is positive for $\frac{1}{3} \le t \le 1$. At $t = 1$,

$$\int_0^1 v\, dt = \int_0^{1/3} v\, dt + \int_{1/3}^1 v\, dt \approx -\frac{5}{3} + 8 \cdot \frac{10}{6} = \frac{35}{3},$$

and the cyclist is about $5 + \frac{35}{3} = \frac{50}{3} = 16\frac{2}{3}$ miles from the lake. Since, starting from the moment $t = \frac{1}{3}$, she moves away from the lake, the cyclist will be farthest from the lake at $t = 1$. The maximal distance equals $16\frac{2}{3}$ miles.

15.

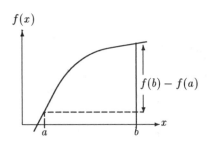

16.

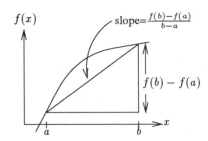

17.

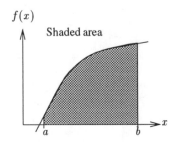

18.

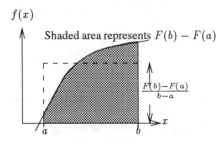

Note that we are using the interpretation of the definite integral as the length of the interval times the average value of the function on that interval, which we developed in Section 3.3.

19.

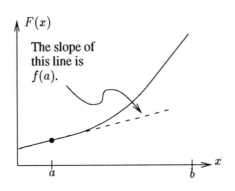

20.

By the FTC, we know that $\int_a^b f(x)\,dx = F(b) - F(a)$.

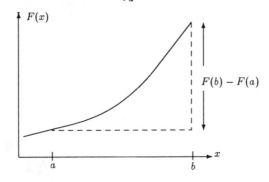

21.

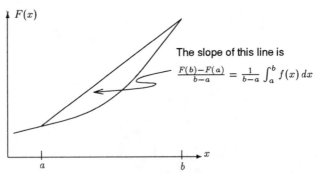

22. Let $v = f(t)$. If we can show that $\int_a^b f(t)dt$ is the change in position of the particle over the time interval $a < t < b$, then $\dfrac{1}{b-a}\int_a^b f(t)dt$ should give us the average velocity. But

$$\int_a^b f(t)\,dt = \int_0^b f(t)\,dt - \int_0^a f(t)\,dt = s(b) - s(a),$$

where $s(b) = \int_0^b f(t)\,dt$ and $s(a) = \int_0^a f(t)\,dt$ are positions of the particle at time $t = b$ and $t = a$, respectively. So $\int_a^b f(t)dt$ is indeed the change of position over $a < t < b$.

3.5 SOLUTIONS

1. For $0 \le t \le 10, 0 \le y \le 1$ the graph of $y = te^{-t}$ looks like the figure to the right.
    Therefore,

    $$\lim_{t \to \infty} te^{-t} = 0.$$

    Also, we are taking the limit of $\dfrac{t}{e^t}$ as $t \to \infty$, and as discussed in Chapter 1, Section 1.4, exponential functions grow much faster than t as $t \to \infty$.

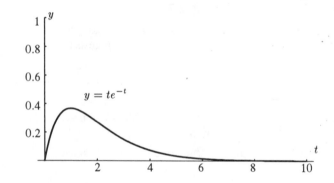

2. For $0 \le t \le 20, 0 \le y \le 1.4$ the graph of $y = t^3 e^{-t}$ looks like the figure to the right.
    Therefore,

    $$\lim_{t \to \infty} t^3 e^{-t} = \lim_{t \to \infty} \frac{t^3}{e^t} = 0.$$

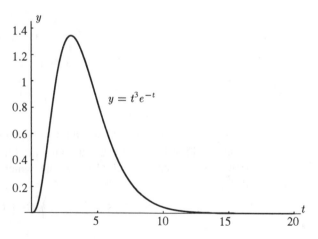

3. For $0 \leq x \leq 25$, $-1 \leq y \leq 1$, the graph of $\frac{\sin x}{x}$ is given to the right. As $x \to \infty$, the graph oscillates about the x-axis, but the amplitude of oscillation is constantly decreasing. By choosing x sufficiently large $y = \frac{\sin x}{x}$ can be brought as close to $y = 0$ as desired; we conclude that

$$\lim_{x \to \infty} \frac{\sin x}{x} = 0.$$

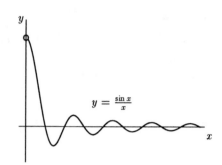

4. (a) For $0 < x \leq 100$, $0 \leq y \leq 3$, the graph is as shown to the right.

(b) Extending the domain to $0 < x \leq 10^6$ we see that $f(x) = \left(1 + \frac{1}{x}\right)^x$ tends, very slowly, towards $2.718\ldots$.

(c) The number above is a good approximation to e, so part (a) strongly suggests that

$$\lim_{x \to \infty} \left(1 + \frac{1}{x}\right)^x = e.$$

Indeed, this limit is sometimes used as the definition of e.

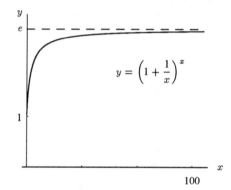

5. (a) It's true, for example, that since

$$\lim_{n \to \infty} \left(1 + \frac{1}{n}\right) = 1,$$

$$\lim_{n \to \infty} \left(1 + \frac{1}{n}\right)^3 = \left(\lim_{n \to \infty} \left(1 + \frac{1}{n}\right)\right)^3 = 1^3,$$

because the exponent, 3, has a fixed value, so we can bring it outside the limit. However, it is *not* true that

$$\lim_{n \to \infty} \left(1 + \frac{1}{n}\right)^n = \lim_{n \to \infty} 1^n = 1$$

since the exponent is not fixed, but rather approaching infinity at the same time as the sum $1 + \frac{1}{n}$ is approaching 1. Thus we are applying the limit only to part of the expression, namely the $\frac{1}{n}$, rather than taking the limit of the whole, which gives the incorrect result. In fact we can verify that

$$2.25 = \left(1 + \frac{1}{2}\right)^2 < \left(1 + \frac{1}{n}\right)^n \quad \text{for any } n > 2.$$

We will prove this result in Exercise 31 in the Review Exercises for Chapter 4.

(b) Your calculator first finds $1 + \frac{1}{n}$ and then raises it to the nth power. But it can only do this with a certain number of digits of accuracy, and so if n gets too large, $\frac{1}{n}$ becomes so small that the calculator rounds $1 + \frac{1}{n}$ down to exactly 1, and returns the result $1^n = 1$.

6.

TABLE 3.7

n	F_n	$G_n = \frac{F_n}{F_{n+1}}$	n	F_n	$G_n = \frac{F_n}{F_{n+1}}$
0	0	0	11	89	0.6180556
1	1	1	12	144	0.6180258
2	1	0.5	13	233	0.6180371
3	2	0.6666667	14	377	0.6180328
4	3	0.6	15	610	0.6180344
5	5	0.625	16	987	0.6180338
6	8	0.6153846	17	1597	0.6180341
7	13	0.6190476	18	2584	0.6180340
8	21	0.6176471	19	4181	0.6180340
9	34	0.6181818	20	6765	0.6180340
10	55	0.6179775			

Let us denote by G_n the entries in the third column; so $G_0 = 0, G_1 = 1, \ldots, G_7 = 0.6190476, \ldots$ Did you notice that the decimal digits of the successive G's stabilize one after another? Thus, G_3 and all subsequent G's begin $0.6 \ldots$; G_6 and all subsequent G's begin $0.61 \ldots$; and G_{11} and all subsequent G's begin $0.6180 \ldots$, etc. (Actually the G_n aren't constant after $n = 18$; your calculator is just rounding off: carried to 13 decimal places, the last four entries of the table are $0.6180340557276, 0.6180339631667$, 0.6180339985218, and 0.6180339850174 so G_{19} and all subsequent entries begin $0.6180339 \ldots$)

When we compute the differences $G_{n+1} - G_n$, we get $G_1 - G_0 = 1, G_2 - G_1 = -\frac{1}{2}, G_3 - G_2 = \frac{1}{6}$, $G_4 - G_3 = -\frac{1}{15}, \ldots$ The signs seem to alternate and the numerators all seem to be 1's. We can check this farther along $G_{17} - G_{16} = \frac{1597}{2584} - \frac{987}{1597} = \frac{1}{(2584)(1597)}$; the pattern seems to hold up.

To prove that this pattern holds forever, we look at $G_{n+1} - G_n = \frac{F_{n+1}}{F_{n+2}} - \frac{F_n}{F_{n+1}} = \frac{F_{n+1}^2 - F_n F_{n+2}}{F_{n+1} F_{n+2}}$. We want to show that the numerator $F_{n+1}^2 - F_n F_{n+2}$ is alternately $+1$ and -1. Let us denote $F_{n+1}^2 - F_n F_{n+2}$ by T_n. We have seen that $T_0 = +1, T_1 = -1, T_2 = -1, T_3 = +1, \ldots, T_{16} = +1, \ldots$ and we want to show that this alternation of $+1$'s and -1's continues indefinitely. To do this we must use the defining relation of the F_n's. For every n, $F_{n+1} = F_n + F_{n-1}$, so $F_{n+2} = F_{n+1} + F_n$. We have

$$\begin{aligned}
T_{n+1} &= F_{n+2}^2 - F_{n+1} F_{n+3} \\
&= F_{n+2}(F_{n+1} + F_n) - F_{n+1}(F_{n+2} + F_{n+1}) \\
&= F_{n+2} F_n - F_{n+1}^2 \\
&= -(F_{n+1}^2 - F_{n+2} F_n) \\
&= -T_n
\end{aligned}$$

Thus, each T is just the opposite of its predecessor, so the sequence $T_0 = +1$, $T_1 = -1$, $T_2 = +1$, ... continues to alternate between $+1$ and -1 for all n.

SOLUTIONS TO REVIEW PROBLEMS FOR CHAPTER THREE

1. For $n = 210$, the left sum ≈ 1.466 (rounding up) and the right sum ≈ 1.417 (rounding down). Since the left and right sums differ by 0.049, their average must be within 0.245 of the true value, so the value of the integral will be 1.442 to one decimal place accuracy.

2. Since $|\sin \theta| \leq 1$, it's clear that $|\sin 2(\frac{\pi}{2})^2 - \sin 0| \leq 1$, so our error estimate is less than $1 \cdot \left(\frac{\frac{\pi}{2}-0}{n}\right) = \frac{\pi}{2n}$. We want $\frac{\pi}{2n} < 0.05$, so $n \geq 32$. We try $n = 32$. [Note: since the function is not monotone over $[0, \frac{\pi}{2}]$, this is not guaranteed to work.]

   For $n = 32$, we get the left sum ≈ 0.501 and the right sum ≈ 0.443. The average of these two sums is 0.472, but, as mentioned above, we are not guaranteed one decimal place accuracy. A way to check this result is to compute the value of the integral for larger values of n. With $n = 100$, the left sum is ≈ 0.481 and the right sum is ≈ 0.462. It seems that the left and right sums are converging, so we can reasonably (but without complete certainty) say that the value of the integral is 0.47 to one decimal place.

3. For $n = 5$, the left sum ≈ 1.338 (rounding up) and the right sum ≈ 1.282 (rounding down). Since the function is monotone over the interval [0,1], as can be seen with a graphing calculator, the actual value is between the two sums. Since the left and right sums differ by 0.056, their average must be within 0.28 of the true value, so the value of the integral correct to one decimal place is 1.31.

4. We begin by noting that $\frac{x^2+1}{x^2-4}$ is not monotone over the interval $[-1, 1]$, as can be seen with a graphing calculator. It is however, even; that is, it is symmetric about the y-axis. We thus have that

$$\int_{-1}^{1} \frac{x^2 + 1}{x^2 - 4}\, dx = 2 \int_{0}^{1} \frac{x^2 + 1}{x^2 - 4}\, dx.$$

   In the second integral, however, the integrand is monotone. Since we want our error to be less than 0.05 for the interval $[-1, 1]$, we want our error to be less than $\frac{1}{2}(0.05) = 0.025$ for the interval [0,1]. For $n = 10$, the left sum ≈ -0.353 (rounding up) and the right sum ≈ -0.396 (rounding down). Since the left and right sums differ by 0.043, their average must be within 0.0215 of the true value, so the value of the integral is $2(-0.3745) = -0.749$ to one decimal place.

5. For $n = 10$, LEFT ≈ -0.086 (rounding down) and RIGHT ≈ -0.080 (rounding up). Since the left and right sums differ by 0.006, their average must be within 0.003 of the true value, so $\int_{2}^{3} -\frac{1}{(r+1)^2}\, dx = -0.083$ to one decimal place.

6. For $n = 20$, LEFT $\approx .534$ (rounding down) and RIGHT $\approx .614$ (rounding up). Since the left and right sums differ by 0.08, their average must be within 0.04 of the true value, so $\int_{0}^{1} \arcsin z\, dz = 0.574$ to one decimal place.

7. (a) $F(0) = 0$.

(b) F increases because $F'(x) = e^{-x^2}$ is positive.

(c) Using right and left sums, we get $F(1) \approx 0.7468$, $F(2) \approx 0.8821$, $F(3) \approx 0.8862$.

8. (a) For $n = 60$, the left sum ≈ 1.673 (rounding down), and the right sum ≈ 1.764 (rounding up). Since the left and right sums differ by 0.091, their average must be within 0.0455 of the true value, so the value of the integral is ≈ 1.7185, and this value is correct to one decimal place.

(b) The Fundamental Theorem of Calculus says we can get the answer by looking at $F(1) - F(0) = e^{1^2} - e^{0^2} = e - 1 = 1.71828$.

9. (a) For $n = 10$, the left sum ≈ 0.054 (rounding down), and the right sum ≈ 0.058 (rounding up). Since the left and right sums differ by 0.004, their average must be within 0.002 of the true value, so the value of the integral is 0.056 to one decimal place.

(b) Using the Fundamental Theorem of Calculus we find that the integral is $F(0.4) - F(0.2) = \frac{1}{2}(\sin^2(0.4) - \sin^2(0.2)) \approx 0.05609$.

10. (a) Since 60 mi/hr = 88 ft/sec, we have $|f(10) - f(0)| = 88$ ft/sec. Thus we would have to measure the car's velocity every $\frac{1}{88}$th of a second to determine the total distance within one foot.

(b) By counting squares and fractions of squares, we find that the area under the graph appears to be around 310 (miles/hour) sec, within about 10. So the distance traveled was about $310 \left(\frac{5280}{3600}\right) \approx 455$ feet, within about $10 \left(\frac{5280}{3600}\right) \approx 15$ feet.

11. (a) If the level first becomes acceptable at time t_1, then $R_0 = 4R(t_1)$, or

$$\frac{1}{4}R_0 = R_0 e^{-0.004t_1}$$

$$\frac{1}{4} = e^{-0.004t_1}.$$

Taking natural logs on both sides yields

$$\ln \frac{1}{4} = -0.004t_1$$

$$t_1 = \frac{\ln \frac{1}{4}}{-0.004} \approx 346.574 \text{ hours.}$$

(b) The acceptable limit is 0.6 millirems/hour, so from the above, $R_0 = 4(0.6) = 2.4$. Since the rate at which radiation is emitted is $R(t) = R_0 e^{-0.004t}$,

$$\text{Total radiation emitted} = \int_0^{346.574} 2.4 e^{-0.004t} \, dt.$$

Approximating the integral using left and right sums with 200 subdivisions, we find that about 450 millirems were emitted over that interval.

12. (a) V, since the slope is constant.

(b)   IV, since the net area under this curve is the most negative.

(c)   III, since the area under the curve is largest.

(d)   II, since the steepest ascent at $t = 0$ occurs on this curve.

(e)   III, since average velocity is $\frac{\text{total distance}}{5}$, and III moves the largest total distance.

(f)   I, since average acceleration is $\dfrac{1}{5}\displaystyle\int_0^5 v'(t)\,dt = \dfrac{1}{5}(v(5) - v(0))$, and in I, the velocity increases the most from start ($t = 0$) to finish ($t = 5$).

13. (a)

$$\text{Average population} = \frac{1}{10}\int_0^{10} 67.38(1.026)^t\,dt$$

Evaluating the integral numerically gives

$$\text{Average population} \approx 76.8 \text{ million}$$

(b)   In 1980, $t = 0$, and $P = 67.38(1.026)^0 = 67.38$.
In 1990, $t = 10$, and $P = 67.38(1.026)^{10} = 87.10$.
Average$= \frac{1}{2}(67.38 + 87.10) = 77.24$ million.

(c)   If P had been linear, the average value found in (a) would have been the one we found in (b). Since the population graph is concave up, it is below the secant line. Thus, the actual values of P are less than the corresponding values on the secant line, and so the average found in (a) is smaller than that in (b).

14. (a)   Using rectangles under the curve, we get

$$\text{Acres defaced} = (1)(0.2 + 0.4 + 1 + 2) = 3.6 \text{ acres}.$$

(b)   Using rectangles above the curve, we get

$$\text{Acres defaced} = (1)(0.4 + 1 + 2 + 3.5) = 6.9 \text{ acres}.$$

(c)   It's between 3.7 and 7, so we'll guess the average: 5.35 acres.

15. (a)   For any star with mass $m(t)$ at time t, growing at a rate of $m'(t)$:

$$\text{mass gained from time } a \text{ to time } b = m(b) - m(a) = \int_a^b m'(t)\,dt$$

Thus, for the first star

$$m_1(1.25) - m_1(0) = \int_0^{1.25} (\tan t)^{t+1}\,dt = 2.00.$$

For the second star

$$m_2(1.25) - m_2(0) = \int_0^{1.25} 2^t\,dt = 1.99.$$

So the first star gains more mass. (Note: to see the difference between these integrals you may need to use a large number of subdivisions, say $n = 500$.)

(b)

$$r'(0.4) = \lim_{h \to 0} \frac{r(0.4 + h) - r(0.4)}{h}$$

$$\approx \frac{(\tan 0.41)^{1.41} - (\tan 0.4)^{1.4}}{0.01} = 0.9126 \cdots$$

$$\approx \frac{(\tan 0.401)^{1.401} - (\tan 0.4)^{1.4}}{0.001} = 0.9116 \cdots$$

so $r'(0.4) = 0.912$ (to three decimal places).

$$p'(0.4) = \lim_{h \to 0} \frac{p(0.4 + h) - p(0.4)}{h}$$

$$\approx \frac{2^{0.401} - 2^{0.4}}{0.001} = 0.9149 \cdots$$

$$\approx \frac{2^{0.4001} - 2^{0.4}}{0.0001} = 0.9146 \cdots$$

so $p'(0.4) = 0.915$ (to three decimal places).

Therefore $p'(0.4)$ is greater. The physical meaning of $r'(0.4)$ is the rate at which the rate of change of mass is changing, when $t = 0.4$.

(c)   The difference in the masses gained by the two stars during the interval from $t = 0$ to $t = 1$, i.e.

$$\int_0^1 (2^t - (\tan t)^{t+1}) \, dt = \left(\begin{array}{c} \text{mass gained by Star 2} \\ \text{during } 0 \le t \le 1 \end{array} \right) - \left(\begin{array}{c} \text{mass gained by Star 1} \\ \text{during } 0 \le t \le 1. \end{array} \right)$$

16.   From the figure, we can determine that $f(x) = 0.5 + \sin\left(\frac{\pi x}{4}\right)$. Using a calculator, you can see that $f(x)$ and $g(x)$ intersect at about $x = 0.50$, $x = 4.19$, and $x = 7.55$. Thus we have:

$$\text{Shaded Area} = \int_0^{0.50} \left(e^{-x/4} - \left(0.5 + \sin\frac{\pi x}{4}\right) \right) \, dx$$

$$+ \int_{0.50}^{4.19} \left(\left(0.5 + \sin\frac{\pi x}{4}\right) - e^{-x/4} \right) \, dx$$

$$+ \int_{4.19}^{7.55} \left(e^{-x/4} - \left(0.5 + \sin\frac{\pi x}{4}\right) \right) \, dx$$

$$\approx 0.12 + 2.15 + 1.57 \approx 3.84$$

17. The length of the curve from O to A is surely
more than OP + PA. Thinking of OP as the
hypotenuse of a right triangle with sides $\frac{\pi}{2}$
and 1, we see that OP = $\sqrt{1 + \frac{\pi^2}{4}} \approx 1.86$.
Similarly, PA ≈ 1.86. So the length of OA is
greater than 3.72.

Now consider a broken line with six segments
as shown. Q =$(\frac{\pi}{6}, \frac{1}{2})$, R =$(\frac{\pi}{3}, \frac{\sqrt{3}}{2})$, S =$(\frac{\pi}{2}, 1)$.

OQ =$\sqrt{(\frac{1}{2})^2 + (\frac{\pi}{6})^2} \approx 0.7240$

QR =$\sqrt{(\frac{1}{2}\sqrt{3} - \frac{1}{2})^2 + (\frac{\pi}{6})^2} \approx 0.6389$

RS =$\sqrt{(1 - \frac{\sqrt{3}}{2})^2 + (\frac{\pi}{6})^2} \approx 0.5405$

The length of the broken line is (using symmetry) 2(OQ + QR + RS) ≈ 3.8068.

The curve must be a little longer than this, but,
as is evident from the figure, very little longer,
so 3.8 is surely close to the exact length of the
curve. We will return to the study of lengths
of curves in Chapter 7.

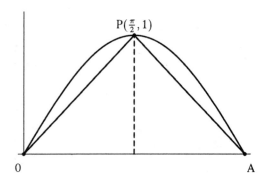

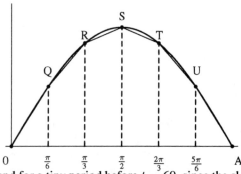

18. (a) The acceleration is positive for $0 \leq t < 40$ and for a tiny period before $t = 60$, since the slope is positive over these intervals. Just to the left of $t = 40$, it looks like the acceleration is approaching 0. Between $t = 40$ and a moment just before $t = 60$, the acceleration is negative.

(b) The maximum altitude was about 500 feet, when t was a little greater than 40 (here we are estimating the area under the graph for $0 \leq t \leq 40$).

(c) The acceleration is greatest when the slope of the velocity is most positive. This happens just before $t = 60$, where the magnitude of the velocity is plunging and the direction of the acceleration is positive, or up.

(d) The deceleration is greatest when the slope of the velocity is most negative. This happens just after $t = 40$.

(e) After the Montgolfier Brothers hit their top climbing speed (at $t = 40$), they suddenly stopped climbing and started to fall. This suggests some kind of catastrophe—the flame going out, the balloon ripping, etc. (In actual fact, in their first flight in 1783, the material covering their balloon, held together by buttons, ripped and the balloon landed in flames.)

(f) The total change in altitude for the Montgolfiers and their balloon is the definite integral of their velocity, or the total area under the given graph (counting the part after $t = 40$ as negative, of course). As mentioned before, the total area of the graph for $0 \leq t \leq 40$ is about 500. The area for $t > 40$ is about 220. So subtracting, we see that the balloon finished 280 feet or so higher than where it began.

19. (a) The mouse changes direction (when its velocity is zero) at times 17, 23, and 27.

    (b) The mouse is moving most rapidly to the right at time 10 and most rapidly to the left at time 40.

    (c) The mouse is farthest to the right when the integral of the velocity, $\int_0^t v(t)\, dt$, is most positive. Since the integral is the sum of the areas above the axis minus the area below the axis, the integral is largest when the velocity is zero at about 17 seconds. The mouse is farthest to the left of center when the integral is most negative at 40 seconds.

    (d) The mouse's speed decreases during seconds 10 to 17, from 20 to 23 seconds, and from 24 seconds to 27 seconds.

    (e) The mouse is at the center of the tunnel at any time t for which the integral from 0 to t of the velocity is zero. This is true at time 0 and again somewhere around 40 seconds.

20. In (a), $f'(1)$ is the slope of a tangent line at $x = 1$, which is negative. As for (c), the rate of change in $f(x)$ is given by $f'(x)$, and the average value of this over $0 \le x \le a$ is

$$\frac{1}{a-0}\int_0^a f'(x)\, dx = \frac{(f(a)-f(0))}{a-0}.$$

This is the slope of the line through the points (0,1) and (a,0), which is less negative that the tangent line at $x = 1$. Therefore $(a) < (c) < 0$. The quantity (b) is

$$\frac{\int_0^a f(x)\, dx}{a}$$

and (d) is $\int_0^a f(x)\, dx$, which is the net area under the graph of f (counting the area as negative for f below the x-axis). Since $a > 1$ and $\int_0^a f(x)\, dx > 0$, we have $0 < (b) < (d)$. Therefore

$$(a) < (c) < (b) < (d).$$

21. (a) The distance traveled is the integral of the velocity, so in T seconds you fall

$$\int_0^T \frac{g}{k}(1 - e^{-kt})\, dt.$$

Putting in the given values we have:

$$\text{distance fallen in } T \text{ seconds} = \int_0^T 49(1 - e^{-0.2t})\, dt \text{ meters}.$$

    (b) We want the number T for which

$$\int_0^T 49(1 - e^{-0.2t})\, dt = 5000.$$

Finding T precisely is difficult, but we can show that $T \approx 107$ as follows:

Since your velocity is always less than 49 m/sec it will take more than $\frac{5000}{49}(\approx 102)$ seconds to fall 5000 meters; i.e. $T > 102$.

If we draw the graph of v versus t we see that it has an asymptote $v = 49$. This is called the *terminal velocity*. Terminal velocity is reached, in a practical sense, fairly soon. When $t = 20$, v is already more than 48.1.

When $t = 100$, $v = 48.999\ldots$, so $v \approx 49$ m/sec.

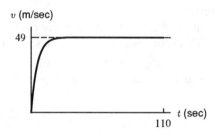

We want to find the time T so that the area under the graph of v from $t = 0$ to $t = T$ is 5000. Since v is increasing, we have:

$$\text{left-hand sum} \leq \int_0^T 49(1 - e^{-0.2t})\, dt \leq \text{right-hand sum}.$$

Since $T > 102$, we try $T = 103$, and using $n = 100$ subdivisions, we have:

$$4775.8 \leq \int_0^{103} 49(1 - e^{-0.2t})\, dt \leq 4826.4$$

Thus, our guess for T is too small, and w need about 173 to 225 meters. since $v \approx 49$ m/sec for $t \geq 1$, we see that each additional second results in approximately 49 meters in distance fallen, so we try $T = 107$. Using $n = 100$ subdivisions, we have:

$$4970.8 \leq \int_0^{107} 49(1 - e^{-0.2t})\, dt \leq 5023.3$$

Therefore $T \approx 107$ seconds.

CHAPTER FOUR

4.1 SOLUTIONS

1. (a) $f(x) = -3x + 2, g(x) = 2x + 1$.

$$k(x) = f(x) + g(x)$$
$$= (-3x + 2) + (2x + 1)$$
$$= -x + 3$$
$$k'(x) = -1.$$

Also, $f'(x) = -3, g'(x) = 2$, so $f'(x) + g'(x) = -3 + 2 = -1$.

(b)

$$j(x) = f(x) - g(x)$$
$$= (-3x + 2) - (2x + 1)$$
$$= -5x + 1$$
$$j'(x) = -5.$$

Also, $f'(x) - g'(x) = -3 - 2 = -5$.

2. $r(t) = 2t - 4$. $r'(t) = 2$.
$s(t) = 3r(t) = 3(2t - 4) = 6t - 12$.
$s'(t) = 6 = 3[r'(t)]$.

3. (a) $f(x) = 5x - 3, g(x) = -2x + 1$.
$f[g(x)] = f(-2x + 1) = 5(-2x + 1) - 3 = -10x + 5 - 3 = -10x + 2$.

So, $\frac{d}{dx}[f[g(x)]] = -10$.

(b) $f'(x) = 5, g'(x) = -2$, and the derivative of $f[g(x)] = -10 = f'(x)g'(x)$. So one might speculate that if f and g are linear functions, then the derivative of $f[g(x)]$ is $f'(x)g'(x)$. This is true, and it can be proved as follows. Consider general linear functions f and g:

$$f(x) = m_1 x + b_1$$
$$f'(x) = m_1$$
$$g(x) = m_2 x + b_2$$
$$g'(x) = m_2.$$

Then

$$f[g(x)] = m_1(m_2 x + b_2) + b_1 = m_1 m_2 x + m_1 b_2 + b_1,$$

and

$$\frac{d}{dx}\left(f[g(x)]\right) = m_1 m_2 = f'(x)g'(x).$$

4.   (a) $r(x) = f(x) + 2g(x) + 3$, $f'(x) = g(x)$, and $g'(x) = r(x)$.

$$
\begin{aligned}
r'(x) &= f'(x) + 2g'(x) \\
&= g(x) + 2r(x) \\
&= g(x) + 2[f(x) + 2g(x) + 3] \\
&= g(x) + 2f(x) + 4g(x) + 6 \\
&= 2f(x) + 5g(x) + 6.
\end{aligned}
$$

(b)

$$
\begin{aligned}
f(x) &= r(x) - 2g(x) - 3 \\
f'(x) &= r'(x) - 2g'(x) \\
&= [2f(x) + 5g(x) + 6] - 2g'(x) \qquad \text{by part (a)} \\
&= 2f(x) + 5f'(x) + 6 - 2r(x),
\end{aligned}
$$

so

$$
4f'(x) = 2r(x) - 2f(x) - 6,
$$

and

$$
f'(x) = \frac{1}{2}r(x) - \frac{1}{2}f(x) - \frac{3}{2}.
$$

5.   Say $\lim_{x \to a} f(x) = A$ and $\lim_{x \to a} g(x) = B$, i.e., as x comes arbitrarily close to a, $f(x)$ comes arbitrarily close to A and $g(x)$ comes arbitrarily close to B. So, as $x \to a$, the sum $f(x) + g(x)$ comes arbitrarily close to $A + B$, i.e.,

$$
\lim_{x \to a}[f(x) + g(x)] = A + B = \lim_{x \to a} f(x) + \lim_{x \to a} g(x).
$$

4.2 SOLUTIONS

1. $y' = 12x^{11}$.

2. $y' = -12x^{-13}$.

3. $y' = \frac{4}{3}x^{\frac{1}{3}}$.

4. $y' = \frac{3}{4}x^{-\frac{1}{4}}$.

5. $y' = -\frac{3}{4}x^{-\frac{7}{4}}$.

6. $f'(x) = -4x^{-5}$

7. $f'(x) = \frac{1}{4}x^{-\frac{3}{4}}$.

8. $f'(x) = ex^{e-1}$.

9. $y' = 6x^{\frac{1}{2}} - \frac{5}{2}x^{-\frac{1}{2}}$.

10. $y' = 18x^2 + 8x - 2$.

11. $y' = -12x^3 - 12x^2 - 6$.

12. $y' = 15t^4 - \frac{5}{2}t^{-\frac{1}{2}} - \frac{7}{t^2}$.

13. $y' = 6t - \frac{6}{t^{3/2}} + \frac{2}{t^3}$.

14. $y' = 2z - \frac{1}{2z^2}$.

15. $y = x + \frac{1}{x}$, so $y' = 1 - \frac{1}{x^2}$.

16. $g(z) = z^5 + 5z^4 - z$
    $g'(z) = 5z^4 + 20z^3 - 1$

17. $f(t) = \dfrac{1}{t^2} + \dfrac{1}{t} - \dfrac{1}{t^4} = t^{-2} + t^{-1} - t^{-4}$
    $f'(t) = -2t^{-3} - t^{-2} + 4t^{-5}$

18. $y = \dfrac{\theta}{\sqrt{\theta}} - \dfrac{1}{\sqrt{\theta}} = \sqrt{\theta} - \dfrac{1}{\sqrt{\theta}}$
    $y' = \dfrac{1}{2\sqrt{\theta}} + \dfrac{1}{2\theta^{3/2}}$.

19. The functions whose derivatives don't exist at $x = 0$ are in problems 2, 4, 5, 6, 7, and 9.

20. $y' = \frac{1}{2}x^{-\frac{1}{2}}$.   (power rule)

21. So far, we can only take the derivative of powers of x and the sums of constant multiples of powers of x. Since we cannot write $\sqrt{x+3}$ in this form, we cannot yet take its derivative.

22. $y' = 6x$.   (power rule and sum rule)

23. $y' = -\frac{2}{3z^3}$.   (power rule and sum rule)

24. $y' = -\dfrac{1}{6x^{3/2}}$.   (power rule and sum rule)

25. We cannot write $\frac{1}{3x^2+4}$ as the sum of powers of x multiplied by constants.

26. The x is in the exponent and we haven't learned how to handle that yet.

27. $y' = 3x^2$.   (power rule)

28. $y' = \pi x^{\pi-1}$.   (power rule)

29. Once again, the x is in the exponent and we haven't learned how to handle that yet.

30. $f'(t) = 6t^2 - 8t + 3$ and $f''(t) = 12t - 8$.

31. (a) Since the power of x will go down by one every time you take a derivative (until the exponent is zero after which the derivative will be zero), we can see immediately that $f^{(8)}(x) = 0$.
    (b) $f^{(7)}(x) = 7 \cdot 6 \cdot 5 \cdot 4 \cdot 3 \cdot 2 \cdot 1 \cdot x^0 = 5040$.

32.

$$f'(x) = 6x^2 - 4x \quad \text{so} \quad f'(1) = 6 - 4 = 2.$$

Thus the equation of the tangent line is $(y - 1) = 2(x - 1)$ or $y = 2x - 1$.

33.

$$y' = 3x^2 - 18x - 16 = 5$$
$$3x^2 - 18x - 21 = 0$$
$$x^2 - 6x - 7 = 0$$
$$(x + 1)(x - 7) = 0$$
$$x = -1 \text{ or } x = 7.$$

$f(-1) = 7, f(7) = -209.$
Thus, the two points are $(-1, 7)$ and $(7, -209)$.

34.

$$f'(x) = -8 + 2\sqrt{2}x$$

$$f'(r) = -8 + 2\sqrt{2}r = 4$$

$$r = \frac{12}{2\sqrt{2}} = 3\sqrt{2}.$$

35. Decreasing means $f'(x) < 0$:
$$f'(x) = 4x^2(x - 3) < 0,$$

so $x < 3$ and $x \neq 0$. Concave up means $f''(x) > 0$:

$$f''(0) = 12x^2 - 24x > 0$$

$$12x(x - 2) > 0$$

$$x < 0 \quad \text{or} \quad x > 2.$$

So, both conditions hold for $x < 0$ or $2 < x < 3$.

36.

$$f'(x) = 12x^2 + 12x - 23 \geq 1$$
$$12x^2 + 12x - 24 \geq 0$$
$$12(x^2 + x - 2) \geq 0$$
$$12(x + 2)(x - 1) \geq 0.$$

Hence $x \geq 1 \quad \text{or} \quad x \leq -2$.

37. (a) $p(x) = x^2 - x$. Now, $p'(x) = 2x - 1 < 0$ when $x < \frac{1}{2}$. So p is decreasing when $x < \frac{1}{2}$.
   (b) $p(x) = x^{\frac{1}{2}} - x$.

$$p'(x) = \frac{1}{2}x^{-\frac{1}{2}} - 1 < 0$$

$$\frac{1}{2}x^{-\frac{1}{2}} < 1$$

$$x^{-\frac{1}{2}} < 2$$

$$x^{\frac{1}{2}} > \frac{1}{2}$$

$$x > \frac{1}{4}.$$

Thus $p(x)$ is decreasing when $x > \frac{1}{4}$.

(c) $p(x) = x^{-1} - x$.

$$p'(x) = -1x^{-2} - 1 < 0$$

$$-x^{-2} < 1$$

$$x^{-2} > -1,$$

which is always true where x^{-2} is defined, since $x^{-2} = \frac{1}{x^2}$ is always positive. Thus $p(x)$ is always decreasing, unless $x = 0$.

38.   The slope of the tangent lines to $y = x^2 - 2x + 4$ is $y' = 2x - 2$. For a line through the origin, $y = mx$. So, at the tangent point, $x^2 - 2x + 4 = mx$ where $m = y' = 2x - 2$.

$$x^2 - 2x + 4 = (2x - 2)x$$

$$x^2 - 2x + 4 = 2x^2 - 2x$$

$$-x^2 + 4 = 0$$

$$-(x + 2)(x - 2) = 0$$

$$x = 2, -2.$$

Thus, the points of tangency are $(2, 4)$ and $(-2, 12)$. The lines through these points and the origin are $y = 2x$ and $y = -6x$, respectively. Graphically:

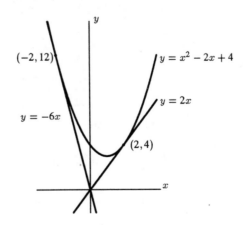

39.   Yes. To see why, we solve the equation $13x\dfrac{dy}{dx} = y$ for $y = x^n$. To solve the equation, we first evaluate $\dfrac{dy}{dx} = \dfrac{d}{dx}(x^n) = nx^{n-1}$. The equation becomes

$$13x(nx^{n-1}) = x^n$$

But $13x(nx^{n-1}) = 13n(x \cdot x^{n-1}) = 13nx^n$, so we have

$$13n(x^n) = x^n$$

For $x \neq 0$, we divide through by x^n to get $13n = 1$, so $n = \frac{1}{13}$. Thus, $y = x^{\frac{1}{13}}$ is a solution.

40.   (a)

$$\begin{aligned}
\frac{d(x^{-1})}{dx} &= \lim_{h \to 0} \frac{(x+h)^{-1} - x^{-1}}{h} = \lim_{h \to 0} \frac{1}{h}\left[\frac{1}{x+h} - \frac{1}{x}\right]\\
&= \lim_{h \to 0} \frac{1}{h}\left[\frac{x - (x+h)}{x(x+h)}\right] = \lim_{h \to 0} \frac{1}{h}\left[\frac{-h}{x(x+h)}\right]\\
&= \lim_{h \to 0} \frac{-1}{x(x+h)} = \frac{-1}{x^2} = -1x^{-2}.
\end{aligned}$$

$$\begin{aligned}
\frac{d(x^{-3})}{dx} &= \lim_{h \to 0} \frac{(x+h)^{-3} - x^{-3}}{h}\\
&= \lim_{h \to 0} \frac{1}{h}\left[\frac{1}{(x+h)^3} - \frac{1}{x^3}\right]\\
&= \lim_{h \to 0} \frac{1}{h}\left[\frac{x^3 - (x+h)^3}{x^3(x+h)^3}\right]\\
&= \lim_{h \to 0} \frac{1}{h}\left[\frac{x^3 - (x^3 + 3hx^2 + 3h^2x + h^3)}{x^3(x+h)^3}\right]\\
&= \lim_{h \to 0} \frac{1}{h}\left[\frac{-3hx^2 - 3xh^2 - h^3}{x^3(x+h)^3}\right]\\
&= \lim_{h \to 0} \frac{-3x^2 - 3xh - h^2}{x^3(x+h)^3}\\
&= \frac{-3x^2}{x^6} = -3x^{-4}.
\end{aligned}$$

(b)   For clarity, let $n = -k$, where k is a positive integer. So $x^n = x^{-k}$.

$$\frac{d(x^{-k})}{dx} = \lim_{h \to 0} \frac{(x+h)^{-k} - x^{-k}}{h}$$

$$= \lim_{h \to 0} \frac{1}{h} \left[\frac{1}{(x+h)^k} - \frac{1}{x^k} \right]$$

$$= \lim_{h \to 0} \frac{1}{h} \left[\frac{x^k - (x+h)^k}{x^k (x+h)^k} \right]$$

$$= \lim_{h \to 0} \frac{1}{h} \left[\frac{x^k - x^k - khx^{k-1} - \overbrace{\ldots - h^k}^{\text{terms involving } h^2 \text{ and higher powers of } h}}{x^k (x+h)^k} \right]$$

$$= \frac{-kx^{k-1}}{x^k (x)^k} = \frac{-k}{x^{k+1}} = -kx^{-(k+1)} = -kx^{-k-1}.$$

41. $\dfrac{dF}{dr} = -\dfrac{2GMm}{r^3}$.

42. (a) $T = 2\pi \sqrt{\dfrac{l}{g}} = \dfrac{2\pi}{\sqrt{g}} \left(l^{\frac{1}{2}} \right)$, so $\dfrac{dT}{dl} = \dfrac{2\pi}{\sqrt{g}} \left(\dfrac{1}{2} l^{-\frac{1}{2}} \right) = \dfrac{\pi}{\sqrt{gl}}$.

    (b) Since $\dfrac{dT}{dl}$ is positive, the period T increases as the length l increases.

43. (a) Velocity $v(t) = \frac{dy}{dt} = \frac{d}{dt}(1250 - 16t^2) = -32t$.
    Since $t \geq 0$, the ball's velocity is negative. This is reasonable, since its height y is decreasing.

    (b) Acceleration $a(t) = \frac{dv}{dt} = \frac{d}{dt}(-32t) = -32$.
    So its acceleration is the negative constant -32.

    (c) The ball hits the ground when its height $y = 0$. This gives

    $$1250 - 16t^2 = 0$$
    $$t = \pm 8.84 \text{ seconds}$$

    We discard $t = -8.84$ because time t is nonnegative. So the ball hits the ground 8.84 seconds after its release, at which time its velocity is

    $$v(8.84) = -32(8.84) = -282.88 \text{ feet/sec} = -192.84 \text{ mph}.$$

44. (a) $A = \pi r^2$
    $\frac{dA}{dr} = 2\pi r$.

    (b) This is the formula for the circumference of a circle.

    (c) $A'(r) = \lim\limits_{h \to 0} \frac{A(r+h) - A(r)}{h}$

    The numerator of the difference quotient denotes the area contained between the inner circle (radius r) and the outer circle (radius $r + h$). As h approaches 0, this area can be approximated by the product of the circumference of the inner circle and the "width" of the area, i.e., h. Dividing this by the denominator, h, we get $A' =$ the circumference of the circle with radius r.

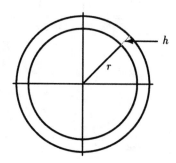

We can also think about the derivative of A as the rate of change of area for a small change in radius. If the radius increases by a tiny amount, the area will increase by a thin ring whose area is simply the circumference at that radius times the small amount. To get the rate of change, we divide by the small amount and obtain the circumference.

45. $V = \frac{4}{3}\pi r^3$

$\frac{dV}{dr} = 4\pi r^2 =$ surface area of a sphere.

Our reasoning is similar to that of Problem 44. The difference quotient $\frac{V(r+h)-V(r)}{h}$ is the volume between two spheres divided by the change in radius. Furthermore, when h is very small (and consequently $V(r+h) \approx V(r)$) this volume is like a coating of paint of depth h applied to the surface of the sphere. The volume of the paint is about $h \cdot$ (Surface Area) for small h: dividing by h gives back the surface area. Also, thinking about the derivative as the rate of change of the function for a small change in the variable, the answer seems clear. If you increase the radius of a sphere the tiniest amount, the volume will increase by a very thin layer whose volume will be the surface area at that radius multiplied by that tiniest amount.

46. $f(x) = \frac{1}{x} = x^{-1}$ $f'(x) = -x^{-2} = -\frac{1}{x^2}$.

The tangent line at $x = 1$ will have slope $f'(1) = -1$. Using the point $(1, 1)$ which lies on the line, we obtain the equation $y = -x + 2$. We approximate $f(2)$ by using the y value corresponding to $x = 2$, so $f(2) \approx 0$.

Similarly, the tangent line at $x = 100$ will have slope $f'(100) = \frac{-1}{(100)^2} = -0.0001$. The equation of the line is then $y = -0.0001x + 0.02$. The approximate value of $f(2)$ predicted by this tangent line is $f(2) \approx 0.0198$.

The actual value of $f(2)$ is $\frac{1}{2}$, so the approximation from $x = 100$ is better than that from $x = 1$. This is because the slope changes less between $x = 2$ and $x = 100$ than it does between $x = 1$ and $x = 2$.

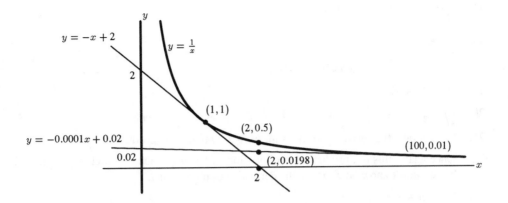

4.3 SOLUTIONS

1. $y' = 10t + 4e^t$.
2. $f'(x) = 2e^x + 2x$.
3. $f'(x) = (\ln 2)2^x + 2(\ln 3)3^x$.
4. $\dfrac{dy}{dx} = 4(\ln 10)10^x - 3x^2$.
5. $\dfrac{dy}{dx} = 3 - 2(\ln 4)4^x$.
6. $\dfrac{dy}{dx} = \dfrac{1}{3}(\ln 3)3^x - \dfrac{33}{2}(x^{-\frac{3}{2}})$.
7. $f'(x) = ex^{e-1}$.
8. $f(x) = e^{1+x} = e^1 \cdot e^x$. Then, since e^1 is just a constant,
   $f'(x) = e \cdot e^x = e^{1+x}$.
9. $f(t) = e^t \cdot e^2$. Then, since e^2 is just a constant, $f'(t) = \frac{d}{dt}(e^t e^2) = e^2 \frac{d}{dt}e^t = e^2 e^t = e^{t+2}$.
10. $y = e^\theta e^{-1}$ $y' = \dfrac{d}{d\theta}(e^\theta e^{-1}) = e^{-1}\dfrac{d}{d\theta}e^\theta = e^\theta e^{-1} = e^{\theta-1}$.
11. $z' = (\ln 4)e^x$.
12. $z' = (\ln 4)^2 4^x$.
13. $f'(z) = (2\ln 3)z + (\ln 4)e^z$.
14. $f'(t) = (\ln(\ln 3))(\ln 3)^t$.
15. $f'(x) = 3x^2 + 3^x \ln 3$

16. $\dfrac{dy}{dx} = 5 \cdot 5^t \ln 5 + 6 \cdot 6^t \ln 6$

17. $\dfrac{dy}{dx} = \pi^x \ln \pi$

18. $f'(x) = \pi^2 x^{(\pi^2 - 1)} + (\pi^2)^x \ln(\pi^2)$

19. $y' = 2x + (\ln 2)2^x$.

20. $y' = \frac{1}{2}x^{-\frac{1}{2}} - \ln\frac{1}{2}(\frac{1}{2})^x = \frac{1}{2\sqrt{x}} + \ln 2(\frac{1}{2})^x$.

21. We can take the derivative of the sum $x^2 + 2^x$, but not the product.

22. Once again, this is a product of two functions, 2^x and $\frac{1}{x}$, each of which we can take the derivative of; but we don't know how to take the derivative of the product.

23. Since $y = e^5 e^x$, $y' = e^5 e^x = e^{x+5}$.

24. $y = e^{5x} = (e^5)^x$, so $y' = \ln(e^5) \cdot (e^5)^x = 5e^{5x}$.

25. $f(s) = 5^s e^s = (5e)^s$, so $f'(s) = \ln(5e) \cdot (5e)^s = (1 + \ln 5)5^s e^s$.

26. The exponent is x^2, and we haven't learned what to do about that yet.

27. $f'(z) = (\ln \sqrt{4})(\sqrt{4})^z = (\ln 2)2^z$.

28. We can't use our rules if the exponent is $\sqrt{\theta}$.

29. This is the composition of two functions each of which we can take the derivative of, but we don't know how to take the derivative of the composition.

30.

TABLE 4.1

x	3^x	Difference Quotient $= \frac{3^{x+h} - 3^x}{h}$	Difference Quotient $\frac{}{3^x}$
0	1	1.09921	1.09921
0.1	1.11612	1.22686	1.09921
0.2	1.24573	1.36932	1.09921
0.3	1.39038	1.52833	1.09921
0.4	1.55184	1.70581	1.09921
0.5	1.73205	1.90389	1.09921

We conclude that $\frac{d}{dx}(3^x) \approx (1.09921) \cdot 3^x$.

31. (a) $f(x) = 1 - e^x$ crosses the x-axis where $0 = 1 - e^x$, which happens when $e^x = 1$, so $x = 0$. Since $f'(x) = -e^x$, $f'(0) = -e^0 = -1$.

    (b) $y = -x$

    (c) The negative of the reciprocal of -1 is 1, so the equation of the normal line is $y = x$.

32. Since $y = 2^x$, $y' = (\ln 2)2^x$. At $(0, 1)$, the tangent line has slope $\ln 2$ so its equation is $y = (\ln 2)x + 1$. At c, $y = 0$, so $0 = (\ln 2)c + 1$, whence $c = -\frac{1}{\ln 2}$.

33. Since $P = 1 \cdot (1.05)^t$, $\frac{dP}{dt} = \ln(1.05)1.05^t$. When $t = 10$,

$$\frac{dP}{dt} = (\ln 1.05)(1.05)^{10} \approx \$0.07947/\text{year} \approx 7.95¢/\text{year}.$$

34.

$$\frac{dP}{dt} = 35{,}000 \cdot (\ln 0.98)(0.98^t).$$

At $t = 23$, this is $35{,}000(\ln 0.98)(0.98^{23}) \approx -444.3\frac{\text{people}}{\text{year}}$. (Note: the negative sign indicates that the population is decreasing.)

35. $\dfrac{dV}{dt} = 75(1.35)^t \ln 1.35 = 22.5(1.35)^t.$

36. (a) $P = 4.1(1 + 0.02)^t = 4.1(1.02)^t.$
    (b)

$$\frac{dP}{dt} = 4.1\frac{d}{dt}(1.02)^t = 4.1(1.02)^t(\ln 1.02)$$

$$\left.\frac{dP}{dt}\right|_{t=0} = 4.1(1.02)^0 \ln 1.02 \approx 0.0812$$

$$\left.\frac{dP}{dt}\right|_{t=15} = 4.1(1.02)^{15} \ln 1.02 \approx 0.11\,.$$

$\dfrac{dP}{dt}$ is the rate of growth of the world's population; $\left.\dfrac{dP}{dt}\right|_{t=0}$ and $\left.\dfrac{dP}{dt}\right|_{t=15}$ are the rates of growth in the years 1975 and 1990, respectively.

37. We are interested in when the derivative $\dfrac{d(a^x)}{dx}$ is positive and when it is negative. The quantity a^x is always positive. However $\ln a > 0$ for $a > 1$ and $\ln a < 0$ for $0 < a < 1$. Thus the function a^x is increasing for $a > 1$ and decreasing for $a < 1$.

38.

$$g(x) = ax^2 + bx + c \qquad\qquad f(x) = e^x$$
$$g'(x) = 2ax + b \qquad\qquad f'(x) = e^x$$
$$g''(x) = 2a \qquad\qquad f''(x) = e^x$$

So, using $g''(0) = f''(0)$, etc., we have $2a = 1$, $b = 1$, and $c = 1$, and thus $g(x) = \frac{1}{2}x^2 + x + 1$.

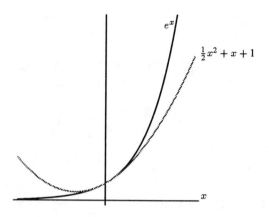

The two functions do look very much alike near $x = 0$. They both increase for large values of x, but e^x increases much more quickly. For very negative values of x, the quadratic goes to ∞ whereas the exponential goes to $-\infty$. By choosing a function whose first few derivatives agreed with the exponential when $x = 0$, we got a function which looks like the exponential for x values near 0.

39. The tangent line has slope $\frac{d}{dx}(e^x) = e^x$. At $x = 0$, this gives us a slope of 1, and the tangent line is $y = x + 1$. A function which is always concave up will always stay above any of its tangent lines. Thus $e^x \geq x + 1$ for all x.

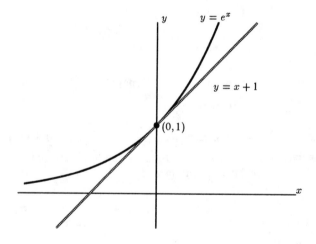

40. The equation $2^x = 2x$ has solutions $x = 1$ and $x = 2$. (Check this by substituting these values into the equation). The graph suggests that these are the only solutions, but how can we be sure?

Lets look at the slope of the curve $f(x) = 2^x$, which is $f'(x) = (\ln 2)2^x \approx (0.693)2^x$, and the slope of the line $g(x) = 2x$ which is 2. At $x = 1$, the slope of $f(x)$ is less than 2; at $x = 2$, the slope of $f(x)$ is more than 2. Since the slope of $f(x)$ is always increasing, there can be no other point of intersection. (If there were another point of intersection, the graph f would have to "turn around".)

Here's another way of seeing this. Suppose $g(x)$ represents the position of a car going a steady 2 mph, while $f(x)$ represents a car which starts ahead of g (because the graph of f is above g) and is initially going slower than g. The car f is first overtaken by g. All the while, however, f is speeding up until eventually it overtakes g again. Notice that the two cars will only meet twice (corresponding to the two intersections of the curve): once when g overtakes f and once when f overtakes g.

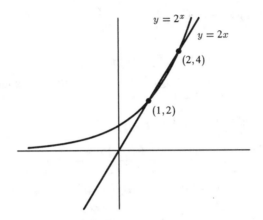

4.4 SOLUTIONS

1. By the product rule,

$$f'(x) = 2x(x^3 + 5) + x^2(3x^2) = 2x^4 + 3x^4 + 10x = 5x^4 + 10x.$$

Alternatively,

$$f'(x) = (x^5 + 5x^2)' = 5x^4 + 10x.$$

The two answers should, and do, match.

2.

$$f'(x) = (\ln 2)2^x 3^x + (\ln 3)2^x 3^x = (\ln 2 + \ln 3)(2^x \cdot 3^x) = \ln(2 \cdot 3)(2 \cdot 3)^x = (\ln 6)6^x$$

or, since $2^x \cdot 3^x = (2 \cdot 3)^x = 6^x$,

$$f'(x) = (6^x)' = (\ln 6)(6^x).$$

The two answers should, and do, match.

3. $f'(x) = x \cdot e^x + e^x \cdot 1 = e^x(x+1)$.

4. $f'(x) = \dfrac{e^x \cdot 1 - x \cdot e^x}{(e^x)^2} = \dfrac{e^x(1-x)}{(e^x)^2} = \dfrac{1-x}{e^x}$.

5. $y' = 2^x + x(\ln 2)2^x = 2^x(1 + x\ln 2)$.

6. $y' = \dfrac{1}{2\sqrt{x}}2^x + \sqrt{x}(\ln 2)2^x$.

7.
$$f'(x) = (x^2 - x^{\frac{1}{2}}) \cdot 3^x(\ln 3) + 3^x\left(2x - \frac{1}{2}x^{-\frac{1}{2}}\right)$$
$$= 3^x\left[(\ln 3)(x^2 - x^{\frac{1}{2}}) + \left(2x - \frac{1}{2\sqrt{x}}\right)\right].$$

8. $w' = (3t^2 + 5)(t^2 - 7t + 2) + (t^3 + 5t)(2t - 7)$.

9. It is easier to do this by multiplying it out first, rather than using the product rule first:
$$z = s^4 - s, \quad z' = 4s^3 - 1.$$

10. $\dfrac{dy}{dt} = 2te^t + (t^2 + 3)e^t = e^t(t^2 + 2t + 3)$

11. $\dfrac{dz}{dt} = \dfrac{3(5t+2) - (3t+1)5}{(5t+2)^2} = \dfrac{15t + 6 - 15t - 5}{(5t+2)^2} = \dfrac{1}{(5t+2)^2}$

12. $y' = (3t^2 - 14t)e^t + (t^3 - 7t^2 + 1)e^t = (t^3 - 4t^2 - 14t + 1)e^t$.

13. $z' = \dfrac{(2t+5)(t+3) - (t^2 + 5t + 2)}{(t+3)^2} = \dfrac{t^2 + 6t + 13}{(t+3)^2}$.

14. $w = y^2 - 6y + 7$. $\quad w' = 2y - 6, y \neq 0$.

15.
$$f'(x) = \dfrac{x(2x) - (x^2 + 3)(1)}{x^2}$$
$$= \dfrac{2x^2 - x^2 - 3}{x^2}$$
$$= \dfrac{x^2 - 3}{x^2}.$$

16. $y' = \dfrac{\frac{1}{2\sqrt{t}}(t^2 + 1) - \sqrt{t}(2t)}{(t^2 + 1)^2}$.

17.
$$f'(x) = \dfrac{(2 + 3x + 4x^2)(1) - (1+x)(3 + 8x)}{(2 + 3x + 4x^2)^2}$$
$$= \dfrac{2 + 3x + 4x^2 - 3 - 11x - 8x^2}{(2 + 3x + 4x^2)^2}$$
$$= \dfrac{-4x^2 - 8x - 1}{(2 + 3x + 4x^2)^2}.$$

18. Notice that you can cancel a z out of the numerator and denominator to get

$$f(z) = \frac{3z}{5z+7}, \qquad z \neq 0$$

Then

$$
\begin{aligned}
f'(z) &= \frac{(5z+7)3 - 3z(5)}{(5z+7)^2} \\
&= \frac{15z + 21 - 15z}{(5z+7)^2} \\
&= \frac{21}{(5z+7)^2}, z \neq 0.
\end{aligned}
$$

[If you used the quotient rule correctly without canceling the z out first, your answer should simplify to this one, but it is usually a good idea to simplify as much as possible before differentiating.]

19.

$$f'(x) = 3(2x - 5) + 2(3x + 8) = 12x + 1$$

$$f''(x) = 12.$$

20.

$$
\begin{aligned}
f(t) &= \frac{1}{e^t} \\
f'(t) &= \frac{e^t \cdot 0 - e^t \cdot 1}{(e^t)^2} \\
&= \frac{-1}{e^t} = -e^{-t}.
\end{aligned}
$$

21. $f(x) = e^x \cdot e^x$
$f'(x) = e^x \cdot e^x + e^x \cdot e^x = 2e^{2x}.$

22.

$$
\begin{aligned}
f(x) &= e^x e^{2x} \\
f'(x) &= e^x(e^{2x})' + (e^x)' e^{2x} \\
&= 2e^x e^{2x} + e^x e^{2x} \text{ (from Problem 21)} \\
&= 3e^{3x}.
\end{aligned}
$$

23. Since $\frac{d}{dx} e^{2x} = 2e^{2x}$ and $\frac{d}{dx} e^{3x} = 3e^{3x}$, we might guess that $\frac{d}{dx} e^{4x} = 4e^{4x}$.

24. (a) Although the answer you would get by using the quotient rule is equivalent, the answer looks simpler in this case if you just use the product rule:

$$\frac{d}{dx}\left(\frac{e^x}{x}\right) = \frac{d}{dx}\left(e^x \cdot \frac{1}{x}\right) = \frac{e^x}{x} - \frac{e^x}{x^2}$$

$$\frac{d}{dx}\left(\frac{e^x}{x^2}\right) = \frac{d}{dx}\left(e^x \cdot \frac{1}{x^2}\right) = \frac{e^x}{x^2} - \frac{2e^x}{x^3}$$

$$\frac{d}{dx}\left(\frac{e^x}{x^3}\right) = \frac{d}{dx}\left(e^x \cdot \frac{1}{x^3}\right) = \frac{e^x}{x^3} - \frac{3e^x}{x^4}.$$

(b) $\dfrac{d}{dx}\dfrac{e^x}{x^n} = \dfrac{e^x}{x^n} - \dfrac{ne^x}{x^{n+1}}.$

25. This is the same function we were asked to differentiate in Problem 18, so we know that, if $x \neq 0$,

$$f'(x) = \frac{21}{(5x+7)^2}.$$

So at $x = 1$,

$$y = f(1) = \frac{3}{12} = \frac{1}{4},$$

$$y' = \frac{21}{144} = \frac{7}{48}.$$

So,

$$y - \frac{1}{4} = \frac{7}{48}(x - 1).$$

$$y = \frac{7}{48}x + \frac{5}{48}.$$

26. (a) $G'(z) = F'(z)H(z) + H'(z)F(z)$, so
$G'(3) = F'(3)H(3) + H'(3)F(3) = 4 \cdot 1 + 3 \cdot 5 = 19.$

(b) $G'(w) = \dfrac{F'(w)H(w) - H'(w)F(w)}{[H(w)]^2}$, so $G'(3) = \frac{4(1)-3(5)}{1^2} = -11.$

27. (a) $f(x) = \frac{x}{x^2-1}.$
$x = 1$ or -1 makes $f(x)$ undefined. All other values of x define f.

$$f'(x) = \frac{x^2 - 1 - (x)(2x)}{(x^2 - 1)^2} = \frac{-x^2 - 1}{(x^2 - 1)^2}.$$

As x gets closer to 1, the denominator of f approaches 0 while the numerator goes to 1. Thus, $f(x)$ approaches infinity, and is large in magnitude at $x \approx 1.01$. Now, observe that $f'(x)$ has $(x^2 - 1)^2$ in the denominator. Since $\frac{1}{(x^2-1)^2}$ is much larger than $\frac{1}{x^2-1}$ as x gets closer to one, $f'(x)$ will be larger in magnitude than $f(x)$ as x goes to 1 (though $f'(x)$ will be negative because its numerator approaches -2).

(b) $g(x) = \frac{x^2+3x-4}{x^2-1}$. $x = 1$ or -1 makes $g(x)$ undefined. All other values of x define g.

$$g'(x) = \frac{(2x+3)(x^2-1)-(2x)(x^2+3x-4)}{(x^2-1)^2} = \frac{-3x^2+6x-3}{(x^2-1)^2}$$

$$= \frac{-3(x-1)^2}{(x^2-1)^2} = \frac{-3}{(x+1)^2}$$

You can factor the numerator and denominator of g to get this formula:

$$g(x) = \frac{(x+4)(x-1)}{(x+1)(x-1)} = \frac{x+4}{x+1}, \quad x \neq 1.$$

At $x = 1$, g is not defined. But it does not go to infinity there. A graph of g would look like a graph of $\frac{x+4}{x+1}$ with a hole at $x = 1$. One can also say the numerator and denominator of g both go to 0 at the same rate as x gets close to 1, so there is no reason for g to be large at 1.01. For $g'(x)$, as x goes to 1, the denominator does not go to 0 but rather to 4 (while the numerator is -3), so $g'(x)$ will not be large.

28.

$$\frac{d(x^2)}{dx} = \frac{d}{dx}(x \cdot x)$$

$$= x\frac{d(x)}{dx} + x\frac{d(x)}{dx}$$

$$= 2x.$$

$$\frac{d(x^3)}{dx} = \frac{d}{dx}(x^2 \cdot x)$$

$$= x^2\frac{d(x)}{dx} + x\frac{d(x^2)}{dx}$$

$$= x^2\frac{d(x)}{dx} + x\left[x\frac{d(x)}{dx} + x\frac{d(x)}{dx}\right]$$

$$= x^2\frac{d(x)}{dx} + x^2\frac{d(x)}{dx} + x^2\frac{d(x)}{dx}$$

$$= 3x^2.$$

29. (a) $f'(x) = (x-2) + (x-1)$.

(b) Think of f as the product of two factors, with the first as $(x-1)(x-2)$. (The reason for this is that we have already differentiated $(x-1)(x-2)$).

$$f(x) = [(x-1)(x-2)](x-3).$$

Now $f'(x) = [(x-1)(x-2)]'(x-3) + [(x-1)(x-2)](x-3)'$
Using the result of a):

$$f'(x) = [(x-2) + (x-1)](x-3) + [(x-1)(x-2)] \cdot 1$$
$$= (x-2)(x-3) + (x-1)(x-3) + (x-1)(x-2).$$

(c) Because we have already differentiated $(x-1)(x-2)(x-3)$, rewrite f as the product of two factors, the first being $(x-1)(x-2)(x-3)$:

$$f(x) = [(x-1)(x-2)(x-3)](x-4)$$

Now $f'(x) = [(x-1)(x-2)(x-3)]'(x-4) + [(x-1)(x-2)(x-3)](x-4)'$.

$$f'(x) = [(x-2)(x-3) + (x-1)(x-3) + (x-1)(x-2)](x-4)$$
$$+ [(x-1)(x-2)(x-3)] \cdot 1$$
$$= (x-2)(x-3)(x-4) + (x-1)(x-3)(x-4)$$
$$+ (x-1)(x-2)(x-4) + (x-1)(x-2)(x-3).$$

From the solutions above, one can observe that when f is a product, its derivative is obtained by differentiating each factor in turn (leaving the other factors alone), and adding the results.

30. From the answer to Problem 29, we find that

$$f'(x) = (x-r_1)(x-r_2)\cdots(x-r_{n-1}) \cdot 1$$
$$+ (x-r_1)(x-r_2)\cdots(x-r_{n-2}) \cdot 1 \cdot (x-r_n)$$
$$+ (x-r_1)(x-r_2)\cdots(x-r_{n-3}) \cdot 1 \cdot (x-r_{n-1})(x-r_n)$$
$$+ \cdots + 1 \cdot (x-r_2)(x-r_3)\cdots(x-r_n)$$
$$= f(x)\left(\frac{1}{x-r_1} + \frac{1}{x-r_2} + \cdots + \frac{1}{x-r_n}\right).$$

31. Assume for $g(x) \neq f(x)$, $g'(x) = g(x)$ and $g(0) = 1$. Then for

$$h(x) = \frac{g(x)}{e^x}$$

$$h'(x) = \frac{g'(x)e^x - g(x)e^x}{(e^x)^2} = \frac{e^x(g'(x) - g(x))}{(e^x)^2} = \frac{g'(x) - g(x)}{e^x}.$$

But, since $g(x) = g'(x)$, $h'(x) = 0$, so $h(x)$ is constant. Thus, the ratio of $g(x)$ to e^x is constant. Since $\frac{g(0)}{e^0} = \frac{1}{1} = 1$, $\frac{g(x)}{e^x}$ must equal 1 for all x. Thus $g(x) = e^x = f(x)$ for all x, so f and g are the same function.

32. We want dR/dr_1. Solving for R:

$$\frac{1}{R} = \frac{1}{r_1} + \frac{1}{r_2} = \frac{r_2 + r_1}{r_1 r_2}$$

gives

$$R = \frac{r_1 r_2}{r_2 + r_1}.$$

So, thinking of r_2 as a constant and using the quotient rule,

$$\frac{dR}{dr_1} = \frac{r_2(r_2 + r_1) - r_1 r_2(1)}{(r_2 + r_1)^2} = \frac{r_2^2}{(r_1 + r_2)^2}.$$

33. (a) $f(140) = 15,000$ says that 15,000 skateboards are sold when the cost is $140 per board.
    $f'(140) = -100$ means that if the price is increased from $140, roughly speaking, every dollar of increase will decrease the total sales by 100 boards.

(b) $\dfrac{dR}{dp} = \dfrac{d}{dp}(p \cdot q) = \dfrac{d}{dp}(p \cdot f(p)) = f(p) + pf'(p).$

So,

$$\left.\frac{dR}{dp}\right|_{p=140} = f(140) + 140 f'(140)$$
$$= 15,000 + 140(-100) = 1000.$$

(c) From (b) we see that $\left.\dfrac{dR}{dp}\right|_{p=140} = 1000 > 0.$ This means that the revenue will increase if the price is raised. (Note we can only be certain that the revenue will increase for a relatively small price increase.)

34. Note first that $f(v)$ is in $\frac{\text{liters}}{\text{km}}$, and v is in $\frac{\text{km}}{\text{hour}}$.

(a) $g(v) = \frac{1}{f(v)}.$ (This is in $\frac{\text{km}}{\text{liter}}$). Differentiating gives

$$g'(v) = \frac{-f'(v)}{\left(f(v)\right)^2}.$$

So,

$$g(80) = \frac{1}{0.05} = 20\,\tfrac{\text{km}}{\text{liter}}.$$

$$g'(80) = \frac{-0.0005}{(0.05)^2} = -\frac{1}{5}\,\tfrac{\text{km}}{\text{liter}} \text{ for each } 1\,\tfrac{\text{km}}{\text{hr}} \text{ increase in speed}.$$

(b) $h(v) = v \cdot f(v).$ (This is in $\frac{\text{km}}{\text{hour}} \cdot \frac{\text{liters}}{\text{km}} = \frac{\text{liters}}{\text{hour}}.$) Differentiating gives

$$h'(v) = f(v) + v \cdot f'(v),$$

so

$$h(80) = 80(0.05) = 4\,\tfrac{\text{liters}}{\text{hr}}.$$

$$h'(80) = 0.05 + 80(0.0005) = 0.09\,\tfrac{\text{liters}}{\text{hr}} \text{ for each } 1\,\tfrac{\text{km}}{\text{hr}} \text{ increase in speed}.$$

(c) Part (a) tells us that at 80 km/hr, the car can go 20 km on 1 liter. Since the first derivative evaluated at this velocity is negative, this implies that as velocity increases, fuel efficiency decreases, i.e., at higher velocities the car will not go as far on 1 liter of gas. Part (b) tells us that at 80 km/hr, the car uses 4 liters in an hour. Since the first derivative evaluated at this velocity is positive, this means that at higher velocities, the car will use more gas per hour.

35. (a) If the museum sells the painting and invests the proceeds $P(t)$ at time t, then t years have elapsed since 1990, and the time span up to the 2010 is $20 - t$. This is how long the proceeds $P(t)$ are earning compound interest in the bank. So, by the compound interest formula,

$$B(t) = P(t)(1 + 0.05)^{20-t} = P(t)(1.05)^{20-t}.$$

(b)

$$B(t) = P(t)(1.05)^{20}(1.05)^{-t} = (1.05)^{20}\frac{P(t)}{(1.05)^t}.$$

(c) By the quotient rule,

$$B'(t) = (1.05)^{20}\left[\frac{P'(t)(1.05)^t - P(t)(1.05)^t \ln 1.05}{(1.05)^{2t}}\right].$$

So,

$$B'(10) = (1.05)^{20}\left[\frac{5000(1.05)^{10} - 150000(1.05)^{10} \ln 1.05}{(1.05)^{20}}\right]$$
$$= (1.05)^{10}(5000 - 150000 \ln 1.05)$$
$$\approx -3776.63.$$

4.5 SOLUTIONS

1. $f'(x) = 99(x + 1)^{98} \cdot 1 = 99(x + 1)^{98}.$

2. $f'(x) = \dfrac{1}{2}(1 - x^2)^{-\frac{1}{2}}(-2x) = \dfrac{-x}{\sqrt{1 - x^2}}.$

3. $w' = 100(t^2 + 1)^{99}(2t) = 200t(t^2 + 1)^{99}.$

4. $w' = 100(t^3 + 1)^{99}(3t^2) = 300t^2(t^3 + 1)^{99}.$

5. $w' = 100(\sqrt{t} + 1)^{99}\left(\frac{1}{2\sqrt{t}}\right) = \frac{50}{\sqrt{t}}(\sqrt{t} + 1)^{99}.$

6. $f'(t) = (e^{3t})(3) = 3e^{3t}.$

7. $y' = \frac{3}{2}e^{\frac{3}{2}w}.$

8. $y' = -4e^{-4t}.$

9. $y' = \dfrac{3s^2}{2\sqrt{s^3 + 1}}.$

10. $w' = \dfrac{1}{2\sqrt{s}}e^{\sqrt{s}}.$

11. $y' = 1 \cdot e^{-t^2} + te^{-t^2}(-2t) = e^{-t^2} - 2t^2e^{-t^2}.$

12. $f'(z) = \dfrac{1}{2\sqrt{z}}e^{-z} - \sqrt{z}e^{-z}$.

13. We can write this as $f(z) = \sqrt{z}e^{-z}$, in which case it is the same as problem 12. So $f'(z) = \dfrac{1}{2\sqrt{z}}e^{-z} - \sqrt{z}e^{-z}$.

14. $z' = 5 \cdot \ln 2 \cdot 2^{5t-3}$.

15. $f'(t) = 1 \cdot e^{5-2t} + te^{5-2t}(-2) = e^{5-2t}(1 - 2t)$

16. $f'(z) = -2(e^z + 1)^{-3} \cdot e^z = \dfrac{-2e^z}{(e^z + 1)^3}$.

17. $f'(\theta) = -1(1 + e^{-\theta})^{-2}(e^{-\theta})(-1) = \dfrac{e^{-\theta}}{(1 + e^{-\theta})^2}$.

18. $f'(x) = 6(e^{5x})(5) + (e^{-x^2})(-2x) = 30e^{5x} - 2xe^{-x^2}$.

19.
$$
\begin{aligned}
f'(w) &= (e^{w^2})(10w) + (5w^2 + 3)(e^{w^2})(2w) \\
&= 2we^{w^2}(5 + 5w^2 + 3) \\
&= 2we^{w^2}(5w^2 + 8).
\end{aligned}
$$

20. $w' = (2t + 3)(1 - e^{-2t}) + (t^2 + 3t)(2e^{-2t})$.

21.
$$
\begin{aligned}
f(y) &= \left[10^{(5-y)}\right]^{\frac{1}{2}} = 10^{\frac{5}{2} - \frac{1}{2}y} \\
f'(y) &= (\ln 10)\left(10^{\frac{5}{2} - \frac{1}{2}y}\right)\left(-\frac{1}{2}\right) = -\frac{1}{2}(\ln 10)(10^{\frac{5}{2} - \frac{1}{2}y}).
\end{aligned}
$$

22. $f'(x) = e^{-(x-1)^2} \cdot (-2)(x - 1)$.

23. $f'(y) = e^{e^{(y^2)}}\left[(e^{y^2})(2y)\right] = 2ye^{[e^{(y^2)}+y^2]}$.

24. $f'(t) = 2(e^{-2e^{2t}})(-2e^{2t})2 = -8(e^{-2e^{2t}+2t})$.

25.
$$
\begin{array}{ll}
f(x) = 6e^{5x} + e^{-x^2} & f'(x) = 30e^{5x} - 2xe^{-x^2} \\
f(1) = 6e^5 + e^{-1} & f'(1) = 30e^5 - 2(1)e^{-1}
\end{array}
$$

$$
\begin{aligned}
y - y_1 &= m(x - x_1) \\
y - (6e^5 + e^{-1}) &= (30e^5 - 2e^{-1})(x - 1) \\
y - (6e^5 + e^{-1}) &= (30e^5 - 2e^{-1})x - (30e^5 - 2e^{-1}) \\
y &= (30e^5 - 2e^{-1})x - 30e^5 + 2e^{-1} + 6e^5 + e^{-1} \\
&\approx 4451.66x - 3560.81.
\end{aligned}
$$

26.   The graph is concave down when $f''(x) < 0$.

$$f'(x) = e^{-x^2}(-2x)$$
$$f''(x) = \left[e^{-x^2}(-2x)\right](-2x) + e^{-x^2}(-2)$$
$$= \frac{4x^2}{e^{x^2}} - \frac{2}{e^{x^2}}$$
$$= \frac{4x^2 - 2}{e^{x^2}} < 0$$

when $4x^2 - 2 < 0$, so $4x^2 < 2$, or $x^2 < \frac{1}{2}$. Hence $-\frac{1}{\sqrt{2}} < x < \frac{1}{\sqrt{2}}$.

27.   (a) $H(x) = F(G(x))$
         $H(4) = F(G(4)) = F(2) = 1$
      (b) $H(x) = F(G(x))$
         $H'(x) = F'(G(x)) \cdot G'(x)$
         $H'(4) = F'(G(4)) \cdot G'(4) = F'(2) \cdot 6 = 5 \cdot 6 = 30$
      (c) $H(x) = G(F(x))$
         $H(4) = G(F(4)) = G(3) = 4$
      (d) $H(x) = G(F(x))$
         $H'(x) = G'(F(x)) \cdot F'(x)$
         $H'(4) = G'(F(4)) \cdot F'(4) = G'(3) \cdot 7 = 8 \cdot 7 = 56$
      (e) $H(x) = \frac{F(x)}{G(x)}$
         $H'(x) = \frac{G(x) \cdot F'(x) - F(x) \cdot G'(x)}{[G(x)]^2}$
         $H'(4) = \frac{G(4) \cdot F'(4) - F(4) \cdot G'(4)}{[G(4)]^2} = \frac{2 \cdot 7 - 3 \cdot 6}{2^2} = \frac{14 - 18}{4} = \frac{-4}{4} = -1$

28.

$$f'(x) = [10(2x+1)^9(2)][(3x-1)^7] + [(2x+1)^{10}][7(3x-1)^6(3)]$$
$$= (2x+1)^9(3x-1)^6[20(3x-1) + 21(2x+1)]$$
$$= [(2x+1)^9(3x-1)^6](102x+1)$$
$$f''(x) = \quad [9(2x+1)^8(2)(3x-1)^6 + (2x+1)^9(6)(3x-1)^5(3)](102x+1)$$
$$+(2x+1)^9(3x-1)^6(102).$$

29.   Yes. To see why, simply plug $x = \sqrt[3]{2t+5}$ into the expression $3x^2 \dfrac{dx}{dt}$ and evaluate it. To do this, first we calculate $\dfrac{dx}{dt}$. By the chain rule,

$$\frac{dx}{dt} = \frac{d}{dt}(2t+5)^{\frac{1}{3}} = \frac{2}{3}(2t+5)^{-\frac{2}{3}} = \frac{2}{3}[(2t+5)^{\frac{1}{3}}]^{-2}.$$

But since $x = (2t + 5)^{\frac{1}{3}}$, we have (by substitution)

$$\frac{dx}{dt} = \frac{2}{3}x^{-2}.$$

It follows that $3x^2 \dfrac{dx}{dt} = 3x^2 \left(\dfrac{2}{3}x^{-2}\right) = 2.$

30. (a)

$$\frac{dQ}{dt} = \frac{d}{dt}e^{-0.000121t}$$
$$= -0.000121e^{-0.000121t}$$

(b)

31. (a)

$$\frac{dH}{dt} = \frac{d}{dt}(40 + 30e^{-2t}) = 30(-2)e^{-2t} = -60e^{-2t}.$$

(b) Since e^{-2t} is always positive, $\dfrac{dH}{dt} < 0$; this makes sense because the temperature of the soda is decreasing.

(c) The magnitude of $\dfrac{dH}{dt}$ is

$$\left|\frac{dH}{dt}\right| = \left|-60e^{-2t}\right| = 60e^{-2t} \leq 60 = \left|\frac{dH}{dt}\right|_{t=0},$$

since $e^{-2t} \leq 1$ for all $t \geq 0$ and $e^0 = 1$. This is just saying that at the moment that the can of soda is put in the refrigerator (at $t = 0$), the temperature difference between the soda and the inside of the refrigerator is the greatest, so the temperature of the soda is dropping the quickest.

32. (a) $\dfrac{dB}{dt} = P\left(1 + \dfrac{r}{100}\right)^t \ln\left(1 + \dfrac{r}{100}\right)$. $\dfrac{dB}{dt}$ tells us how fast the amount of money in the bank is changing with respect to time for fixed initial investment P and interest rate r.

(b) $\dfrac{dB}{dr} = Pt\left(1 + \dfrac{r}{100}\right)^{t-1}\dfrac{1}{100}$. $\dfrac{dB}{dr}$ indicates how fast the amount of money changes with respect to the interest rate r, assuming fixed initial investment P and time t.

33. (a)

$$\frac{dm}{dv} = \frac{d}{dv}\left[m_0\left(1 - \frac{v^2}{c^2}\right)^{-1/2}\right]$$

$$= m_0\left(-\frac{1}{2}\right)\left(1 - \frac{v^2}{c^2}\right)^{-3/2}\left(-\frac{2v}{c^2}\right)$$

$$= \frac{m_0 v}{c^2}\frac{1}{\sqrt{\left(1 - \frac{v^2}{c^2}\right)^3}}.$$

(b) $\dfrac{dm}{dv}$ represents the rate of change of mass with respect to the speed v.

34. Both pressure and volume are functions of time, so if k is the constant,

$$p(t)[v(t)]^{1.4} = k.$$

Since $p = 50$ when $v = 32$, we have $k = 50 \cdot 32^{1.4} = 6400$. Now, write pressure in terms of volume:

$$p(t) = 6400[v(t)]^{-1.4}.$$

By the chain rule, $p'(t) = p'(v(t)) \cdot v'(t)$, so

$$p'(t) = -1.4(6400)[v(t)]^{-2.4}v'(t) = -8960[v(t)]^{-2.4}v'(t).$$

At the moment we are interested in, $v(t) = 32$ and $v'(t) = -4$, so

$$p'(t) = -8960(32^{-2.4})(-4) = 8.75 \text{ lbs/in}^2 \text{ per second}.$$

35. (a)

For $t < 0, I = \dfrac{dQ}{dt} = 0.$

For $t > 0, I = \dfrac{dQ}{dt} = -\dfrac{1}{R}e^{-t/RC}.$

(b) For $t > 0, t \to 0$ (that is, as $t \to 0^+$),

$$I = -\frac{1}{R}e^{-t/RC} \to -\frac{1}{R}.$$

Since $I = 0$ just to the left of $t = 0$ and $I = -1/R$ just to the right of $t = 0$, it is not possible to define I at $t = 0$.

(c) Q is not differentiable at $t = 0$ because there is no tangent line at $t = 0$.

4.6 SOLUTIONS

1.
$$f(x) = (1 - \cos x)^{\frac{1}{2}}$$
$$f'(x) = \frac{1}{2}(1 - \cos x)^{-\frac{1}{2}}(-(-\sin x))$$
$$= \frac{\sin x}{2\sqrt{1 - \cos x}}.$$

2. $f'(x) = [-\sin(\sin x)](\cos x).$

3. $f'(x) = \cos(3x) \cdot 3 = 3\cos(3x).$

4. $z' = -4\sin(4\theta).$

5. $w' = e^t \cos(e^t).$

6. $f'(x) = (2x)(\cos x) + x^2(-\sin x) = 2x\cos x - x^2 \sin x.$

7. $f'(x) = (e^{\cos x})(-\sin x) = -\sin x e^{\cos x}.$

8. $f'(y) = (\cos y)e^{\sin y}.$

9. $z' = e^{\cos \theta} - \theta(\sin \theta)e^{\cos \theta}.$

10. $f'(x) = 2 \cdot (\sin(3x)) + 2x[\cos(3x)] \cdot 3 = 2\sin(3x) + 6x\cos(3x)$

11. $f'(x) = 2\cos(2x)\sin(3x) + 3\sin(2x)\cos(3x).$

12. $y' = e^\theta \sin(2\theta) + 2e^\theta \cos(2\theta).$

13.
$$f'(x) = (e^{-2x})(-2)(\sin x) + (e^{-2x})(\cos x)$$
$$= -2\sin x(e^{-2x}) + (e^{-2x})(\cos x)$$
$$= e^{-2x}[\cos x - 2\sin x].$$

14. $z' = \dfrac{\cos t}{2\sqrt{\sin t}}.$

15. $y' = 5\sin^4 \theta \cos \theta.$

16. $g'(z) = \dfrac{e^z}{\cos^2(e^z)}.$

17. $z' = \dfrac{-3e^{-3\theta}}{\cos^2(e^{-3\theta})}.$

18. $w' = (-\cos \theta)e^{-\sin \theta}.$

19. $h'(t) = 1 \cdot (\cos t) + t(-\sin t) + \frac{1}{\cos^2 t} = \cos t - t\sin t + \frac{1}{\cos^2 t}.$

20. $f'(\theta) = 2\theta \sin \theta + \theta^2 \cos \theta + 2\cos \theta - 2\theta \sin \theta - 2\cos \theta = \theta^2 \cos \theta.$

21.

TABLE 4.2

x	$\cos x$	Difference Quotient	$-\sin x$
0	1.0	−0.0005	0.0
0.1	0.995	−0.10033	−0.099833
0.2	0.98007	−0.19916	−0.19867
0.3	0.95534	−0.296	−0.29552
0.4	0.92106	−0.38988	−0.38942
0.5	0.87758	−0.47986	−0.47943
0.6	0.82534	−0.56506	−0.56464

22. (a) $v(t) = \dfrac{dy}{dt} = \dfrac{d}{dt}(15 + \sin 2\pi t) = 2\pi \cos 2\pi t.$

(b)

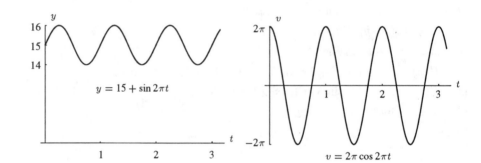

23. (a) $\dfrac{dy}{dt} = -\dfrac{4.9\pi}{6}\sin\left(\dfrac{\pi}{6}t\right)$. It represents the rate of change of the depth of the water.

(b) $\dfrac{dy}{dt}$ is zero where the tangent line to the curve $y(t)$ is horizontal. $\dfrac{dy}{dt} = 0$ occurs when $\sin(\frac{\pi}{6}t) = 0$, or at $t = 6$am, 12 noon, 6pm and 12 midnight. When $\dfrac{dy}{dt} = 0$, the depth of the water is no longer changing. Therefore, it has either just finished rising or just finished falling, and we know that the harbor's level is at a maximum or a minimum.

24. (a) When $\sqrt{\frac{k}{m}}\,t = \frac{\pi}{2}$ the spring is farthest from the equilibrium position. This occurs at time $t = \frac{\pi}{2}\sqrt{\frac{m}{k}}$

$v = A\sqrt{\frac{k}{m}}\cos\left(\sqrt{\frac{k}{m}}\,t\right)$, so the maximum velocity occurs when $t = 0$

$a = -A\frac{k}{m}\sin\left(\sqrt{\frac{k}{m}}\,t\right)$, so the maximum acceleration occurs when $\sqrt{\frac{k}{m}}\,t = \frac{3\pi}{2}$, which is at time $t = \frac{3\pi}{2}\sqrt{\frac{m}{k}}$

(b) $T = \dfrac{2\pi}{\sqrt{k/m}} = 2\pi\sqrt{\dfrac{m}{k}}$

(c) $\dfrac{dT}{dm} = \dfrac{2\pi}{\sqrt{k}} \cdot \dfrac{1}{2}m^{-\frac{1}{2}} = \dfrac{\pi}{\sqrt{km}}$

Since $\dfrac{dT}{dm} > 0$, an increase in the mass causes the period to increase.

25. f is certainly periodic. Since sine is periodic with period 2π, we know that $\sin w = \sin(w + 2\pi)$. Since these have the same value, $e^{\sin w} = e^{\sin(w+2\pi)}$, so f also has period 2π. It does not grow unboundedly, though. Sine cannot get bigger than 1 or less than -1. Consequently, the biggest f can get is $e^1 = e$ and the smallest is $e^{-1} = \frac{1}{e}$. (f has no zeros and is never negative.) See the following figure.

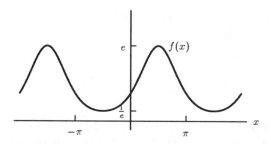

26. Even though sine is a periodic function, this one is not. Since e^x grows more rapidly for larger numbers and increases from near zero (for very negative numbers) to near infinity (for very positive numbers), this graph will look like the standard sine curve for angles from zero to infinity but stretched and squashed. For example, the part of the standard sine curve, $\sin z$, between $z = 0$ and $z = 1$ is in this case stretched out on the negative x-axis. On the positive x-axis, the sine curve is squashed more and more as the numbers get larger. $f(x)$ still has 1 as a max and -1 as a min. f has many zeros and can be negative. See the figure below.

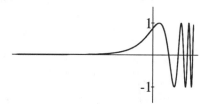

27.

TABLE 4.3

h (degrees)	$\sin h$	$\dfrac{\sin h}{h}$
± 1	0.0174524	0.0174524
± 0.1	0.0017453	0.0174533
± 0.01	0.0001745	0.0174533
± 0.001	0.0000174	0.0174533

Thus, the limit appears to be approximately 0.0174533. Consider the ratio $\frac{\sin h}{h}$. Let's take some values of h as before: $\pm 1, \pm 0.1, \pm 0.01, \pm 0.001$. As we approach 0, however, the numerator, $\sin h$, will be much smaller in magnitude if h is in degrees rather than in radians. For example, if $h = 1$ radian, $\sin h = 0.8415$, but if $h = 1°$, $\sin h = 0.01745$. Thus, since the numerator is smaller for h measured in degrees while the denominator is numerically the same, we expect the ratio $\frac{\sin h}{h}$ to be smaller.

28.
$$\frac{d}{dx}(\sin x)|_{x=35°} = \lim_{h \to 0} \frac{\sin(35° + h) - \sin 35°}{h}$$

Using $h = \pm 0.1, \pm 0.01, \pm 0.001$, we get $\frac{d}{dx}(\sin 35°) \approx 0.014$.

29.
$$w'(t) = u'(v(t)) \cdot v'(t) = u'(\cos t)(-\sin t)$$
$$w'(\pi) = u'(\cos \pi)(-\sin \pi)$$
$$= u'(-1)(-\sin \pi)$$
$$= 2 \cdot 0$$
$$= 0.$$

30. The answer would be 0 no matter what $u'(-1)$ is. Algebraically, you can see this by noting that whatever $u'(-1)$ is, it gets multiplied by zero. Intuitively, the fact that the derivative of cosine is 0 at π means that it is not changing at π. Then, if you are looking at the value of $u(\cos t)$ at π, its value can't be changing either since $\cos t$ is not changing.

31. (a) $k'(p) = \frac{2}{\cos^2(2p)}$. Since $-1 \le \cos(2p) \le 1$, $0 \le \cos^2(2p) \le 1$, and it follows that $k'(p) \ge 2 > 1$. So there is no p such that $k'(p) = 1$.
$r'(p) = \frac{1}{2\cos^2 \frac{1}{2}p}$. Setting $r'(p) = 1$, we get $\cos^2 \frac{1}{2}p = \frac{1}{2}$, or

$\cos \frac{1}{2}p = \pm\sqrt{\frac{1}{2}} = \pm\frac{1}{\sqrt{2}}$. So $\frac{1}{2}p = \pm\frac{\pi}{4}$ since $-\pi < p < \pi$, and $p = \pm\frac{\pi}{2}$.

(b) Graphically, this implies that the tangent to $k(p)$ is steeper than the line $y = x$, at every point on the graph.

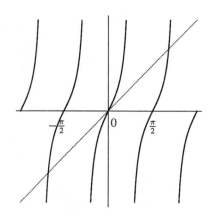

The tangent to $r(p)$ is as steep as $y = x$ for $p = \pm\frac{\pi}{2}$.

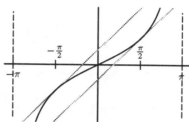

32. The tangent lines to $f(x) = \sin x$ have slope $\frac{d}{dx}(\sin x) = \cos x$. The tangent line at $x = 0$ has slope $f'(0) = \cos 0 = 1$ and goes through the point $(0,0)$. Consequently, its equation is $y = g(x) = x$. The approximate value of $\sin\frac{\pi}{6}$ given by this equation is then $g(\frac{\pi}{6}) = \frac{\pi}{6} \approx 0.524$.

Similarly, the tangent line at $x = \frac{\pi}{3}$ has slope $f'(\frac{\pi}{3}) = \cos\frac{\pi}{3} = \frac{1}{2}$ and goes through the point $(\frac{\pi}{3}, \frac{\sqrt{3}}{2})$. Consequently, its equation is $y = h(x) = \frac{1}{2}x + \frac{3\sqrt{3}-\pi}{6}$. The approximate value of $\sin\frac{\pi}{6}$ given by this equation is then $h(\frac{\pi}{6}) = \frac{6\sqrt{3}-\pi}{12} \approx 0.604$.

The actual value of $\sin\frac{\pi}{6}$ is $\frac{1}{2}$, so the approximation from 0 is better than that from $\frac{\pi}{3}$. This is because the slope of the function changes less between $x = 0$ and $x = \frac{\pi}{6}$ than it does between $x = \frac{\pi}{6}$ and $x = \frac{\pi}{3}$.

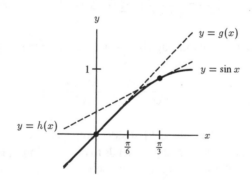

33. (a) If $f(x) = \sin x$, then

$$f'(x) = \lim_{h \to 0} \frac{\sin(x+h) - \sin x}{h}$$
$$= \lim_{h \to 0} \frac{(\sin x \cos h + \sin h \cos x) - \sin x}{h}$$
$$= \lim_{h \to 0} \frac{\sin x(\cos h - 1) + \sin h \cos x}{h}$$
$$= \sin x \lim_{h \to 0} \frac{\cos h - 1}{h} + \cos x \lim_{h \to 0} \frac{\sin h}{h}.$$

(b) $\frac{\cos h - 1}{h} \to 0$ and $\frac{\sin h}{h} \to 1$, as $h \to 0$. Thus, $f'(x) = \sin x \cdot 0 + \cos x \cdot 1 = \cos x$.

(c)   Similarly,

$$\begin{aligned} g'(x) &= \lim_{h \to 0} \frac{\cos(x + h) - \cos x}{h} \\ &= \lim_{h \to 0} \frac{(\cos x \cos h - \sin x \sin h) - \cos x}{h} \\ &= \lim_{h \to 0} \frac{\cos x (\cos h - 1) - \sin x \sin h}{h} \\ &= \cos x \lim_{h \to 0} \frac{\cos h - 1}{h} - \sin x \lim_{h \to 0} \frac{\sin h}{h} \\ &= -\sin x. \end{aligned}$$

34.   (a)   Sector OAQ is a sector of a circle with radius $\frac{1}{\cos \theta}$ and angle $\Delta\theta$. Thus its area is the left side of the inequality. Similarly, the area of Sector OBR is the right side of the equality. The area of the triangle OQR is $\frac{1}{2}\Delta \tan \theta$ since it is a triangle with base $\Delta \tan \theta$ (the segment QR) and height 1 (if you turn it sideways, it is easier to see this). Thus, using the given fact about areas (which is also clear from looking at the picture), we have

$$\frac{\Delta\theta}{2\pi} \cdot \pi \left(\frac{1}{\cos \theta} \right)^2 \leq \frac{1}{2} \cdot \Delta(\tan \theta) \leq \frac{\Delta\theta}{2\pi} \cdot \pi \left(\frac{1}{\cos(\theta + \Delta\theta)} \right)^2.$$

(b)   Dividing the inequality through by $\frac{\Delta\theta}{2}$ and canceling the π's gives:

$$\left(\frac{1}{\cos \theta} \right)^2 \leq \frac{\Delta \tan \theta}{\Delta\theta} \leq \left(\frac{1}{\cos(\theta + \Delta\theta)} \right)^2.$$

Then as $\Delta\theta \to 0$, the right and left sides both tend towards $\left(\frac{1}{\cos \theta} \right)^2$ while the middle (which is the difference quotient for tangent) tends to $(\tan \theta)'$. Thus, the derivative of tangent is "squeezed" between two values heading towards the same thing and must, itself, also tend to that value. Therefore, $(\tan \theta)' = \left(\frac{1}{\cos \theta} \right)^2$.

(c)   Take the identity $\sin^2 \theta + \cos^2 \theta = 1$ and divide through by $\cos^2 \theta$ to get $(\tan \theta)^2 + 1 = \left(\frac{1}{\cos \theta} \right)^2$. Differentiating with respect to θ yields:

$$\begin{aligned} 2(\tan \theta) \cdot (\tan \theta)' &= 2 \left(\frac{1}{\cos \theta} \right) \cdot \left(\frac{1}{\cos \theta} \right)' \\ 2 \left(\frac{\sin \theta}{\cos \theta} \right) \cdot \left(\frac{1}{\cos \theta} \right)^2 &= 2 \left(\frac{1}{\cos \theta} \right) \cdot (-1) \left(\frac{1}{\cos \theta} \right)^2 (\cos \theta)' \\ 2 \frac{\sin \theta}{\cos^3 \theta} &= (-1)2 \frac{1}{\cos^3 \theta} (\cos \theta)' \\ -\sin \theta &= (\cos \theta)'. \end{aligned}$$

(d)

$$\frac{d}{d\theta}\left(\sin^2\theta + \cos^2\theta\right) = \frac{d}{d\theta}(1)$$
$$2\sin\theta \cdot (\sin\theta)' + 2\cos\theta \cdot (\cos\theta)' = 0$$
$$2\sin\theta \cdot (\sin\theta)' + 2\cos\theta \cdot (-\sin\theta) = 0$$
$$(\sin\theta)' - \cos\theta = 0$$
$$(\sin\theta)' = \cos\theta.$$

4.7 SOLUTIONS

1. $f'(x) = \frac{-1}{1-x} = \frac{1}{x-1}$.

2. $f'(t) = \frac{2t}{t^2+1}$.

3. $f'(z) = -1(\ln z)^{-2} \cdot \frac{1}{z} = \frac{-1}{z(\ln z)^2}$.

4. $f'(\theta) = \frac{-\sin\theta}{\cos\theta} = -\tan\theta$.

5. $f'(x) = \frac{1}{1-e^{-x}} \cdot -e^{-x}(-1) = \frac{e^{-x}}{1-e^{-x}}$.

6. $f'(\alpha) = \frac{1}{\sin\alpha} \cdot \cos\alpha = \frac{\cos\alpha}{\sin\alpha}$.

7. $f'(x) = \frac{1}{e^x+1} \cdot e^x$.

8. $f'(t) = \dfrac{1}{\ln t} \cdot \dfrac{1}{t} = \dfrac{1}{t\ln t}$

9. $f'(x) = \frac{1}{e^{7x}} \cdot (e^{7x})7 = 7$.
    (Note also that $\ln(e^{7x}) = 7x$ implies $f'(x) = 7$.)

10. Note that $f(x) = e^{\ln x} \cdot e^1 = x \cdot e = ex$. So $f'(x) = e$. (Remember, e is just a constant.) You might also use the chain rule to get:
    $$f'(x) = e^{(\ln x)+1} \cdot \frac{1}{x}.$$
    [Are the two answers the same? Of course they are, since
    $$e^{(\ln x)+1}\left(\frac{1}{x}\right) = e^{\ln x} \cdot e\left(\frac{1}{x}\right) = xe\left(\frac{1}{x}\right) = e.]$$

11. $f'(w) = \frac{1}{\cos(w-1)}[-\sin(w-1)] = -\tan(w-1)$.
    [This could be done easily using the answer from Problem 4 and the chain rule.]

12. $f(t) = \ln t$ (because $\ln e^x = x$ *or* because $e^{\ln t} = t$), so $f'(t) = \frac{1}{t}$.

13. $f'(y) = \dfrac{2y}{\sqrt{1-y^4}}$.

14. $g'(t) = \dfrac{3}{(3t-4)^2 + 1}$.

15. $h'(w) = \arcsin w + \dfrac{w}{\sqrt{1-w^2}}$.

16. $g(\alpha) = \alpha$, so $g'(\alpha) = 1$.

17. Let

$$g(x) = \arcsin x$$

so

$$\sin[g(x)] = x.$$

Differentiating,

$$\cos[g(x)] \cdot g'(x) = 1$$

$$g'(x) = \frac{1}{\cos[g(x)]}$$

Using the fact that $\sin^2 \theta + \cos^2 \theta = 1$, and $\cos[g(x)] \geq 0$, since $-\frac{\pi}{2} \leq g(x) \leq \frac{\pi}{2}$, we get

$$\cos[g(x)] = \sqrt{1 - (\sin[g(x)])^2}.$$

Therefore,

$$g'(x) = \frac{1}{\sqrt{1 - (\sin[g(x)])^2}}$$

Since $\sin[g(x)] = x$, we have

$$g'(x) = \frac{1}{\sqrt{1-x^2}}, \quad -1 < x < 1.$$

18.

Let

$$g(x) = \log x$$

Then

$$10^{g(x)} = x$$

Differentiating,

$$(\ln 10)[10^{g(x)}]g'(x) = 1$$

$$g'(x) = \frac{1}{(\ln 10)[10^{g(x)}]}$$

$$g'(x) = \frac{1}{(\ln 10)x}.$$

19. pH $= 2 = -\log x$ means $\log x = -2$ so $x = 10^{-2}$. Rate of change of pH with hydrogen ion concentration is

$$\frac{d}{dx}\text{pH} = -\frac{d}{dx}(\log x) = \frac{-1}{x(\ln 10)} = -\frac{1}{(10^{-2})\ln 10} = -43.4$$

20. (a) $P = 10.8(0.998)^{10} = 10.59$ million.
    (b)

$$\frac{dP}{dt} = 10.8(\ln 0.998)(0.998)^{t}$$

$$\text{so} \quad \frac{dP}{dt}\bigg|_{t=10} = 10.8(\ln 0.998)(0.998)^{10} = -0.02 \text{ million/year}$$

21. The closer you look at the function, the more it begins to look like a line with slope equal to the derivative of the function at $x = 0$. Hence, functions whose derivatives at $x = 0$ are equal will look the same there.

   The following functions look like the line $y = x$ since, in all cases, $y' = 1$ at $x = 0$.
   $y = x$ $y' = 1$
   $y = \sin x$ $y' = \cos x$
   $y = \tan x$ $y' = \frac{1}{\cos^2 x}$
   $y = \ln(x + 1)$ $y' = \frac{1}{x+1}$

   The following functions look like the line $y = 0$ since, in all cases, $y' = 0$ at $x = 0$.
   $y = x^2$ $y' = 2x$
   $y = x \sin x$ $y' = x \cos x + \sin x$
   $y = x^3$ $y' = 3x^2$
   $y = \frac{1}{2}\ln(x^2 + 1)$ $y' = 2x \cdot \frac{1}{2} \cdot \frac{1}{x^2+1} = \frac{x}{x^2+1}$
   $y = 1 - \cos x$ $y' = \sin x$

   The following functions look like the line $x = 0$ since, in all cases, as $x \to 0^+$, the slope $y' \to \infty$.
   $y = \sqrt{x}$ $y' = \frac{1}{2\sqrt{x}}$
   $y = \sqrt{\frac{x}{x+1}}$ $y' = \frac{(x+1)-x}{(x+1)^2} \cdot \frac{1}{2} \cdot \frac{1}{\sqrt{\frac{x}{x+1}}} = \frac{1}{2(x+1)^2} \cdot \sqrt{\frac{x+1}{x}}$
   $y = \sqrt{2x - x^2}$ $y' = (2 - 2x)\frac{1}{2} \cdot \frac{1}{\sqrt{2x-x^2}} = \frac{1-x}{\sqrt{2x-x^2}}$

22. (a) $y = \ln x$, $y' = \frac{1}{x}$; $f'(1) = \frac{1}{1} = 1$.
    $y - y_1 = m(x - x_1)$, $y - 0 = 1(x - 1)$; $y = g(x) = x - 1$.
    (b) $g(1.1) = 1.1 - 1 = 0.1$; $g(2) = 2 - 1 = 1$.
    (c) $f(1.1)$ and $f(2)$ are below $g(x) = x - 1$. $f(0.9)$ and $f(0.5)$ are also below $g(x)$. This would be true for any approximation of this function by a tangent line since f is concave down ($f''(x) = -\frac{1}{x^2} < 0$ for all $x \neq 0$.) Thus, for a given x value, the y value given by the function is always below the value given by the tangent line.

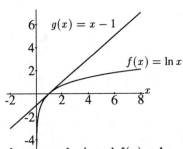

23. (a) Let $g(x) = ax^2 + bx + c$ be our quadratic and $f(x) = \ln x$. For the best approximation, we want
to find a quadratic with the same value as $\ln x$ at $x = 1$ and the same first and second derivatives
as $\ln x$ at $x = 1$. $g'(x) = 2ax + b, g''(x) = 2a, f'(x) = \frac{1}{x}, f''(x) = -\frac{1}{x^2}$.

$$g(1) = a(1)^2 + b(1) + c \quad f(1) = 0$$
$$g'(1) = 2a(1) + b \quad f'(1) = 1$$
$$g''(1) = 2a \quad f''(1) = -1$$

Thus, we obtain the equations

$$a + b + c = 0$$
$$2a + b = 1$$
$$2a = -1$$

We find $a = -\frac{1}{2}$, $b = 2$ and $c = -\frac{3}{2}$. Thus our approximation is:

$$g(x) = -\frac{1}{2}x^2 + 2x - \frac{3}{2}$$

(b) From the graph on the right, we noticed that around $x = 1$, the value of $f(x) = \ln x$ and the value
of $g(x) = -\frac{1}{2}x^2 + 2x - \frac{3}{2}$ are very close.

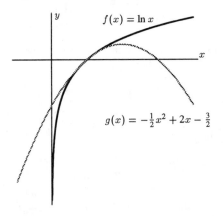

(c) $g(1.1) = 0.095 \quad g(2) = 0.5$
Compare with $f(1.1) = 0.0953, f(2) = 0.693$.

24. (a)

$$f'(x) = \frac{1}{1+x^2} + \frac{1}{1+\frac{1}{x^2}} \cdot (-\frac{1}{x^2})$$

$$= \frac{1}{1+x^2} + \left(-\frac{1}{x^2+1}\right)$$

$$= \frac{1}{1+x^2} - \frac{1}{1+x^2}$$

$$= 0$$

(b) f is a constant function. Checking at a few values of x,

TABLE 4.4

x	arctan x	arctan x^{-1}	$f(x) = \arctan x + \arctan x^{-1}$
1	0.785392	0.7853982	1.5707963
2	1.1071487	0.4636476	1.5707963
3	1.2490458	0.3217506	1.5707963

25. (a) Since the elevator is descending at 30 ft/sec, its height from the ground is given by $h(t) = 300 - 30t$,   for $0 \le t \le 10$.

(b) From the triangle in the figure,

$$\tan \theta = \frac{h(t) - 100}{150} = \frac{300 - 30t - 100}{150} = \frac{200 - 30t}{150}.$$

Therefore

$$\theta = \arctan\left(\frac{200 - 30t}{150}\right)$$

and

$$\frac{d\theta}{dt} = \frac{1}{1 + \left(\frac{200-30t}{150}\right)^2} \cdot \left(\frac{-30}{150}\right) = -\frac{1}{5}\left(\frac{150^2}{150^2 + (200 - 30t)^2}\right).$$

Notice that $\frac{d\theta}{dt}$ is always negative, which is reasonable since θ decreases as the elevator descends.

(c) If we want to know when θ changes (decreases) the fastest, we want to find out when $d\theta/dt$ has the largest magnitude. This will occur when the denominator, $150^2 + (200 - 30t)^2$, in the expression for $d\theta/dt$ is the smallest, or when $200 - 30t = 0$. This occurs when $t = \frac{200}{30}$ seconds, and so $h(\frac{200}{30}) = 100$ feet, i.e., when the elevator is at the level of the observer.

4.8 SOLUTIONS

1. We differentiate implicitly both sides of the equation with respect to x.

$$2x + \left(y + x\frac{dy}{dx}\right) - 3y^2\frac{dy}{dx} = y^2 + x(2y)\frac{dy}{dx},$$

$$x\frac{dy}{dx} - 3y^2\frac{dy}{dx} - 2xy\frac{dy}{dx} = y^2 - y - 2x,$$

$$\frac{dy}{dx} = \frac{y^2 - y - 2x}{x - 3y^2 - 2xy}.$$

2. We differentiate implicitly both sides of the equation with respect to x.

$$2x + 2y\frac{dy}{dx} = 0,$$

$$\frac{dy}{dx} = -\frac{2x}{2y} = -\frac{x}{y}.$$

3. We differentiate implicitly both sides of the equation with respect to x.

$$x^{\frac{1}{2}} + y^{\frac{1}{2}} = 25,$$

$$\frac{1}{2}x^{-\frac{1}{2}} + \frac{1}{2}y^{-\frac{1}{2}}\frac{dy}{dx} = 0,$$

$$\frac{dy}{dx} = -\frac{\frac{1}{2}x^{-\frac{1}{2}}}{\frac{1}{2}y^{-\frac{1}{2}}} = -\frac{x^{-\frac{1}{2}}}{y^{-\frac{1}{2}}} = -\frac{\sqrt{y}}{\sqrt{x}} = -\sqrt{\frac{y}{x}}.$$

4. $\dfrac{2}{3}x^{-1/3} + \dfrac{2}{3}y^{-1/3} \cdot \dfrac{dy}{dx} = 0, \dfrac{dy}{dx} = -\dfrac{x^{-1/3}}{y^{-1/3}} = -\dfrac{y^{1/3}}{x^{1/3}}.$

5. We differentiate implicitly both sides of the equation with respect to x.

$$\cos(xy)\left(y + x\frac{dy}{dx}\right) = 2,$$

$$y\cos(xy) + x\cos(xy)\frac{dy}{dx} = 2,$$

$$\frac{dy}{dx} = \frac{2 - y\cos(xy)}{x\cos(xy)}.$$

6. We differentiate implicitly both sides of the equation with respect to x.

$$\ln y + x\frac{1}{y}\frac{dy}{dx} + 3y^2\frac{dy}{dx} = \frac{1}{x},$$

$$\frac{x}{y}\frac{dy}{dx} + 3y^2\frac{dy}{dx} = \frac{1}{x} - \ln y,$$

$$\frac{dy}{dx}\left(\frac{x}{y} + 3y^2\right) = \frac{1 - x\ln y}{x},$$

$$\frac{dy}{dx}\left(\frac{x + 3y^3}{y}\right) = \frac{1 - x\ln y}{x},$$

$$\frac{dy}{dx} = \frac{(1 - x\ln y)}{x} \cdot \frac{y}{(x + 3y^3)}.$$

7. We differentiate implicitly both sides of the equation with respect to x.

$$e^{\cos y}(-\sin y)\frac{dy}{dx} = 3x^2 \arctan y + x^3\frac{1}{1 + y^2}\frac{dy}{dx}$$

$$\frac{dy}{dx}\left(-e^{\cos y}\sin y - \frac{x^3}{1 + y^2}\right) = 3x^2 \arctan y$$

$$\frac{dy}{dx} = \frac{3x^2 \arctan y}{-e^{\cos y}\sin y - x^3(1 + y^2)^{-1}}.$$

8. Using the relation $\cos^2 y + \sin^2 y = 1$, the equation becomes:
$1 = y + 2$ or $y = -1$. Hence, $\dfrac{dy}{dx} = 0$.

9. First, we must find the slope of the tangent, i.e. $\left.\dfrac{dy}{dx}\right|_{(1,-1)}$. Differentiating implicitly, we have:

$$y^2 + x(2y)\frac{dy}{dx} = 0,$$

$$\frac{dy}{dx} = -\frac{y^2}{2xy} = -\frac{y}{2x}.$$

Substitution yields $\left.\dfrac{dy}{dx}\right|_{(1,-1)} = -\dfrac{-1}{2} = \dfrac{1}{2}$. Using the point-slope formula for a line, we have that the equation for the tangent line is $y + 1 = \frac{1}{2}(x - 1)$ or $y = \frac{1}{2}x - \frac{3}{2}$.

10. First, we must find the slope of the tangent, $\left.\dfrac{dy}{dx}\right|_{(4,2)}$. Implicit differentiation yields:

$$2y\frac{dy}{dx} = \frac{2x(xy - 4) - x^2\left(x\frac{dy}{dx} + y\right)}{(xy - 4)^2}.$$

Given the complexity of the above equation, we first want to substitute 4 for x and 2 for y (the coordinates of the point where we are constructing our tangent line), then solve for $\dfrac{dy}{dx}$. Substitution yields:

$$2 \cdot 2\frac{dy}{dx} = \frac{(2 \cdot 4)(4 \cdot 2 - 4) - 4^2\left(4\frac{dy}{dx} + 2\right)}{(4 \cdot 2 - 4)^2} = \frac{8(4) - 16(4\frac{dy}{dx} + 2)}{16} = -4\frac{dy}{dx}.$$

$$4\frac{dy}{dx} = -4\frac{dy}{dx},$$

Solving for $\dfrac{dy}{dx}$, we have:

$$\frac{dy}{dx} = 0.$$

The tangent is a horizontal line, through $(4, 2)$, hence its equation is $y = 2$.

11. First, we must find the slope of the tangent, $\left.\dfrac{dy}{dx}\right|_{(a,0)}$. We differentiate implicitly, obtaining:

$$\frac{2}{3}x^{-\frac{1}{3}} + \frac{2}{3}y^{-\frac{1}{3}}\frac{dy}{dx} = 0,$$

$$\frac{dy}{dx} = -\frac{\frac{2}{3}x^{-\frac{1}{3}}}{\frac{2}{3}y^{-\frac{1}{3}}} = -\frac{\sqrt[3]{y}}{\sqrt[3]{x}}.$$

Substitution yields, $\dfrac{dy}{dx}\Big|_{(a,0)} = \dfrac{\sqrt[3]{0}}{\sqrt[3]{a}} = 0$. The tangent is a horizontal line through $(a, 0)$, hence its equation is $y = 0$.

12. Taking derivatives implicitly, we find

$$\frac{dy}{dx} + \cos y \frac{dy}{dx} + 2x = 0$$

$$\frac{dy}{dx} = \frac{-2x}{1 + \cos y}$$

So, at the point $x = 3, y = 0$,

$$\frac{dy}{dx} = \frac{(-2)(3)}{1 + \cos 0} = \frac{-6}{2} = -3.$$

13. $y = x^{\frac{m}{n}}$. Taking n^{th} powers of both sides of this expression yields $(y)^n = (x^{\frac{m}{n}})^n$, or $y^n = x^m$.

$$\frac{d}{dx}(y^n) = \frac{d}{dx}(x^m)$$

$$ny^{n-1}\frac{dy}{dx} = mx^{m-1}$$

$$\frac{dy}{dx} = \frac{m}{n}\frac{x^{m-1}}{y^{n-1}}$$

$$= \frac{m}{n}\frac{x^{m-1}}{(x^{m/n})^{n-1}}$$

$$= \frac{m}{n}\frac{x^{m-1}}{x^{m-\frac{m}{n}}}$$

$$= \frac{m}{n}x^{(m-1)-(m-\frac{m}{n})}$$

$$= \frac{m}{n}x^{\frac{m}{n}-1}.$$

14. (a) If $x = 4$ then $16 + y^2 = 25$, so $y = \pm 3$. We find $\dfrac{dy}{dx}$ implicitly:

$$2x + 2y\frac{dy}{dx} = 0$$

$$\frac{dy}{dx} = -\frac{x}{y}$$

So the slope at $(4, 3)$ is $-\frac{4}{3}$ and at $(4, -3)$ is $\frac{4}{3}$. The tangent lines are:

$$(y - 3) = -\frac{4}{3}(x - 4) \quad \text{and} \quad (y + 3) = \frac{4}{3}(x - 4)$$

(b)   The normal lines have slopes that are the negative of the reciprocal of the slopes of the tangent lines. Thus,

$$(y - 3) = \frac{3}{4}(x - 4) \quad \text{so} \quad y = \frac{3}{4}x$$

and

$$(y + 3) = -\frac{3}{4}(x - 4) \quad \text{so} \quad y = -\frac{3}{4}x$$

are the normal lines.

(c)   These lines meet at the origin, which is the center of the circle.

15.   (a)   Taking derivatives implicitly, we get

$$\frac{2}{25}x + \frac{2}{9}y\frac{dy}{dx} = 0$$

$$\frac{dy}{dx} = \frac{-9x}{25y}$$

(b)   The slope is not defined anywhere along the line $y = 0$. This ellipse intersects that line in two places, $(-5, 0)$ and $(5, 0)$. (These are, of course, the "ends" of the ellipse where the tangent is vertical.)

16.   Solving the equation for x we get

$$x = \frac{6}{y} + y^2$$

whose graph looks like:

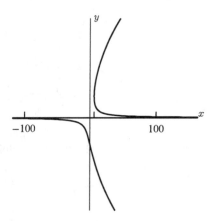

There appears to be one point where the tangent line is vertical. (The exact x-value of this point is indicated by a tick mark on the x-axis.) From the example, we see that this value is $x \approx 6.240$. For each x less than this value, there is one corresponding y value. For $x \approx 6.240$, there are two y values, and for each x greater than 6.240, there are three corresponding y values.

17. (a) Solving for $\frac{dy}{dx}$ by implicit differentiation yields

$$3x^2 + 3y^2\frac{dy}{dx} - y^2 - 2xy\frac{dy}{dx} = 0$$
$$\frac{dy}{dx} = \frac{y^2 - 3x^2}{3y^2 - 2xy}.$$

(b) We can approximate the curve near $x = 1$, $y = 2$ by its tangent line. The tangent line will have slope $\frac{(2)^2-3(1)^2}{3(2)^2-2(1)(2)} = \frac{1}{8} = 0.125$. Thus its equation is

$$y = 0.125x + 1.875$$

Using the y values of the tangent line to approximate the y values of the curve, we get:

TABLE 4.5

x	0.96	0.98	1	1.02	1.04
approximate y	1.995	1.9975	2.000	2.0025	2.005

(c) When $x = 0.96$, we get the equation $0.96^3 + y^3 - 0.96y^2 = 5$, whose solution by numerical methods is 1.9945, which is close to the one above.

(d) The tangent line is horizontal when $\frac{dy}{dx}$ is zero and vertical when $\frac{dy}{dx}$ is undefined. These will occur when the numerator is zero and when the denominator is zero, respectively.

Thus, we know that the tangent is horizontal when $y^2 - 3x^2 = 0 \Rightarrow y = \pm\sqrt{3}x$. To find the points that satisfy this condition, we substitute back into the original equation for the curve:

$$x^3 + y^3 - xy^2 = 5$$
$$x^3 \pm 3\sqrt{3}x^3 - 3x^3 = 5$$
$$x^3 = \frac{5}{\pm 3\sqrt{3} - 2}$$

So $x \approx 1.1609$ or $x \approx -0.8857$.

Substituting,

$$y = \pm\sqrt{3}x \text{ so } y \approx 2.0107 \quad \text{or} \quad y \approx 1.5341.$$

Thus, the tangent line is horizontal at $(1.1609, 2.0107)$ and $(-0.8857, 1.5341)$.

Also, we know that the tangent is vertical whenever $3y^2 - 2xy = 0$, that is, when $y = \frac{2}{3}x$ or $y = 0$. Substituting into the original equation for the curve gives us $x^3 + (\frac{2}{3}x)^3 - (\frac{2}{3})^2x^3 = 5$, whence $x^3 \approx 5.8696$, so $x \approx 1.8039$, $y \approx 1.2026$. The other vertical tangent is at $y = 0$, $x = \sqrt[3]{5}$.

18. (a) Taking derivatives implicitly yields

$$e^{5y} + 5xe^{5y}\frac{dy}{dx} = 3\frac{dy}{dx}$$
$$\frac{dy}{dx} = \frac{e^{5y}}{3 - 5xe^{5y}}.$$

(b)   Thus the slope at $(0,0)$ is $\dfrac{e^{5.0}}{3 - (5 \cdot 0)e^{5.0}} = \dfrac{1}{3}$. Then the equation of the tangent line is $y = \frac{1}{3}x$.

(c)   When $x = 0.1$, $y \approx \frac{1}{3} \cdot 0.1 = 0.0333$.

4.9 SOLUTIONS

1. With $f(x) = 1/x$, we see that the tangent line approximation to f near $x = 1$ is

$$f(x) \approx f(1) + f'(1)(x - 1),$$

which becomes

$$\frac{1}{x} \approx 1 + f'(1)(x - 1).$$

Since $f'(x) = -1/x^2$, $f'(1) = -1$. Thus our formula reduces to

$$\frac{1}{x} \approx 1 - (x - 1) = 2 - x.$$

This is the local linearization of $1/x$ near $x = 1$.

2. With $f(x) = 1/(\sqrt{1 + x})$, we see that the tangent line approximation to f near $x = 0$ is

$$f(x) \approx f(0) + f'(0)(x - 0),$$

which becomes

$$\frac{1}{\sqrt{1 + x}} \approx 1 + f'(0)x.$$

Since $f'(x) = (-1/2)(1 + x)^{-3/2}$, $f'(0) = -1/2$. Thus our formula reduces to

$$\frac{1}{\sqrt{1 + x}} \approx 1 - x/2.$$

This is the local linearization of $\dfrac{1}{\sqrt{1 + x}}$ near $x = 0$.

3. Let $f(x) = e^{-x}$. Then $f'(x) = -e^{-x}$. So $f(0) = 1$, $f'(0) = -e^0 = -1$. Therefore, $e^{-x} \approx f(0) + f'(0)x = 1 - x$.

4. Using local linearization, as in Example 3 we see that when h is small, $e^{kh} \approx 1 + kh$, so that $\dfrac{e^{kh} - 1}{h} \approx k$. Thus

$$\lim_{h \to 0} \frac{e^{kh} - 1}{h} = k.$$

5. If $\$P$ were deposited, then Pe^{rt} would be the balance after t years if interest were compounded continuously at the nominal rate r (see Section 4.4). If interest were compounded n times a year, then the balance would be $P(1 + \frac{r}{n})^{nt}$. The local linearization $e^{rt} \approx 1 + rt$ tells us that for small values of t, say $t = \frac{1}{n}$,

$$Pe^{r(\frac{1}{n})} \approx P\left(1 + r\left(\frac{1}{n}\right)\right) = P(1 + \frac{1}{n}).$$

In other words, the balance after one compounding period is approximately the same whether interest is compounded n times a year or continuously.

6. (a) Let $f(x) = (1 + x)^k$. Then $f'(x) = k(1 + x)^{k-1}$. Since

$$f(x) \approx f(0) + f'(0)(x - 0)$$

is the tangent line approximation, and $f(0) = 1$, $f'(0) = k$, for small x we get

$$f(x) \approx 1 + kx.$$

   (b) Since $\sqrt{1.1} = (1 + 0.1)^{1/2} \approx 1 + (1/2)0.1 = 1.05$ by the above method, this estimate is about right.

   (c) The real answer is less than 1.05. Since $(1.05)^2 = (1 + 0.05)^2 = 1 + 2(1)(0.05) + (0.05)^2 = 1.1 + (0.05)^2 > 1.1$, we have $(1.05)^2 > 1.1$ Therefore

$$\sqrt{1.1} < 1.05.$$

   Graphically, we can see this because the graph of $\sqrt{1 + x}$ is concave down, so it bends below its tangent line. (See Figure 4.29 on page 235.) Therefore the true value ($\sqrt{1.1}$) which is on the curve is below the approximate value (1.05) which is on the tangent line.

7. (a) Since $\sin x \approx x$ for small x, we have

$$\cos x = 1 - 2\sin^2 \frac{x}{2} \approx 1 - 2\left(\frac{x}{2}\right)^2 = 1 - \frac{x^2}{2}.$$

   (b) (i) $\displaystyle\lim_{h \to 0} \frac{\cos h - 1}{h} = \lim_{h \to 0} \frac{\left(1 - \frac{h^2}{2}\right) - 1}{h} = \lim_{h \to 0} \left(\frac{-h^2/2}{h}\right) = \lim_{h \to 0} -\frac{h}{2} = 0.$

   (ii) $\displaystyle\lim_{h \to 0} \frac{\cos h - 1}{h^2} = \lim_{h \to 0} \frac{\left(1 - \frac{h^2}{2}\right) - 1}{h^2} = \lim_{h \to 0} \frac{-h^2/2}{h^2} = \lim_{h \to 0} \left(-\frac{1}{2}\right) = -\frac{1}{2}.$

8. The local linearization of e^x near $x = 0$ is $1 + 1x$ so

$$e^x \approx 1 + x.$$

Squaring this yields, for small x,

$$e^{2x} = (e^x)^2 \approx (1 + x)^2 = 1 + 2x + x^2.$$

Local linearization of e^{2x} directly yields

$$e^{2x} \approx 1 + 2x$$

for small x. The two approximations are consistent because they agree: the tangent line approximation to $1 + 2x + x^2$ is just $1 + 2x$.

The first approximation is more accurate. One can see this numerically or by noting that the approximation for e^{2x} given by $1 + 2x$ is really the same as approximating e^y at $y = 2x$. Since the other approximation approximates e^y at $y = x$, which is twice as close to 0 and therefore a better general estimate, it's more likely to be correct.

9. (a) Let $f(x) = 1/(1+x)$. Then $f'(x) = -1/(1+x)^2$ by the chain rule. So $f(0) = 1$, and $f'(0) = -1$. Therefore, for x near 0, $1/(1+x) \approx f(0) + f'(0)x = 1 - x$.

   (b) We know that for small y, $1/(1+y) \approx 1 - y$. Let $y = x^2$; when x is small, so is $y = x^2$. Hence, for small x, $1/(1+x^2) \approx 1 - x^2$.

   (c) Since the linearization of $1/(1+x^2)$ is the line $y = 1$, and this line has a slope of 0, the derivative of $1/(1+x^2)$ is zero at $x = 0$.

10. The local linearizations of $f(x) = e^x$ and $g(x) = \sin x$ near $x = 0$ are

$$f(x) = e^x \approx 1 + x$$

and

$$g(x) = \sin x \approx x.$$

Thus, the local linearization of $e^x \sin x$ is the local linearization of the product:

$$e^x \sin x \approx (1 + x)x = x + x^2 \approx x.$$

We therefore know that the derivative of $e^x \sin x$ at $x = 0$ must be 1. Similarly, using the local linearization of $1/(1 + x)$ near $x = 0$, $1/(1 + x) \approx 1 - x$, we have

$$\frac{e^x \sin x}{1 + x} = (e^x)(\sin x)\left(\frac{1}{1 + x}\right) \approx (1 + x)(x)(1 - x) = x - x^3$$

so the local linearization of the triple product $\dfrac{e^x \sin x}{1 + x}$ at $x = 0$ is simply x. And therefore the derivative of $\dfrac{e^x \sin x}{1 + x}$ at $x = 0$ is 1.

11. Note that

$$[f(x)g(x)]' = \lim_{h \to 0} \frac{f(x + h)g(x + h) - f(x)g(x)}{h}.$$

We use the hint: For small h, $f(x + h) \approx f(x) + f'(x)h$, and $g(x + h) \approx g(x) + g'(x)h$. Therefore

$$\begin{aligned}
f(x + h)g(x + h) - f(x)g(x) &\approx [f(x) + hf'(x)][g(x) + hg'(x)] - f(x)g(x) \\
&= f(x)g(x) + hf'(x)g(x) + hf(x)g'(x) \\
&\quad + h^2 f'(x)g'(x) - f(x)g(x) \\
&= hf'(x)g(x) + hf(x)g'(x) + h^2 f'(x)g'(x).
\end{aligned}$$

Therefore

$$\lim_{h \to 0} \frac{f(x+h)g(x+h) - f(x)g(x)}{h} = \lim_{h \to 0} \frac{hf'(x)g(x) + hf(x)g'(x) + h^2 f'(x)g'(x)}{h}$$

$$= \lim_{h \to 0} \frac{h\left(f'(x)g(x) + f(x)g'(x) + hf'(x)g'(x)\right)}{h}$$

$$= \lim_{h \to 0} \left(f'(x)g(x) + f(x)g'(x) + hf'(x)g'(x)\right)$$

$$= f'(x)g(x) + f(x)g'(x).$$

12. Note that

$$[f(g(x))]' = \lim_{h \to 0} \frac{f(g(x+h)) - f(g(x))}{h}.$$

Using the local linearizations of f and g, we get that

$$f(g(x+h)) - f(g(x)) \approx f\left(g(x) + g'(x)h\right) - f(g(x))$$

$$\approx f\left(g(x)\right) + f'(g(x))g'(x)h) - f(g(x))$$

$$= f'(g(x))g'(x)h.$$

Therefore,

$$[f(g(x))]' = \lim_{h \to 0} \frac{f(g(x+h)) - f(g(x))}{h}$$

$$= \lim_{h \to 0} \frac{f'(g(x))g'(x)h}{h}$$

$$= \lim_{h \to 0} f'(g(x))g'(x)$$

$$= f'(g(x))g'(x).$$

SOLUTIONS TO REVIEW PROBLEMS FOR CHAPTER FOUR

1. $f'(x) = 6x(e^x - 4) + (3x^2 + \pi)e^x = 6xe^x - 24x + 3x^2 e^x + \pi e^x.$

2. $g'(x) = \dfrac{d}{dx}(2x - x^{-1/3} + 3^x - e) = 2 + \dfrac{1}{3x^{\frac{4}{3}}} + 3^x \ln 3.$

3. $\dfrac{d}{dz}\left(\dfrac{z^2 + 1}{\sqrt{z}}\right) = \dfrac{d}{dz}(z^{\frac{3}{2}} + z^{-\frac{1}{2}}) = \dfrac{3}{2}z^{\frac{1}{2}} - \dfrac{1}{2}z^{-\frac{3}{2}} = \dfrac{\sqrt{z}}{2}(3 - z^{-2}).$

4. $h'(r) = \dfrac{d}{dr}\left(\dfrac{r^2}{2r+1}\right) = \dfrac{(2r)(2r+1) - 2r^2}{(2r+1)^2} = \dfrac{2r(r+1)}{(2r+1)^2}.$

5. $\dfrac{d}{dt} e^{(1+3t)^2} = e^{(1+3t)^2} \cdot 2(1+3t) \cdot 3 = 6(1+3t)e^{(1+3t)^2}.$

6. $f'(t) = \dfrac{d}{dt}\left(2te^t - \dfrac{1}{\sqrt{t}}\right) = 2e^t + 2e^t t + \dfrac{1}{2t^{3/2}}.$

7. $\dfrac{d}{dx} xe^{\tan x} = e^{\tan x} + xe^{\tan x}\dfrac{1}{\cos^2 x}.$

8. $g'(w) = \dfrac{d}{dw}\left(\dfrac{1}{2^w + e^w}\right) = -\dfrac{2^w \ln 2 + e^w}{(2^w + e^w)^2}.$

9. $\dfrac{d}{dy} \ln \ln(2y^3) = \dfrac{1}{\ln(2y^3)}\dfrac{1}{2y^3}6y^2.$

10. $f'(x) = \dfrac{d}{dx}(2 - 4x - 3x^2)(6x^e - 3\pi) = (-4 - 6x)(6x^e - 3\pi) + (2 - 4 - 3x^2)(6exe^{-1}).$

11. $r'(\theta) = \dfrac{d}{d\theta} \sin[(3\theta - \pi)^2] = \cos[(3\theta - \pi)^2] \cdot 2(3\theta - \pi) \cdot 3 = 6(3\theta - \pi)\cos[(3\theta - \pi)^2].$

12. $s'(\theta) = \dfrac{d}{d\theta} \sin^2(3\theta - \pi) = 6\cos(3\theta - \pi)\sin(3\theta - \pi).$

13. $\dfrac{d}{d\theta} \sqrt{a^2 - \sin^2 \theta} = \dfrac{1}{2\sqrt{a^2 - \sin^2 \theta}}(-2\sin\theta\cos\theta) = -\dfrac{\sin\theta\cos\theta}{\sqrt{a^2 - \sin^2 \theta}}.$

14. $g'(x) = \dfrac{d}{dx}\left(x^{\frac{1}{2}} + x^{-1} + x^{-\frac{3}{2}}\right) = \dfrac{1}{2}x^{-\frac{1}{2}} - x^{-2} - \dfrac{3}{2}x^{-\frac{5}{2}}.$

15. $w'(\theta) = \dfrac{1}{\sin^2 \theta} - \dfrac{2\theta\cos\theta}{\sin^3 \theta}$

16.

$$\dfrac{d}{d\theta}\left(\dfrac{\sin(5-\theta)}{\theta^2}\right) = \dfrac{\cos(5-\theta)(-1)\theta^2 - \sin(5-\theta)(2\theta)}{\theta^4}$$

$$= -\dfrac{\theta\cos(5-\theta) + 2\sin(5-\theta)}{\theta^3}.$$

17. $h'(t) = \dfrac{d}{dt}\left(\ln\left(e^{-t} - t\right)\right) = \dfrac{1}{e^{-t} - t}\left(-e^{-t} - 1\right).$

18. $g'(x) = \dfrac{d}{dx}\left(x^k + k^x\right) = kx^{k-1} + k^x \ln k.$

19. $s'(x) = \dfrac{d}{dx}\left(\arctan(2 - x)\right) = \dfrac{-1}{1 + (2 - x)^2}.$

20. $r'(\theta) = \dfrac{d}{d\theta}\left(e^{\left(e^\theta + e^{-\theta}\right)}\right) = e^{\left(e^\theta + e^{-\theta}\right)}\left(e^\theta - e^{-\theta}\right).$

21. $\dfrac{d}{dy}\left(\dfrac{y}{\cos y + a}\right) = \dfrac{\cos y + a - y(-\sin y)}{(\cos y + a)^2} = \dfrac{\cos y + a + y\sin y}{(\cos y + a)^2}.$

22. (a) $H'(2) = r'(2)s(2) + r(2)s'(2) = -1 \cdot 1 + 4 \cdot 3 = 11.$

     (b) $H'(2) = \dfrac{r'(2)}{2\sqrt{r(2)}} = \dfrac{-1}{2\sqrt{4}} = -\dfrac{1}{4}.$

     (c) $H'(2) = r'(s(2))s'(2) = r'(1) \cdot 3,$ but we don't know $r'(1).$

     (d) $H'(2) = s'(r(2))r'(2) = s'(4)r'(2) = -3.$

23. When we zoom in on the origin, we find that two functions are not defined there. The other functions all look like straight lines through the origin. The only way we can tell them apart is their slope.

     The following functions all have slope 0 and are therefore indistinguishable:

$\sin x - \tan x,\ \dfrac{x^2}{x^2+1},\ x - \sin x,$ and $\dfrac{1-\cos x}{\cos x}.$

These functions all have slope 1 at the origin, and are thus indistinguishable:

$\arcsin x,\ \dfrac{\sin x}{1+\sin x},\ \arctan x,\ e^x - 1,\ \dfrac{x}{x+1},$ and $\dfrac{x}{x^2+1}.$

     Now, $\dfrac{\sin x}{x} - 1$ and $-x\ln x$ both are undefined at the origin, so they are distinguishable from the other functions. In addition, while $\dfrac{\sin x}{x} - 1$ has a slope that approaches zero near the origin, $-x\ln x$ becomes vertical near the origin, so they are distinguishable from each other.

     Finally, $x^{10} + \sqrt[10]{x}$ is the only function defined at the origin and with a vertical tangent there, so it is distinguishable from the others.

24. It makes sense to define the angle between two curves to be the angle between their tangent lines. (The tangent lines are the best linear approximations to the curves). The functions $\sin x$ and $\cos x$ are equal at $x = \dfrac{\pi}{4}.$

For $f_1(x) = \sin x,\ f_1'(\frac{\pi}{4}) = \cos(\frac{\pi}{4}) = \dfrac{\sqrt{2}}{2}.$

For $f_2(x) = \cos x,\ f_2'(\frac{\pi}{4}) = -\sin(\frac{\pi}{4}) = -\dfrac{\sqrt{2}}{2}.$

Using the point $(\frac{\pi}{4}, \frac{\sqrt{2}}{2})$ for each tangent line we get $y = \dfrac{\sqrt{2}}{2}x + \dfrac{\sqrt{2}}{2}(1 - \frac{\pi}{4})$ and $y = -\dfrac{\sqrt{2}}{2}x + \dfrac{\sqrt{2}}{2}(1 + \frac{\pi}{4}),$ respectively.

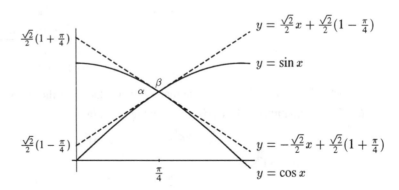

There are two possibilities of how to define the angle between the tangent lines, indicated by α and β above. The choice is arbitrary, so we will solve for both.

     To find the angle, $\alpha,$ we consider the triangle formed by these two lines and the y-axis.

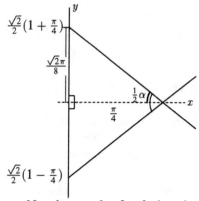

$$\tan\left(\frac{1}{2}\alpha\right) = \frac{\sqrt{2}\pi/8}{\pi/4}$$

$$\tan\left(\frac{1}{2}\alpha\right) = \frac{\sqrt{2}}{2}$$

$$\frac{1}{2}\alpha = 0.61548 \text{ radians}$$

$$\alpha = 1.231 \text{ radians, or } 70.5°.$$

Now let us solve for β, the other possible measure of the angle between the two tangent lines. Since α and β are supplementary,

$$\beta = \pi - 1.231 = 1.909 \text{ radians, or } 109.4°.$$

25. (a) $\dfrac{dg}{dr} = GM\dfrac{d}{dr}\left(\dfrac{1}{r^2}\right) = GM\dfrac{d}{dr}\left(r^{-2}\right) = GM(-2)r^{-3} = -\dfrac{2GM}{r^3}.$

(b) $\dfrac{dg}{dr}$ is the rate of change of acceleration due to the pull of gravity. The further away from the center of the earth, the weaker the pull of gravity is. So g is decreasing and therefore its derivative, $\dfrac{dg}{dr}$, is negative.

(c) By part (a),

$$\left.\frac{dg}{dr}\right|_{r=6400} = \left.-\frac{2GM}{r^3}\right|_{r=6400}$$

$$= -\frac{2(6.67\times 10^{-20})(6\times 10^{24})}{(6400)^3}$$

$$\approx -3.05\times 10^{-6}.$$

(d) It is reasonable to assume that g is a constant near the surface of the earth.

26. The population of Mexico is given by the formula

$$M = 84(1+0.026)^t = 84(1.026)^t \text{ million}$$

and that of the US by

$$U = 250(1+0.007)^t = 250(1.007)^t \text{ million},$$

where t is measured in years ($t = 0$ corresponds to the year 1975). So,

$$\left.\frac{dM}{dt}\right|_{t=0} = \left.84\frac{d}{dt}(1.026)^t\right|_{t=0} = \left.84(1.026)^t \ln(1.026)\right|_{t=0} \approx 2.156$$

and

$$\left.\frac{dU}{dt}\right|_{t=0} = 250\frac{d}{dt}(1.007)^t\Big|_{t=0} = 250(1.007)^t\ln(1.007)\Big|_{t=0} \approx 1.744$$

Since $\left.\dfrac{dM}{dt}\right|_{t=0} > \left.\dfrac{dU}{dt}\right|_{t=0}$, the population of Mexico was growing faster in 1975.

27. (a) If the distance $s(t) = 20e^{\frac{t}{2}}$, then the velocity, $v(t)$, is given by

$$v(t) = s'(t) = \left(20e^{\frac{t}{2}}\right)' = \left(\frac{1}{2}\right)\left(20e^{\frac{t}{2}}\right) = 10e^{\frac{t}{2}}.$$

(b) Observing the differentiation in (a), we note that

$$s'(t) = v(t) = \frac{1}{2}\left(20e^{\frac{t}{2}}\right).$$

Substituting $s(t)$ for $20e^{\frac{t}{2}}$, we obtain $s'(t) = \frac{1}{2}s(t)$.

28. (a)

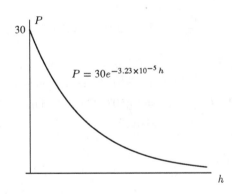

(b)

$$\frac{dP}{dh} = 30e^{-3.23\times10^{-5}h}(-3.23\times10^{-5})$$

so

$$\left.\frac{dP}{dh}\right|_{h=0} = -30(3.23\times10^{-5}) = -9.69\times10^{-4}$$

Hence, at $h = 0$, the slope of the tangent line is -9.69×10^{-4}, so the equation of the tangent line is

$$y - 30 = (-9.69\times10^{-4})(h - 0)$$

or

$$y = (-9.69 \times 10^{-4})h + 30.$$

(c)   The rule of thumb says

$$\left(\begin{array}{c}\text{Drop in pressure from} \\ \text{sea level to height } h\end{array}\right) = \frac{h}{1000}$$

But since the pressure at sea level is 30 inches of mercury, this drop in pressure is also $(30 - P)$, so

$$30 - P = \frac{h}{1000}$$

giving

$$P = 30 - 0.001h.$$

(d)   The equations in (b) and (c) are almost the same: both have P intercepts of 30, and the slopes are almost the same $(9.69 \times 10^{-4} \approx 0.001)$. The rule of thumb calculates values of P which are very close to the tangent lines, and therefore yields values very close to the curve.

(e)   The tangent line is slightly below the curve, and the rule of thumb line, having a slightly more negative slope, is slightly below the tangent line (for $h > 0$). Thus, the rule of thumb values are slightly smaller.

29.

$$\frac{dy}{dt} = -7.5(0.507)\sin(0.507t) = -3.80\sin(0.507t)$$

(a)   When $t = 6$, $\frac{dy}{dt} = -3.80\sin(0.507 \cdot 6) = -0.38$ meters/hour. So it's falling at 0.38 meters/hour.

(b)   When $t = 9$, $\frac{dy}{dt} = -3.80\sin(0.507 \cdot 9) = 3.76$ meters/hour. So it's rising at 3.76 meters/hour.

(c)   When $t = 12$, $\frac{dy}{dt} = -3.80\sin(0.507 \cdot 12) = 0.75$ meters/hour. So it's rising at 0.75 meters/hour.

(d)   When $t = 18$, $\frac{dy}{dt} = -3.80\sin(0.507 \cdot 18) = -1.12$ meters/hour. So it's falling at 1.12 meters/hour.

30.   (a)   Using the chain rule,

$$g'(x) = e^{n \ln x} \cdot \frac{d}{dx}(n \ln x) = e^{n \ln x} \cdot \frac{n}{x}$$

(b) $x^n = e^{n \ln x}$, so

$$\begin{aligned}
\frac{d}{dx}(x^n) &= \frac{d}{dx}(e^{n \ln x}) \\
&= e^{n \ln x} \cdot \frac{n}{x} \\
&= x^n \cdot \frac{n}{x} \\
&= nx^{n-1}.
\end{aligned}$$

31. (a) From the figure, the slope of the secant to $y = \ln x$ between $x = 1$ and $x = 1 + \frac{1}{t}$ is given by

$$\text{slope} = \frac{\ln(1 + \frac{1}{t}) - 0}{(1 + \frac{1}{t}) - 1} = \frac{\ln(1 + \frac{1}{t})}{\frac{1}{t}} = t\ln(1 + \frac{1}{t}).$$

As $t \to \infty$, this slope approaches the value of the slope of the tangent line to $y = \ln x$ at $x = 1$. We know that the derivative of $\ln x$ is $\frac{1}{x}$, so $f'(1) = \frac{1}{1} = 1$, and we have $\lim\limits_{t \to \infty} t\ln(1 + \frac{1}{t}) = 1$. Thus,

$$\lim_{n \to \infty}\left(1 + \frac{1}{n}\right)^n = \lim_{n \to \infty} e^{n\ln(1 + \frac{1}{n})}$$
$$= e^{\left[\lim\limits_{n \to \infty} n\ln(1 + \frac{1}{n})\right]}$$
$$= e^1 = e.$$

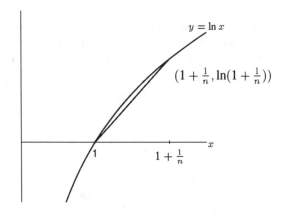

$$y = \ln x$$

$$\left(1 + \tfrac{1}{n}, \ln(1 + \tfrac{1}{n})\right)$$

$$x$$

$$1 \qquad 1 + \tfrac{1}{n}$$

(b) We have $\lim\limits_{x \to \infty}(1 + \frac{1}{x})^x = e$ from the above, replacing t by x. Now suppose r is a positive constant, and consider $\lim\limits_{x \to \infty}(1 + \frac{r}{x})^x$. As $x \to \infty$, $rx \to \infty$ as well. Thus replacing x with rx, we have

$$\lim_{x \to \infty}\left(1 + \frac{r}{x}\right)^x = \lim_{rx \to \infty}\left(1 + \frac{r}{rx}\right)^{rx} = \lim_{rx \to \infty}\left(1 + \frac{1}{x}\right)^{rx}$$
$$= \lim_{x \to \infty}\left(1 + \frac{1}{x}\right)^{rx} = \left[\lim_{x \to \infty}\left(1 + \frac{1}{x}\right)^x\right]^r = e^r.$$

Suppose one deposits P dollars in an account that gives an interest r. If this is compounded n times a year, at the end of that year the balance becomes

$$P\left(1 + \frac{r}{n}\right)^n.$$

By the preceding, as the number of times interest is compounded goes to infinity, the balance approaches

$$\lim_{n \to \infty} P\left(1 + \frac{r}{n}\right)^n = Pe^r.$$

Thus, if $r = 1$ (the interest rate is 100%), the balance is multiplied by a factor of e each year.

One might expect that if the interest were compounded a large number of times, the balance after one year would be a sizable fortune. The following argument shows that this is not the case. For example, if an initial sum of \$100 is placed into an account which compounds interest twice annually at a rate $r = 0.07$, then after one year there is

$$\$100 \left(1 + \frac{0.07}{2}\right)^2 = \$107.12$$

in the account. On the other hand, no matter how many times the interest is compounded, the balance could be no greater than

$$\lim_{n \to \infty} \$100 \left(1 + \frac{0.07}{n}\right)^n = \$100 e^{0.07} = \$107.25.$$

Thus the number of times a balance is compounded has very little effect on the overall interest.

(c) Suppose an initial balance is compounded n times annually at a rate of $r = 1$. The balance after one year is $P(1 + \frac{1}{n})^n$. Clearly if P is compounded $n + 1$ times, the balance will be greater, i.e.

$$P\left(1 + \frac{1}{n+1}\right)^{n+1} > P\left(1 + \frac{1}{n}\right)^n$$

or,

$$\left(1 + \frac{1}{n+1}\right)^{n+1} > \left(1 + \frac{1}{n}\right)^n.$$

(d) Using the argument in (a) we have:

$$\text{slope of secant line} = n \ln(1 + \tfrac{1}{n})$$

and

$$\text{slope of secant line } 2 = n + 1 \ln(1 + \tfrac{1}{n+1})$$

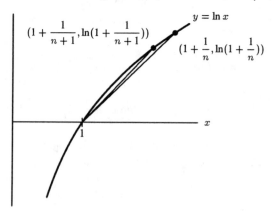

32. If $a = e$, the only solution is $(0,1)$.

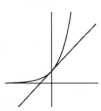

If $1 < a < e$, there are two solutions as illustrated:

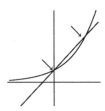

and if $a > e$, there are also two solutions.

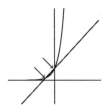

One way to prove the above is to compare the slopes of the lines. For example, e^x will have slope greater than 1 for all $x > 0$ and less than 1 for all $x < 0$, so it cannot meet the line $1 + x$ at any other points. Similar arguments can be made for the other cases.

33. Since we're given the instantaneous rate of change T at $t = 30$ is 2, we want to choose a and b so that the derivative of T agrees with this value. Differentiating, $T'(t) = ab \cdot e^{-bt}$. Then we have

$$2 = T'(30) = abe^{-30b} \text{ or } e^{-30b} = \frac{2}{ab}$$

We also know that at $t = 30$, $T = 120$, so

$$120 = T(30) = 200 - ae^{-30b} \text{ or } e^{-30b} = \frac{80}{a}$$

Thus $\dfrac{80}{a} = e^{-30b} = \dfrac{2}{ab}$, so $b = \frac{1}{40} = 0.025$ and $a = 169.36$.

34. We are given that the volume is increasing at a constant rate $\frac{dV}{dt} = 400$. The radius r is related to the volume by the formula $V = \frac{4}{3}\pi r^3$. By implicit differentiation, we have

$$\frac{dV}{dt} = \frac{4}{3}\pi 3r^2 \frac{dr}{dt} = 4\pi r^2 \frac{dr}{dt}$$

Plugging in $\frac{dV}{dt} = 400$ and $r = 10$, we have

$$400 = 400\pi \frac{dr}{dt}$$

so $\frac{dr}{dt} = \frac{1}{\pi} \approx 0.32\mu m/day$.

35. The radius r is related to the volume by the formula $V = \frac{4}{3}\pi r^3$. By implicit differentiation, we have

$$\frac{dV}{dt} = \frac{4}{3}\pi 3r^2 \frac{dr}{dt} = 4\pi r^2 \frac{dr}{dt}$$

The surface area of a sphere is $4\pi r^2$, so if $\frac{dV}{dt} = \frac{1}{3} \cdot S$, then

$$\frac{dV}{dt} = (4\pi r^2)\frac{dr}{dt} = S\frac{dr}{dt} \text{ so } \frac{dr}{dt} = \frac{1}{3}\mu m^3/day.$$

36. (a) $\displaystyle\lim_{t\to\infty} e^{-0.1t} = 0$

$\displaystyle\lim_{t\to\infty} \frac{1000000}{1+5000e^{-0.1t}} = 1000000.$

Thus, in the long run, close to 1,000,000 people will have had the disease.

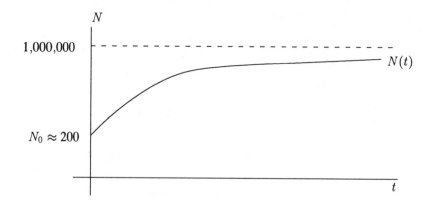

(b)   The rate at which people fall sick is given by the first derivative $N'(t)$.
$N'(t) \approx \frac{\Delta N}{\Delta t}$, where $\Delta t = 1$ day.

$$N'(t) = \frac{500{,}000{,}000}{e^{0.1t}(1 + 5000e^{-0.1t})^2} = \frac{500{,}000{,}000}{e^{0.1t} + 25{,}000{,}000e^{-0.1t} + 10^4}$$

Graphing this we see that the maximum value of $N'(t)$ is approximately 25,000. Therefore the maximum number of people to fall sick on any given day is 25,000.

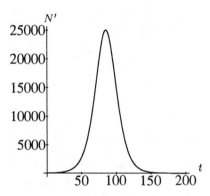

37.   (a)   We can approximate $\frac{d}{dx}[F(x)G(x)H(x)]$ using the large rectangular solids by which our original cube is increased:

$$\text{Volume of whole} - \text{volume of original solid} = \text{change in volume.}$$

$$F(x+h)G(x+h)H(x+h) - F(x)G(x)H(x) = \text{change in volume.}$$

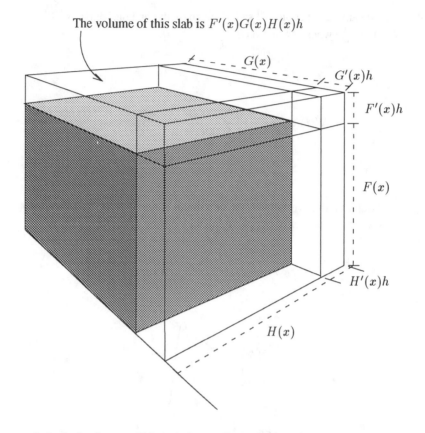

The volume of this slab is $F'(x)G(x)H(x)h$

As in the book, we will ignore the <u>smaller</u> regions which are added (the long, thin rectangular boxes and the small cube in the corner.) This can be justified by recognizing that as $h \to 0$, these volumes will shrink much faster than the volumes of the big slabs and will therefore be insignificant. (Note that these smaller regions have an h^2 or h^3 in the formulas of their volumes.) Then we can approximate the change in volume above by:

$$F(x + h)G(x + h)H(x + h) - F(x)G(x)H(x)$$
$$\approx F'(x)G(x)H(x)h \quad \text{(top slab)}$$
$$+ F(x)G'(x)H(x)h \quad \text{(front slab)}$$
$$+ F(x)G(x)H'(x)h \quad \text{(other slab)},$$

dividing by h gives

$$\frac{F(x + h)G(x + h)H(x + h) - F(x)G(x)H(x)}{h}$$
$$\approx F'(x)G(x)H(x) + F(x)G'(x)H(x) + F(x)G(x)H'(x),$$

letting $h \to 0$

$$(FGH)' = F'GH + FG'H + FGH'.$$

(b) Verifying,

$$\frac{d}{dx}[(F(x) \cdot G(x)) \cdot H(x)]$$
$$= (F \cdot G)'(H) + (F \cdot G)(H)'$$
$$= [F'G + FG']H + FGH'$$
$$= F'GH + FG'H + FGH'$$

as before.

(c) From the answer to (b), we observe that the derivative of a product is obtained by differentiating each factor in turn (leaving the other factors alone), and adding the results. So, in general,

$$(f_1 \cdot f_2 \cdot f_3 \cdot \ldots \cdot f_n)' = f_1' f_2 f_3 \cdots f_n + f_1 f_2' f_3 \cdots f_n + \cdots + f_1 \cdots f_{n-1} f_n'.$$

38. We want to find dP/dV. Solving $PV = k$ for P gives

$$P = k/V$$

so,

$$\frac{dP}{dV} = -\frac{k}{V^2}.$$

39. (a) Since $V = k/P$, the volume decreases.

(b) Since $PV = k$ and $P = 2$ when $V = 10$, we have $k = 20$, so

$$V = \frac{20}{P}.$$

We think of both P and V as functions of time, so by the chain rule

$$\frac{dV}{dt} = \frac{dV}{dP}\frac{dP}{dt},$$
$$\frac{dV}{dt} = -\frac{20}{P^2}\frac{dP}{dt}.$$

We know that $dP/dt = 0.05$ atm/min when $P = 2$ atm, so

$$\frac{dV}{dt} = -\frac{20}{2^2} \cdot (0.05) = -0.25 \text{ cc/min}.$$

40. (a) Plotting $f(r)$ for r near 0 shows a parabola-shaped graph which appears smooth at $r = 0$ even after zooming in. This suggests that $f(r)$ *is* differentiable at $r = 0$.

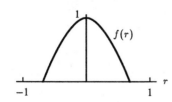 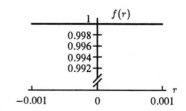

(b) For $r > 0$, $|r| = r$, so

$$f(r) = -2r + \sqrt{1 - 4r^2 + 4r}.$$

Thus, for $r > 0$,

$$f'(r) = -2 + \frac{1}{2}(1 - 4r^2 + 4r)^{-1/2}(-8r + 4).$$

Now let $r \to 0^+$, and we have

$$\text{Slope to right of } r = 0 \text{ is } \lim_{r \to 0^+} f'(r) = -2 + \frac{1}{2}(1)^{-1/2}4 = 0.$$

(c) For $r < 0$, $|r| = -r$, so

$$f(r) = 2r + \sqrt{1 - 4r^2 - 4r}.$$

Thus, for $r < 0$,

$$f'(r) = 2 + \frac{1}{2}(1 - 4r^2 - 4r)^{-1/2}(-8r - 4).$$

Now let $r \to 0^-$ and we have

$$\text{Slope to left of } r = 0 \text{ is } \lim_{r \to 0^-} f'(r) = 2 + \frac{1}{2}(1)^{-1/2}(-4) = 0.$$

(d) Since the slope to the right of $r = 0$ and the slope to the left of $r = 0$ are equal, there is no corner at $r = 0$ and so the function is differentiable there.

CHAPTER FIVE

5.1 SOLUTIONS

1.

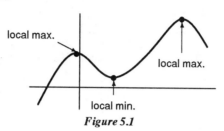

local max.

local max.

local min.

Figure 5.1

2. (a)   (b)

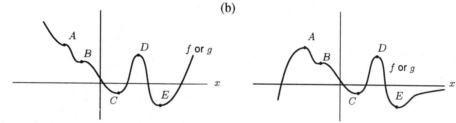

3. Let's look at the critical points of f. Just to the left of the first critical point $f' > 0$, so f is increasing. Immediately to the right of the first critical point $f' < 0$, so f is decreasing. Thus, the first point must be a maximum. To the left of the second critical point, $f' < 0$, and to its right, $f' > 0$; hence it is a minimum. On either side of the last critical point, $f' > 0$, so it is neither a maximum nor a minimum.

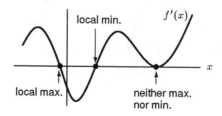

local min.

$f'(x)$

local max.

neither max. nor min.

4. One. The derivative of $f(x) = x^5 + x + 7$ is $f'(x) = x^4 + 1$, which is positive for all x. So the function is increasing over its entire domain, and hence can only cross the x-axis once. Since $f(x) \to +\infty$ as $x \to +\infty$ and $f(x) \to -\infty$ as $x \to -\infty$, the graph of f must cross the x-axis.

5. $f'(x) = 6x^2 + 6x - 36$. To find critical points, we set $f'(x) = 0$. Then

    $$6(x^2 + x - 6) = 6(x + 3)(x - 2) = 0.$$

    Therefore, the critical points of f are $x = -3$ and $x = 2$. To the left of $x = -3$, $f'(x) > 0$. Between $x = -3$ and $x = 2$, $f'(x) < 0$. To the right of $x = 2$, $f'(x) > 0$. Thus $f(-3)$ is a local maximum, $f(2)$ a local minimum.

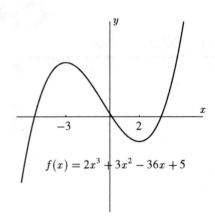

$f(x) = 2x^3 + 3x^2 - 36x + 5$

6. $f'(x) = 12x^3 - 12x^2$. To find critical points, we set $f'(x) = 0$. This implies $12x^2(x-1) = 0$. So the critical points of f are $x = 0$ and $x = 1$. To the left of $x = 0$, $f'(x) < 0$. Between $x = 0$ and $x = 1$, $f'(x) < 0$. To the right of $x = 1$, $f'(x) > 0$. Therefore, $f(1)$ is a local minimum, but $f(0)$ is not a local extremum.

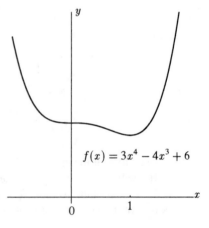

$f(x) = 3x^4 - 4x^3 + 6$

7. $f'(x) = 7(x^2 - 4)^6 2x = 14x(x - 2)^6(x + 2)^6$. The critical points of f are $x = 0$, $x = \pm 2$. To the left of $x = -2$, $f'(x) < 0$. Between $x = -2$ and $x = 0$, $f'(x) < 0$. Between $x = 0$ and $x = 2$, $f'(x) > 0$. To the right of $x = 2$, $f'(x) > 0$. Thus, $f(0)$ is a local minimum, whereas $f(-2)$ and $f(2)$ are not local extrema.

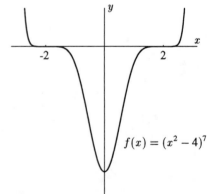

$f(x) = (x^2 - 4)^7$

8. $f'(x) = 4(x^3 - 8)^3 3x^2$
$= 12x^2(x - 2)^3(x^2 + 2x + 4)^3$.
So the critical points are $x = 0$ and $x = 2$.
To the left of $x = 0$, $f'(x) < 0$.
Between $x = 0$ and $x = 2$, $f'(x) < 0$.
To the right of $x = 2$, $f'(x) > 0$.
Thus, $f(2)$ is a local minimum, whereas $f(0)$ is not a local extremum.

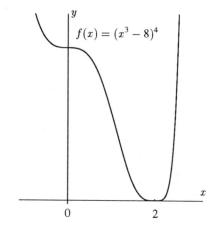

9.

$$f'(x) = \frac{x^2 + 1 - x \cdot 2x}{(x^2 + 1)^2} = \frac{1 - x^2}{(x^2 + 1)^2} = \frac{(1 - x)(1 + x)}{(x^2 + 1)^2}.$$

Critical points are $x = \pm 1$. To the left of $x = -1$, $f'(x) < 0$.
Between $x = -1$ and $x = 1$, $f'(x) > 0$.
To the right of $x = 1$, $f'(x) < 0$.
So, $f(-1)$ is a local minimum, $f(1)$ a local maximum.

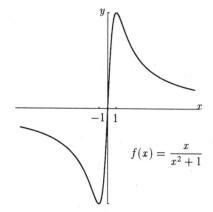

10. $f'(x) = 4xe^{5x} + 2x^2e^{5x} \cdot 5 = 2e^{5x}x(5x + 2)$. Notice that $e^{5x} > 0$ for all x. So, the critical points are $x = 0$ and $x = -2/5$.
To the left of $x = -2/5$, $f'(x) > 0$.
Between $x = -2/5$ and $x = 0$, $f'(x) < 0$.
To the right of $x = 0$, $f'(x) > 0$.
So, $f(-2/5)$ is a local maximum, $f(0)$ a local minimum. Notice that in the figure, you can barely discern the local maximum and minimum.

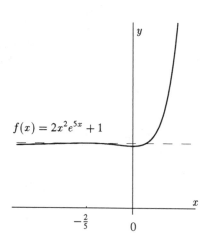

11. Using a computer to plot pictures of both the function, $f(x) = x^3 - e^x$, and its derivative, $f'(x) = 3x^2 - e^x$, we find that the derivative crosses the x-axis three times in the intervals we are interested in.

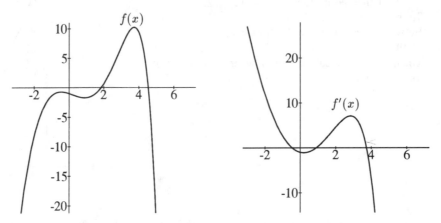

Through trial and error, we obtain approximations: local maximum at $x \approx 3.73$, local minimum at $x \approx 0.91$ and local maximum at $x \approx -0.46$. We can use the approximate values at these points, along with a picture as a guide, to find the global maximum and minimum on any interval.

(a) We find the global minimum and maximum on the interval $-1 \leq x \leq 4$ by examining every critical point, as well as its endpoints. Since $f(-1) = -1.3679$, $f(-0.46) = -0.7286$, $f(0.91) = -1.7308$, $f(3.73) = 10.2160$, $f(4) = 9.4018$, $x \approx 0.91$ gives a local (and global) minimum on the interval and $x \approx 3.73$ gives a local (and global) maximum.

(b) We find the global minimum and maximum on the interval $-3 \leq x \leq 2$ by examining every critical point, as well as its endpoints. Since $f(-3) = -27.0498$, $f(-0.46) = -0.7286$, $f(0.91) = -1.7308$, $f(2) = 0.6109$, $x = -3$ gives a global min and $x = 2$ a global max. (Even though $x \approx -0.46$ gives a local maximum, it does not give the greatest maximum on this interval; even though $x \approx 0.91$ gives a local minimum, it is not the smallest minimum on this interval.)

12. (a) We have $f'(x) = 10x^9 - 10 = 10(x^9 - 1)$. This is zero when $x = 1$, so $x = 1$ is a critical point of f. For values of x less than 1, x^9 is less than 1, and thus $f'(x)$ is negative when $x < 1$. Similarly, $f'(x)$ is positive for $x > 1$. Thus $f(1) = -9$ is a local minimum.

(b) We have, by looking at the endpoints and the critical point, $f(0) = 0$, $f(1) = -9$, and $f(2) = 1004$. Thus the global minimum is at $x = 1$, and the global maximum is at $x = 2$.

13. $f(x) = x - \ln x$, where $0.1 \leq x \leq 2$.

(a) $f'(x) = 1 - \frac{1}{x}$. This is zero only when $x = 1$, and so $x = 1$ is the only critical point of f. $f'(x)$ is positive when $x > 1$, and negative when $x < 1$. Thus $f(1) = 1$ is a local minimum.

(b) We have, by looking at the endpoints and the critical point,

$$f(0.1) = 0.1 - \ln(0.1) \approx 2.4026$$
$$f(1) = 1$$
$$f(2) = 2 - \ln 2 \approx 1.3069.$$

Thus $x = 0.1$ gives the global maximum and $x = 1$ gives the global minimum.

14. (a)

$$f(x) = \sin^2 x - \cos x \quad \text{for } 0 \le x \le \pi$$
$$f'(x) = 2\sin x \cos x + \sin x = (\sin x)(2\cos x + 1)$$

$f'(x) = 0$ when $\sin x = 0$ or when $2\cos x + 1 = 0$. Now, $\sin x = 0$ when $x = 0$ or when $x = \pi$. On the other hand, $2\cos x + 1 = 0$ when $\cos x = \frac{-1}{2}$, which happens when $x = \frac{2\pi}{3}$. So the critical points are $x = 0$, $x = \frac{2\pi}{3}$, and $x = \pi$.

Note that $\sin x > 0$ for $0 < x < \pi$. Also, $2\cos x + 1 < 0$ if $\frac{2\pi}{3} < x \le \pi$ and $2\cos x + 1 > 0$ if $0 < x < \frac{2\pi}{3}$. Therefore,

$$f'(x) < 0 \quad \text{for} \quad \frac{2\pi}{3} < x < \pi$$
$$f'(x) > 0 \quad \text{for} \quad 0 < x < \frac{2\pi}{3}.$$

Thus f has a local maximum at $x = \frac{2\pi}{3}$ and local minima at $x = 0$ and $x = \pi$.

(b) We have

$$f(0) = [\sin(0)]^2 - \cos(0) = -1$$
$$f\left(\frac{2\pi}{3}\right) = \left[\sin\left(\frac{2\pi}{3}\right)\right]^2 - \cos\frac{2\pi}{3} = 1.25$$
$$f(\pi) = [\sin(\pi)]^2 - \cos(\pi) = 1.$$

Thus the global maximum is at $x = \frac{2\pi}{3}$, and the global minimum is at $x = 0$.

15. (a) Since the volume of water in the container is proportional to its depth, and the volume is increasing at a constant rate,

$$d(t) = \text{ Depth at Time } t = Kt,$$

where K is some positive constant. So the graph is linear, as shown. Since initially no water is in the container, we have $d(0) = 0$, and the graph starts from the origin.

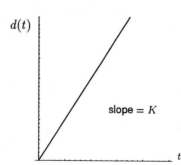

(b)   As time increases, the additional volume needed to raise the water level by a fixed amount increases. Thus, although the depth of water in the cone at time t, $d(t)$, continues to increase, it does so more and more slowly. This means $d'(t)$ is positive but decreasing.

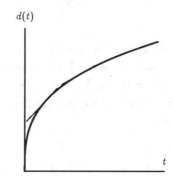

Figure 5.2: Graph of Depth against Time

16.   Using the product rule on the function $f(x) = axe^{bx}$, we have $f'(x) = ae^{bx} + abxe^{bx}$. We want $f(\frac{1}{3}) = 1$, and since this is to be a maximum, we require $f'(\frac{1}{3}) = 0$. These conditions give

$$f\left(\frac{1}{3}\right) = a\left(\frac{1}{3}\right)e^{\left(\frac{1}{3}\right)b} = 1,$$

$$f'\left(\frac{1}{3}\right) = ae^{\left(\frac{1}{3}\right)b} + ab\left(\frac{1}{3}\right)e^{\left(\frac{1}{3}\right)b} = 0.$$

Since $ae^{\left(\frac{1}{3}\right)b}$ is non-zero, we can divide both sides of the second equation by $ae^{\left(\frac{1}{3}\right)b}$ to obtain $0 = 1 + \frac{b}{3}$. This implies $b = -3$. Plugging $b = -3$ into the first equation gives us $a(\frac{1}{3})e^{-1} = 1$, or $a = 3e$. How do we know we have a maximum at $x = \frac{1}{3}$ and not a minimum? Since $f'(x) = ae^{bx}(1 + bx) = (3e)e^{-3x}(1 - 3x)$, and $(3e)e^{-3x}$ is always positive, it follows that $f'(x) > 0$ when $x < \frac{1}{3}$ and $f'(x) < 0$ when $x > \frac{1}{3}$. Since f' is positive to the left of $x = \frac{1}{3}$ and negative to the right of $x = \frac{1}{3}$, $f(\frac{1}{3})$ is a local maximum.

17.

$$f(x) = \frac{x + 50}{x^2 + 525},$$

$$f'(x) = \frac{x^2 + 525 - 2x(x + 50)}{(x^2 + 525)^2} = \frac{-x^2 - 100x + 525}{(x^2 + 525)^2}.$$

Since the denominator is positive for all x, setting $f'(x) = 0$ gives:

$$x^2 + 100x - 525 = 0$$

$$(x - 5)(x + 105) = 0$$

$$x = 5, -105$$

These are the only two critical points. Checking signs using the formula for $f'(x)$, we find $f(x)$ is decreasing for $-105 < x < 5$ and $f(x)$ is increasing for $x < -105$ and $x > 5$.

It is difficult to solve this problem with a calculator for two reasons. First, the critical points are at -105 and 5, which are very far apart. To find both of these points, one would have to search a large portion of the domain. Second, the range of values around the critical points is very small. For example,

$$f(-100) = -0.0047506$$
$$f(-105) = -0.0047619$$
$$f(-110) = -0.0047525$$

As you can see, although $x = -105$ gives a local minimum, f is extremely flat in the neighborhood of -105. Even 5 units away, the difference is less than 1% of the value at -105. It is very hard to see these small differences on a calculator, so solving the problem on a calculator is difficult.

18. Since $f(x) = 2x^3 - 9x^2 + 12x + 1$, $f'(x) = 6x^2 - 18x + 12 = 6(x^2 - 3x + 2) = 6(x - 2)(x - 1)$. Thus there are critical points at $x = 2$, $x = 1$. Using the formula, we find that $f(1) = 6$ and $f(2) = 5$. Using a graphing calculator and the above information as a guide, we can construct the following graph. We see that $x = 1$ gives a local max while $x = 2$ gives a local min. Furthermore, the only interval on which f is decreasing is $1 < x < 2$. Thus $f(x) = 10$ can have only one solution, $f(x) = 5$ has two solutions, $f(x) = 0$ has only one solution, and since $5 < 2e < 6$, $f(x) = 2e$ has 3 solutions.

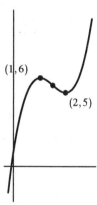

19. Let $f(x) = \sin x$ and $g(x) = x$. Then $f(0) = 0$ and $g(0) = 0$. Also $f'(x) = \cos x$ and $g'(x) = 1$, so for all $x \geq 0$: $f'(x) \leq g'(x)$. So the graphs of f and g both go through the origin and the graph of f climbs slower than the graph of g. Thus the graph of f is below the graph of g for $x \geq 0$. Thus $\sin x < x$ for $x > 0$ and $\sin x \leq x$ for $x \geq 0$.

20. Local maximum for some θ, $1.1 < \theta < 1.2$
Local minimum for some θ, $1.5 < \theta < 1.6$
Local maximum for some θ, $2.0 < \theta < 2.1$

21.

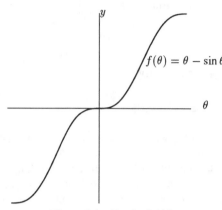

Figure 5.3: Graph of $f(\theta)$

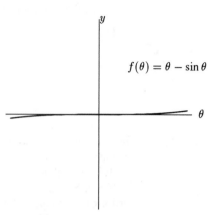

Figure 5.4: Graph of $f(\theta)$ Zoomed In

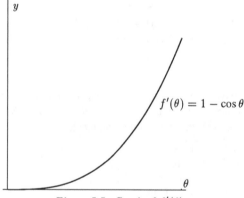

Figure 5.5: Graph of $f'(\theta)$

(a) In Figure 5.3, we see that $f(\theta) = \theta - \sin\theta$ definitely has a zero at $\theta = 0$. To see if it has any other zeros near the origin, we use our calculator to zoom in. (See Figure 5.4.) No extra root seems to appear no matter how close to the origin we zoom. However, zooming can never tell you for sure that there is not a root that you have not found yet.

(b) Using the derivative we can argue that for sure that there is no other zero. $f'(\theta) = 1 - \cos\theta$. Since $\cos\theta < 1$ for $0 < \theta \le 1$, $f'(\theta) > 0$ for $0 < \theta \le 1$. Thus, f increases for $0 < \theta \le 1$. Consequently, we conclude that the only zero of f is the one at the origin. If f had another zero at x_0, $x_0 > 0$, f would have to "turn around", and recross the x-axis at x_0. But if this were the case, f' would be nonpositive somewhere, which we know to be impossible.

22. Since f is differentiable everywhere, f' must be zero (not undefined) at any critical points; thus, $f'(3) = 0$. Since f has exactly one critical point, f' may change sign only at $x = 3$. Thus f is always increasing or always decreasing for $x < 3$ or $x > 3$. The possible cases for f (there are 4) determine whether $x = 3$ is a local minimum, local maximum, or neither.

(a) $x = 3$ is a local (as well as a global) maximum because $f(x)$ is increasing when $x < 3$ and decreasing when $x > 3$.

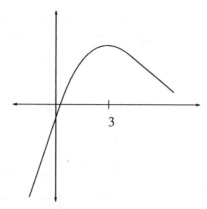

(b) $x = 3$ is a local (as well as a global) minimum because $f(x)$ heads to infinity to either side of $x = 3$.

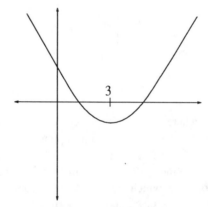

(c) $x = 3$ is neither a local minimum nor a local maximum. This is simply because there are points where $f(x) < f(3)$, and points where $f(x) > f(3)$, so f must be increasing for $x < 3$ and $x > 3$.

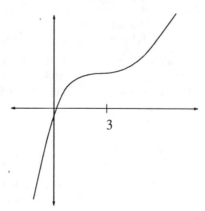

(d) $x = 3$ is a local (as well as a global) minimum because $f(x)$ is decreasing to the left of $x = 3$ and must increase to the right of $x = 3$, as eventually $f(x)$ will become close to 3.

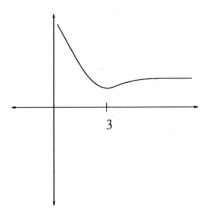

3

23.   (a)   We want to find where $x > 2\ln x$, which is the same as solving $x - 2\ln x > 0$. Let $f(x) = x - 2\ln x$. Then $f'(x) = 1 - \frac{2}{x}$, which implies that $x = 2$ is the only critical point of f. Since $f'(x) < 0$ for $x < 2$ and $f'(x) > 0$ for $x > 2$, by the first derivative test we see that f has a local minimum at $x = 2$. Since $f(2) = 2 - 2\ln 2 \approx 0.61$, then for all $x > 0$, $f(x) \geq f(2) > 0$. Thus $f(x)$ is always positive, which means $x > 2\ln x$ for any $x > 0$.

(b)   We've shown that $x > 2\ln x = \ln(x^2)$ for all $x > 0$. Thus $e^x > e^{\ln x^2} = x^2$, so $e^x > x^2$ for all $x > 0$.

(c)   Let $f(x) = x - 3\ln x$. Then $f'(x) = 1 - \frac{3}{x} = 0$ at $x = 3$. By the first derivative test, f has a local minimum at $x = 3$. But, $f(3) \approx -0.295$, which is less than zero. Thus $3\ln x > x$ at $x = 3$. So, x is not less than $3\ln x$ for all $x > 0$.
    (One could also see this by plugging in $x = e$: since $3\ln e = 3$, $x < 3\ln x$ when $x = e$.)

24.   Let $f(x) = x^4 - 4x$. We want to show that $f(x) > -4$ for all x. Since $f'(x) = 4x^3 - 4 = 4(x^3 - 1)$, $f(x)$ has only one critical point, at $x = 1$. Furthermore, $f'(x) < 0$ for $x < 1$ and $f'(x) > 0$ for $x > 1$. Hence $f(x)$ has a global minimum at $x = 1$. Thus $f(x)$ is never less than $f(1) = -3$. In particular, $f(x) > -4$.

25.   (a)

$$P(t) = \frac{2000}{1 + e^{(5.3 - 0.4t)}}$$

Population of Rabbits

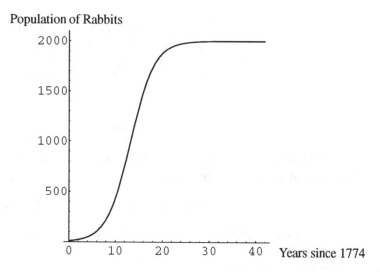

(b) The population appears to have been growing fastest when there were about 500 rabbits, just over 10 years after Captain Cook left them there.
(c) The rabbits reproduce quickly, so their population initially grew very rapidly. Limited food and space availability or perhaps predators on the island probably accounts for the population being unable to grow past 2000.

5.2   SOLUTIONS

1. To find inflection points of the function f we must find points where f'' changes sign. However, because f'' is the derivative of f', any point where f'' changes sign will be a local maximum or minimum on the graph of f'.

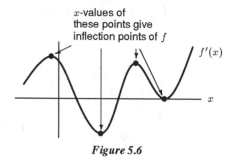

Figure 5.6

2.

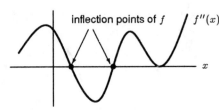

Figure 5.7

The inflection points of f are the points where f'' changes sign.

3. First, check that $x = 0$ is a critical point.

$$f'(0) = \cos 0 + 2 \cdot 0 - 1 = 1 + 0 - 1 = 0$$

so $x = 0$ is a critical point. Now, $f''(x) = -2x\sin(x^2) + 2$. So $f''(0) = 0 + 2 = 2 > 0$. Thus $x = 0$ is a local minimum.

4. $f(x) = \frac{1}{2}xe^{-10x}$. We have

$$f'(x) = \frac{1}{2}e^{-10x} - 5xe^{-10x} = e^{-10x}\left(\frac{1}{2} - 5x\right)$$

Since $f'(\frac{1}{10}) = 0$, this is a critical point. We can use the second derivative test to decide whether it is a local maximum or minimum.

We have

$$f''(x) = -5e^{-10x} - 5e^{-10x} + 50xe^{-10x} = (50x - 10)e^{-10x}$$

Since $f''(\frac{1}{10})$ is negative, $f(\frac{1}{10}) = \frac{1}{20e}$ is a local maximum. Furthermore, since $f''(x)$ changes sign at $x = \frac{1}{5}$, $x = \frac{1}{5}$ is an inflection point of f.

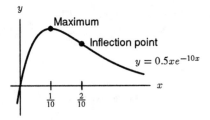

5.

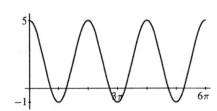

$f(x) = 2 + 3\cos x$, so $f'(x) = -3\sin x$, which is zero when $x = n\pi$ for $n = 0, 1, \ldots 5$.

The local maxima are where n is even, at $x = 0$, $x = 2\pi$, $x = 4\pi$, $x = 6\pi$. The local minima are where n is odd, at $x = \pi$, $x = 3\pi$, $x = 5\pi$. This is because when n is even, $\cos n\pi = 1$, the maximum of cosine, and so $f(x) = 5$ here, maximizing $f(x)$. When n is odd, $\cos n\pi = -1$, the minimum of cosine, and so $f(x) = -1$ here, minimizing $f(x)$..

$f''(x) = -3\cos x$, which is zero when $x = (2n+1)\pi/2$ for $n = 0, 1, \ldots 5$, so there are inflection points at $x = \pi/2, 3\pi/2, 5\pi/2, 7\pi/2, 9\pi/2$, and $11\pi/2$. These are the points with the steepest slopes, since $f'(x)$ is either maximized or minimized here.

6.

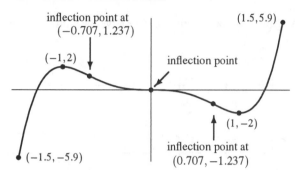

inflection point at
$(-0.707, 1.237)$

$(-1, 2)$

inflection point

$(1.5, 5.9)$

$(1, -2)$

$(-1.5, -5.9)$

inflection point at
$(0.707, -1.237)$

We see that $f'(x) = 15x^4 - 15x^2$ and $f''(x) = 60x^3 - 30x$. Since $f'(x) = 15x^2(x^2 - 1)$, the critical points are $x = 0, \pm 1$. Since $15x^2$ is always positive, $f'(x) < 0$ when $x^2 - 1 < 0$, or when $|x| < 1$. $f'(x) \geq 0$ otherwise. This tells us that $f(x)$ increases for $|x| > 1$, and decreases for $|x| < 1$. Thus f has a local minimum at $x = 1$ and a local maximum at $x = -1$.

We check critical points and the endpoints of the interval: $f(1.5) = 5.9$, $f(1) = -2$, $f(-1) = 2$, $f(-1.5) = -5.9$. Therefore f has a global minimum at $x = -1.5$ and a global maximum at $x = 1.5$, To find possible inflection points, we determine when $f''(x) = 0$. This means that $60x^3 - 30x = 0$, so the inflection points are $x = 0$ or $x = \pm 1/\sqrt{2}$. The coordinates of the graph at the inflection points are $(0, 0)$, $(1/\sqrt{2}, -7/(4\sqrt{2})) \approx (0.707, -1.237)$, and $(-1/\sqrt{2}, 7/(4\sqrt{2})) \approx (-0.707, 1.237)$.

7. (If you read Chapter 9, you'll see that this curve is just $\sqrt{2}\sin(x + \pi/4)$, making this problem fairly simple. We'll proceed without that helpful fact.)

Since both $\sin x$ and $\cos x$ have period 2π, the same is true for $f(x)$. Therefore we need only graph $f(x)$ for $0 \leq x \leq 2\pi$ and repeat the graph two more times.

We have $f'(x) = \cos x - \sin x = 0$ when $\cos x = \sin x$, or when $1 = \frac{\sin x}{\cos x} = \tan x$. For $0 \leq x \leq 2\pi$, this has the solutions $x = \pi/4$ and $x = 5\pi/4$. Thus $f(x)$ has critical points at $x = \frac{\pi}{4}$ and $x = \frac{5\pi}{4}$.

We have (checking endpoints and critical points):

$$f(0) = f(2\pi) = \sin(0) + \cos(0) = 1,$$
$$f\left(\frac{\pi}{4}\right) = \sin\left(\frac{\pi}{4}\right) + \cos\left(\frac{\pi}{4}\right) \approx 1.414,$$
$$\text{and } f\left(\frac{5\pi}{4}\right) = \sin\left(\frac{5\pi}{4}\right) + \cos\left(\frac{5\pi}{4}\right) \approx -1.414.$$

Since $f(0) < f(\frac{\pi}{4})$, $f(x)$ is increasing for $0 < x < \pi/4$. Since $f(\frac{\pi}{4}) > f(\frac{5\pi}{4})$, $f(x)$ is decreasing for $\pi/4 < x < 5\pi/4$. And since $f(\frac{5\pi}{4}) < f(2\pi)$, $f(x)$ is again increasing for $5\pi/4 < x < 2\pi$.

Thus f has a local maximum at $x = \pi/4$, and a local minimum at $x = 5\pi/4$.

We have $f''(x) = -\sin x - \cos x = 0$ when $-\sin x = \cos x$, i.e. when $\tan x = -1$. This has solutions $x = 3\pi/4$ and $x = 7\pi/4$. Furthermore, $f''(x) < 0$ for $0 \le x < 3\pi/4$, $f''(x) > 0$ for $3\pi/4 < x < 7\pi/4$, and $f''(x) < 0$ for $7\pi/4 < x \le 2\pi$. Therefore, f is concave down for $0 < x < \frac{3\pi}{4}$, concave up for $\frac{3\pi}{4} < x < \frac{7\pi}{4}$, and concave down for $\frac{7\pi}{4} < x < 2\pi$. Thus, the inflection points are $x = \frac{3\pi}{4}, \frac{7\pi}{4}$.

Combining this with our results for $f'(x)$, we have this diagram:

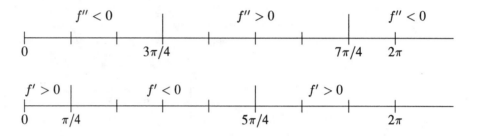

and the graph:

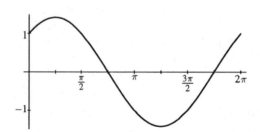

Thus the completed graph for $f(x) = \sin x + \cos x$ with $0 \le x \le 6\pi$ is:

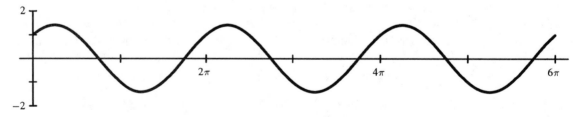

The coordinates of the local and global maxima are $(\pi/4, \sqrt{2})$, $(9\pi/4, \sqrt{2})$, $(17\pi/4, \sqrt{2})$.

The coordinates of the local and global minima are $(5\pi/4, \sqrt{2})$, $(13\pi/4, \sqrt{2})$, $(21\pi/4, \sqrt{2})$.

The inflection points are $x = \frac{3\pi}{4}, \frac{7\pi}{4}, \frac{11\pi}{4}, \frac{15\pi}{4}, \frac{19\pi}{4}$, and $\frac{23\pi}{4}$.

8. There is no way to do this algebraically since there is no way to solve the necessary equations: $f(x) = 0$, $f'(x) = 0$, and $f''(x) = 0$. To find the maxima, minima, and inflection points, we must use a calculator to approximate the solutions of these equations. We have

$$f'(x) = e^{\frac{x}{2}}\left(\frac{1}{2}\right) - \frac{1}{x^2 + 1}(2x) = \frac{1}{2}e^{\frac{x}{2}} - \frac{2x}{x^2 + 1},$$

$$f''(x) = \frac{1}{2}e^{\frac{x}{2}}\left(\frac{1}{2}\right) - \frac{(x^2 + 1)(2) - 2x(2x)}{(x^2 + 1)^2} = \frac{1}{4}e^{\frac{x}{2}} + \frac{2(x^2 - 1)}{(x^2 + 1)^2}$$

By looking at the graph of f closely with a calculator, we find that the intercepts are exactly $(0, 1)$ and approximately $(-0.934, 0)$. To find the local maxima and minima, we look for zeros on the graph of f'. There are zeros at 0.325 and 1.313. Plugging these values into f, we get a local maximum at $(0.325, 1.076)$ and a local minimum at $(1.313, 0.926)$. These are, however, only local, since $f(x) \to \pm\infty$ as $x \to \pm\infty$. To find inflection points, we look for zeros of f''. Again, by the graphing calculator, there are zeros (and thus inflection points) at $x = 0.747$ and $x = -0.867$. The coordinates of the curve at the inflection points are $(0.747, 1.009)$ and $(-0.867, 0.088)$.

9. We have

$$f'(x) = 10x^9 - 10$$

and

$$f''(x) = 90x^8.$$

Since $90x^8 \geq 0$ for all x, this shows that $f'(x)$ is increasing, in particular for $0 \leq x \leq 2$. Thus $f'(x)$ is maximized on the given interval when $x = 2$. Since $f'(2) = 10(2^9) - 10 = 5110 > 0$, f is increasing most rapidly when $x = 2$. Similarly, $f'(x)$ is least on the given interval when $x = 0$. $f'(0) = -10$, so this is where $f(x)$ is decreasing most rapidly.

10. We have $f'(x) = 1 - \frac{1}{x}$. Since $\frac{1}{x}$ decreases as x increases, $1 - \frac{1}{x}$ increases as x increases. Thus $f'(x)$ is smallest when $x = 0.1$ and largest when $x = 2$. Since $f'(0.1) = 1 - \frac{1}{0.1} = -9 < 0$, $f(x)$ is decreasing most rapidly when $x = 0.1$. We have $f'(2) = 1 - \frac{1}{2} = \frac{1}{2} > 0$, so $f(x)$ is increasing most rapidly when $x = 2$.

11. (a) To find the critical points, set $f' = 0$. Since $f'(x) = 1 + \sin x$, we want $\sin x = -1$. This is never possible for $0 \leq x \leq \pi$. Thus there are no local minima or maxima, so the global maximum and minimum must be at the endpoints. If we check them, we see that $f(0) = -1$ and $f(\pi) = \pi + 1$. So $f(x)$ is least at $x = 0$ and greatest at $x = \pi$.

    (b) $f''(x) = \cos x$. $\cos x = 0$ at $x = \frac{\pi}{2}$. Thus $x = \frac{\pi}{2}$ is a critical point for $f'(x)$. Since $f'(\frac{\pi}{2}) = 2$, and since $f'(0) = f'(\pi) = 1$, $f'(\frac{\pi}{2}) = 2$ is a local maximum of $f'(x)$, and $f'(x)$ is never less than 1. So, $f(x)$ is increasing most rapidly at $x = \frac{\pi}{2}$ and decreasing nowhere.

    (c) Since $f'(x)$ gives the slope of the line tangent to f at x, we want $f'(x)$ to be increasing most rapidly. This is when $f''(x)$ is largest. To find the critical points of f'', we set $f'''(x) = 0$. But $f'''(x) = -\sin x = 0$ at $x = 0, \pi$. Now, $f''(0) = 1$, and $f''(\pi) = -1$. So $f'(x)$, the slope of the tangent lines, is decreasing most rapidly at $x = \pi$ and increasing most rapidly at $x = 0$.

12.   (a)

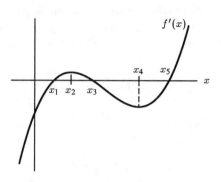

(b) $f'(x)$ changes sign at x_1, x_3, and x_5.

(c) $f'(x)$ has local extrema at x_2 and x_4.

13.   The local maxima and minima of f correspond to places where f' is zero and changes sign. The points at which f changes concavity correspond to local maxima and minima of f'. The change of sign of f', from positive to negative corresponds to a maximum of f and change of sign of f' from negative to positive corresponds to a minimum of f.

14.   Since $f'(x) = (\ln x)^2 - 2(\sin x)^4$, we have

$$f''(x) = 2(\ln x)\frac{1}{x} - 2 \cdot 4(\sin x)^3(\cos x) = \frac{2\ln x}{x} - 8(\sin x)^3 \cos x.$$

We now graph both f' and f''.

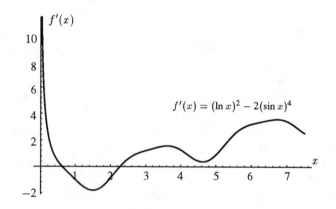

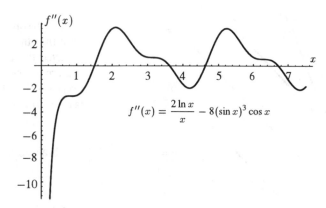

$$f''(x) = \frac{2\ln x}{x} - 8(\sin x)^3 \cos x$$

$f(x)$ is increasing where $f'(x) > 0$: $0 < x < 0.6, 2.3 < x \le 7.5$.
$f(x)$ is decreasing where $f'(x) < 0$: $0.6 < x < 2.3$.
$f(x)$ is concave up where $f''(x) > 0$: $1.5 < x < 3.6, 4.6 < x < 6.7$.
$f(x)$ is concave down where $f''(x) < 0$: $0 < x < 1.5, 3.6 < x < 4.6, 6.7 < x \le 7.5$.

Using this information, we sketch $f(x)$:

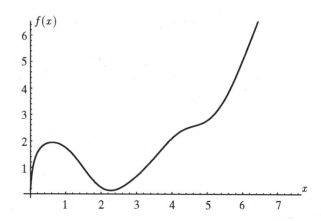

15. Remember that if a function is concave down on some interval, it will be below any line tangent to it on that interval. If we let $f(x) = \ln x$, then $f'(x) = \frac{1}{x}$ and $f''(x) = -\frac{1}{x^2}$. Since $f''x$ is everywhere negative, $f(x)$ is everywhere concave down, and will thus remain below any of its tangent lines forever. Now, the tangent line to $f(x) = \ln x$ at $x = 1$ is $y = x - 1$. This is because $f'(1) = 1$, and $f(1) = 0$. Thus $f(x)$ stays below this line, which is the same as saying $\ln x \le x - 1$.

16.

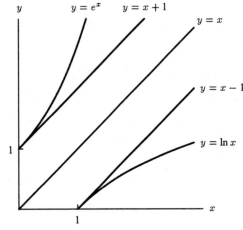

Graphical solution: If f and g are inverse functions then the graph of g is just the graph of f reflected through the line $y = x$. But e^x and ln x are inverse functions, and so are the functions $x + 1$ and $x - 1$. Thus the equivalence is clear from the figure.

Algebraic solution: If

$$x + 1 \le e^x$$

then, replacing x by $x - 1$, we have

$$x \le e^{x-1}.$$

Taking logs, and using the fact that the log is an increasing function, gives

$$\ln x \le x - 1.$$

17. (a) As $x \to \infty$, $f(x) \to 1$. As $x \to -\infty$, $f(x) \to 1$. As $x \to 0^+$, $f(x) \to \infty$. As $x \to 0^-$, $f(x) \to 0$.

  (b) $f'(x) = (\frac{-1}{x^2})(e^{\frac{1}{x}})$. Thus $f'(x) < 0$ for all $x \ne 0$, which means $f(x)$ is decreasing everywhere it is defined.

  (c) $f''(x) = \frac{1}{x^4}e^{\frac{1}{x}} + \frac{2}{x^3}e^{\frac{1}{x}} = \frac{(2x+1)}{x^4}e^{\frac{1}{x}}$.
    $f''(x) = 0$ when $x = -1/2$.
    $f''(x) < 0$ for $x < -1/2$ and $f''(x) > 0$ for $-1/2 < x < 0$ and $x > 0$.
    So, $f(x)$ is concave up for $x > 0$ and $-1/2 < x < 0$, and concave down for $x < -1/2$.

  (d)

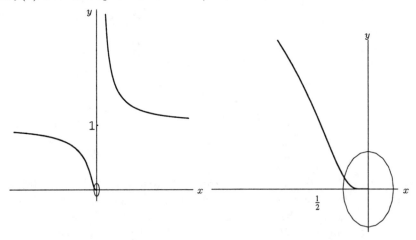

The figure on the left is not drawn to scale so that we can see the graph more globally. The figure on the right is a blow-up of the graph on the left for values of x between -1 and 0. In this picture, we have a better view of the inflection point at $x = -1/2$.

18. (a) as $x \to \infty$, $y \to \infty$

as $x \to -1^+$, $y \to -\infty$

(Note: as $x \to -1^-$, y is undefined. This is because if x is even slightly less than -1, x^3 is also less than -1, which means $x^3 + 1 < 0$, and $\ln(x^3 + 1)$ is undefined.)

(b) To determine where f is increasing or decreasing, we first locate its critical points. Since $f'(x) = \frac{3x^2}{x^3+1}$, $f'(x) \geq 0$ for $x > -1$. Since $f'(x)$ is positive for $x > -1$ (except at the origin), $f(x)$ is increasing for $x > -1$ and is undefined elsewhere.

(c)

$$f''(x) = \frac{(x^3 + 1)(6x) - (3x^2)^2}{(x^3 + 1)^2} = \frac{-3x(x^3 - 2)}{(x^3 + 1)^2}$$

$f''(x) = 0$ for $x = 0, \sqrt[3]{2}$. Thus if $f(x)$ has points of inflection, they are at $x = 0$ and $x = \sqrt[3]{2}$. $f(x)$ is concave down for $-1 < x < 0$ and $x > \sqrt[3]{2}$, since $f''(x)$ is negative on these intervals. $f(x)$ is concave up for $0 < x < \sqrt[3]{2}$, since $f''(x)$ is positive here. This means that $x = 0$ and $x = \sqrt[3]{2}$ are indeed inflection points for f.

(d)

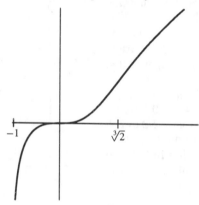

19. (a) This is one of many possible graphs.

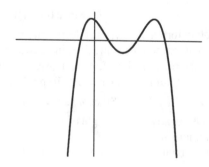

(b) Since f must have a bump between each pair of zeros, f could have at most four zeros.

(c) f could well have no zeros at all. To see this, consider the graph of the above function shifted vertically downwards.

(d) f must have at least two inflection points. Since f has 3 maxima or minima, it has 3 critical points. Consequently f' will have 3 corresponding zeros. Between each pair of these zeroes is a "bump," that is, a maximum or minimum. Thus f' will have at at least two maxima or minima, which implies that f'' will have two zeros. These values, where the second derivative is zero, correspond to points of inflection on the graph of f.

(e) f is of even degree since there are an odd number of critical points. A critical point is a zero of f', so f' has odd degree, implying f has even degree.

(f) The smallest degree f could have is four, since f' has degree at least 3.

(g) For example:

$$f(x) = k(x - a)(x - b)(x - c)(x - d)$$

for some real numbers a, b, c, d, and k. Note that a, b, c, and d are zeros and that k is a stretch factor.

20. One possible idea is to use the a parabola $f(x) = k(x-5)^2$. By carefully choosing the value of k, we can be sure that $|f''|$ is small enough. The reason for the $(x-5)$ is that the curve, being shifted to the right by 5, is now centered in the interval $0 \leq x \leq 10$. We have $f'(x) = 2k(x - 5)$, $f''(x) = 2k$. So if we take $k = 0.22$, say, then $|f''(x)| \leq 0.44 < 0.5$ for all x, while $f'(x)$ grows from -2.2 to 2.2. Unfortunately, this function has f'' constant. So we "perturb" it a little bit so that f'' varies in a small interval. The result is the graph to right.

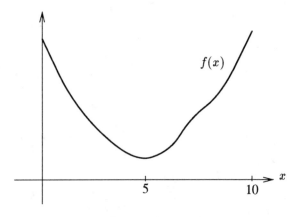

21. (a) When a number grows larger, its reciprocal grows smaller. Therefore, since f is increasing near x_0, we know that g (its reciprocal) must be decreasing. Another argument can be made using derivatives. We know that (since f is increasing) $f'(x) > 0$ near x_0. We also know (by the chain rule) that $g'(x) = (f(x)^{-1})' = -\frac{f'(x)}{f(x)^2}$. Since both $f'(x)$ and $f(x)^2$ are positive, this means $g'(x)$ is negative, which in turn means $g(x)$ is decreasing near $x = x_0$.

(b) Since f has a local maximum near x_1, $f(x)$ increases as x nears x_1, and then $f(x)$ decreases as x exceeds x_1. Thus the reciprocal of f, g, decreases as x nears x_1 and then increases as x exceeds x_1. Thus g has a local minimum at $x = x_1$. To put it another way, since f has a local maximum at $x = x_1$, we know $f'(x_1) = 0$. Since $g'(x) = -\frac{f'(x)}{f(x)^2}$, $g'(x_1) = 0$. To the left of x_1, $f'(x_1)$ is positive, so $g'(x)$ is negative. To the right of x_1, $f'(x_1)$ is negative, so $g'(x)$ is positive. Therefore, g has a local minimum at x_1.

(c) Since f is concave down at x_2, we know $f''(x_2) < 0$. We also know (from above) that

$$g''(x_2) = \frac{2f'(x_2)^2}{f(x_2)^3} - \frac{f''(x_2)f(x_2)}{f(x_2)^3} = \frac{1}{f(x_2)^2}\left(\frac{2f'(x_2)^2}{f(x_2)} - f''(x_2)\right).$$

Since $\frac{1}{f(x_2)^2} > 0$ and $2f'(x_2)^2 > 0$, and since $f(x_2) > 0$ (since f is assumed to be everywhere positive), we see that $g''(x_2)$ is positive. Thus g is concave up at x_2.

Note that for the first two parts of the problem, we didn't need to require f to be positive (only non-zero). However, it was necessary here.

22.

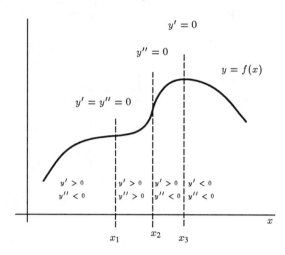

23.

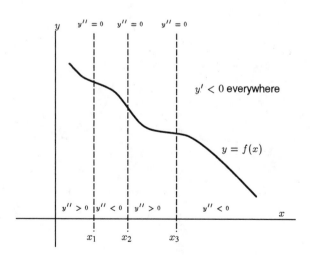

24.

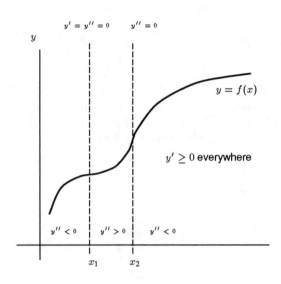

25.

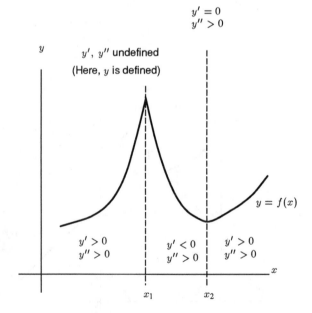

26.

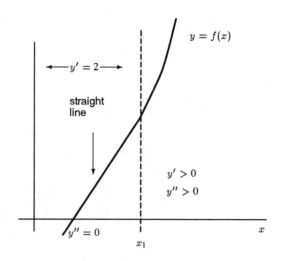

27.

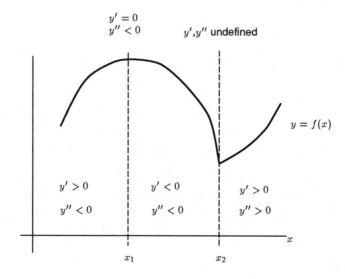

28.

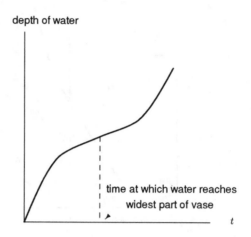

29.

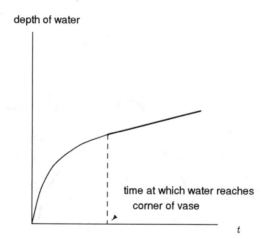

30. We have the inequality $e^x \geq 1 + x$ for all x. Let n be a positive integer, and take $x = 1/n$. Then the above inequality becomes

$$e^{\frac{1}{n}} \geq 1 + \frac{1}{n}$$

This means (since both sides are positive)

$$\left(e^{\frac{1}{n}}\right)^n \geq \left(1 + \frac{1}{n}\right)^n,$$

$$e \geq \left(1 + \frac{1}{n}\right)^n.$$

If $x \neq 0$, we actually have the strict inequality

$$e^x > 1 + x,$$

because the graph of e^x lies above the line $y = 1 + x$ except at the point $(0, 1)$. Thus $e > \left(1 + \frac{1}{n}\right)^n$.

Now let $x = -1/(n + 1)$. Then from the above inequality

$$e^{-\frac{1}{n+1}} > 1 - \frac{1}{n + 1} = \frac{n}{n + 1}.$$

Writing this as

$$\frac{1}{e^{\frac{1}{n+1}}} > \frac{n}{n + 1},$$

we see (by cross multiplying) that

$$e^{\frac{1}{n+1}} < \frac{n + 1}{n} = 1 + \frac{1}{n},$$

and raising both sides to the $(n + 1)^{\text{st}}$ power yields

$$e < \left(1 + \frac{1}{n}\right)^{n+1}.$$

Therefore

$$\left(1 + \frac{1}{n}\right)^n < e < \left(1 + \frac{1}{n}\right)^{n+1}$$

for any positive integer n.

Trying $n = 100$, we find

$$\left(1 + \frac{1}{100}\right)^{100} < e < \left(1 + \frac{1}{100}\right)^{101},$$

so $2.7048 < e < 2.7319$. For a given value of n, the distance between the lower and upper bound for e is

$$\left(1 + \frac{1}{n}\right)^{n+1} - \left(1 + \frac{1}{n}\right)^n = \left(1 + \frac{1}{n}\right)^n \left(1 + \frac{1}{n} - 1\right) = \left(1 + \frac{1}{n}\right)^n \frac{1}{n}.$$

Since $\left(1 + \frac{1}{n}\right)^n < e$, this error is less than e/n. So to be sure of being off by no more that 10^{-10}, we need to take $n > 10^{10} e$. For example, we could take $n = 3 \times 10^{10}$.

If you do not get a reasonable answer on your calculator, it is probably because it is rounding off some digit which affects the answer. For example, if you take $n = 10^{10}$, you calculator will first add $1/n = 10^{-10}$ to 1, getting a number which rounds to 1. Then your estimate for e will be 1, far off the true answer!

5.3   SOLUTIONS

1. If $f'(x) > 0$ for all x then $f(x)$ is increasing everywhere. Since $f'(x) = 3x^2 + 2ax + b$, the condition is $3x^2 + 2ax + b > 0$ for all x. Since f' is positive for large $|x|$, this is the same as saying that f' has no zeros. (For f' to go from negative to positive, crossing the x-axis, would require a zero.) By the quadratic formula, that happens when the discriminant $(2a)^2 - 4(3)(b)$ is negative, that is, when $a^2 - 3b < 0$.

2. (a) Let $p(x) = x^3 - ax$, and suppose $a < 0$. Then $p'(x) = 3x^2 - a > 0$ for all x, so $p(x)$ is always increasing.

    (b) Now suppose $a > 0$. We have $p'(x) = 3x^2 - a = 0$ when $x^2 = \frac{a}{3}$, i.e., when $x = \sqrt{\frac{a}{3}}$ and $x = -\sqrt{\frac{a}{3}}$.

    We have $p''(x) = 6x$; since $6\sqrt{a/3} > 0$, $f(\sqrt{a/3})$ is a local minimum, and since $-6\sqrt{a/3} < 0$, $f(-\sqrt{a/3})$ is a local maximum.

    (c) <u>Case 1:</u> $a < 0$

    $p(x)$ is always increasing. $p''(x) = 6x > 0$ if $x > 0$, in which case the graph is concave up; $6x < 0$ if $x < 0$, in which case the graph is concave down. Thus $x = 0$ is an inflection point.

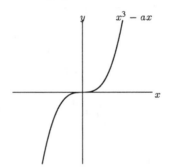

<u>Case 2:</u> $a > 0$

We have

$$p\left(\sqrt{\frac{a}{3}}\right) = \left(\sqrt{\frac{a}{3}}\right)^3 - a\sqrt{\frac{a}{3}} = \frac{a\sqrt{a}}{\sqrt{27}} - \frac{a\sqrt{a}}{\sqrt{3}} < 0,$$

$$\text{and} \quad p\left(-\sqrt{\frac{a}{3}}\right) = -\frac{a\sqrt{a}}{\sqrt{27}} + \frac{a\sqrt{a}}{\sqrt{3}} = -p\left(\sqrt{\frac{a}{3}}\right) > 0.$$

$$p'(x) = 3x^2 - a \begin{cases} = 0 & \text{if } |x| = \sqrt{\frac{a}{3}}; \\ > 0 & \text{if } |x| > \sqrt{\frac{a}{3}}; \\ < 0 & \text{if } |x| < \sqrt{\frac{a}{3}}. \end{cases}$$

So p is increasing for $x < -\sqrt{a/3}$, decreasing for $-\sqrt{a/3} < x < \sqrt{a/3}$, and increasing for $x > \sqrt{a/3}$. Since $p''(x) = 6x$, the graph of $p(x)$ is concave down for values of x less than zero and concave up for values greater than zero. Putting this together:

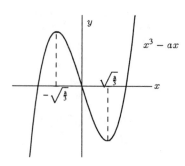

3. (a) We have $p'(x) = 3x^2 - a$, and (see solution to 2)

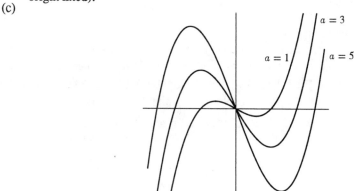

Local maximum: $p\left(-\sqrt{\frac{a}{3}}\right) = \frac{-a\sqrt{a}}{\sqrt{27}} + \frac{a\sqrt{a}}{\sqrt{3}} = +\frac{2a\sqrt{a}}{3\sqrt{3}}$

Local minimum: $p\left(\sqrt{\frac{a}{3}}\right) = -p\left(-\sqrt{\frac{a}{3}}\right) = -\frac{2a\sqrt{a}}{3\sqrt{3}}$

(b) Increasing the value of a moves the critical points of p away from the y-axis, and moves the critical values away from the x-axis. Thus, the "bumps" get higher and further apart. At the same time, increasing the value of a spreads the zeros of p further apart (while leaving the one at the origin fixed).

(c)

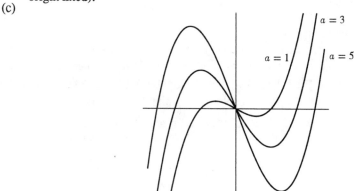

4. We have $f(x) = x^2 + 2ax = x(x + 2a) = 0$ when $x = 0$ or
    $x = -2a$.

    $$f'(x) = 2x + 2a = 2(x + a) \begin{cases} = 0 & \text{when } x = -a \\ > 0 & \text{when } x > -a \\ < 0 & \text{when } x < -a. \end{cases}$$

    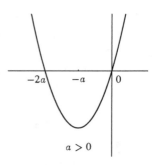

    $a > 0$

    Furthermore, $f''(x) = 2$, so that $f(-a)$ is a global minimum,
    and the graph is always concave up.

    Increasing $|a|$ stretches the graph horizontally. Also, the critical value (the value of f at the critical
    point) drops further beneath the x-axis.

5. (a) $f'(x) = 4x^3 + 2ax = 2x(2x^2 + a)$; so $x = 0$ and $x = \pm\sqrt{-\frac{a}{2}}$ (if $\pm\sqrt{-\frac{a}{2}}$ is real, i.e. $-\frac{a}{2} \geq 0$)
        are critical points.
    (b) $x = 0$ is a critical point for any value of a. In order to guarantee that $x = 0$ is the only critical
        point, the factor $2x^2 + a$ should not have a root other than $x = 0$. This means $a \geq 0$, since $2x^2 + a$
        has only one root ($x = 0$) for $a = 0$, and no roots for $a > 0$. There is no restriction on the constant
        b.
        $f''(x) = 12x^2 + 2a$. $f''(0) = 2a$.
        If $a > 0$, then by the second derivative test, $f(0)$ is a local minimum.
        If $a = 0$, then $f(x) = x^4 + b$, which has a local minimum at $x = 0$.
        So $x = 0$ is a local minimum when $a \geq 0$.
    (c) Again, b will have no effect on the location of the critical points. In order for $f'(x) = 2x(2x^2 + a)$
        to have three different roots, the constant a has to be negative. Let $a = -2c^2$, for some $c > 0$.
        Then
        $f'(x) = 4x(x^2 - c^2) = 4x(x - c)(x + c)$.
        The critical points of f are $x = 0$ and $x = \pm c$.
        To the left of $x = -c$, $f'(x) < 0$.
        Between $x = -c$ and $x = 0$, $f'(x) > 0$.
        Between $x = 0$ and $x = c$, $f'(x) < 0$.
        To the right of $x = c$, $f'(x) > 0$.
        So, $f(-c)$ and $f(c)$ are local minima and $f(0)$ is a local maximum.
    (d) For $a \geq 0$, there is exactly one critical point, $x = 0$. For $a < 0$ there are exactly three different
        critical points. These exhaust all the possibilities. (Notice that the value of b is irrelevant here.)

6. Since $\lim\limits_{t \to \infty} N = a$, we have $a = 200{,}000$. Note that while $N(t)$ will never actually reach $200{,}000$, it
    will become arbitrarily close to $200{,}000$. Since N represents the number of people, it makes sense to
    round up long before $t \to \infty$. When $t = 1$, $N = 0.1(200{,}000) = 20{,}000$ people, so plugging into our
    formula gives

    $$N(1) = 20{,}000 = 200{,}000 \left(1 - e^{-k(1)}\right).$$

Solving for k gives

$$2 = 20 \left(1 - e^{-k}\right)$$
$$0.1 = 1 - e^{-k}$$
$$e^{-k} = 0.9$$
$$k = -\ln 0.9 \approx 0.105.$$

7. (a) We have $\lim_{t \to \infty} e^{-\frac{kt}{m}} = 0$ (k and m are positive), so the terminal velocity is $\dfrac{mg}{k}$ ft/sec.

(b) At $t = 10$ seconds, your velocity is $0.8mg/k$, or 80% of terminal velocity. By plugging into our formula,

$$v(10) = 0.8\frac{mg}{k}$$
$$= \frac{mg}{k}\left(1 - e^{-10k/m}\right)$$

so that

$$1 - e^{-10k/m} = 0.8,$$
$$e^{-10k/m} = 0.2.$$

Taking logs, we obtain

$$\frac{10k}{m} = -\ln 0.2,$$

and since $m = \dfrac{\text{weight}}{g} = \frac{150}{32} \approx 4.7$ slugs (a slug is the unit of mass),

$$k = \frac{(-\ln 0.2)(4.7)}{10} \approx 0.76\frac{\text{ft·lbs}}{\text{sec}}.$$

(c) Still assuming a 150-pound skydiver, we have terminal velocity

$$\frac{mg}{k} \approx \frac{150}{0.76} \approx 197.4\frac{\text{ft}}{\text{sec}}\left(\frac{1\text{mph}}{(22/15)\text{ft/sec}}\right) \approx 134.6 \text{ mph}.$$

8. $T(t) = $ the temperature at time $t = a(1 - e^{-kt}) + b$.

(a) Since at time $t = 0$ the yam is 20°C, we have

$$T(0) = 20° = a\left(1 - e^0\right) + b = a(1 - 1) + b = b.$$

Thus $b = 20°$C. Now, common sense tells us that after a period of time, the yam will heat up to about 200°, or oven temperature. Thus the temperature T should approach 200° as the time t grows large:

$$\lim_{t \to \infty} T(t) = 200°\text{C} = a(1 - 0) + b = a + b.$$

Since $a + b = 200°$, and $b = 20°$C, this means $a = 180°$C.

(b) Since we're talking about how quickly the yam is heating up, we need to look at the derivative, $T'(t) = ake^{-kt}$:

$$T'(t) = (180°)ke^{-kt}.$$

We know $T'(0) = \frac{2°}{\text{min}}$, so

$$\frac{2°}{\text{min}} = (180°)ke^{-k(0)} = (180°)(k).$$

So $k = \frac{2°/\text{min}}{180°} = \frac{1}{90}\text{min}^{-1}$.

9. (a) We have $y' = 2A(x + B)$ and $y'' = 2A$.

   (i) If A is positive, the graph concaves upward, if A is negative, the graph concaves downward.

   (ii) The larger A is in magnitude, the steeper the graph is.

   (b) B shifts the graph to the left or right depending on whether it is increased or decreased. Note that the x-intercept of the graph is at $x = -B$.

   (c) The graph is a parabola with a maximum (if A is negative) or minimum (if A is positive) at $x = -B$, where the steepness depends on the magnitude of A.

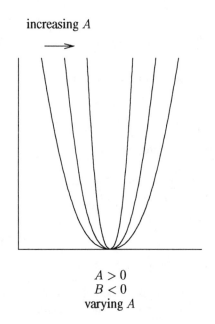

increasing A

$A > 0$
$B < 0$
varying A

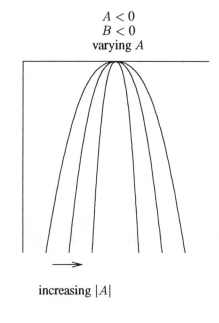

$A < 0$
$B < 0$
varying A

increasing $|A|$

10. (a) The larger the value of $|A|$, the steeper the graph.

   (b) The graph is shifted horizontally by B. The shift is to the left for positive B, to the right for negative B. There is a vertical asymptote at $x = -B$.

(c)

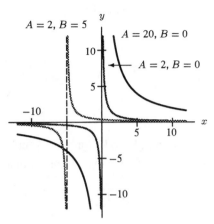

11. Let $f(x) = ae^{-bx^2}$. Since

$$f(x) = ae^{-bx^2} = ae^{-\frac{(x-0)^2}{(1/b)}},$$

this is just the family of curves $y = e^{\frac{(x-A)^2}{B}}$ multiplied by a constant a. This family of curves is discussed in the text; here, $A = 0$, $B = \frac{1}{b}$. When $x = 0$, $y = ae^0 = a$, so a determines the y-intercept. a also serves to flatten or stretch the graph of e^{-bx^2} vertically. Since $f'(x) = -2abxe^{-bx^2}$, $f(x)$ has a critical point at $x = 0$. For $b > 0$, the graphs are bell-shaped curves centered at $x = 0$, and $f(0) = a$ is a global maximum.

To find the inflection points of f, we solve $f''(x) = 0$. Since $f'(x) = -2abxe^{-bx^2}$,

$$f''(x) = -2abe^{-bx^2} + 4ab^2x^2e^{-bx^2}$$

Since e^{-bx^2} is always positive, $f''(x) = 0$ when

$$-2ab + 4ab^2x^2 = 0$$
$$x^2 = \frac{2ab}{4ab^2}$$
$$x = \pm\sqrt{\frac{1}{2b}}$$

These are points of inflection, since the second derivative changes sign here. Thus for large values of b, the inflection points are close to $x = 0$, and for smaller values of b the inflection points are further from $x = 0$. Therefore b affects the width of the graph.

In the graphs below, a is held constant, and slight variations in b are shown.

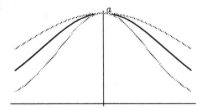

12. (a) Let $f(x) = axe^{-bx}$. To find the maxima and minima of f, we solve

$$f'(x) = ae^{-bx} - abxe^{-bx} = ae^{-bx}(1 - bx) \begin{cases} = 0 & \text{if } x = \frac{1}{b} \\ < 0 & \text{if } x > \frac{1}{b} \\ > 0 & \text{if } x < \frac{1}{b}. \end{cases}$$

Therefore, f is increasing ($f' > 0$) for $x < \frac{1}{b}$ and decreasing ($f' > 0$) for $x > \frac{1}{b}$. A local maximum occurs at $x = \frac{1}{b}$. There are no local minima. To find the points of inflection, we write

$$\begin{aligned} f''(x) &= -abe^{-bx} + ab^2xe^{-bx} - abe^{-bx} \\ &= -2abe^{-bx} + ab^2xe^{-bx} \\ &= ab(bx - 2)e^{-bx}, \end{aligned}$$

so $f'' = 0$ at $x = \frac{2}{b}$. Therefore, f is concave up for $x < \frac{2}{b}$ and concave down for $x > \frac{2}{b}$, and the inflection point is $x = \frac{2}{b}$.

(b) Varying a stretches or flattens the graph but does not affect the critical point $x = \frac{1}{b}$ and the inflection point $x = \frac{2}{b}$. Since the critical and inflection points are inversely proportional to b, varying b will change these points, as well as the maximum $f(\frac{1}{b}) = \frac{a}{be}$. For example, an increase in b will shift the critical and inflection points to the left, and also lower the maximum value of f.

(c)

13. A affects the amplitude (e.g. height) of the curve. B affects the frequency. C causes a phase shift to the left or right.

Changing A:

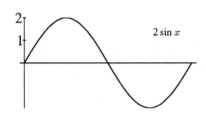

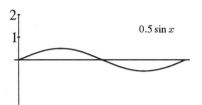

Changing B:

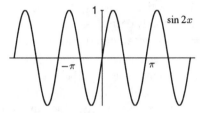

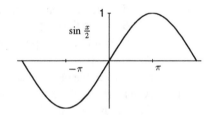

Changing C:

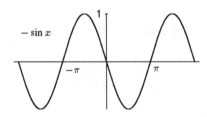

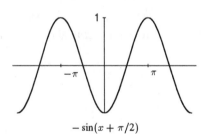

$-\sin(x + \pi/2)$

14.   (a) $y = e^{-ax} \sin x$, $a > 0$, $x \geq 0$. To find the critical points, we'll solve $y' = 0$.
$y' = e^{-ax} \cos x - ae^{-ax} \sin x = -e^{-ax}(a \sin x - \cos x).$
Since the $-e^{-ax}$ factor is never zero, $y' = 0$ when $a \sin x - \cos x = 0$, or

$$a\frac{\sin x}{\cos x} - 1 = 0$$
$$a \tan x = 1$$
$$\tan x = \frac{1}{a}$$

The graph of $e^{-ax} \sin x$ looks like:

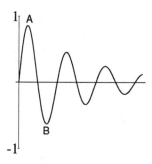

For $x \geq 0$, there are infinitely many local maxima and minima. Since $e^{-ax} \to 0$ as $x \to \infty$, A and B are the global maximum and minimum respectively. That is, A will be the highest peak, and B will be the deepest valley because e^{-ax} continually decreases.

Since the critical points are where $\tan x = \frac{1}{a}$, the maximum occurs at $x_{max} = \tan^{-1}(\frac{1}{a})$. Since $\frac{1}{a} > 0$, $0 < x_{max} < \frac{\pi}{2}$ by definition of the inverse tangent function. Since tangent has a period of π, the next critical point, which is the global minimum, will be at $x_{min} = x_{max} + \pi$.

(b)   As a increases, $\frac{1}{a}$ decreases, so that $\tan^{-1}(\frac{1}{a})$ gets closer and closer to 0. Thus, the x values giving the maximum and minimum become close to 0 and π respectively. Since the values of $\sin x$ lie between -1 and 1, and $\lim\limits_{a \to \infty} e^{-ax} = 0$, the absolute values of the maximum and minimum descend to 0 as $a \to \infty$.

15.   (a)   To find the critical points we must first take a derivative of y.

$$y' = -1((1-x^2)^2 + 2ax^2)^{-2}((1-x^2)^2 + 2ax^2)'$$
$$= -((1-x^2)^2 + 2ax^2)^{-2}(2(1-x^2)(-2x) + 4ax)$$
$$= -\frac{4x^3 - 4x + 4ax}{((1-x^2)^2 + 2ax^2)^2}.$$

Set $\dfrac{dy}{dx} = 0$. Thus,

$$4x^3 - 4x + 4ax = 0$$
$$4x\left(x^2 - 1 + a\right) = 0.$$

So, we have critical points when $x = 0$, and $x = +\sqrt{1-a}$. [Note: No negative root since $x \geq 0$.]

What kind of critical point is $x = 0$? First, note that the denominator of $\dfrac{dy}{dx}$ is always positive. Since the numerator is made up of odd powers of x, it will change sign at $x = 0$ regardless of the value of a. The sign of the numerator, $-4x(x^2 - 1 + a)$, does depend on the value of a. If $a > 1$, the factor $(x^2 - 1 + a)$ is positive when $x = 0$, so the sign of $\dfrac{dy}{dx}$ switches from positive to negative across $x = 0$, hence we get a local maximum. If $0 < a < 1$, the factor $(x^2 - 1 + a)$ is negative when $x = 0$, so the sign of $\dfrac{dy}{dx}$ switches from negative to positive across $x = 0$ and we get a local minimum. When $a = 1$, the function is $y = 1/(1 + x^4)$ which has a local maximum at the origin.

What kind of critical point is $x = \sqrt{1 - a}$*?* Again, look at the numerator of $\dfrac{dy}{dx}$. For x slightly greater than $\sqrt{1 - a}$, the quantity $-4x(x^2 - 1 + a)$ will be negative. For x slightly less than $\sqrt{1 - a}$, the quantity $-4x(x^2 - 1 + a)$ will be positive. Hence, there is a maximum at $x = \sqrt{1 - a}$.

For $0 < a < 1$, both roots exist, making the family more interesting. If $a > 1$, then $\sqrt{1 - a}$ does not exist and we get only a critical point at $x = 0$. For $a = 1$, $\sqrt{1 - a} = 0$ and again there is only one critical point at $x = 0$.

(b)   At the critical point where $x = \sqrt{1 - a}$, we calculate the y-coordinate.

$$y = \frac{1}{(1 - (1 - a))^2 + 2a(1 - a)}$$
$$= \frac{1}{a^2 + 2a - 2a^2}$$
$$= \frac{1}{2a - a^2}$$

When a is small, we can neglect the a^2 term, so we get a critical point very close to $\left(1, \dfrac{1}{2a}\right)$.

(c)   For $x > 0$, $(1 - x^2)^2 + 2ax^2 > (1 - x^2)^2$. So, $y = \dfrac{1}{(1 - x^2)^2 + 2ax^2} < \dfrac{1}{(1 - x^2)^2}$ and hence $y < \dfrac{1}{(1 - x^2)^2}$.

(d)

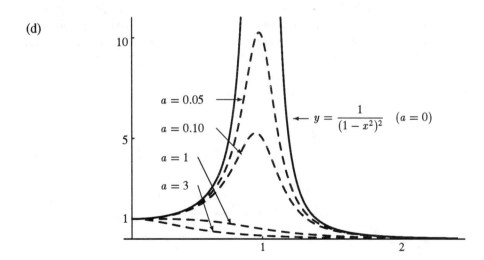

(e)   For this family, a determines whether there will be a hill or valley at $x = 0$. If $a \geq 1$ there is a hill at $x = 0$. If $0 < a < 1$, the valley at $x = 0$ is bounded to the right by a peak at $x = \sqrt{1 - a}$.

5.4   SOLUTIONS

1.   (a) $N = 100 + 20x$, graphed in Figure 5.8.

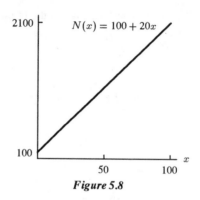

Figure 5.8

(b) $N'(x) = 20$ and its graph is just a horizontal line. This means that rate of increase of the number of bees with acres of clover is constant – each acre of clover brings 20 more bees.

On the other hand, $\frac{N(x)}{x} = \frac{100}{x} + 20$ means that the average number of bees per acre of clover approaches 20 as more acres are put under clover. As x increases, $\frac{100}{x}$ decreases to 0, so $\frac{N(x)}{x}$ approaches 20 (i.e. $\frac{N(x)}{x} \rightarrow 20$). Since the total number of bees is 20 per acre plus the original 100, the average number of bees per acre is 20 plus the 100 shared out over x acres. As x increases, the 100 are shared out over more acres, and so its contribution to the average becomes less. Thus the average number of bees per acre approaches 20 for large x.

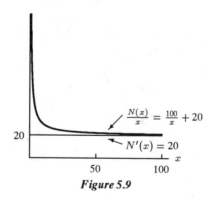

Figure 5.9

2.

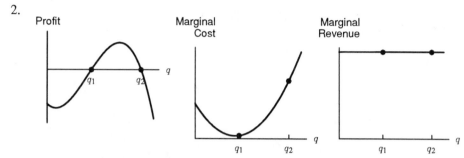

3. (a) $C(0)$ represents the fixed costs before production, that is, the cost of producing zero units, incurred for initial investments in equipment, etc.

(b) The marginal cost decreases slowly, and then increases as quantity produced increases. See Problem 2, graph (b).

(c) Concave down implies decreasing marginal cost, while concave up implies increasing marginal cost.

(d) An inflection point of the cost function is (locally) the point of maximum or minimum marginal cost.

(e) One would think that the more of an item you produce, the less it would cost to produce extra items. In economic terms, one would expect the marginal cost of production to decrease, so we would expect the cost curve to be concave down. In practice, though, it eventually becomes more expensive to produce more items, because workers and resources may become scarce as you increase production. Hence after a certain point, the marginal cost may rise again. This happens in oil production, for example.

4. (a) $\pi(q)$ is maximized when $R(q) > C(q)$ and they are as far apart as possible:

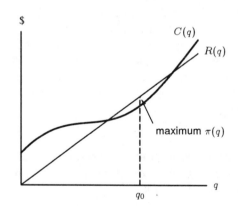

(b) $\pi'(q_0) = R'(q_0) - C'(q_0) = 0$ implies that $C'(q_0) = R'(q_0) = p$.

Graphically, the slopes of the two curves at q_0 are equal. This is plausible because if $C'(q_0)$ were greater than p or less than p, the maximum of $\pi(q)$ would be to the left or right of q_0, respectively. In economic terms, if the cost were rising more quickly than revenues, the profit would be maximized at a lower quantity (and if the cost were rising more slowly, at a higher quantity).

(c)

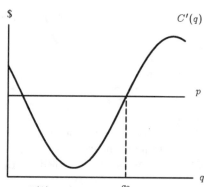

5. (a) The fixed cost is 0 because $C(0) = 0$.
    (b) Profit, $\pi(q)$, is equal to money from sales, $7q$, minus total cost to produce those items, $C(q)$.

$$\pi = 7q - 0.01q^3 + 0.6q^2 - 13q$$
$$\pi' = -0.03q^2 + 1.2q - 6 = 0$$
$$q = \frac{-1.2 \pm \sqrt{(1.2)^2 - 4(0.03)(6)}}{-0.06} \approx 5.9 \text{ min}, \ 34.1 \text{ max}$$

Since

$$\pi(35) = 7(35) - 0.01(35)^3 + 0.6(35)^2 - 13(35) = 245 - 148.75 = 96.25$$

$$\pi(34) = 7(34) - 0.01(34)^3 + 0.6(34)^2 - 13(34) = 238 - 141.44 = 96.56$$

The maximum profit is $\pi(34) = 96.56$. The money from sales is $238, the cost to produce the items is $141.44, resulting in a profit of $96.56.

(c) The money from sales is equal to price×quantity sold. If the price is raised from $7 by $x to $(7 + x)$, the result is a reduction in sales from 34 items to $(34 - 2x)$ items. So the result of raising the price by $x is to change the money from sales from $7(34)$ to $(7 + x)(34 - 2x)$. If the production level is fixed at 34, then the production costs are fixed at $141.44, as found in part (b), and the profit is given by:

$$\pi(x) = (7 + x)(34 - 2x) - 141.44$$

This expression gives us the profit as a function of the change in price x, rather than as a function of quantity as found in part (b). We take the derivative of π with respect to x to find the change in price that maximizes the profit.

$$\pi' = (1)(34 - 2x) + (7 + x)(-2) = 34 - 14 - 4x = 0$$

So $x = 5$, and this must give a maximum for $\pi(x)$ since the graph of π is a parabola which opens downwards. The profit when the price is $12 $(= 7 + x = 7 + 5)$ is thus $\pi(5) = (7 + 5)(34 - 2(5)) - 141.44 = \$146.56$. This is indeed higher than the profit when the price is $7, so the smart thing to do is to raise the price by $5.

6.

$$\text{Profit} = \text{Revenue} - \text{Cost}$$
$$\pi = pq - wL = pcK^\alpha L^\beta - wL$$

The variable on the right is L, so at the maximum

$$\frac{d\pi}{dL} = \beta pc K^\alpha L^{\beta-1} - w = 0$$

Now $\beta - 1$ is negative, since $0 < \beta < 1$, so $1 - \beta$ is positive and we can write

$$\frac{\beta pc K^\alpha}{L^{1-\beta}} = w$$

giving

$$L = \left(\frac{\beta pc K^\alpha}{w} \right)^{\frac{1}{1-\beta}}$$

Since $\beta - 1$ is negative, when L is just above 0, the quantity $L^{\beta-1}$ is huge and positive, so $d\pi/dL > 0$. When L is large, $L^{\beta-1}$ is small, so $d\pi/dL < 0$. Thus the value of L we have found gives a global maximum, since it is the only critical point.

7. (a)

$$C'(q) = \frac{K}{a} q^{(1/a)-1}, \quad C''(q) = \frac{K}{a} \left(\frac{1}{a} - 1 \right) q^{(1/a)-2}.$$

If $a > 1$, $C''(q) < 0$, so C is concave down.

(b)

$$a(q) = \frac{C(q)}{q} = \frac{Kq^{1/a} + F}{q}$$

$$M(q) = \frac{K}{a} q^{1/a}$$

so $a(q) = M(q)$ means

$$\frac{Kq^{1/a} + F}{q} = \frac{K}{a} q^{(1/a)-1}.$$

Solving,

$$Kq^{1/a} + F = \frac{K}{a} q^{1/a}$$

$$K \left(\frac{1}{a} - 1 \right) q^{1/a} = F$$

$$q = \left[\frac{Fa}{K(1-a)} \right]^a.$$

8. (a) $a(q) = \frac{C(q)}{q}$, so $C(q) = 0.01q^3 - 0.6q^2 + 13q$.

(b) Taking the derivative of $C(q)$ gives an expression for the marginal cost:

$$C'(q) = MC(q) = 0.03q^2 - 1.2q + 13.$$

To find the smallest MC we take its derivative and find the value of q that makes it zero. So: $MC'(q) = 0.06q - 1.2 = 0$ so $q = \frac{1.2}{0.06} = 20$. This value of q must give a minimum because the graph of $MC(q)$ is a parabola opening upwards. Therefore the minimum marginal cost is $MC(20) = 1$. So the marginal cost is at a minimum when the additional cost per item is \$1.

(c) $a'(q) = 0.02q - 0.6$
Setting $a'(q) = 0$ and solving for q gives $q = 30$ as the quantity at which the average is minimized, since the graph of a is a parabola which opens upwards. The minimum average cost is $a(30) = 4$.

(d) The marginal cost at $q = 30$ is $MC(30) = 0.03(30)^2 - 1.2(30) + 13 = 4$. This is the same as the average cost at this quantity. Note that since $a(q) = C(q)/q$, we have $a'(q) = \frac{qC'(q)-C(q)}{q^2}$. At a critical point, q_0,

$$0 = a'(q_0) = \frac{q_0 C'(q_0) - C(q_0)}{q_0^2},$$

so $C'(q_0) = \frac{C(q_0)}{q_0} = a(q_0)$. Therefore $C'(30) = a(30) = 4$.

Another way to see why the marginal cost at $q = 30$ must equal the minimum average cost $a(30) = 4$ is to view $C'(30)$ as the approximate cost of producing the 30th or 31st good. If $C'(30) < a(30)$, then producing the 31st good would lower the average cost, i.e. $a(31) < a(30)$. If $C'(30) > a(30)$, then producing the 30th good would raise the average cost, i.e. $a(30) > a(29)$. Since $a(30)$ is the global minimum, we must have $C'(30) = a(30)$.

9. It is interesting to note that to draw a graph of $C'(q)$ for this problem, you never have to know what $C(q)$ looks like, although you *could* draw a graph of $C(q)$ if you wanted to. By the formula given in the problem, we know that $C(q) = q \cdot a(q)$. Using the product rule we get that $C'(q) = a(q) + q \cdot a'(q)$.

We are given a graph of $a(q)$ which is linear, so $a(q) = b + mq$, where $b = a(0)$ is the y-intercept and m is the slope. Therefore

$$C'(q) = a(q) + q \cdot a'(q) = b + mq + q \cdot m$$
$$= b + 2mq.$$

In other words, $C'(q)$ is also linear, and it has twice the slope and the same y–intercept as $a(q)$.

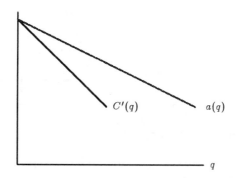

10. Since $a(q) = \frac{C(q)}{q}$, $C(q) = a(q) \cdot q$. Thus $C'(q) = q \cdot a'(q) + a(q)$, and so $C'(q_0) = q_0 \cdot a'(q_0) + a(q_0)$.

Since t_1 is the line tangent to $a(q)$ at $q = q_0$, the slope of the line t_1 is $a'(q_0)$, and the equation of the line is

$$y = a(q_0) + a'(q_0) \cdot (q - q_0) = a'(q_0) \cdot q + \big(a(q_0) - a'(q_0) \cdot q_0\big).$$

Thus the y-intercept of t_1 is given by $a(q_0) - q_0 \cdot a'(q_0)$, and the equation of the line t_2 is

$$y = 2 \cdot a'(q_0) \cdot q + \big(a(q_0) - a'(q_0) \cdot q_0\big)$$

since t_2 has twice the slope of t_1. Let's compute y for $q = q_0$:

$$y = 2 \cdot a'(q_0) \cdot q_0 + \big(a(q_0) - a'(q_0) \cdot q_0\big) = q_0 \cdot a'(q_0) + a(q_0) = C'(q_0).$$

Hence $C'(q_0)$ is given by the point on t_2 where $q = q_0$.

(This rule also would work to solve Problem 9. In that case, t_1 coincides with $a(q)$, and so $C'(q)$ is the line with the same y–intercept and twice the slope as t_1.)

5.5 SOLUTIONS

1. We have that $v(r) = a(R - r)r^2 = aRr^2 - ar^3$, and $v'(r) = 2aRr - 3ar^2 = 2ar(R - \frac{3}{2}r)$, which is zero if $r = \frac{2}{3}R$, or if $r = 0$, and so $v(r)$ has critical points here.
$v''(r) = 2aR - 6ar$, and thus $v''(0) = 2aR > 0$, which by the second derivative test implies that v has a minimum at $r = 0$. $v''(\frac{2}{3}R) = 2aR - 4aR = -2aR < 0$, and so by the second derivative test v has a maximum at $r = \frac{2}{3}R$.

2. (a) We have $T(D) = (\frac{C}{2} - \frac{D}{3})D^2 = \frac{CD^2}{2} - \frac{D^3}{3}$, and $\frac{dT}{dD} = CD - D^2 = D(C - D)$, Since, by this formula, $\frac{dT}{dD}$ is zero when $D = 0$ or $D = C$, negative when $D > C$, and positive when $D < C$, we have (by the first derivative test) that the temperature change is maximized when $D = C$.

(b) The sensitivity is $\frac{dT}{dD} = CD - D^2$; its derivative is $\frac{d^2T}{dD^2} = C - 2D$, which is zero if $D = \frac{C}{2}$, negative if $D > \frac{C}{2}$, and positive if $D < \frac{C}{2}$. Thus by the first derivative test the sensitivity is maximized at $D = \frac{C}{2}$.

3. Call the stacks A and B. (See below.)

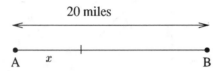

Suppose the point where the concentration of deposit is a minimum occurs at a distance of x miles from stack A. We want to find x such that

$$S = \frac{k_1}{x^2} + \frac{k_2}{(20-x)^2} = k_2 \left(\frac{7}{x^2} + \frac{1}{(20-x)^2} \right)$$

is a minimum, which is the same thing as minimizing $f(x) = 7x^{-2} + (20-x)^{-2}$ since k_2 is nonnegative. We have

$$f'(x) = -14x^{-3} - 2(20-x)^{-3}(-1) = \frac{-14}{x^3} + \frac{2}{(20-x)^3} = \frac{-14(20-x)^3 + 2x^3}{x^3(20-x)^3}.$$

Thus we want to find x such that $-14(20-x)^3 + 2x^3 = 0$, which implies $2x^3 = 14(20-x)^3$. That's equivalent to $x^3 = 7(20-x)^3$, or $\frac{20-x}{x} = (\frac{1}{7})^{1/3} \approx 0.523$. Solving for x, we have $20 - x = 0.523x$, whence $x = \frac{20}{1.523} \approx 13.13$.

To verify that this minimizes f, we take the second derivative:

$$f''(x) = 42x^{-4} + 6(20-x)^{-4} = \frac{42}{x^4} + \frac{6}{(20-x)^4} > 0$$

for any $0 < x < 20$, so by the second derivative test the concentration is minimized 13.13 miles from A.

4. The question points out that s is 0 at both of the endpoints of the interval, and that it is positive for any x inside the interval. Let's look for critical points of s:

$$s'(x) = 1 - 2x$$
$$0 = 1 - 2x$$
$$x = \frac{1}{2}.$$

So there is only one critical point ($x = 1/2$) in the interval. We can see that $x = 1/2$ is a local maximum since $s' > 0$ when $x < 1/2$ and $s' < 0$ when $x > 1/2$. Now consider the endpoints, $x = 0$ and $x = 1$. Since s is 0 at both endpoints, $x = 1/2$ is the global maximum. The maximum difference is $s(1/2) = 1/2 - (1/2)^2 = 1/4$.

Alternatively, we could have recognized that the graph of s is just a parabola, and we know about parabolas: this one is concave down, with zeros at $x = 0, 1$, so it must have its maximum at $x = 1/2$.

5. $f'(x) = 2(x - a_1) + 2(x - a_2) + 2(x - a_3)$.
   $f'(x) = 0$ when $3x - a_1 - a_2 - a_3 = 0$, i.e. $x = \frac{a_1 + a_2 + a_3}{3}$, the average of a_1, a_2 and a_3.
   This is where $f(x)$ is a minimum, since f is a parabola which opens upwards.
   This is a reasonable answer since it keeps each squared term in $f(x)$ somewhat small.

6. (a) Note that

   $$f'(x) = 2(x - a_1) + 2(x - a_2) + 2(x - a_3) + 2(x - a_4).$$

   Setting $f'(x) = 0$ yields

   $$x = \frac{2(a_1 + a_2 + a_3 + a_4)}{8} = \frac{a_1 + a_2 + a_3 + a_4}{4}.$$

   Since $f''(x) = 8 > 0$, this is a local minimum.

   (b) The mean, $\frac{a_1 + a_2 + \cdots + a_n}{n}$, minimizes this sum of squares. We check just as before:

   $$f'(x) = 2(x - a_1) + 2(x - a_2) + \cdots + 2(x - a_n),$$

   so if $f'(x) = 0$, $2nx = 2(a_1 + a_2 + \cdots + a_n)$, so $x = \frac{a_1 + a_2 + \cdots + a_n}{n}$. This is a minimum because
   $f''(x) = 2n > 0$.

7. (a) At higher speeds, more energy is used so the graph rises to the right. The initial drop is explained
   by the fact that the energy it takes a bird to start its flight is greater than that needed to maintain
   the low speed following that start. The bird consumes more energy at the beginning of its flight
   because it is more difficult to maintain its balance and take off. When it flies slightly faster, the
   amount of energy consumed decreases. But when it flies at very high speeds, the bird consumes
   a lot more energy (this is analogous to our swimming in a pool).

   (b) $f(v)$ measures energy per second; $a(v)$ measures energy per meter. A bird traveling at rate v will
   in 1 second travel v meters, and thus will consume $v \cdot a(v)$ joules of energy in that 1 second
   period. Thus $v \cdot a(v)$ represents the energy consumption per second, and so $f(v) = v \cdot a(v)$.

   (c) Since $v \cdot a(v) = f(v)$, $a(v) = \frac{f(v)}{v}$. But this ratio has the same value as the slope of a line passing
   from the origin through the point $(v, f(v))$ on the curve (see figure). Thus $a(v)$ is minimal when
   the slope of this line is minimal. To find the value of v minimizing $a(v)$, we solve $a'(v) = 0$. By
   the quotient rule,

   $$a'(v) = \frac{v f'(v) - f(v)}{v^2}.$$

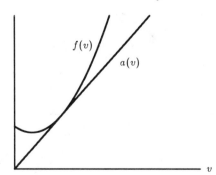

Thus $a'(v) = 0$ when $vf'(v) = f(v)$, or when $f'(v) = \frac{f(v)}{v} = a(v)$. Thus since $a(v)$ is represented by the slope of a line through the origin and a point on the curve, $a(v)$ is minimized when this line is tangent to $f(v)$, since then the slope $a(v)$ equals $f'(v)$.

(d) The bird should minimize $a(v)$ assuming it wants to go from one particular point to another, i.e. where the distance is set. Then minimizing $a(v)$ minimizes the total energy used for the flight.

8. (a) To maximize benefit (surviving young), we pick 10, because that's the highest point of the benefit graph.

   (b) To optimize (the vertical distance between the curves) we can either do it by inspection or note that the slopes of the two curves will be the same where the difference is maximized. Either way, one gets approximately 9.

9. This question implies that the line from the origin to the point $(x, R(x))$ has some relationship to $r(x)$. The slope of this line is $\frac{R(x)}{x}$, which is $r(x)$. So the point x_0 at which $r(x)$ is maximal will also be the point at which the slope of this line is maximal. The question claims that the line from the origin to $(x_0, R(x_0))$ will be tangent to the graph of $R(x)$. We can understand this by trying to see what would happen if it were otherwise.

If the line from the origin to $(x_0, R(x_0))$ intersects the graph of $R(x)$, then there are points of this graph on both sides of the line — and, in particular, there is some point x_1 such that the line from the origin to $(x_1, R(x_1))$ has larger slope than the line to $(x_0, R(x_0))$. (See the graph below.) But we picked x_0 so that no other line had larger slope, and therefore no such x_1 exists. So the original supposition is false, and the line from the origin to $(x_0, R(x_0))$ is tangent to the graph of $R(x)$.

(a) See (b).
(b)

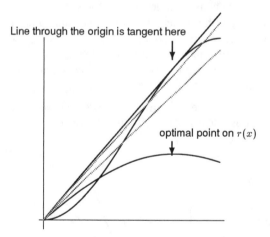

Line through the origin is tangent here

optimal point on $r(x)$

(c)

$$r(x) = \frac{R(x)}{x}$$

$$r'(x) = \frac{xR'(x) - R(x)}{x^2}$$

So when $r(x)$ is maximized $0 = \frac{R'(x)}{x} - \frac{R(x)}{x^2}$, or $R'(x) = \frac{R(x)}{x} = r(x)$. i.e. when $r(x)$ is maximized, $r(x) = R'(x)$.

Let us call the x value at which the maximum of r occurs x_m. Then the line passing through $R(x_m)$ and the origin is $y = x \cdot \frac{R(x_m)}{x_m}$. Its slope is $\frac{R(x_m)}{x_m}$, which also happens to be $r(x_m)$. In the previous paragraph, we showed that at x_m, this is also equal to the slope of the tangent to $R(x)$. So, the line through the origin *IS* the tangent line.

10.

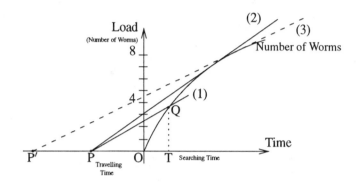

(a) See line (1). For any point Q on the loading curve, the line joining PQ has slope

$$\frac{QT}{PT} = \frac{QT}{PO + OT} = \frac{\text{load}}{\text{traveling time} + \text{searching time}}.$$

(b) The slope of the line PQ is maximized when the line is tangent to the loading curve, which happens with line (2). The load is then approximately 7 worms.

(c) If the traveling time is increased, the point P moves to the left, to point P', say. If line (3) is tangent to the curve, it will be tangent to the curve further to the right than line (2), so the optimal load is larger. This makes sense: if the bird has to fly further, you'd expect it to bring back more worms each time.

11. Let $y = e^{-x^2}$. Since $y' = -2xe^{-x^2}$, y is increasing for $x < 0$ and decreasing for $x > 0$. Hence $y = e^0 = 1$ is a maximum.

When $x = \pm 0.3$, $y = e^{-0.09} \approx 0.9139$, which is a minimum on the given interval. Thus $e^{-0.09} \le y \le 1$, so

12. Let $y = \ln(1 + x)$. Since $y' = \frac{1}{1+x}$, y is increasing for all $x \ge 0$. The lower bound is at $x = 0$, so, $\ln(1) = 0 \le y$. There is no upper bound.

13. Let $y = \ln(1 + x^2)$. Then $y' = \frac{2x}{1+x^2}$. Since the denominator is always positive, the sign of y' is determined by the numerator $2x$. Thus $y' > 0$ when $x > 0$, and $y' < 0$ when $x < 0$, and we have a local (and global) minimum for y at $x = 0$. Since $y(-1) = \ln 2$ and $y(2) = \ln 5$, the global maximum is at $x = 2$. Thus $0 \le y \le \ln 5$, or (in decimals) $0 \le y < 1.61$. (Note that our upper bound has been rounded *up* from 1.6094.)

14. Let $y = x^3 - 4x^2 + 4x$. To locate the critical points, we solve $y' = 0$. Since $y' = 3x^2 - 8x + 4 = (3x - 2)(x - 2)$, the critical points are $x = 2/3$ and $x = 2$. To find the global minimum and maximum on $0 \leq x \leq 4$, we check the critical points and the endpoints: $y(0) = 0$; $y(\frac{2}{3}) = \frac{32}{27}$; $y(2) = 0$; $y(4) = 16$. Thus, the global minimum is at $x = 2$, the global maximum is at $x = 4$, and $0 \leq y \leq 16$.

15. The graph of f in Figure 5.10 suggests that f is nondecreasing over the entire interval. You can confirm this by looking at the derivative:

$$f'(x) = 1 + \cos x$$

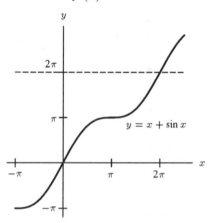

Figure 5.10: Graph of $y = x + \sin x$

Since $\cos x \geq -1$, we have $f' \geq 0$ everywhere, so f never decreases. This means that a lower bound for f is 0 (its value at the left endpoint of the interval) and an upper bound is 2π (its value at the right endpoint). That is, if $0 \leq x \leq 2\pi$:

$$0 \leq f(x) \leq 2\pi.$$

These are the best bounds for the function f over the interval.

16. (a) We have $x^{1/x} = e^{(1/x)\ln x}$. Thus

$$\frac{d(x^{1/x})}{dx} = \frac{d(e^{(1/x)\ln x})}{dx} = \frac{d(\frac{1}{x}\ln x)}{dx} e^{(1/x)\ln x}$$

$$= \left(-\frac{\ln x}{x^2} + \frac{1}{x^2} \right) x^{1/x}$$

$$= \frac{x^{1/x}}{x^2}(1 - \ln x) \begin{cases} = 0 & \text{when } x = e \\ < 0 & \text{when } x > e \\ > 0 & \text{when } x < e \end{cases}$$

Hence $e^{1/e}$ is the global maximum for $x^{1/x}$, by the first derivative test.

(b) Since $x^{1/x}$ is increasing for $0 < x < e$ and decreasing for $x > e$, and 2 and 3 are the closest integers to e, either $2^{1/2}$ or $3^{1/3}$ is the maximum for $n^{1/n}$. We have $2^{1/2} \approx 1.414$ and $3^{1/3} \approx 1.442$, so $3^{1/3}$ is the maximum.

(c) Since $e < 3 < \pi$, and $x^{1/x}$ is decreasing for $x > e$, $3^{1/3} > \pi^{1/\pi}$.

17. (a) If, following the hint, we set $f(x) = \frac{a+x}{2} - \sqrt{ax}$, then $f(x)$ represents the difference between the arithmetic and geometric means for some fixed a and any x. We can find where this difference is minimized by solving $f'(x) = 0$. Since $f'(x) = \frac{1}{2} - \frac{1}{2}\sqrt{a}x^{-\frac{1}{2}}$, if $f'(x) = 0$ then $\frac{1}{2}\sqrt{a}x^{-\frac{1}{2}} = \frac{1}{2}$, or $x = a$. Since $f''(x) = \frac{1}{4}\sqrt{a}x^{-\frac{3}{2}}$ is positive for all positive x, by the second derivative test $f(x)$ has a minimum at $x = a$ of $f(a) = 0$. Thus $f(x) = \frac{a+x}{2} - \sqrt{ax} \geq 0$ for all $x > 0$, which means $\frac{a+x}{2} \geq \sqrt{ax}$. Taking $x = b$, we have $\frac{a+b}{2} \geq \sqrt{ab}$. This means that the arithmetic average is greater than the geometric average unless $a = b$, in which case the two averages are equal.

Alternatively (and without using calculus): Since

$$\frac{a+b}{2} - \sqrt{ab} = \frac{a - 2\sqrt{ab} + b}{2}$$

$$= \frac{(\sqrt{a} - \sqrt{b})^2}{2} > 0,$$

$\frac{a+b}{2} > \sqrt{ab}$.

(b) Following the hint, set $f(x) = \frac{a+b+x}{3} - \sqrt[3]{abx}$. Then $f(x)$ represents the difference between the arithmetic and geometric means for some fixed a, b and any x. We can find where this difference is minimized by solving $f'(x) = 0$. Since $f'(x) = \frac{1}{3} - \frac{1}{3}\sqrt[3]{ab}x^{-2/3}$, $f'(x) = 0$ implies that $\frac{1}{3}\sqrt[3]{ab}x^{-2/3} = \frac{1}{3}$, or $x = \sqrt{ab}$. Since $f''(x) = \frac{2}{9}\sqrt[3]{ab}x^{-5/3}$ is positive for all positive x, by the second derivative test $f(x)$ has a minimum at $x = \sqrt{ab}$. But

$$f(\sqrt{ab}) = \frac{a+b+\sqrt{ab}}{3} - \sqrt[3]{ab\sqrt{ab}} = \frac{a+b+\sqrt{ab}}{3} - \sqrt{ab} = \frac{a+b-2\sqrt{ab}}{3}.$$

By the first part of this problem, we know that $\frac{a+b}{2} - \sqrt{ab} \geq 0$, which implies that $a+b-2\sqrt{ab} \geq 0$. Thus $f(\sqrt{ab}) = \frac{a+b-2\sqrt{ab}}{3} \geq 0$. Since f has a maximum at $x = \sqrt{ab}$, $f(x)$ is always nonnegative. Thus $f(x) = \frac{a+b+x}{3} - \sqrt[3]{abx} \geq 0$, so $\frac{a+b+c}{3} \geq \sqrt[3]{abc}$. Note that equality holds only when $a = b = c$. (This may also be done without calculus, but it's harder than (a).)

5.6 SOLUTIONS

1. Let w and l be the width and length, respectively, of the rectangular area you wish to enclose. Then

$$w + w + l = 100 \text{ feet}$$
$$l = 100 - 2w$$
$$\text{Area} = w \cdot l = w(100 - 2w) = 100w - 2w^2$$

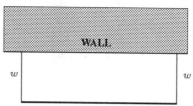

To maximize area, we solve $A' = 0$ to find critical points. This gives $A' l = 100 - 4w = 0$, so $w = 25$, $l = 50$. So the area is $25 \cdot 50 = 1250$ square feet. This is a local maximum by the second derivative test because $A'' = -4 < 0$. Since the graph of A is a parabola, the local maximum is in fact a global maximum.

2. Volume: $V = x^2 y$,
   Surface: $S = 2x^2 + 4xy = 2x^2 + 4xV/x^2 = 2x^2 + 4V/x$.
   To find the dimensions which minimize the area, find x such that $dS/dx = 0$.

$$\frac{dS}{dx} = 4x - \frac{4V}{x^2} = 0,$$

so

$$x^3 = V,$$

and solving for x gives $x = \sqrt[3]{V} = y$. To see that this gives a minimum, note that for small x, $S \approx 4V/x$ is decreasing. For large x, $S \approx 2x^2$ is increasing. Since there is only one critical point, this must give a global minimum. Therefore, when the length equals the height, the surface area is minimized.

3. Volume: $V = x^2 y$,
   Surface: $S = x^2 + 4xy = x^2 + 4xV/x^2 = x^2 + 4V/x$.
   To find the dimensions which minimize the area, find x such that $dS/dx = 0$.

$$\frac{dS}{dx} = 2x - \frac{4V}{x^2} = 0,$$

so

$$x^3 = 2V,$$

and solving for x gives $x = \sqrt[3]{2V}$. To see that this gives a minimum, note that for small x, $S \approx 4\frac{V}{x}$ is decreasing. For large x, $S \approx x^2$ is increasing. Since there is only one critical point, this must give a global minimum. Using x to find y gives $y = V^{1/3}/2^{2/3} = \sqrt[3]{V/4}$.

4.

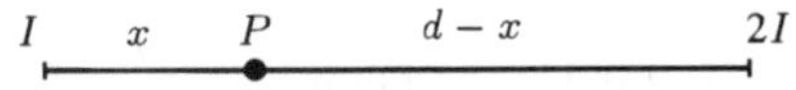

Figure 5.11

Suppose L is the illumination at point P. Then

$$L = \frac{kI}{x^2} + \frac{k2I}{(d-x)^2}$$

Differentiating gives

$$\frac{dL}{dx} = \frac{-2kI}{x^3} - \frac{4kI(-1)}{(d-x)^3} = 0, \text{ so } \frac{1}{x^3} = \frac{2}{(d-x)^3}.$$

Solving for x gives

$$d - x = 2^{1/3}x \quad \text{so} \quad x = \frac{d}{1 + 2^{1/3}}.$$

To see that this is where the illumination is least, note that for small x, the kI/x^2 term dominates, so $L \approx kI/x^2$ decreases initially. For values of x slightly less than d, the $2kI/(d-x)^2$ term dominates, so $L \approx 2kI/(d-x)^2$ increases as x approaches d. Since there is only one critical point, it must give the global minimum.

5. Let x equal the number of chairs ordered in excess of 300, so $0 \le x \le 100$.

$$\text{Revenue} = R = (90 - 0.25x)(300 + x)$$
$$= 27,000 - 75x + 90x - 0.25x^2 = 27,000 + 15x - 0.25x^2$$

At a critical point $dR/dx = 0$. $dR/dx = 15 - 0.5x$ so $x = 30$ gives a maximum revenue of $27,225$ since the graph of R is a parabola which opens downwards. The minimum is $0 (when no chairs are sold).

6. If v is the speed of the boat, then

$$\text{Cost of fuel per hour (in \$/hour)} = kv^3,$$

where k is the constant of proportionality. To find k, use the information that the boat uses $100 worth of fuel per hour when cruising at 10 miles per hour: $100 = k10^3$, so $k = 100/10^3 = 0.1$. Thus,

$$\text{Cost of fuel per hour (in \$/hour)} = 0.1v^3.$$

From the given information, we also have

$$\text{Cost of other operations (labor, maintenance, etc.) per hour (in \$/hour)} = 675.$$

So

$$\text{Total Cost (in \$/hour)} = \text{Cost of fuel (in \$/hour)} + \text{Cost of other (in \$/hour)}$$
$$= 0.1v^3 + 675.$$

However, we want to find the Cost per *mile*, which is the Total Cost per *hour* divided by the number of miles that the ferry travels in one hour. If v is the speed in miles/hour at which the ferry travels, the number of miles that the ferry travels in one hour is simply v miles. Let $C =$ Cost per *mile*. Then

$$\text{Cost per } \textit{mile} \text{ (in \$/mile)} = \frac{\text{Total Cost per } \textit{hour} \text{ (in \$/hour)}}{\text{Distance traveled per hour (in miles/hour)}}$$
$$C = \frac{0.1v^3 + 675}{v} = 0.1v^2 + \frac{675}{v}$$

We also know that $0 < v < \infty$. To find the speed at which Cost per *mile* is minimized, set

$$\frac{dC}{dv} = 2(0.1)v - \frac{675}{v^2} = 0$$

so

$$2(0.1)v = \frac{675}{v^2}$$
$$v^3 = \frac{675}{2(0.1)} = 3375$$
$$v = 15 \text{ miles/hour}$$

Since

$$\frac{d^2C}{dv^2} = 0.2 + \frac{2(675)}{v^3} > 0$$

for $v > 0$, by the second-derivative test, $v = 15$ gives a local minimum for C. Since this is the only critical point for $0 < v < \infty$, it must give a global minimum.

7. (a) The disk takes the same amount of time to go around, regardless of the radius of the track, so the same amount of music is stored on each track.

(b) If the amount of information on each track is the same, then the information must be densest on the innermost track (call this radius r). Furthermore, the information density on this track is b, so $(2\pi r)b = $ amount of information per track. The number of tracks on the disk is $(R - r)a$. The total amount of information stored is thus: $A = (2\pi r)b \cdot (R - r)a$.

To find the inner radius that maximizes the amount of information stored, we take the first derivative and set it equal to 0 gives:

$$\frac{dA}{dr} = 2\pi abR - 4\pi abr = 0.$$

So $r = R/2$. This gives a maximum for A since the graph of A is a parabola which opens downwards.

8. Let $(x, 0)$ be the coordinates of the bottom left corner of the rectangle. Then the width of the rectangle is $(9 - x)$, and the height is $\sqrt{x}$. Thus the area $A = (9 - x)(\sqrt{x}) = 9x^{\frac{1}{2}} - x^{\frac{3}{2}}$, and $A' = \frac{9}{2}x^{-\frac{1}{2}} - \frac{3}{2}x^{\frac{1}{2}}$. To maximize area, we solve $A' = 0$, or $\frac{9}{2}x^{-\frac{1}{2}} = \frac{3}{2}x^{\frac{1}{2}}$, meaning $3 = x$. Evaluating A at $x = 3$ and at the endpoints, $x = 0$ and $x = 9$, shows the maximum occurs at $x = 3$. The dimensions which maximize the area are $6 \times \sqrt{3}$.

Similarly, we let the perimeter be $P = 2(9 - x) + 2\sqrt{x} = 18 - 2x + 2x^{\frac{1}{2}}$. So $P' = -2 + x^{-\frac{1}{2}}$. To maximize perimeter, we solve $P' = 0$, getting $x^{-\frac{1}{2}} = 2$, or $x = \frac{1}{4}$. Evaluating $P(2)$, $P(0)$ and $P(9)$ shows the maximum is $P(2)$. The dimensions for maximal perimeter are $\frac{35}{4} \times \frac{1}{2}$.

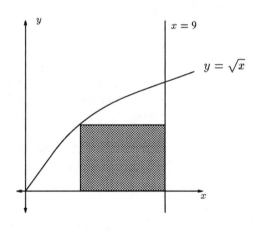

9. The distance from a given point on the parabola (x, x^2) to $(1, 0)$ is given by

$$D = \sqrt{(x - 1)^2 + (x^2 - 0)^2}.$$

Minimizing this is equivalent to minimizing $d = (x - 1)^2 + x^4$. (We can ignore the square root if we are only interested in minimizing because the square root is smallest when the thing it is the square root of is smallest.) To minimize d, we find its critical points by solving $d' = 0$. Since $d = (x - 1)^2 + x^4 = x^2 - 2x + 1 + x^4$,

$$d' = 2x - 2 + 4x^3$$
$$d' = 2(2x^3 + x - 1)$$

By graphing $d' = 2x^3 + x - 1$ on a calculator, we see that it has only 1 root, $x \approx 0.59$. This must give a minimum (as we can make d as large as we please); but this is confirmed by the second derivative test, as $d'' = 6x^2 + 1$, which is always positive. Thus the point $(0.59, 0.59^2) \approx (0.59, 0.35)$ is approximately the closest point of $y = x^2$ to $(1, 0)$.

10. (a) Since $y^2 = 1 - x^2/9$, we wish to minimize the distance

$$D = \sqrt{(x - 2)^2 + (y - 0)^2} = \sqrt{(x - 2)^2 + 1 - \frac{x^2}{9}}.$$

To do so, we find the value of x minimizing D^2. This x also minimizes D. Since $d = (x - 2)^2 + 1 - \frac{x^2}{9}$, we have

$$d' = 2(x - 2) - \frac{2x}{9} = \frac{16x}{9} - 4,$$

which is 0 when $x = 9/4$. Since $d'' = 16/9 > 0$, d is at a local minimum when $x = 9/4$. Since the graph of d is a parabola, the local minimum is in fact a global minimum. Solving for y, we have

$$y^2 = 1 - \frac{x^2}{9} = 1 - \left(\frac{9}{4}\right)^2 \cdot \frac{1}{9} = \frac{7}{16},$$

so $y = \pm\frac{\sqrt{7}}{4}$. Therefore, the closest points are $(\frac{9}{4}, \pm\frac{\sqrt{7}}{4})$.

(b) This time, we wish to minimize

$$D = \sqrt{(x - \sqrt{8})^2 + 1 - \frac{x^2}{9}}.$$

Again, let $d = D^2$ and minimize d. Since $d = (x - \sqrt{8})^2 + 1 - \frac{x^2}{9}$,

$$d' = 2(x - 2\sqrt{2}) - \frac{2x}{9} = \frac{16x}{9} - 4\sqrt{2}.$$

Therefore, $d' = 0$ when $x = 9\sqrt{2}/4$. But $9\sqrt{2}/4 > 3$, an impossibility if (x, y) is to lie on the ellipse! The major axis is only 6 units long. Therefore, there aren't any critical points on the interval from -3 to 3, so the minimum distance must be attained at an endpoint. Since $d' < 0$ for all x between -3 and 3, the minimum must be at $x = 3$. So $(3, 0)$ is the point on the ellipse closest to $(\sqrt{8}, 0)$.

11.

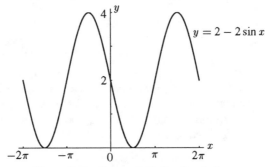

Figure 5.12: Graph of $f(x) = 2 - 2\sin x$

Let $p(x)$ represent the distance from the origin to the point $(x, f(x))$ on the graph of f.
By the Pythagorean Theorem,

$$p(x) = \sqrt{x^2 + (f(x))^2} = \sqrt{x^2 + (2 - 2\sin x)^2}.$$

We can determine the minimum of p by looking at its graph drawn on a calculator or computer. (see Figure 5.13).

From the above graph of $f(x) = 2 - 2\sin x$, it is clear that we need only look at values of x between 0 and $\frac{\pi}{2}$, since those points on the graph of f are clearly the closest to the origin (see Figure 5.12).

We see that $p(x)$ reaches its minimum when $x \approx 0.8$.

The minimum distance is then $\sqrt{0.8^2 + (2 - 2\sin 0.8)^2} \approx 0.98$.

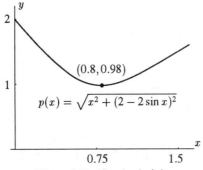

Figure 5.13: Graph of $p(x)$

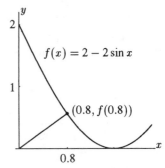

Figure 5.14: The Closest Point to the Origin

12.   Let x be as indicated in the figure in the text. Then the distance from S to Town 1 is $\sqrt{1 + x^2}$ and the distance from S to Town 2 is $\sqrt{(4 - x)^2 + 4^2} = \sqrt{x^2 - 8x + 32}$.

$$\text{Total length of pipe } = f(x) = \sqrt{1 + x^2} + \sqrt{x^2 - 8x + 32}.$$

We want to look for critical points of f. The easiest way is to graph f and see that it has a local minimum at about $x = 0.8$ miles. Alternatively, we can use the formula:

$$f'(x) = \frac{2x}{2\sqrt{1+x^2}} + \frac{2x - 8}{2\sqrt{x^2 - 8x + 32}}$$

$$= \frac{x}{\sqrt{1+x^2}} + \frac{x - 4}{\sqrt{x^2 - 8x + 32}}$$

$$= \frac{x\sqrt{x^2 - 8x + 32} + (x - 4)\sqrt{1 + x^2}}{\sqrt{1 + x^2}\sqrt{x^2 - 8x + 32}} = 0.$$

$f'(x)$ is equal to zero when the numerator is equal to zero.

$$(*) \qquad x\sqrt{x^2 - 8x + 32} + (x - 4)\sqrt{1 + x^2} = 0$$

$$x\sqrt{x^2 - 8x + 32} = (4 - x)\sqrt{1 + x^2}.$$

Squaring both sides and simplifying, we get

$$15x^2 + 8x - 16 = 0,$$

$$(3x + 4)(5x - 4) = 0.$$

So $x = 4/5$. (Discard $x = -4/3$ since we are only interested in x between 0 and 4, between the two towns.) Using the second derivative test, we can verify that $x = 4/5$ is a local minimum.

13. (a) Let's suppose Bueya finds an apartment x miles from Washington University. Then her total traveling distance for the day is

$$2x + 2(14 - x) + 2|x - 5| = 2x + 28 - 2x + 2|x - 5|$$

$$= 28 + 2|x - 5|$$

Note that we had to take $|x - 5|$ as the distance to and from the bar, since we do not know whether $x \geq 5$ or $x < 5$. Since $|x - 5| \geq 0$, $28 + |x - 5|$ is minimized when $|x - 5| = 0$, i.e. when $x = 5$. So Bueya should look for an apartment as close to the bar as possible. (Is there a moral to this story?)

(b) Now let's suppose Marie-Josée finds an apartment x miles from Washington University. Her total travel distance is

$$2x + 2(14 - x) + 2|x - 5| + 2|x - 13| = 28 + 2|x - 5| + 2|x - 13|.$$

This last sum is minimized for any x between 5 and 13. Indeed, if $5 \leq x \leq 13$, then the sum

$$28 + 2(x - 5) + 2(13 - x) = 44.$$

Thus Marie-Josée should try to live anywhere between the bar and the Gateway Arch.

14. (a) The distance the pigeon flies over water is

$$\overline{BP} = \frac{\overline{AB}}{\sin\theta} = \frac{500}{\sin\theta},$$

and over land is

$$\overline{PL} = \overline{AL} - \overline{AP} = 2000 - \frac{500}{\tan\theta} = 2000 - \frac{500\cos\theta}{\sin\theta}.$$

Therefore the energy required is

$$E = 2e\left(\frac{500}{\sin\theta}\right) + e\left(2000 - \frac{500\cos\theta}{\sin\theta}\right)$$

$$= 500e\left(\frac{2-\cos\theta}{\sin\theta}\right) + 2000e, \quad \text{for} \quad \arctan\left(\frac{500}{2000}\right) \leq \theta \leq \frac{\pi}{2}$$

(b) Notice that E and the function $f(\theta) = \dfrac{2-\cos\theta}{\sin\theta}$ must have the same critical points since the graph of E is just a stretch and a vertical shift of the graph of f. The graph of $\dfrac{2-\cos\theta}{\sin\theta}$ for $\arctan(\frac{500}{2000}) \leq \theta \leq \frac{\pi}{2}$ in Figure 5.15 shows that E has precisely one critical point, and that a minimum for E occurs at this point.

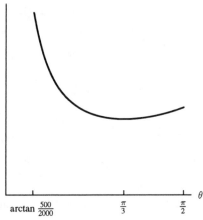

Figure 5.15: Graph of $f(\theta) = \frac{2-\cos\theta}{\sin\theta}$ for $\arctan(\frac{500}{2000}) \leq \theta \leq \frac{\pi}{2}$

To find the critical point θ, we solve $f'(\theta) = 0$ or

$$E' = 0 = 500e\left(\frac{\sin\theta\cdot\sin\theta - (2-\cos\theta)\cdot\cos\theta}{\sin^2\theta}\right)$$

$$= 500e\left(\frac{1-2\cos\theta}{\sin^2\theta}\right).$$

Therefore $1 - 2\cos\theta = 0$ and so $\theta = \dfrac{\pi}{3}$.

(c) Letting $a = \overline{AB}$ and $b = \overline{AL}$, our formula for E becomes

$$E = 2e\left(\frac{a}{\sin\theta}\right) + e\left(b - \frac{a\cos\theta}{\sin\theta}\right)$$

$$= ea\left(\frac{2 - \cos\theta}{\sin\theta}\right) + eb, \quad \text{for} \quad \arctan\left(\frac{a}{b}\right) \le \theta \le \frac{\pi}{2}$$

Again, the graph of E is just a stretch and a vertical shift of the graph of $\dfrac{2 - \cos\theta}{\sin\theta}$. Thus, our answer $\theta = \frac{\pi}{3}$ is independent of e, but is, however, dependent on the ratio $\dfrac{a}{b} = \dfrac{\overline{AB}}{\overline{AL}}$ since $\arctan(\frac{a}{b}) \le \theta \le \frac{\pi}{2}$. In other words, the optimal angle is $\theta = \frac{\pi}{3}$ provided $\arctan(\frac{a}{b}) \le \frac{\pi}{3}$; otherwise, the optimal angle is $\arctan(\frac{a}{b})$, which means the pigeon should fly over the lake for the entire trip – this occurs when $\frac{a}{b} > 1.733$.

15. We want to maximize the viewing angle, which is $\theta = \theta_1 - \theta_2$.

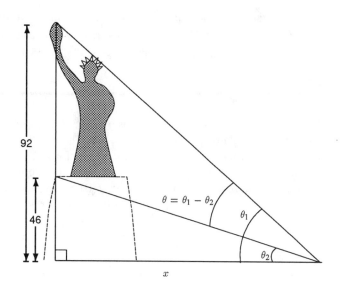

Now

$$\tan(\theta_1) = \frac{92}{x} \quad \text{so } \theta_1 = \arctan\left(\frac{92}{x}\right)$$

$$\tan(\theta_2) = \frac{46}{x} \quad \text{so } \theta_2 = \arctan\left(\frac{46}{x}\right)$$

Then

$$\theta = \arctan\left(\frac{92}{x}\right) - \arctan\left(\frac{46}{x}\right) \quad \text{for} \quad x > 0.$$

We look for critical points of the function by computing $d\theta/dx$:

$$
\begin{aligned}
\frac{d\theta}{dx} &= \frac{1}{1 + (92/x)^2}\left(\frac{-92}{x^2}\right) - \frac{1}{1 + (46/x)^2}\left(\frac{-46}{x^2}\right) \\
&= \frac{-92}{x^2 + 92^2} - \frac{-46}{x^2 + 46^2} \\
&= \frac{-92(x^2 + 46^2) + 46(x^2 + 92^2)}{(x^2 + 92^2) \cdot (x^2 + 46^2)} \\
&= \frac{46(4232 - x^2)}{(x^2 + 92^2) \cdot (x^2 + 46^2)}
\end{aligned}
$$

Setting $d\theta/dx = 0$ gives

$$x^2 = 4232$$
$$x = \pm\sqrt{4232}$$

Since $x > 0$, the critical point is $x = \sqrt{4232} \approx 65.1$ meters. To verify that this is indeed where θ attains a maximum, we note that $d\theta/dx > 0$ for $0 < x < \sqrt{4232}$ and $d\theta/dx < 0$ for $x > \sqrt{4232}$. By the First Derivative Test, θ attains a maximum at $x = \sqrt{4232} \approx 65.1$.

5.7 SOLUTIONS

1. (a) $f'(x) = 3x^2 + 6x + 3 = 3(x + 1)^2$. Thus $f'(x) > 0$ everywhere except at $x = -1$, so it is increasing everywhere except perhaps at $x = -1$. The function is in fact increasing at $x = -1$ since $f(x) > f(-1)$ for $x > -1$, and $f(x) < f(-1)$ for $x < -1$.

   (b) The original equation can have at most one root, since it can only pass through the x-axis once if it never decreases. It must have one root, since $f(0) = -6$ and $f(1) = 1$.

   (c) The root is in the interval $[0, 1]$, since $f(0) < 0 < f(1)$.

   (d) Let $x_0 = 1$.

$$
\begin{aligned}
x_0 &= 1 \\
x_1 &= 1 - \frac{f(1)}{f'(1)} \\
&= 1 - \frac{1}{12} = \frac{11}{12} \approx 0.917 \\
x_2 &= \frac{11}{12} - \frac{f\left(\frac{11}{12}\right)}{f'\left(\frac{11}{12}\right)} \approx 0.913 \\
x_3 &= 0.913 - \frac{f(0.913)}{f'(0.913)} \approx 0.913.
\end{aligned}
$$

Since the digits repeat, they should be accurate. Thus $x \approx 0.913$.

2. Let $f(x) = x^3 - 50$. Then $f(\sqrt[3]{50}) = 0$, so we can use Newton's method to solve $f(x) = 0$ to obtain $x = \sqrt[3]{50}$. Since $f'(x) = 3x^2$, f' is always positive, and f is therefore increasing. Consequently, f has only one zero. Since $3^3 = 27 < 50 < 64 = 4^3$, let $x_0 = 3.5$. Then

$$x_0 = 3.5$$
$$x_1 = 3.5 - \frac{f(3.5)}{f'(3.5)} \approx 3.694$$

Continuing, we find

$$x_2 \approx 3.684$$
$$x_3 \approx 3.684.$$

Since the digits repeat, x_3 should be correct, as can be confirmed by calculator.

3. Let $f(x) = x^4 - 100$. Then $f(\sqrt[4]{100}) = 0$, so we can use Newton's method to solve $f(x) = 0$ to obtain $x = \sqrt[4]{100}$. $f'(x) = 4x^3$. Since $3^4 = 81 < 100 < 256 = 4^4$, try 3.1 as an initial guess.

$$x_0 = 3.1$$
$$x_1 = 3.1 - \frac{f(3.1)}{f'(3.1)} \approx 3.164$$
$$x_2 = 3.164 - \frac{f(3.164)}{f'(3.164)} \approx 3.162$$
$$x_3 = 3.162 - \frac{f(3.162)}{f'(3.162)} \approx 3.162$$

Thus $\sqrt[4]{100} \approx 3.162$.

4. Let $f(x) = x^3 - \frac{1}{10}$. Then $f(10^{-1/3}) = 0$, so we can use Newton's method to solve $f(x) = 0$ to obtain $x = 10^{-1/3}$. $f'(x) = 3x^2$. Since $\sqrt[3]{\frac{1}{27}} < \sqrt[3]{\frac{1}{10}} < \sqrt[3]{\frac{1}{8}}$, try $x_0 = \frac{1}{2}$. Then $x_1 = 0.5 - \frac{f(0.5)}{f'(0.5)} \approx 0.467$. Continuing, we find $x_2 \approx 0.464$. $x_3 \approx 0.464$. Since $x_2 \approx x_3$, $10^{-\frac{1}{3}} \approx 0.464$.

5. Let $f(x) = \sin x - 1 + x$; we want to find all zeros of f, because $f(x) = 0$ implies $\sin x = 1 - x$. Graphing $\sin x$ and $1 - x$, we see that $f(x)$ has one solution at $x \approx \frac{1}{2}$.

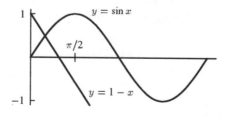

Letting $x_0 = 0.5$, and using Newton's method, we have $f'(x) = \cos x + 1$, so that

$$x_1 = 0.5 - \frac{\sin(0.5) - 1 + 0.5}{\cos(0.5) + 1} \approx 0.511,$$

$$x_2 = 0.511 - \frac{\sin(0.511) - 1 + 0.511}{\cos(0.511) + 1} \approx 0.511.$$

Thus $\sin x = 1 - x$ has one solution at $x \approx 0.511$.

6. Let $f(x) = \cos x - x$. We want to find all zeros of f, because $f(x) = 0$ implies that $\cos x = x$. Since $f'(x) = -\sin x - 1$, f' is always negative (as $-\sin x$ never exceeds 1). This means f is always decreasing and consequently has at most 1 root. We now use Newton's method. Since $\cos 0 > 0$ and $\cos \frac{\pi}{2} < \frac{\pi}{2}$, $\cos x = x$ for $0 < x < \frac{\pi}{2}$. Thus, try $x_0 = \frac{\pi}{6}$.

$$x_1 = \frac{\pi}{6} - \frac{\cos \frac{\pi}{6} - \frac{\pi}{6}}{-\sin \frac{\pi}{6} - 1} \approx 0.7519,$$

$$x_2 \approx 0.7391,$$

$$x_3 \approx 0.7390.$$

$x_2 \approx x_3 \approx 0.739$. Thus $x \approx 0.739$ is the solution.

7. Let $f(x) = e^{-x} - \ln x$. Then $f'(x) = -e^{-x} - \frac{1}{x}$. We want to find all zeros of f, because $f(x) = 0$ implies that $e^{-x} = \ln x$. Since e^{-x} is always decreasing and $\ln x$ is always increasing, there must be only 1 solution. Since $e^{-1} > \ln 1 = 0$, and $e^{-e} < \ln e = 1$, then $e^{-x} = \ln x$ for some x, $1 < x < e$. Try $x_0 = 1$. We now use Newton's method.

$$x_1 = 1 - \frac{e^{-1} - 0}{-e^{-1} - 1} \approx 1.2689,$$

$$x_2 \approx 1.309,$$

$$x_3 \approx 1.310.$$

Thus $x \approx 1.310$ is the solution.

8. Let $f(x) = e^x \cos x - 1$. Then $f'(x) = -e^x \sin x + e^x \cos x$. Now we use Newton's method, guessing $x_0 = 1$ initially.

$$x_1 = 1 - \frac{f(1)}{f'(1)} \approx 1.5725$$

Continuing: $x_2 \approx 1.364$, $x_3 \approx 1.299$, $x_4 \approx 1.293$, $x_5 \approx 1.293$. Thus $x \approx 1.293$ is a solution. Looking at a graph of $f(x)$ suffices to convince us that there is only one solution.

9. Let $f(x) = \ln x - \frac{1}{x}$, so $f'(x) = \frac{1}{x} + \frac{1}{x^2}$.
Now use Newton's method with an initial guess of $x_0 = 2$.

$$x_1 = 2 - \frac{\ln 2 - \frac{1}{2}}{\frac{1}{2} + \frac{1}{4}} \approx 1.7425,$$

$$x_2 \approx 1.763,$$
$$x_3 \approx 1.763.$$

Thus $x \approx 1.763$ is a solution. Since $f'(x) > 0$ for positive x, f is increasing: it must be the only solution.

10. (a) One zero in the interval $0.6 < x < 0.7$.
    (b) Three zeros in the intervals $-1.55 < x < -1.45$, $x = 0$, $1.45 < x < 1.55$.
    (c) Two zeros in the intervals $0.1 < x < 0.2$, $3.5 < x < 3.6$.

11. $f'(x) = 3x^2 + 1$. Since f' is always positive, f is everywhere increasing. Thus f has only one zero. Since $f(0) < 0 < f(1), 0 < x_0 < 1$. Pick $x_0 = 0.68$.

$$x_0 = 0.68,$$
$$x_1 = 0.6823278,$$
$$x_2 \approx 0.6823278.$$

Thus $x \approx 0.682328$ (rounded up) is a root. Since $x_1 \approx x_2$, the digits should be correct.

12. Let $f(x) = x^2 - a$, so $f'(x) = 2x$.

Then by Newton's method, $x_{n+1} = x_n - \frac{x_n^2 - a}{2x_n}$

For $a = 2$:

$x_0 = 1, x_1 = 1.5, x_2 \approx 1.416, x_3 \approx 1.414215, x_4 \approx 1.414213$ so $\sqrt{2} \approx 1.4142$.

For $a = 10$:

$x_0 = 5, x_1 = 3.5, x_2 \approx 3.17857, x_3 \approx 3.162319, x_4 \approx 3.162277$ so $\sqrt{10} \approx 3.1623$.

For $a = 1000$:

$x_0 = 500, x_1 = 251, x_2 \approx 127.49203, x_3 \approx 67.6678, x_4 \approx 41.2229, x_5 \approx 32.7406, x_6 \approx 31.6418$, $x_7 \approx 31.62278, x_8 \approx 31.62277$ so $\sqrt{1000} \approx 31.6228$.

For $a = \pi$:

$x_0 = \frac{\pi}{2}, x_1 \approx 1.7853, x_2 \approx 1.7725 \ x_3 \approx 1.77245, x_4 \approx 1.77245$ so $\sqrt{\pi} \approx 1.77245$.

13. (a) Set $f(x) = \sin x$, so $f'(x) = \cos x$. Guess $x_0 = 3$. Then

$$x_1 = 3 - \frac{\sin 3}{\cos 3} \approx 3.1425$$
$$x_2 \approx 3.141592653, \text{ which is correct to one billionth!}$$

(b) Newton's method uses the tangent line at $x = 3$, i.e. $y - \sin 3 = \cos(3)(x - 3)$. Around $x = 3$, however, $\sin x$ is almost linear, since the second derivative $\sin''(\pi) = 0$. Thus using the tangent line to get an approximate value for the root gives us a very good approximation.

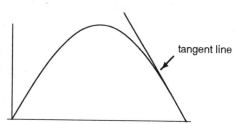

tangent line

(c) $f(x) = \sin x$

$$[3,4]: f(3) = 0.14112$$
$$f(4) = -0.7568$$

The root is in

$$[3, 3.5]: f(3.5) = -0.35078 \text{ (bisection 1)}$$
$$[3, 3.25]: f(3.25) = -0.10819 \text{ (bisection 2)}$$
$$[3.125, 3.25]: f(3.125) = \quad 0.01659 \text{ (bisection 3)}$$
$$[3.125, 3.1875]: f(3.1875) = -0.04584 \text{ (bisection 4)}$$

We continue this process; after 11 bisections, we know the root lies between 3.1411 and 3.1416, which still is not as good an approximation as what we get from Newton's method.

14.   (a)   We have $f(x) = \sin x - \frac{2}{3}x$ and $f'(x) = \cos x - \frac{2}{3}$.
Using $x_0 = 0.904$,

$$x_1 = 0.904 - \frac{\sin(0.904) - \frac{2}{3}(0.904)}{\cos(0.904) - \frac{2}{3}} \approx 4.704,$$

$$x_2 = 4.704 - \frac{\sin(4.704) - \frac{2}{3}(4.704)}{\cos(4.704) - \frac{2}{3}} \approx -1.423,$$

$$x_3 = -1.433 - \frac{\sin(-1.423) - \frac{2}{3}(-1.423)}{\cos(-1.423) - \frac{2}{3}} \approx -1.501,$$

$$x_4 = -1.499 - \frac{\sin(-1.501) - \frac{2}{3}(-1.501)}{\cos(-1.501) - \frac{2}{3}} \approx -1.496,$$

$$x_5 = -1.496 - \frac{\sin(-1.496) - \frac{2}{3}(-1.496)}{\cos(-1.496) - \frac{2}{3}} \approx -1.496.$$

Using $x_0 = 0.905$,

$$x_1 = 0.905 - \frac{\sin(0.905) - \frac{2}{3}(0.905)}{\cos(0.905) - \frac{2}{3}} \approx 4.643,$$

$$x_2 = 4.643 - \frac{\sin(4.643) - \frac{2}{3}(4.643)}{\cos(4.643) - \frac{2}{3}} \approx -0.918,$$

$$x_3 = -0.918 - \frac{\sin(-0.918) - \frac{2}{3}(-0.918)}{\cos(-0.918) - \frac{2}{3}} \approx -3.996,$$

$$x_4 = -3.996 - \frac{\sin(-3.996) - \frac{2}{3}(-3.996)}{\cos(-3.996) - \frac{2}{3}} \approx -1.413,$$

$$x_5 = -1.413 - \frac{\sin(-1.413) - \frac{2}{3}(-1.413)}{\cos(-1.413) - \frac{2}{3}} \approx -1.502,$$

$$x_6 = -1.502 - \frac{\sin(-1.502) - \frac{2}{3}(-1.502)}{\cos(-1.502) - \frac{2}{3}} \approx -1.496.$$

Now using $x_0 = 0.906$,

$$x_1 = 0.906 - \frac{\sin(0.906) - \frac{2}{3}(0.906)}{\cos(0.906) - \frac{2}{3}} \approx 4.584,$$

$$x_2 = 4.584 - \frac{\sin(4.584) - \frac{2}{3}(4.584)}{\cos(4.584) - \frac{2}{3}} \approx -0.509,$$

$$x_3 = -0.510 - \frac{\sin(-0.509) - \frac{2}{3}(-0.509)}{\cos(-0.509) - \frac{2}{3}} \approx .207,$$

$$x_4 = -1.300 - \frac{\sin(.207) - \frac{2}{3}(.207)}{\cos(.207) - \frac{2}{3}} \approx -0.009,$$

$$x_5 = -1.543 - \frac{\sin(-0.009) - \frac{2}{3}(-0.009)}{\cos(-0.009) - \frac{2}{3}} \approx 0,$$

(b) Starting with 0.904 and 0.905 yields the same value, but the two paths to get to the root are very different. Starting with 0.906 leads to a different root. Our starting points were near the maximum value of f: consequently, a small change in x_0 makes a large change in x_1.

SOLUTIONS TO REVIEW PROBLEMS FOR CHAPTER FIVE

1. (a) We wish to investigate the behavior of $f(x) = x^3 - 3x^2$ on the interval $-1 \le x \le 3$. We find:

$$f'(x) = 3x^2 - 6x = 3x(x - 2)$$
$$f''(x) = 6x - 6 = 6(x - 1)$$

(b) The critical points of f are $x = 2, 0$, since $f'(x) = 0$ here. Using the second derivative test, we find that $x = 0$ is a local maximum since $f'(0) = 0$ and $f''(0) = -6 < 0$, that $x = 2$ is a local minimum since $f'(2) = 0$ and $f''(2) = 6 > 0$.

   (c)   There is an inflection point at $x = 1$ since f'' changes sign at $x = 1$.

   (d)   At the critical points, $f(0) = 0$ and $f(2) = -4$.

        At the endpoints: $f(-1) = -4, f(3) = 0$.

        So the global maxima are $f(0) = 0$ and $f(3) = 0$, while the global minima are $f(-1) = -4$ and $f(2) = -4$.

   (e)

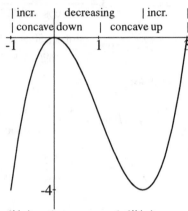

2.   (a)   First we find f' and f''; $f'(x) = 1 + \cos x$ and $f''(x) = -\sin x$.

   (b)   The critical point of f is $x = \pi$, since $f'(\pi) = 0$.

   (c)   Since f'' changes sign at $x = \pi$, it means that $x = \pi$ is an inflection point.

   (d)   Evaluating f at the critical point and endpoints, we find $f(0) = 0$, $f(2\pi) = 2\pi, f(\pi) = \pi$. Therefore, the global maximum is $f(2\pi) = 2\pi$, and the global minimum is $f(0) = 0$. Note that $x = \pi$ isn't a local maximum or minimum of f, and that the second derivative test is inconclusive here.

   (e)

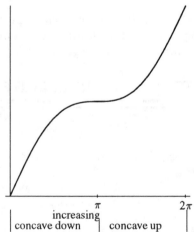

3.   (a)   First we find f' and f'':

$$f'(x) = -e^{-x} \sin x + e^{-x} \cos x$$

$$f''(x) = e^{-x}\sin x - e^{-x}\cos x$$
$$-e^{-x}\cos x - e^{-x}\sin x$$
$$= -2e^{-x}\cos x$$

(b) The critical points are $x = \frac{\pi}{4}, \frac{5\pi}{4}$, since $f'(x) = 0$ here.

(c) The inflection points are $x = \frac{\pi}{2}, \frac{3\pi}{2}$, since f'' changes sign at these points.

(d) At the endpoints, $f(0) = 0$, $f(2\pi) = 0$. So we have $f(\frac{\pi}{4}) = (e^{-\frac{\pi}{4}})(\frac{\sqrt{2}}{2})$ as the local and global maximum; $f(\frac{5\pi}{4}) = -e^{\frac{-5\pi}{4}}(\frac{\sqrt{2}}{2})$ as the local and global minimum.

(e)

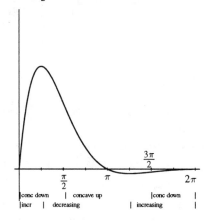

4. (a) We first find f' and f'':

$$f'(x) = -\frac{2}{3}x^{-\frac{5}{3}} + \frac{1}{3}x^{-\frac{2}{3}} = \frac{1}{3}x^{-\frac{5}{3}}(x - 2)$$
$$f''(x) = \frac{10}{9}x^{-\frac{8}{3}} - \frac{2}{9}x^{-\frac{5}{3}} = -\frac{2}{9}x^{-\frac{8}{3}}(x - 5)$$

(b) Critical point: $x = 2$.

(c) There are no inflection points, since f'' does not change sign on the interval $1.2 \le x \le 3.5$.

(d) At the endpoints, $f(1.2) \approx 1.94821$ and $f(3.5) \approx 1.95209$. Also $f(2) \approx 1.88988$ is a local minimum. So, the global minimum is $f(2) \approx 1.88988$ and the global maximum is $f(3.5) \approx 1.95209$.

(e)

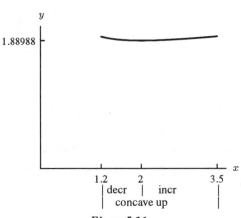

Figure 5.16

5. The polynomial $f(x)$ behaves like $2x^3$ as x goes to ∞. Therefore, $\lim\limits_{x \to \infty} f(x) = \infty$ and $\lim\limits_{x \to -\infty} f(x) = -\infty$.

    We have $f'(x) = 6x^2 - 18x + 12 = 6(x - 2)(x - 1)$, which is zero when $x = 1$ or $x = 2$.

    Also, $f''(x) = 12x - 18 = 6(2x - 3)$, which is zero when $x = \frac{3}{2}$. For $x < \frac{3}{2}$, $f''(x) < 0$; for $x > \frac{3}{2}$, $f''(x) > 0$. Thus $x = \frac{3}{2}$ is an inflection point.

    The critical points are $x = 1$ and $x = 2$, and $f(1) = 6$, $f(2) = 5$. By the second derivative test, $f''(1) = -6 < 0$, so $x = 1$ is a local maximum; $f''(2) = 6 > 0$, so $x = 2$ is a local minimum.

    Now we can draw the diagrams below.

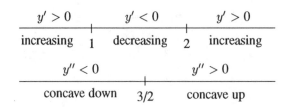

The graph of $f(x) = 2x^3 - 9x^2 + 12x + 1$ looks like this.

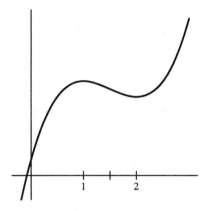

$f(x)$ has no global maximum or minimum.

6. If we divide the denominator and numerator of $f(x)$ by x^2 we have

$$\lim_{x \to \pm\infty} \frac{4x^2 \frac{1}{x^2}}{x^2 + 1 \frac{1}{x^2}} = \lim_{x \to \pm\infty} \frac{4}{1 + \frac{1}{x^2}} = 4$$

since

$$\lim_{x \to \pm\infty} \frac{1}{x^2} = 0.$$

Using the quotient rule we get

$$f'(x) = \frac{(x^2 + 1)8x - 4x^2(2x)}{(x^2 + 1)^2} = \frac{8x}{(x^2 + 1)^2},$$

which is zero when $x = 0$, positive when $x > 0$, and negative when $x < 0$. Thus $f(x)$ has a local minimum when $x = 0$, with $f(0) = 0$.

Because $f'(x) = \frac{8x}{(x^2+1)^2}$, the quotient rule implies that

$$f''(x) = \frac{(x^2 + 1)^2 8 - 8x[2(x^2 + 1)2x]}{(x^2 + 1)^4}$$

$$= \frac{8x^2 + 8 - 32x^2}{(x^2 + 1)^3}$$

$$= \frac{8(1 - 3x^2)}{(x^2 + 1)^3}$$

The denominator is always positive, so $f''(x) = 0$ when $x = \pm\sqrt{1/3}$, positive when $-\sqrt{1/3} < x < \sqrt{1/3}$, and negative when $x > \sqrt{1/3}$ or $x < -\sqrt{1/3}$. This gives the diagram

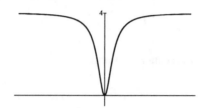

and the graph of f looks like:

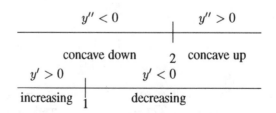

with inflection points $x = \pm\sqrt{1/3}$, a global minimum at $x = 0$, and no local or global maxima (since $f(x)$ never achieves 4).

7. As $x \to -\infty$, $e^{-x} \to \infty$, so $xe^{-x} \to -\infty$. Thus $\lim_{x \to -\infty} xe^{-x} = -\infty$.
    As $x \to \infty$, $\frac{x}{e^x} \to 0$, since e^x grows much more quickly than x. Thus $\lim_{x \to \infty} xe^{-x} = 0$.
    Using the product rule,

    $$f'(x) = e^{-x} - xe^{-x} = (1 - x)e^{-x},$$

which is zero when $x = 1$, negative when $x > 1$, and positive when $x < 1$. Thus $f(1) = \frac{1}{e^1} = \frac{1}{e}$ is a local maximum.

Again, using the product rule,

$$f''(x) = -e^{-x} - e^{-x} + xe^{-x}$$
$$= xe^{-x} - 2e^{-x}$$
$$= (x - 2)e^{-x},$$

which is zero when $x = 2$, positive when $x > 2$, and negative when $x < 2$, giving an inflection point at $(2, \frac{2}{e^2})$. With the above, we have the following diagram:

$y'' < 0$		$y'' > 0$
concave down	2	concave up
$y' > 0$		$y' < 0$
increasing	1	decreasing

The graph of f is:

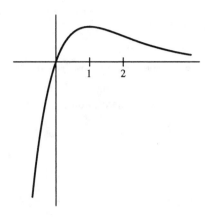

and $f(x)$ has one global maximum and no local or global minima.

8. We first compute f' and f'':

$$f'(x) = -xe^{-\frac{x^2}{2}}$$
$$f''(x) = -e^{-\frac{x^2}{2}} + x^2 e^{-\frac{x^2}{2}}$$
$$= e^{-\frac{x^2}{2}}(x^2 - 1)$$

$x = 0$ is a critical point, since $f'(0) = 0$. Since $f''(0) = -1$, by the second derivative test $f(0) = 1$ is a local maximum. $x = 1$ and $x = -1$ are inflection points, because $f''(x)$ changes sign there.

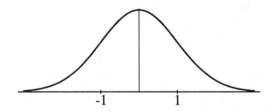

9. $\lim_{x \to \infty} f(x) = +\infty$, and $\lim_{x \to -\infty} f(x) = -\infty$.
    There are no asymptotes.
    $f'(x) = 3x^2 + 6x - 9 = 3(x + 3)(x - 1)$. Critical points are $x = -3$, $x = 1$.
    $f''(x) = 6(x + 1)$.

TABLE 5.1

x		-3		-1		1	
f'	$+$	0	$-$		$-$	0	$+$
f''	$-$		$-$	0	$+$		$+$
f	↗⌢		↘⌢		↘⌣		↗⌣

Thus, $x = -1$ is an inflection point. $f(-3) = 12$ is a local maximum; $f(1) = -20$ is a local minimum. There are no global maxima or minima.

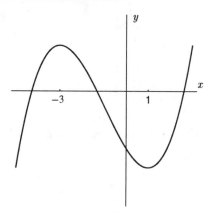

10. $\lim\limits_{x \to +\infty} f(x) = +\infty$, and $\lim\limits_{x \to -\infty} f(x) = -\infty$.

There are no asymptotes.

$f'(x) = 5x^4 - 45x^2 = 5x^2(x^2 - 9) =$
$5x^2(x + 3)(x - 3)$.

The critical points are $x = 0$, $x = \pm 3$. f' changes sign at 3 and -3 but not at 0.

$f''(x) = 20x^3 - 90x = 10x(2x^2 - 9)$. f'' changes sign at $0, \pm 3/\sqrt{2}$.

So, inflection points are at $x = 0$, $x = \pm\frac{3}{\sqrt{2}}$.

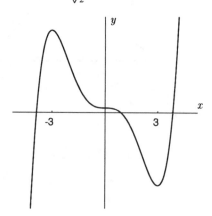

TABLE 5.2

x		-3		$\frac{-3}{\sqrt{2}}$		0		$\frac{3}{\sqrt{2}}$		3	
f'	$+$	0	$-$		$-$	0	$-$		$-$	0	$+$
f''	$-$		$-$	0	$+$	0	$-$	0	$+$		$+$
f	↗⌢		↘⌢		↘⌣		↘⌢		↘⌣		↗⌣

Thus, $f(-3)$ is a local maximum; $f(3)$ is a local minimum. There are no global maxima or minima.

11. $\displaystyle\lim_{x \to +\infty} f(x) = +\infty$, and $\displaystyle\lim_{x \to 0^+} f(x) = +\infty$.

Hence, $x = 0$ is a vertical asymptote.

$f'(x) = 1 - \dfrac{2}{x} = \dfrac{x-2}{x}$, so $x = 2$ is the only critical point.

$f''(x) = \dfrac{2}{x^2}$, which can never be zero. So there are no inflection points.

TABLE 5.3

x		2	
f'	$-$	0	$+$
f''	$+$		$+$
f	↘⌣		↗⌣

Thus, $f(2)$ is a local and global minimum.

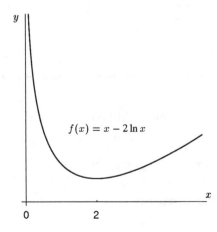

$f(x) = x - 2\ln x$

12. $\lim\limits_{x \to +\infty} f(x) = +\infty$, $\lim\limits_{x \to -\infty} f(x) = 0$.

$y = 0$ is the horizontal asymptote.

$f'(x) = 2xe^{5x} + 5x^2e^{5x} = xe^{5x}(5x + 2)$.

Thus, $x = -\frac{2}{5}$ and $x = 0$ are the critical points.

$$\begin{aligned}
f''(x) \\
&= 2e^{5x} + 2xe^{5x} \cdot 5 + 10xe^{5x} + 25x^2e^{5x} \\
&= e^{5x}(25x^2 + 20x + 2).
\end{aligned}$$

So, $x = \dfrac{-2 \pm \sqrt{2}}{5}$ are inflection points.

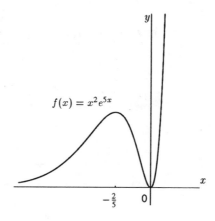

$f(x) = x^2e^{5x}$

TABLE 5.4

x		$\frac{-2-\sqrt{2}}{5}$		$-\frac{2}{5}$		$\frac{-2+\sqrt{2}}{5}$		0	
f'	+		+	0	−		−	0	+
f''	+	0	−		−	0	+		+
f	⌣↗		↗⌢		↘⌢		↘⌣		↗⌣

So, $f(-\frac{2}{5})$ is a local maximum; $f(0)$ is a local and global minimum.

13. Since $\lim\limits_{x \to -\infty} f(x) = \lim\limits_{x \to +\infty} f(x) = 0$, $y = 0$ is a horizontal asymptote.

$f'(x) = -2xe^{-x^2}$. So, $x = 0$ is the only critical point.

$f''(x) = -2(e^{-x^2} + x(-2x)e^{-x^2}) = 2e^{-x^2}(2x^2 - 1) = 2e^{-x^2}(\sqrt{2}x - 1)(\sqrt{2}x + 1)$.

Thus, $x = \pm\frac{1}{\sqrt{2}}$ are inflection points.

TABLE 5.5

x		$\frac{-1}{\sqrt{2}}$		0		$\frac{1}{\sqrt{2}}$	
f'	$+$		$+$	0	$-$		$-$
f''	$+$	0	$-$		$-$	0	$+$
f	⌣↗		⌢↗		⌢↘		⌣↘

Thus, $f(0) = 1$ is a local and global maximum.

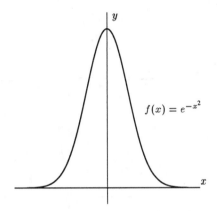

$$f(x) = e^{-x^2}$$

14. $\displaystyle\lim_{x \to +\infty} f(x) = \lim_{x \to -\infty} f(x) = 1.$

Thus, $y = 1$ is a horizontal asymptote. Since $x^2 + 1$ is never 0, there are no vertical asymptotes.

$$f'(x) = \frac{2x(x^2+1) - x^2(2x)}{(x^2+1)^2} = \frac{2x}{(x^2+1)^2}.$$

So, $x = 0$ is the only critical point.

$$
\begin{aligned}
f''(x) \\
&= \frac{2(x^2+1)^2 - 2x \cdot 2(x^2+1) \cdot 2x}{(x^2+1)^4} \\
&= \frac{2(x^2+1-4x^2)}{(x^2+1)^3} \\
&= \frac{2(1-3x^2)}{(x^2+1)^3}.
\end{aligned}
$$

So, $x = \pm\frac{1}{\sqrt{3}}$ are inflection points.

TABLE 5.6

x		$\frac{-1}{\sqrt{3}}$		0		$\frac{1}{\sqrt{3}}$	
f'	$-$		$-$	0	$+$		$+$
f''	$-$	0	$+$		$+$	0	$-$
f	$\searrow\frown$		$\searrow\smile$		$\nearrow\smile$		$\nearrow\frown$

Thus, $f(0) = 0$ is a local and global minimum.

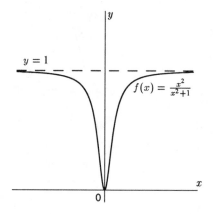

15. By Problem 14, Section 5.3, the maximum of $f(x) = e^{-ax}\sin x$, for $a > 0$, $x > 0$, occurs at $x = \arctan(\frac{1}{a})$, and the minimum at $x = \pi + \arctan(\frac{1}{a})$:

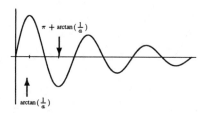

Letting $a = 1$, we have $\arctan(1) = \pi/4$ and $\pi + \arctan(1) = 5\pi/4$. Thus

$$e^{-5\pi/4}\sin(5\pi/4) \le e^{-x}\sin x \le e^{-\pi/4}\sin(\pi/4),$$

or

$$-0.014 \le e^{-x}\sin x \le 0.322.$$

16. Let $f(x) = x \sin x$. Then $f'(x) = x \cos x + \sin x$.

$f'(x) = 0$ when $x = 0$, $x \approx 2$, and $x \approx 5$.

Using Newton's method (or some other approximation method), we can find the zeros of $f'(x)$ with more precision. First, $(f')'(x) = f''(x) = -x \sin x + 2 \cos x$. Guess $x_0 = 2$:

$$x_1 = 2 - \frac{f'(2)}{f''(2)} \approx 2.029,$$

$$x_2 \approx 2.029.$$

To find another zero, guess $x_0 = 5$.

$$x_1 = 5 - \frac{f'(5)}{f''(5)} \approx 4.914,$$

$$x_2 \approx 4.913,$$

$$x_3 \approx 4.913.$$

Thus the zeros of $f'(x)$ are (approximately) 0, 2.029, and 4.913. We check the endpoints and critical points for the global maximum and minimum.

$$f(0) = 0, \qquad f(2\pi) = 0,$$
$$f(2.029) \approx 1.8197, \ f(4.914) \approx -4.814.$$

Thus for $0 \le x \le 2\pi$, $-4.82 \le f(x) \le 1.82$.

17. (a) $(-\infty, 0)$ decreasing, $(0, \infty)$ increasing.

(b) $f(0)$ is a local and global minimum.

18. (a) increasing for all x.

(b) no maxima or minima

19. (a) $(-\infty, 0)$ decreasing, $(0, 4)$ increasing, $(4, \infty)$ decreasing.

(b) local minimum at $f(0)$, local maximum at $f(4)$.

20. (a) $(-\infty, -1)$ decreasing, $(-1, 0)$ increasing, $(0, 1)$ decreasing, $(1, \infty)$ increasing.

(b) local minima at $f(-1)$ and $f(1)$, local maximum at $f(0)$.

21. (a) The concavity changes at t_1 and t_3.

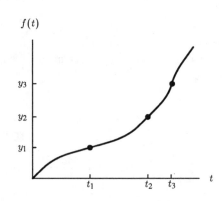

(b) $f(t)$ grows fastest where the vase is skinniest (at y_3) and slowest where the vase is widest (at y_1). The diameter of the widest part of the vase looks to be about 4 times as large as the diameter at the skinniest part. Since the area of a cross section is given by πr^2, where r is the radius, the ratio between areas of cross sections at these two places is about 4^2, so the growth rates are in a ratio of about 1 to 16 (the wide part being 16 times slower).

22.

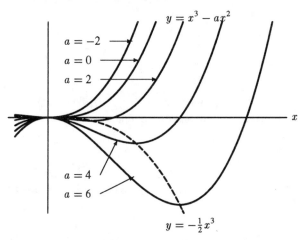

To solve for the critical points, we set $\dfrac{dy}{dx} = 0$. Since $\dfrac{d}{dx}\left(x^3 - ax^2\right) = 3x^2 - 2ax$, we want $3x^2 - 2ax = 0$, so $x = 0$ or $x = \frac{2}{3}a$.

At $x = 0$, we have $y = 0$. This first critical point is independent of a and lies on the curve $y = -\frac{1}{2}x^3$. At $x = \frac{2}{3}a$, we calculate $y = -\frac{4}{27}a^3 = -\frac{1}{2}\left(\frac{2}{3}a\right)^3$. Thus the second critical point also lies on the curve $y = -\frac{1}{2}x^3$.

23.   (a)   We have $g'(t) = \dfrac{t(1/t) - \ln t}{t^2} = \dfrac{1 - \ln t}{t^2}$, which is zero if $t = e$, negative if $t > e$, and positive if $t < e$, since $\ln t$ is increasing. Thus $g(e) = \frac{1}{e}$ is a global maximum for g. Since $t = e$ was the only point at which $g'(t) = 0$, there is no minimum.

(b)   Now $\frac{\ln t}{t}$ is increasing for $0 < t < e$, $\frac{\ln 1}{1} = 0$, and $\frac{\ln 5}{5} \approx 0.322 < \frac{\ln(e)}{e}$. Thus, for $0 < t < e$, $\frac{\ln t}{t}$ increases from 0 to above $\frac{\ln 5}{5}$, so there must be a t between 0 and e such that $\frac{\ln t}{t} = \frac{\ln 5}{5}$. For $t > e$, there is only one solution to $\frac{\ln t}{t} = \frac{\ln 5}{5}$, namely $t = 5$, since $\frac{\ln t}{t}$ is decreasing for $t > e$. Thus $\frac{\ln x}{x} = \frac{\ln 5}{5}$ has exactly two solutions.

(c)   The graph of $\frac{\ln t}{t}$ intersects the horizontal line $y = \frac{\ln 5}{5}$, at $x = 5$ and $x \approx 1.75$.

24.   (a) x-intercept: $(a, 0)$, y-intercept: $(0, \frac{1}{a^2+1})$

(b)   Area $= \frac{1}{2}(a)(\frac{1}{a^2+1}) = \frac{a}{2(a^2+1)}$

(c)

$$A = \frac{a}{2(a^2+1)}$$

$$A' = \frac{2(a^2+1) - a(4a)}{4(a^2+1)^2}$$

$$= \frac{2(1-a^2)}{4(a^2+1)^2}$$

$$= \frac{(1-a^2)}{2(a^2+1)^2}$$

If $A' = 0$, then $a = \pm 1$. We only consider positive values of a, and we note that A' changes sign from positive to negative at $a = 1$. Hence $a = 1$ is a local maximum of A which is a global maximum because $A' < 0$ for all $a > 1$ and $A' > 0$ for $0 < a < 1$.

(d) $A = \frac{1}{2}(1)(\frac{1}{2}) = \frac{1}{4}$

(e) $a = 2$ and $a = \frac{1}{2}$.

25.   (a) $a(q)$ is represented by the slope of the line from the origin to the graph. For example, the slope of line (1) through (0,0) and $(p, C(p))$ is $\frac{C(p)}{p} = a(p)$.

(b) $a(q)$ is minimal where $a(q)$ is tangent to the graph (line (2)).

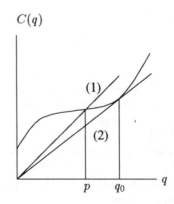

(c)   We have $a(q) = \frac{C(q)}{q}$; by the quotient rule

$$a'(q) = \frac{qC'(q) - C(q)}{q^2}$$
$$= \frac{C'(q) - \frac{C(q)}{q}}{q}$$
$$= \frac{1}{q}(C'(q) - a(q)).$$

Thus if $q = q_0$, then $a'(q_0) = \frac{1}{q}(C'(q_0) - a(q_0)) = 0$, so that $C'(q_0) = a(q_0)$; or, the average cost is minimized when it equals the marginal cost.

(d)

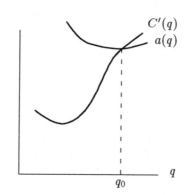

26.   (a)   If the water is colder, the air warms it. If the water is warmer, the air cools it.
      (b)

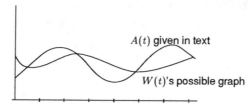

(c)   When the graphs intersect, the water temperature is not changing (since it is exactly the same as the air temperature). In other words, the derivative of the water temperature will be zero. Thus, the extrema of the water temperature occur at these intersections.
(d)   The greater $A(t) - W(t)$ is, the greater the rate of change of the water temperature.
(e)   When $A(t) - W(t)$ reaches a maximum or minimum, the rate at which $W(t)$ changes reaches a maximum or minimum. In other words, $W'(t)$ is at a maximum or minimum and therefore $W''(t) = 0$ and $W''(t)$ changes sign. Thus $W(t)$ has inflection points whenever $A(t) - W(t)$ reaches a maximum or minimum.

(f)

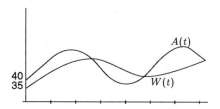

27. $r(\lambda) = a(\lambda)^{-5}(e^{\frac{b}{\lambda}} - 1)^{-1}$

$r'(\lambda) = a(-5\lambda^{-6})(e^{\frac{b}{\lambda}} - 1)^{-1} + a(\lambda^{-5})(\frac{b}{\lambda^2}e^{\frac{b}{\lambda}})(e^{\frac{b}{\lambda}} - 1)^{-2}$

$(0.96, 3.13)$ is a maximum, so $r'(0.96) = 0$ implies that the following holds, with $\lambda = 0.96$:

$$5\lambda^{-6}(e^{\frac{b}{\lambda}} - 1)^{-1} = \lambda^{-5}\left(\frac{b}{\lambda^2}e^{\frac{b}{\lambda}}\right)(e^{\frac{b}{\lambda}} - 1)^{-2}$$

$$5\lambda(e^{\frac{b}{\lambda}} - 1) = be^{\frac{b}{\lambda}}$$

$$5\lambda e^{\frac{b}{\lambda}} - 5\lambda = be^{\frac{b}{\lambda}}$$

$$5\lambda e^{\frac{b}{\lambda}} - be^{\frac{b}{\lambda}} = 5\lambda$$

$$\left(\frac{5\lambda - b}{5\lambda}\right)e^{\frac{b}{\lambda}} = 1$$

$$\frac{4.8 - b}{4.8}e^{\frac{b}{0.96}} - 1 = 0.$$

Using Newton's method, or some other approximation method, we search for a root. The root should be near 4.8. Using our initial guess, we get $b \approx 4.7665$. At $\lambda = 0.96$, $r = 3.13$, so

$$3.13 = \frac{a}{0.96^5(e^{\frac{b}{0.96}} - 1)} \qquad \text{or}$$

$$a = 3.13(0.96)^5(e^{\frac{b}{0.96}} - 1)$$

$$\approx 363.23.$$

As a check, we try $r(4) \approx 0.155$, which looks about right on the given graph.

28. '

(a)

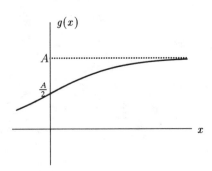

A is the limiting value of $g(x)$ for large values of x.

(b)   Calculating $g(x) + g(-x)$ directly, we have

$$g(x) + g(-x)$$

$$= \frac{A}{1 + e^{-Cx}} + \frac{A}{1 + e^{Cx}}$$

$$= \frac{A(1 + e^{Cx}) + A(1 + e^{-Cx})}{(1 + e^{-Cx})(1 + e^{Cx})}$$

$$= \frac{A(2 + e^{Cx} + e^{-Cx})}{1 + 1 + e^{-Cx} + e^{Cx}} = A.$$

This is the sum of two mirror-image functions. Their sum is A for any value of x.

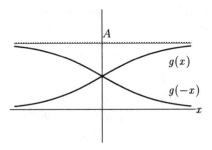

(c)   If C is increased, then the slope near $x = 0$ increases.

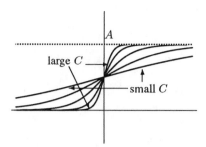

(d)   Consider a horizontal shift of $g(x)$. Replacing x by $x - b$ in the function $g(x)$, we get a shift to the right by the distance b.

$$g(x - b) = \frac{A}{1 + e^{-C(x-b)}}$$

$$= \frac{A}{1 + e^{-Cx+bC}}$$

$$= \frac{A}{1 + e^{bC}e^{-Cx}}$$

Since e^{bC} is a constant, we can rename it B. Thus $g(x - b) = \dfrac{A}{1 + Be^{-Cx}}$. A horizontal shift can be written in terms of B instead of b.

CHAPTER SIX

6.1 SOLUTIONS

1. Left-hand sum gives: $1^2(1/4) + (1.25)^2(1/4) + (1.5)^2(1/4) + (1.75)^2(1/4) = 1.96875$.
   Right-hand sum gives: $(1.25)^2(1/4) + (1.5)^2(1/4) + (1.75)^2(1/4) + (2)^2(1/4) = 2.71875$.
   We estimate the value of the integral by taking the average of these two sums, which is 2.34375.
   Since x^2 is monotonic on $1 \le x \le 2$, the true value of the integral lies between 1.96875 and 2.71875. Thus the most our estimate could be off is 0.375. We expect it to be much closer. (And it is — the true value of the integral is $7/3 \approx 2.333$.)

2. The integral represents the area below the graph of $f(x)$ but above the x-axis.

   (a) Since each square has area 1, by counting squares and half-squares we find

   $$\int_1^6 f(x)\,dx = 8.5.$$

   (b) The average value is $\dfrac{1}{6-1}\displaystyle\int_1^6 f(x)\,dx = \dfrac{8.5}{5} = \dfrac{17}{10} = 1.7$.

3. Since $2x^2 + 7x$ is an antiderivative of $(4x + 7)$, by the Fundamental Theorem we have

   $$\int_1^3 (4x + 7)\,dx = 2x^2 + 7x \Big|_1^3 = 30.$$

   Thus the average value is $\dfrac{1}{3-1}\displaystyle\int_1^3 (4x + 7)\,dx = \dfrac{30}{2} = 15$. Another way to work this problem is to sketch the graph of f on $1 \le x \le 3$. Then the integral is represented by the area underneath the trapezoid, which can easily be found.

4.

   $$\int_a^b f(x)\,dx = \int_a^b x\,dx = \frac{x^2}{2}\Big|_a^b = \frac{1}{2}(b^2 - a^2) = \frac{1}{2}(b - a)(b + a),$$

   so the average value of f on $[a, b]$ is

   $$\frac{1}{(b-a)}\int_a^b f(x)\,dx = \frac{b + a}{2}.$$

   So all we need to consider is whether $\frac{(b-a)(b+a)}{2}$ is less than, greater than, or equal to $\frac{b+a}{2}$.

   (a) $\int_a^b f(x)\,dx$ will be greater than the average value of f on the interval $[a, b]$ if $\frac{(b-a)(b+a)}{2} < \frac{b+a}{2}$. This will be true if either $b + a > 0$ and $b - a < 1$ or $b + a < 0$ and $b - a > 1$. An interval is $[0, \frac{1}{2}]$.

(b) $\int_a^b f(x)\,dx$ will be the same as the average value of f on the interval $[a, b]$ if $\frac{(b-a)(b+a)}{2} = \frac{b+a}{2}$. This will be true if either $b - a = 1$ and $b + a$ takes any values, or $b + a = 0$ and $b - a$ takes any values. An interval is $[0, 1]$.

(c) $\int_a^b f(x)\,dx$ is greater than the average value of f on $[a, b]$ if $\frac{(b-a)(b+a)}{2} > \frac{b+a}{2}$. This will be true if either $b + a > 0$ and $b - a > 1$, or $b + a < 0$ and $b - a < 1$. An interval is $[0, 2]$.

5. Since $\frac{d}{dx}(x^3 + x) = 3x^2 + 1$, by the Fundamental Theorem of Calculus,
$\int_0^2 (3x^2 + 1)\,dx = (x^3 + x)|_0^2 = 10$.

6.

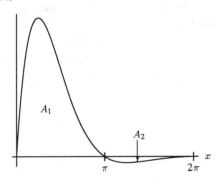

Looking at the above graph of $e^{-x} \sin x$ for $0 \le x \le 2\pi$, we see that the area below the curve for $0 \le x \le \pi$, A_1, is much greater than the area above the curve for $\pi \le x \le 2\pi$, A_2. Thus, since the integral is $A_1 - A_2$,

$$\int_0^{2\pi} e^{-x} \sin x\,dx > 0.$$

7. (a) One small box on the graph corresponds to moving at 750 ft/min for 15 seconds, which corresponds to a distance of 187.5 ft. Estimating the area beneath the velocity curves, we find:
Distance traveled by car 1 $\approx$ 5.5 boxes $= 1031.25$ ft.
Distance traveled by car 2 $\approx$ 3 boxes $= 562.5$ ft.

(b) The two cars will have gone the same distance when the area beneath their velocity curves are equal. Since the two areas overlap, they are equal when the two shaded regions have equal areas, at $t \approx 1.6$ minutes.

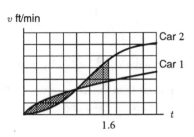

8. (a) At 3 pm, the car is traveling with a velocity of about 67 mph, while the truck has a velocity of 50 mph. Because the car is ahead of the truck at 3 pm and is traveling at a greater velocity, the distance between the car and the truck is increasing at this time. If d_{car} and d_{truck} represent the distance traveled by the car and the truck respectively, then

$$\text{distance apart} = d_{car} - d_{truck}.$$

The rate of change of the distance apart is given by its derivative:

$$(\text{distance apart})' = (d_{car})' - (d_{truck})'$$
$$= v_{car} - v_{truck}$$

At 3 pm, we get $(\text{distance apart})' = 67 \text{ mph} - 50 \text{ mph} = 17 \text{ mph}$. Thus, at 3 pm the car is traveling with a velocity 17 mph greater than the truck's velocity, and the distance between them is increasing at 17 mph.

(b) At 2 pm, the car's velocity is greatest. Because the truck's velocity is constant, $v_{car} - v_{truck}$ will be largest when the car's velocity is largest. Thus, at 2 pm the distance between the car and the truck is increasing fastest—i.e., the car is pulling away at the greatest rate.

(Note: This only takes into account the time when the truck is moving. When the truck <u>isn't</u> moving from 12:00 to 1:00 the car pulls away from the truck at an even greater rate.)

9. (a)

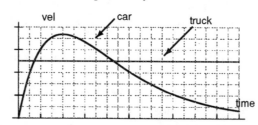

(b) The graphs intersect twice, at about 0.7 hours and 4.3 hours. At each intersection point, the velocity of the car is equal to the velocity of the truck. If the distance apart is written as $d_{car} - d_{truck}$, then its derivative is $(\text{distance apart})' = (d_{car})' - (d_{truck})' = v_{car} - v_{truck}$. At our intersection points $v_{car} = v_{truck}$, so $(\text{distance apart})' = 0$. Thus these points are where the distance between the two vehicles is at a local extremum. To see this, note that from the time they start until 0.7 hours later the truck is traveling at a greater velocity than the car, so the truck is ahead of the car and pulling farther away. At 0.7 hours they are traveling at the same velocity, and after 0.7 hours the car is traveling faster than the truck, so that the car begins to gain on the truck. Thus, at 0.7 hours the truck is farther from the car than it is immediately before or after 0.7 hours. Note that this says nothing about what the distance between the two is doing outside of a small interval around 0.7 hours (later, perhaps, the truck could be even farther from the car): this is only a local extremum. Similarly, because the car's velocity is greater than the truck's after 0.7 hours, it will catch up with the truck and eventually pass and pull away from the truck until 4.3 hours, at which point the two are again traveling at the same velocity. After 4.3 hours the truck travels faster than the car, so that it now gains on the car. Thus, 4.3 hours represents the point where the car is farthest ahead of the truck.

10. Since $\dfrac{d}{dt}(\sin t) = \cos t$, and since $v(t)$ is the derivative of distance traveled, by the Fundamental Theorem of Calculus,

$$\text{distance} = \int_0^{\pi/2} v(t)\, dt = \int_0^{\pi/2} \cos t\, dt = \sin t \Big|_0^{\pi/2} = 1.$$

11. (a) The equation $v = 6 - 2t$ implies that $v > 0$ (the car is moving forwards) if $0 \le t < 3$ and that $v < 0$ (the car is moving backwards) if $t > 3$. When $t = 3$, $v = 0$, so the car is not moving at the instant $t = 3$. The car is decelerating when $|v|$ is decreasing; since v decreases (from 6 to 0) on the interval $0 \le t < 3$, the car decelerates on that interval. The car accelerates when $|v|$ is increasing, which occurs on the domain $t > 3$.

(b) The car moves forward on the interval $0 \le t < 3$, so it is furthest to the right at $t = 3$. For all $t > 3$, the car is decelerating. There is no upper bound on the car's distance behind its starting point since it is decelerating for all $t > 3$.

(c) Let $s(t)$ be the position of the car at time t. Then

$$v(t) = \frac{d}{dt}s(t),$$

so $s(t)$ is an antiderivative of $v(t)$. Thus,

$$s(t) = \int v(t)\, dt = \int (6 - 2t)\, dt = 6t - t^2 + C.$$

Since the car's position is measured from its starting point, we have $s(0) = 0$, so $C = 0$. Thus, $s(t) = 6t - t^2$.

12. (a) The distance traveled is equal to the area of the region under the graph of $v(t)$ between $t = 0$ and $t = 10$, or, the area of the trapezoid T.

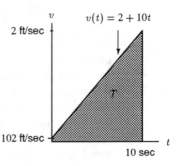

$$\text{Area of } T = \frac{v(0) + v(10)}{2}\Delta t$$
$$= \frac{(2 + 10 \cdot 0) + (2 + 10 \cdot 10)}{2}(10)$$
$$= 520 \text{ ft}.$$

(b) Since $v(t) = 2 + 10t > 0$ for all $t \ge 0$, the car is always moving in the same direction. If the car's initial position is $s(0)$, then its position at time t is simply $s(0)+$ distance traveled in t seconds. To find this distance we calculate the area of the trapezoid where the right-hand limit is t rather than 10.

$$\text{Area of Trapezoid} = \frac{v(0) + v(t)}{2}\Delta t = \frac{(2 + 10 \cdot 0) + (2 + 10t)}{2}t$$

$$= \frac{4 + 10t}{2} t = 5t^2 + 2t.$$

Thus $s(t) = s(0) + 5t^2 + 2t$ feet.

(c) The distance traveled by the car between $t = 0$ and $t = 10$ seconds is found by plugging into $s(t)$:

$$s(10) - s(0) = \left(s(0) + 5(10)^2 + 2 \cdot 10\right) - s(0)$$
$$= 5(10)^2 + 2 \cdot 10 = 520 \text{ ft}.$$

This is the same answer we found in part (a).

(d) The distance traveled by the car between $t = 0$ and $t = 10$ is the area of the region under the graph of $v(t)$ and between $t = 0$ and $t = 10$, i.e.,

$$\text{Total Distance} = \int_0^{10} v(t)\, dt = \int_0^{10} (2 + 10t)\, dt$$

The Fundamental Theorem of Calculus asserts that, if $V(t)$ is an antiderivative for $v(t)$, then

$$\int_0^{10} (2 + 10t)\, dt = V(10) - V(0).$$

If C is any constant, then an antiderivative for $v(t)$ is given by

$$V(t) = 5t^2 + 2t + C.$$

For example, the equation in part (b), $s(t) = 5t^2 + 2t + s(0)$, is such an antiderivative, where C is $s(0)$. Since the total distance $= s(10) - s(0)$, this is an example of the Fundamental Theorem of Calculus. Notice that the C's cancel when computing a definite integral. In this situation this corresponds to the fact that the distance traveled is independent of the starting point.

13. (a) For the first twelve months, the total number of appliances sold is

$$7 + 9 + 11 + \cdots + 29 = 216,$$

so the average number $= \frac{216}{12} = 18$ appliances per month.

(b) Average $= \dfrac{1}{12} \displaystyle\int_0^{12} (2t + 5)\, dt$, which by the Fundamental Theorem is given by $\dfrac{1}{12}(t^2 + 5t)\Big|_0^{12} =$ $\dfrac{204}{12} = 17$ appliances per month.

(c) They are close, but not equal. Using integration gives an underestimate of the true value. This is because the function $2t + 5$ equals the rate at which she sells only at the end of each month; see the figure below.

(d) The integral is easier to calculate than the sum, particularly for a large number of months.

(e)   The rectangles represent the true answer. The shaded region is the error.

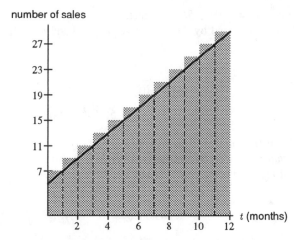

14.   Let C be the rate of the flow through the hose. At $t = t_0$, the volume of water in the tank is equal to the area under the lower curve (flow rate through the hose) minus the area under the upper curve (flow rate through the hole) in the region to the left of the vertical line $t = t_0$. Since the overlap of these regions cancels, the volume is also equal to $5C$ (that's the area under the lower curve from $t = 0$ to $t = 5$) minus the region bounded by the upper curve, the horizontal line of height C, the vertical line $t = t_0$, and the vertical line $t = 5$. If $t_0 > 15$, movement of the vertical line $t = t_0$ doesn't change the area of the latter region, so the difference becomes constant. Thus the volume of water in the tank becomes constant, and the physical system is in a steady state.

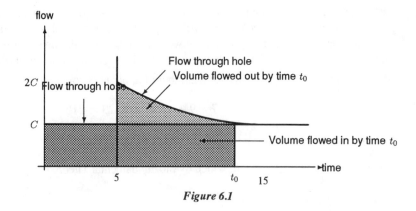

Figure 6.1

15.   (a) $F(x)$ represents the unshaded region under the curve between the y-axis and x; $F(x + h)$ represents this region together with the shaded region. Thus the shaded region alone is given by the difference $F(x + h) - F(x)$.

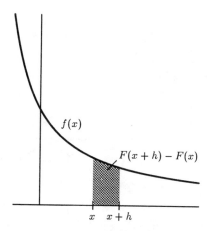

(b) Enlarging the shaded area in part (a), we see that the area of the large box, $(A_1 + A_2 + A_3)$, is $h \cdot f(x)$, the area of the shaded region, $(A_1 + A_2)$, is $F(x + h) - F(x)$ and the area of the small box, A_1, is $h \cdot f(x + h)$. Thus

$$h \cdot f(x) > F(x + h) - F(x) > h \cdot f(x + h).$$

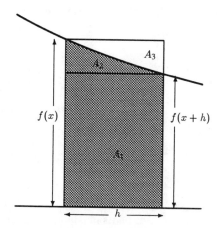

(c) $F'(x) = \lim\limits_{h \to 0} \dfrac{F(x + h) - F(x)}{h}$. From part (b) we have

$$h \cdot f(x) > F(x + h) - F(x) > h \cdot f(x + h).$$

Dividing by h (for $h > 0$) gives

$$f(x) > \frac{F(x + h) - F(x)}{h} > f(x + h).$$

Therefore, $\dfrac{F(x+h)-F(x)}{h}$ is trapped between $f(x)$ and $f(x+h)$. Since in the limit as $h \to 0$, $f(x+h) \to f(x)$, we see that

$$F'(x) = \lim_{h \to 0} \frac{F(x+h)-F(x)}{h} = f(x).$$

16. (a)

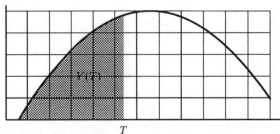

Figure 6.2

$Y(T)$ is the area of the shaded region in the picture. Thus, $Y(T) = \int_0^T y(t)\,dt$.

(b) Here is a graph of $Y(T)$. Note that the graph of y looked like the graph of a quadratic function. Thus, the graph of Y should look like a cubic, which indeed it does.

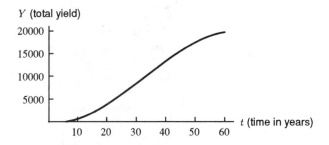

(c) $a(T) = \frac{1}{T}Y(T) = \frac{1}{T}\int_0^T y(t)\,dt$.

(d) (i) If the function $a(T)$ takes on its maximum at some point T, then $a'(T) = 0$. Since $a(T) = \frac{1}{T}Y(T)$, we may differentiate using the quotient rule to show that this condition is equivalent to

$$\frac{TY'(T)-Y(T)}{T^2} = 0;$$

or, equivalently, $Y(T) = TY'(T)$.

(ii) The expression above may be rewritten in terms of y, giving us

$$T\frac{d}{dT}\int_0^T y(t)\,dt = \int_0^T y(t)\,dt.$$

Simplifying, we obtain $Ty(T) = \int_0^T y(t)\, dt$, or, equivalently,

$$y(T) = \frac{1}{T} \int_0^T y(t)\, dt = a(T),$$

which is our desired condition on $y(T)$.

To find the value of T which satisfies $Ty(T) = Y(T)$, notice that $Y(T)$ is the area under the curve from 0 to T, and that $Ty(T)$ is the area of a rectangle of height $y(T)$. Thus we want the area under the curve to be equal to the area of the rectangle, or $A = B$ in the figure below. This happens when $T \approx 50$ years. In other words, the orchard should be cut down after about 50 years.

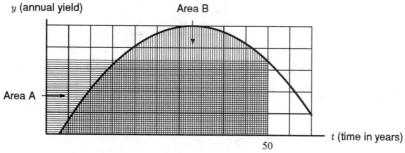

Figure 6.3: The Yield from an Orchard

6.2 SOLUTIONS

1. $\int_1^3 (x^2 - x)\, dx = \int_1^3 x^2\, dx - \int_1^3 x\, dx$.
    $\int_1^3 3x^2\, dx = 26$, so $\int_1^3 x^2\, dx = 26/3$, since $\int_1^3 3x^2\, dx = 3 \int_1^3 x^2\, dx$.
    $\int_1^3 2x\, dx = 8$, so $\int_1^3 x\, dx = 4$, since $\int_1^3 2x\, dx = 2 \int_1^3 x\, dx$.
    Thus, $\int_1^3 (x^2 - x)\, dx = \frac{26}{3} - 4 = \frac{14}{3}$.

2. (a) The integral represents the area of a rectangle with height 1 and base $b - a$. Thus $\int_a^b 1\, dx = b - a$.

    (b) (i) $\int_2^5 1\, dx = 3$.

    (ii) $\int_{-3}^8 1\, dx = 11$.

    (iii) $\int_1^3 23\, dx = 23 \int_1^3 1\, dx = 46$.

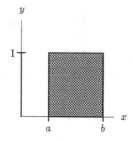

3. (a) The integral represents the area above the x-axis and below the line $y = x$ between $x = a$ and $x = b$. This area is $A_1 + A_2 = a(b-a) + \frac{1}{2}(b-a)^2 = (a + \frac{b-a}{2})(b-a) = \frac{b+a}{2}(b-a) = \frac{b^2-a^2}{2}$. The formula holds similarly for negative values.

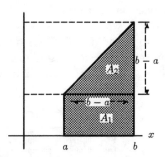

    (b) (i) $\int_2^5 x\, dx = 21/2$. (ii) $\int_{-3}^8 x\, dx = 55/2$. (iii) $\int_1^3 5x\, dx = 5\int_1^3 x\, dx = 20$.

4. This integral represents the area of two triangles, each of base 1 and height 1. Therefore:

$$\int_{-1}^1 |x|\, dx = \frac{1}{2} \cdot 1 \cdot 1 + \frac{1}{2} \cdot 1 \cdot 1 = 1.$$

5. (a) $\frac{1}{\sqrt{2\pi}} \int_1^3 e^{-\frac{x^2}{2}}\, dx$

$$= \frac{1}{\sqrt{2\pi}} \int_0^3 e^{-\frac{x^2}{2}}\, dx - \frac{1}{\sqrt{2\pi}} \int_0^1 e^{-\frac{x^2}{2}}\, dx$$
$$\approx 0.4987 - 0.3413 = 0.1574.$$

    (b) $\left(\text{by symmetry of } e^{x^2/2}\right)$ $\frac{1}{\sqrt{2\pi}} \int_{-2}^3 e^{-\frac{x^2}{2}}\, dx = \frac{1}{\sqrt{2\pi}} \int_{-2}^0 e^{-\frac{x^2}{2}}\, dx + \frac{1}{\sqrt{2\pi}} \int_0^3 e^{-\frac{x^2}{2}}\, dx$

$$= \frac{1}{\sqrt{2\pi}} \int_0^2 e^{-\frac{x^2}{2}}\, dx + \frac{1}{\sqrt{2\pi}} \int_0^3 e^{-\frac{x^2}{2}}\, dx$$
$$\approx 0.4772 + 0.4987 = 0.9759.$$

6. By the given property, $\int_a^a f(x)\, dx = -\int_a^a f(x)\, dx$, so (reversing the a's) $2\int_a^a f(x)\, dx = 0$. Thus $\int_a^a f(x)\, dx = 0$.

7. $\int_{-1}^1 e^{x^2}\, dx > 0$, since $e^{x^2} > 0$, and $\int_{-1}^1 e^{x^2}\, dx$ represents the area below the curve $y = e^{x^2}$.

8. Looking at the figure , we see that $\int_0^1 e^{x^2}\, dx$ represents the area under the curve. This area is clearly greater than zero, but it is less than e since it fits inside a rectangle of width 1 and height e (with room to spare). Thus

$$0 < \int_0^1 e^{x^2}\, dx < e < 3$$

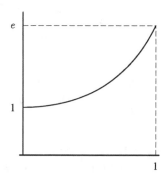

9. (a)

TABLE 6.1

x	0	1	2	3	4	5
$F(x)$	0	1	4	9	16	25

(b) F is clearly increasing for $x > 0$; as x increases, so does the area under the curve. F is also concave up for $x > 0$ — as x gets bigger the size of the area added to the integral gets bigger as well.

(c) $F(-1) = \int_0^{-1} 2t\, dt = -(\int_{-1}^0 2t\, dt)$. The quantity inside the parentheses represents the area between $y = 2t$ and the t-axis for $-1 \le t \le 0$. This area is below the t-axis, hence it is negative. So $F(-1) = -(\text{negative area})$. Thus $F(-1)$ is positive.

10. (a) We find F for each piece, $0 \le x \le 1$ and $1 \le x \le 2$.
     For $0 \le x \le 1$, f is $-x + 1$, so F is of the form

$$\int (-x + 1)\, dx = -\frac{x^2}{2} + x + C.$$

Since we want $F(1) = 1$, we need $C = \frac{1}{2}$.
For $1 \le x \le 2$, f is $x - 1$, so F is of the form

$$\int (x - 1)\, dx = \frac{x^2}{2} - x + C.$$

Again, since we want $F(1) = 1$, we have $C = \frac{3}{2}$.

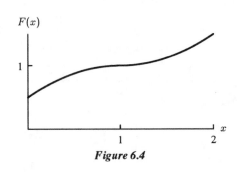

Figure 6.4

(b) $F(2) - F(0) = \frac{3}{2} - \frac{1}{2} = 1$.

The area under the graph of f is the area of the two triangles, which is $\frac{1}{2} + \frac{1}{2} = 1$.

(c) The Fundamental Theorem of Calculus says

$$\int_0^2 f(x)\,dx = F(2) - F(0).$$

Since the value of the integral is just the area under the curve, we have shown this in part (b).

6.3 SOLUTIONS

1.

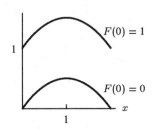

2.

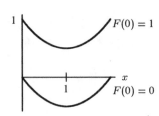

3.

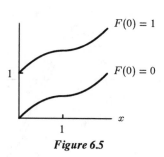

Figure 6.5

4.

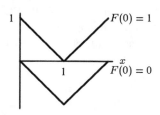

5.

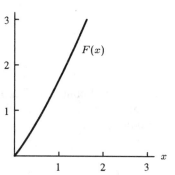

F is increasing because f is positive; F
is concave up because f is increasing.

6.

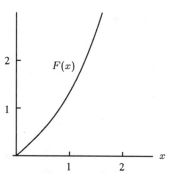

F is increasing because f is positive; F
is concave up because f is increasing.

7.

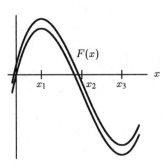

Note that since $f(x_1) = 0$ and $f'(x_1) < 0$, $F(x_1)$ is a local maximum; since $f(x_3) = 0$ and $f'(x_3) > 0$, $F(x_3)$ is a local minimum. Also, since $f'(x_2) = 0$ and f changes from decreasing to increasing about $x = x_2$, F has an inflection point at $x = x_2$.

8.

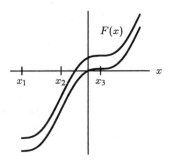

Note that since $f(x_1) = 0$ and $f'(x_1) > 0$, $F(x_1)$ is a local minimum. Since $f'(x_3) = 0$, and f' changes sign around $x = x_2$, $F(x_3)$ is an inflection point. Also, since $f'(x_2) = 0$ and f changes from increasing to decreasing about $x = x_2$, F has another inflection point at $x = x_2$.

9.

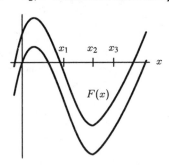

Note that since $f(x_2) = 0$, $f'(x_2) > 0$, so $F(x_2)$ is a local minimum. Since $f'(x_1) = 0$ and f changes from decreasing to increasing at $x = x_1$, F has an inflection point at $x = x_1$.

10.   The derivative, $f'(x)$, graphed with the function, would look something like

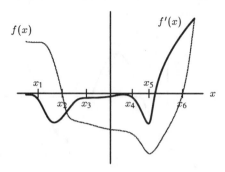

The antiderivative, $F(x)$, graphed with the function, would look something like

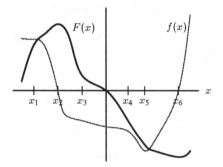

11.   Between time $t = 0$ and time $t = B$, the velocity of the cork is always positive, which means the cork is moving upwards. At time $t = B$, the velocity is zero, and so the cork has stopped moving altogether. Since shortly thereafter the velocity of the cork becomes negative, the cork will next begin to move downwards. Thus when $t = B$ the cork has risen as far as it ever will, and is riding on top of the crest of the wave.

From time $t = B$ to time $t = D$, the velocity of the cork is negative, which means it is falling. When $t = D$, the velocity is again zero, and the cork has ceased to fall. Thus when $t = D$ the cork is riding on the bottom of the trough of the wave.

Since the cork is on the crest at time B and in the trough at time D, it is probably midway between crest and trough when the time is midway between B and D. Thus at time $t = C$ the cork is moving through the equilibrium position on its way down. (The equilibrium position is where the cork would be if the water were absolutely calm.) By symmetry, $t = A$ is the time when the cork is moving through the equilibrium position on the way up.

Since acceleration is the derivative of velocity, points where the acceleration is zero would be critical points of the velocity function. Since point A (a maximum) and point C (a minimum) are critical points, the acceleration is zero there.

A possible graph of the height of the cork is shown below. The horizontal axis represents a height equal to the average depth of the ocean at that point (the equilibrium position of the cork).

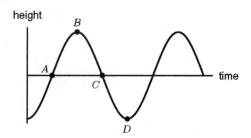

12. Looking at the graph of g', we see that the critical points of g occur when $x = 15$ and $x = 40$, since $g'(x) = 0$ at these values. Inflection points of g occur when $x = 10$ and $x = 20$, because $g'(x)$ has a local maximum or minimum at these values. Knowing these four key points, we sketch the graph of $g(x)$ as follows.

We start at $x = 0$, where $g(0) = 50$. Since g' is negative on the interval $[0, 10]$, the value of $g(x)$ is decreasing there. At $x = 10$ we have

$$g(10) = g(0) + \int_0^{10} g'(x)\, dx$$
$$= 50 - (\text{area of shaded trapezoid } T_1)$$
$$= 50 - \left(\frac{10+20}{2} \cdot 10\right) = -100.$$

Similarly,

$$g(15) = g(10) + \int_{10}^{15} g'(x)\, dx$$
$$= -100 - (\text{area of triangle } T_2)$$
$$= -100 - \frac{1}{2}(5)(20) = -150.$$

Continuing,

$$g(20) = g(15) + \int_{15}^{20} g'(x)\, dx = -150 + \frac{1}{2}(5)(10) = -125,$$

and

$$g(40) = g(20) + \int_{20}^{40} g'(x)\, dx = -125 + \frac{1}{2}(20)(10) = -25.$$

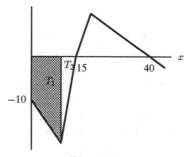

Figure 6.6

We now find concavity of $g(x)$ in the intervals $[0, 10]$, $[10, 15]$, $[15, 20]$, $[20, 40]$ by checking whether $g'(x)$ increases or decreases in these same intervals. If $g'(x)$ decreases, then $g(x)$ is concave up; if $g'(x)$ increases, then $g(x)$ is concave down. Thus we finally have our graph of $g(x)$:

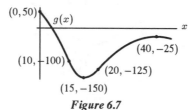

Figure 6.7

13. Let $y'(t) = \frac{dy}{dt}$. Then y is the antiderivative of y' such that $y(0) = 0$. We know that

$$y(x) = \int_0^x y'(t)\, dt.$$

Thus, $y(x)$ is the area under the graph of $\frac{dy}{dt}$ from $t = 0$ to $t = x$ (note: we interpret "area" to be negative if a region lies below the t-axis). We therefore know that $y(t_1) = 2$, $y(t_3) = 2 - 2 = 0$, and $y(t_5) = 2$.

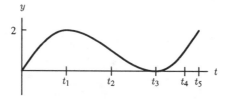

The function y' is positive on the intervals $(0, t_1)$ and (t_3, ∞), so y is increasing on those intervals. y' is negative on the interval (t_1, t_3), so y is decreasing on that interval. y' is increasing on the interval (t_2, t_4), so y is concave up on that interval; y' is decreasing on $(0, t_2)$, so y is concave down there. t_2, the point where the concavity changes, is an inflection point. Finally, since y' is constant on the interval (t_4, ∞), y's graph is linear with positive slope on this interval. $y(t_1) = 2$ is a local maximum, and $y(t_3) = 0$ is a local minimum.

14. Let $y'(t) = \frac{dy}{dt}$. Then y is the antiderivative of y' such that $y(0) = 0$. We know that $y(x) = \int_0^x y'(t)\, dt$. Thus $y(x)$ is the area under the graph of $\frac{dy}{dt}$ from $t = 0$ to $t = x$ (note: we interpret "area" to be negative if a region lies below the t-axis). We therefore know that $y(t_1) = -2$, $y(t_3) = -2 + 2 = 0$, and $y(t_5) = -2$.

   The function y' is positive on the interval (t_1, t_3), so y is increasing on that interval. y' is negative on the intervals $(0, t_1)$ and (t_3, ∞), so y is decreasing on those intervals. y' is increasing on $(0, t_2)$, so y is concave up on that interval; y' is decreasing on (t_2, t_4), so y is concave down there. t_2, the point where concavity changes, is an inflection point. Finally, since y' is a negative constant on the interval (t_4, ∞), y has a linear graph with a negative slope on this interval. $y(t_1) = -2$ is a local minimum, and $y(t_3) = 0$ is a local maximum.

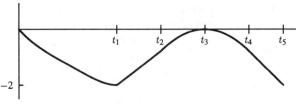

Figure 6.8

15.

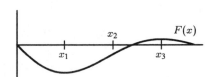

Figure 6.9

16.

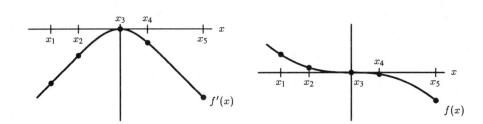

   (a) $f(x)$ is greatest at x_1.
   (b) $f(x)$ is least at x_5.
   (c) $f'(x)$ is greatest at x_3..
   (d) $f'(x)$ is least at x_5.
   (e) $f''(x)$ is greatest at x_1.
   (f) $f''(x)$ is least at x_5.

17. Let's start by making sure that we know what the graph is telling us. This car starts by going 50 mph for two hours, turns around quickly and goes 50 mph in the opposite direction for one hour, turns around again, and goes 50 mph for another hour in the original direction. The distance, D, it has moved by time T is given by the integral of the velocity up to that time:

$$D(T) = \int_0^T v(t)\, dt.$$

We calculate this integral from the area under the curve, with area below the curve being subtracted. For the first two hours the distance moved is given by the area shown in Figure 6.10; this area has magnitude $50T$. Thus

$$D(T) = 50T \qquad \text{for } 0 \leq T < 2.$$

At the end of the first two hours, the car is 100 miles from its starting point. If T is between 2 and 3 hours, the car has moved forwards for 2 hours, and backwards for the remainder of the time, namely $(T - 2)$ hours. (See Figure 6.11.) Thus the car has gone forward 100 miles, and backwards $50(T - 2)$ miles. The total distance from its starting point is given by

$$D(T) = 100 - 50(T - 2) \qquad \text{for } 2 \leq T < 3$$

which simplifies to

$$D(T) = 200 - 50T \qquad \text{for } 2 \leq T < 3.$$

By the end of three hours, the car is $100 - 50 = 50$ miles from its starting point. During the last hour, the car travels in the original direction again. See Figure 6.12. For T over 3 hours, the car starts 50 miles from its starting point and then moves in the original direction for another $(T - 3)$ hours, covering an additional $50(T - 3)$ miles. Thus

$$D(T) = 50 + 50(T - 3) \qquad \text{for } 3 \leq T \leq 4,$$

giving

$$D(T) = 200 - 50T \qquad \text{for } 3 \leq T \leq 4.$$

A graph of the function $D(T)$ is in Figure 6.13.

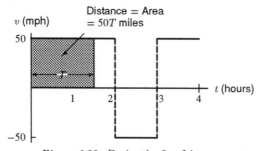

Figure 6.10: During the first 2 hours

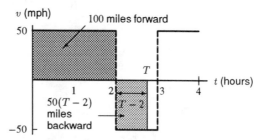

Figure 6.11: Between the 2nd and 3rd hour

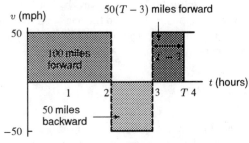

Figure 6.12: The last hour

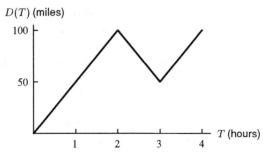

Figure 6.13: Distance of car from starting point as a function of time

18. (a) Suppose $Q(t)$ is the amount of water in the reservoir at time t. Then

$$Q'(t) = \begin{array}{c} \text{Rate at which water} \\ \text{in reservoir is increasing} \end{array} = \begin{array}{c} \text{inflow} \\ \text{rate} \end{array} - \begin{array}{c} \text{outflow} \\ \text{rate} \end{array}$$

Thus the amount of water in the reservoir is increasing when the inflow curve is above the outflow, and decreasing when it is below. This means that $Q(t)$ is a maximum where the curves cross in July 1993 (as shown in Figure 6.14), and $Q(t)$ is decreasing fastest when the outflow is farthest above the inflow curve, which occurs about October 1993 (see Figure 6.14).

To estimate values of $Q(t)$, we use the Fundamental Theorem which says that the change in the total quantity of water in the reservoir is given by

$$Q(t) - Q(\text{Jan'93}) = \int_{\text{Jan93}}^{t} (\text{inflow rate} - \text{outflow rate})dt$$

or

$$Q(t) = Q(\text{Jan'93}) + \int_{\text{Jan93}}^{t} (\text{inflow rate} - \text{outflow rate})dt$$

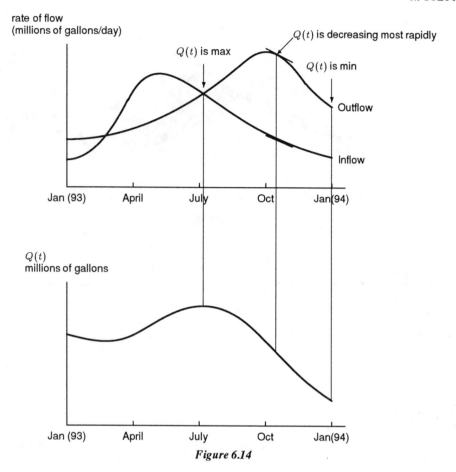

Figure 6.14

(b)   See Figure 6.14. Maximum in July 1993. Minimum in Jan 1994.

(c)   See Figure 6.14. Increasing fastest in May 1993. Decreasing fastest in Oct 1993.

(d)   In order for the water to be the same as Jan'93 the total amount of water which has flowed into the reservoir must be 0, so

$$\int_{\text{Jan93}}^{\text{July94}} (\text{inflow} - \text{outflow})dt = -A_1 + A_2 - A_3 + A_4 = 0$$

giving $A_1 + A_3 = A_2 + A_4$

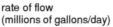

rate of flow
(millions of gallons/day)

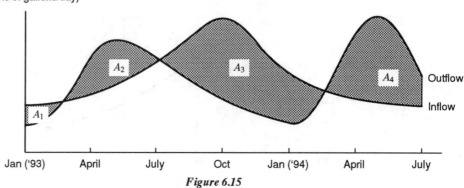

Figure 6.15

6.4 SOLUTIONS

1. $5x$

2. $\frac{5}{2}x^2$

3. $\frac{1}{3}x^3$

4. $\frac{1}{3}t^3 + \frac{1}{2}t^2$

5. $\sin t$

6. $\frac{2}{3}z^{\frac{3}{2}}$

7. $\ln z$

8. $-\dfrac{1}{t}$

9. $-\dfrac{1}{2z^2}$

10. e^z

11. $-\cos t$

12. $\frac{2}{3}t^3 + \frac{3}{4}t^4 + \frac{4}{5}t^5$

13. $\frac{t^4}{4} - \frac{t^3}{6} - \frac{t^2}{2}$

14. $\frac{y^5}{5} + \ln y$

15. $\dfrac{5}{2}x^2 - \dfrac{2}{3}x^{\frac{3}{2}}$

16. $\dfrac{t^2+1}{t} = t + \dfrac{1}{t}$, which has antiderivative $\dfrac{t^2}{2} + \ln|t|$

17. $-\cos 2\theta$

18. $e^t + 5\frac{1}{5}e^{5t} = e^t + e^{5t}$

19. $\frac{1}{3}(t+1)^3$

20. $\dfrac{5^x}{\ln 5}$

21. $\sin t + \tan t$

22. $\sin(t^2)$

23. $\dfrac{1}{2}\sin(t^2)$

24. $\sin(x^3 + 7)$

25. $e^2 y + \dfrac{2^y}{\ln 2}$

26. $-\cos\theta + \arctan\theta$

27. $\dfrac{1}{2}e^{x^2}$

28. $4x^{\frac{3}{2}} + \dfrac{1}{x} + 10\ln x$

29. The general antiderivative of $f(x)$ is $F(x) = 3x + C$. Since $F(0) = 2$, we have $F(0) = 3(0) + C = C = 2$. Thus $C = 2$, and $F(x) = 3x + 2$.

30. The general antiderivative of $f(x)$ is $F(x) = e^x + C$. Since $F(0) = 2$, we have $F(0) = e^0 + C = 1 + C = 2$. Thus $C = 1$, and $F(x) = e^x + 1$.

31. The general antiderivative of $f(x)$ is $F(x) = \frac{1}{3}x^3 + C$. Since $F(0) = 2$, we have $F(0) = \frac{1}{3}(0)^3 + C = C = 2$. Thus $C = 2$, and $F(x) = \frac{1}{3}x^3 + 2$.

32. The general antiderivative of $f(x)$ is $F(x) = \sin x + C$. Since $F(0) = 2$, we have $F(0) = \sin 0 + C = 0 + C = 2$. Thus $C = 2$, and $F(x) = \sin x + 2$.

33. The general antiderivative of $f(x)$ is $F(x) = -\cos x + C$. Since $F(0) = 2$, we have $F(0) = -\cos 0 + C = -1 + C = 2$. Thus $C = 3$, and $F(x) = -\cos x + 3$.

34. The general antiderivative of $f(x)$ is $F(x) = \frac{1}{3}(x-1)^3 + C$. Since $F(0) = 2$, we have $F(0) = \frac{1}{3}(0-1)^3 + C = -\frac{1}{3} + C = 2$. Thus $C = \frac{7}{3}$, and $F(x) = \frac{1}{3}(x-1)^3 + \frac{7}{3}$.

35. $\dfrac{3x^2}{2} + C$

36. $2t^2 + 7t + C$

37. $\sin\theta + C$

38. $5e^z + C$

39. $\dfrac{x^2}{2} + 2x^{1/2} + C$

40. $-\cos t + C$

41. $\pi x + \dfrac{x^{12}}{12} + C$

42. $\displaystyle\int \left(t^{3/2} + t^{-3/2}\right)\, dt = \dfrac{2t^{5/2}}{5} - 2t^{-1/2} + C$

43. $\sin(x + 1) + C$

44. $\frac{1}{2}e^{2r} + C$

45. $\displaystyle\int \dfrac{1}{e^z}\, dz = \int e^{-z}\, dz = -e^{-z} + C$

46. $\displaystyle\int \left(y - \dfrac{1}{y}\right)^2 dy = \int (y^2 - 2 + \dfrac{1}{y^2})\, dy = \dfrac{y^3}{3} - 2y - \dfrac{1}{y} + C$

47.

$$\frac{dy}{dt} = k\sqrt{t} = kt^{1/2}$$

$$y = \frac{2}{3}kt^{3/2} + C.$$

Since $y = 0$ when $t = 0$, we have $C = 0$, so

$$y = \frac{2}{3}kt^{3/2}.$$

48. Since the car's acceleration is constant, a graph of its velocity against time t is linear.

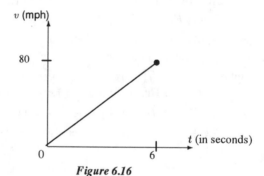

Figure 6.16

The acceleration is just the slope of this line:

$$\frac{dv}{dt} = \frac{80 - 0\ \text{mph}}{6\ \text{sec}} = \frac{40}{3} = 13.33\frac{\text{mph}}{\text{sec}}.$$

To convert our units into ft/sec^2,

$$\frac{40}{3} \cdot \frac{\text{mph}}{\text{sec}} \cdot \frac{5280\ \text{ft}}{1\ \text{mile}} \cdot \frac{1\ \text{hour}}{3600\ \text{sec}} = 19.55\frac{\text{ft}}{\text{sec}^2}$$

49. (a)

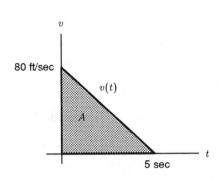

(b) The total distance is represented by the shaded region A, the area under the graph of $v(t)$.

(c) The area A, a triangle, is given by

$$A = \frac{1}{2}(\text{base})(\text{height}) = \frac{1}{2}(5 \sec)(80 \text{ ft/sec}) = 200 \text{ ft}.$$

(d) Using integration and the Fundamental Theorem of Calculus, we have $A = \int_0^5 v(t)\,dt$ or $A = s(5) - s(0)$, where $s(t)$ is an antiderivative of $v(t)$.

   We have that $a(t)$, the acceleration, is constant: $a(t) = k$ for some constant k. Therefore $v(t) = kt + C$ for some constant C. We have $80 = v(0) = k(0) + C = C$, so that $v(t) = kt + 80$. Putting in $t = 5, 0 = v(5) = (k)(5) + 80$, or $k = -80/5 = -16$.

   Thus $v(t) = -16t + 80$, and an antiderivative for $v(t)$ is $s(t) = -8t^2 + 80t + C$. Since the total distance traveled at $t = 0$ is 0, we have $s(0) = 0$ which means $C = 0$. Finally, $A = \int_0^5 v(t)\,dt = s(5) - s(0) = (-8(5)^2 + (80)(5)) - (-8(0)^2 + (80)(0)) = 200 \text{ ft}$, which agrees with the previous part.

50. Since the acceleration is constant, a graph of the velocity versus time looks like this:

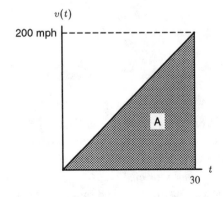

   The distance traveled in 30 seconds, which is how long the runway must be, is equal to the area represented by A. We have $A = \frac{1}{2}(\text{base})(\text{height})$. First we convert the required velocity into miles per second.

$$200 \text{ mph} = \frac{200 \text{ miles}}{\text{hour}} \left(\frac{1 \text{ hour}}{60 \text{ minutes}} \right) \left(\frac{1 \text{ minute}}{60 \text{ seconds}} \right)$$

$$= \frac{200}{3600} \frac{\text{miles}}{\text{second}}$$

$$= \frac{1}{18} \text{ miles/second}.$$

Therefore $A = \frac{1}{2}(30 \text{ sec})(320 \text{ mph}) = \frac{1}{2}(30 \text{ sec}) \left(\frac{1}{18} \text{ miles/sec} \right) = \frac{5}{6} \text{ miles}.$

51. (a)

t (sec)	0	0.5	1	1.5	2	2.5	3	3.5	4	4.5	5	5.5	6
$v(t)$ (ft/sec)	30	27.5	25	22.5	20	17.5	15	12.5	10	7.5	5	2.5	0

Since the velocity is constantly decreasing, and $v(6) = 0$, the car comes to rest after 6 seconds.

(b) Over the interval $a \leq t \leq a + \frac{1}{2}$, the left-hand velocity is $v(a)$, and the right-hand velocity is $v(a + \frac{1}{2})$. Since we are considering half-second intervals, $\Delta t = \frac{1}{2}$, and $n = 12$. Computing, LEFT(12) = 97.5 ft., and RIGHT(12) = 82.5 ft.

(c) Area A represents distance traveled.

$$A = \frac{1}{2}(\text{base})(\text{height}) = \frac{1}{2} \cdot 6 \cdot 30 = 90 \text{ ft}.$$

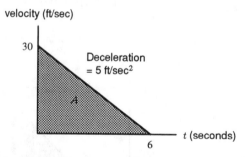

velocity (ft/sec)

30

Deceleration = 5 ft/sec²

A

t (seconds)

6

(d) The velocity is constantly decreasing at a rate of 5 ft/sec per second, i.e. after each second the velocity has dropped by 5 units. Therefore $v(t) = 30 - 5t$.

An antiderivative for $v(t)$ is $s(t)$, where $s(t) = 30t - \frac{5}{2}t^2$. Thus by the Fundamental Theorem of Calculus, the distance traveled = $s(6) - s(0) = (30(6) - \frac{5}{2}(6)^2) - (30(0) - \frac{5}{2}(0)^2) = 90$ ft. Since $v(t)$ is decreasing, the left-hand sum in part (b) overestimates the distance traveled, while the right-hand sum underestimates it.

The area A is equal to the average of the left-hand and right-hand sums: 90 ft = $\frac{1}{2}(97.5 \text{ ft} + 82.5 \text{ ft})$. The left-hand sum is an overestimate of A; the right-hand sum is an underestimate.

52. The equation of motion is $y = -\frac{gt^2}{2} + v_0 t + y_0 = -16t^2 + 128t + 320$. Taking the first derivative, we get $v = -32t + 128$. The second derivative gives us $a = -32$.

(a) At its highest point, the stone's velocity is zero:
$v = 0 = -32t + 128$, so $t = 4$.

(b) At $t = 4$, the height is $y = -16(4)^2 + 128(4) + 320 = 576$ ft

(c) When the stone hits the beach

$$y = 0 = -16t^2 + 128t + 320$$
$$0 = -t^2 + 8t + 20 = (10 - t)(2 + t).$$

So $t = 10$.

(d) Impact is at $t = 10$. The velocity, v, at this time is $v(10) = -32(10) + 128 = -192$ ft/sec.

53. (a) $a(t) = 1.6$, so $v(t) = 1.6t + v_0 = 1.6t$, since the initial velocity is 0.

(b) $s(t) = 0.8t^2 + s_0$

54. (a) $s = v_0 t - 16t^2$, where v_0 = initial velocity, and $v = s' = v_0 - 32t$. At the maximum height, $v = 0$, so $v_0 = 32t$. Plugging into the distance equation yields $100 = 32t^2 - 16t^2 = 16t^2$, so $t = \frac{5}{2}$ seconds, whence $v_0 = 32\left(\frac{5}{2}\right) = 80$ ft/sec.

(b) This time $g = 5$ ft/sec^2, so $s = v_0 t - 2.5t^2 = 80t - 2.5t^2$, and $v = s' = 80 - 5t$. At the highest point, $v = 0$, so $t = \frac{80}{5} \approx 16$. Plugging into the distance equation yields $s = 80(16) - 2.5(16)^2 = 640$ ft.

6.5 SOLUTIONS

1. The velocity as a function of time is given by: $v = v_0 + at$. Since the object starts from rest, $v_0 = 0$, and the velocity is just the acceleration times time: $v = -32t$. Integrating this, we get position as a function of time: $y = -16t^2 + y_0$, where the last term, y_0, is the initial position at the top of the tower, so $y_0 = 400$ feet. Thus we have a function giving position as a function of time: $y = -16t^2 + 400$.

To find at what time the object hits the ground, we find t when $y = 0$. We solve $0 = -16t^2 + 400$ for t, getting $t^2 = \frac{400}{16} = 25$, so $t = 5$. Therefore the object hits the ground after 5 seconds. At this time it is moving with a velocity $v = -32(5) = -160$ feet/second.

2. In Problem 1 we used the equation $0 = -16t^2 + 400$ to learn that the object hits the ground after 5 seconds. In a more general form this is the equation $y = -\frac{g}{2}t^2 + v_0 t + y_0$, and we know that $v_0 = 0$, $y_0 = 400$ ft. So the moment the object hits the ground is given by $0 = -\frac{g}{2}t^2 + 400$. In Problem 1 we used $g = 32$ ft/sec^2, but in this case we want to find a g that results in the object hitting the ground after only 5/2 seconds. So we put in 5/2 for t and solve for g getting: $0 = -\frac{g}{2}\left(\frac{5}{2}\right)^2 + 400$, so $g = \frac{2(400)}{(5/2)^2} = 128$ ft/sec^2.

3. $a(t) = -32$

Since $v(t)$ is the antiderivative of $a(t)$, $v(t) = -32t + v_0$. But $v_0 = 0$, so $v(t) = -32t$. Since $s(t)$ is the antiderivative of $v(t)$, $s(t) = -16t^2 + s_0$, where s_0 is the height of the building. Since the ball hits the ground in 5 seconds, $s(5) = 0 = -400 + s_0$. Hence $s_0 = 400$ feet, so the window is 400 feet high.

4. Let time $t = 0$ be the moment when the astronaut jumps up. If acceleration due to gravity is 5 ft/sec^2 and initial velocity is 10 ft/sec, then the velocity of the astronaut is described by

$$v(t) = 10 - 5t.$$

Suppose $y(t)$ describes his distance from the surface of the moon. By the Fundamental Theorem,

$$y(t) - y(0) = \int_0^t (10 - 5x) \, dx$$

$$y(t) = 10t - \frac{1}{2}5t^2.$$

since $y(0) = 0$ (assuming the astronaut jumps off the surface of the moon).

The astronaut reaches the maximum height when his velocity is 0, i.e. when

$$\frac{dy}{dt} = v(t) = 10 - 5t = 0.$$

Solving for t, we get $t = 2$ sec as the time at which he reaches the maximum height from the surface of the moon. At this time his height is

$$y(2) = 10(2) - \frac{1}{2}5(2)^2 = 10 \text{ ft.}$$

When the astronaut is at height $y = 0$, he either just landed or is about to jump. To find how long it is before he comes back down, we find when he is at height $y = 0$. Set $y(t) = 0$ to get

$$0 = 10t - \frac{1}{2}5t^2$$
$$0 = 20t - 5t^2$$
$$0 = 4t - t^2$$
$$0 = t(t - 4).$$

So we have $t = 0$ sec (when he jumps off) and $t = 4$ sec (when he lands, which gives the time he spent in the air).

5. Let the acceleration due to gravity equal $-k$ meters/sec^2, for some positive constant k, and suppose the object falls from an initial height of $s(0)$ meters.

We have $a(t) = \frac{dv}{dt} = -k$, so that $v(t) = -kt + v_0$. Since the initial velocity is zero, we have $v(0) = -k(0) + v_0 = 0$, which means $v_0 = 0$. Our formula becomes $v(t) = \frac{ds}{dt} = -kt$. This means $s(t) = \frac{-kt^2}{2} + s_0$. Since $s(0) = \frac{-k(0)^2}{2} + s_0$, we have $s_0 = s(0)$, and our formula becomes $s(t) = \frac{-kt^2}{2} + s(0)$. Suppose that the object falls for t seconds. Assuming it hasn't hit the ground, its height is $\frac{-kt^2}{2} + s(0)$, so that the distance traveled is $s(0) - (\frac{-kt^2}{2} + s(0)) = \frac{kt^2}{2}$ meters, which is proportional to t^2.

6. (a) $t = \dfrac{s}{\frac{1}{2}v_{\max}}$.

   t is the time it takes for an object to travel the distance s, starting from rest with uniform acceleration a. $v_{\max}$ is the highest velocity the object reaches. Since its initial velocity is 0, the mean of its highest velocity and initial velocity is $\frac{1}{2}v_{\max}$.

   (b) By Problem 5, $s = \frac{1}{2}gt^2$, where g is the acceleration due to gravity, so it takes $\sqrt{\frac{200}{32}} = \frac{5}{2}$ seconds for the body to hit the ground. Since $v = gt$, $v_{\max} = 32(\frac{5}{2}) = 80$ ft/sec.
   (100 ft)/(40 ft/sec) $= 5/2$, so Galileo's result is verified.

   (c) If the acceleration is a constant a, then $s = \frac{1}{2}at^2$, and $v_{\max} = at$. Thus

   $$\frac{s}{\frac{1}{2}v_{\max}} = \frac{\frac{1}{2}at^2}{\frac{1}{2}at} = t.$$

7. (a) Since $s(t) = -\frac{1}{2}gt^2$, the distance a body falls in the first second is

   $$s(1) = -\frac{1}{2} \cdot g \cdot 1^2 = -\frac{g}{2}.$$

   In the second second, the body travels

   $$s(2) - s(1) = -\frac{1}{2}\left(g \cdot 2^2 - g \cdot 1^2\right) = -\frac{1}{2}(4g - g) = -\frac{3g}{2}.$$

   In the third second, the body travels

   $$s(3) - s(2) = -\frac{1}{2}\left(g \cdot 3^2 - g \cdot 2^2\right) = -\frac{1}{2}(9g - 4g) = -\frac{5g}{2},$$

   and in the fourth second, the body travels

   $$s(4) - s(3) = -\frac{1}{2}\left(g \cdot 4^2 - g \cdot 3^2\right) = -\frac{1}{2}(16g - 9g) = -\frac{7g}{2}.$$

   (b) Galileo seems to have been correct. His observation follows from the fact that the differences between consecutive squares are consecutive odd numbers. For, if n is any number, then $n^2 - (n-1)^2 = 2n - 1$, which is the nth odd number (where 1 is the first).

8. If r is the distance from the center of the earth,

   $$g = \frac{GM}{r^2},$$

   so at 2 meters

   $$9.8 = \frac{GM}{(6.4 \times 10^6 + 2)^2}.$$

   At 100 meters above the ground,

   $$g_{\text{new}} = \frac{GM}{(6.4 \times 10^6 + 100)^2}.$$

so

$$\frac{g_{new}}{9.8} = \frac{GM}{(6.4 \times 10^6 + 100)^2} \bigg/ \frac{GM}{(6.4 \times 10^6 + 2)^2}$$

$$g_{new} = 9.8 \left(\frac{6,400,002}{6,400,100}\right)^2 = 9.79969\ldots \text{ m/sec}^2.$$

Thus, to the first decimal place, the acceleration due to gravity is still 9.8 m/sec^2 at 100 m above the ground.

At 100,000 meters above the ground,

$$g_{new} = 9.8 \left(\frac{6,400,002}{6,500,000}\right)^2 = 9.5 \text{m/sec}^2.$$

SOLUTIONS TO REVIEW PROBLEMS FOR CHAPTER SIX

1. True. The antiderivatives of $3x^2$ are of the form $x^3 + C$. No two such curves intersect. (If they did, then we'd have $x^3 + C = x^3 + C'$, so $C = C'$, but then the curves are the same!)

2. False.

$$\int_0^2 x\,dx = \frac{x^2}{2}\bigg|_0^2 = 2,$$

but

$$2\int_0^1 x\,dx = 2\left(\frac{x^2}{2}\bigg|_0^1\right) = 1.$$

3. True. $\int_0^x f(t)\,dt = \int_0^1 f(t)\,dt + \int_1^x f(t)\,dt$, and $\int_0^1 f(t)\,dt$ is a constant given f.

4. Answers may vary, but should discuss Riemann Sums (see Sections 3.2 and 6.1), antiderivatives (Section 5.8) and the Fundamental Theorem of Calculus (Sections 3.4 and 6.1).

5. $f(x) = \frac{1}{2}x^4 - \ln|x| + \frac{1}{x} + C.$

6. $f(x) = e^x + \frac{1}{1+e}x^{1+e} + C.$

7. $f(x) = e^\pi x - \frac{2}{\sqrt{x}} + C.$

8.

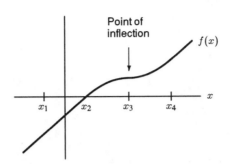

9.

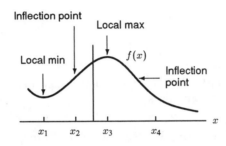

10. Antiderivative $F(x) = \frac{x^2}{2} + \frac{x^6}{6} - \frac{x^{-4}}{4}$.

11. $\ln |x| - \dfrac{1}{x} - \dfrac{1}{2x^2} + C$

12. Antiderivative $F(x) = \frac{x^7}{7} - \frac{1}{7}(\frac{x^{-5}}{-5}) = \frac{x^7}{7} + \frac{1}{35}x^{-5}$.

13. Antiderivative $G(t) = 5t + \sin t$

14. $-\cos(3\alpha) + C$

15. Antiderivative $H(r) = 2\frac{r^{3/2}}{3/2} + \frac{1}{2}\frac{r^{1/2}}{1/2} = \frac{4}{3}r^{3/2} + r^{1/2}$.

16. Antiderivative $G(x) = \frac{x^4}{4} + x^3 + \frac{3x^2}{2} + x$.

17. Antiderivative $H(t) = t - 2\ln|t| - 1/t$.

18. $P(y) = \ln|y| + y^2/2 + y$

19. $F(z) = e^z + 3z$

20. $e^{x^2} + C$

21. $e^x + e^{1+x} + C$

22. $G(\theta) = -\cos\theta - 2\sin\theta$

23. $P(r) = \pi r^2$

24. $\dfrac{2^x}{\ln 2} - \dfrac{2^{-x}}{\ln 2} + C$

25. $\dfrac{(1 + \sin t)^{30}}{30} + C$

26. $\dfrac{2}{3}t^{3/2} + \dfrac{t^{10}}{10} + C$

27. $\sin(2x) + C$

28. $\tan\theta + C$

29. $3e^x + \dfrac{2^x}{\ln 2} + C$

30. $\displaystyle\int (x^2 - 4x + 4)\,dx = \dfrac{x^3}{3} - 2x^2 + 4x + C$

31. $\ln|x + 5| + C$

32. $e^{\sin\theta} + C$

33. $\displaystyle\int \sqrt{x}\left(1 - \dfrac{1}{x^{\frac{3}{2}}}\right) dx = \int \left(x^{1/2} - \dfrac{1}{x}\right) dx = \dfrac{2}{3}x^{3/2} - \ln|x| + C$

34. From Example 2 on page 328, we know that the height of an object above the ground which begins at rest and then falls for t seconds is

$$s(t) = -16t^2 + K,$$

where K is the initial height. Here the flower pot falls from 200 ft, so we have

$$s(t) = -16t^2 + 200.$$

To see when the pot hits the ground, solve $s(t) = 0$: $-16t^2 + 200 = 0$, so $t^2 = 200/16$, and

$$t = \sqrt{\dfrac{200}{16}} \approx 3.54 \text{ seconds.}$$

Now, the velocity of the flower pot is given by $s'(t) = v(t) = -32t$. So, its velocity when it hits the sidewalk is

$$v(3.54) \approx -113.1 \text{ ft/sec,}$$

which is approximately 77 mph downwards.

35. The first thing we should do is convert our units. We'll bring everything into feet and seconds. Thus, the initial speed of the car is

$$\dfrac{70\,\text{miles}}{\text{hour}} \left(\dfrac{1\,\text{hour}}{3600\,\text{sec}}\right) \left(\dfrac{5280\,\text{feet}}{1\,\text{mile}}\right) \approx 102.7\,\text{ft/sec.}$$

We assume that the acceleration is constant as the car comes to a stop. A graph of its velocity versus time is given in Figure 6.17. We know that the area under the curve in Figure 6.17 represents the distance that the car travels before it comes to a stop, 157 feet. But this area is a triangle, so it is easy to find t_0, the time the car comes to rest. We solve

$$\dfrac{1}{2}(102.7)t_0 = 157,$$

which gives

$$t_0 \approx 3.06 \text{ sec.}$$

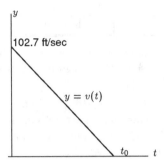

Figure 6.17: Graph of velocity versus time

Since acceleration is the rate of change of velocity, the car's acceleration is given by the slope of the line in Figure 6.17. Thus, the acceleration, k, is given by

$$k = \frac{102.7 - 0}{0 - 3.06} \approx -33.56 \text{ ft/sec}^2.$$

(k is negative because the car is slowing down.)

36. (a) See (b).
      (b)

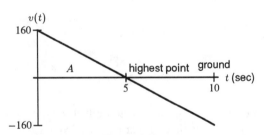

Figure 6.18

The highest point is at $t = 5$ seconds. The object hits the ground at $t = 10$ seconds, since by symmetry if the object takes 5 seconds to go up, it takes 5 seconds to come back down.

(c) The maximum height is the distance traveled when going up, which is represented by the area A of the triangle above the time axis.

$$\text{Area} = \frac{1}{2}(160 \text{ ft/sec})(5 \text{ sec}) = 400 \text{ feet.}$$

(d) The slope of the line is -32, so $v(t) = -32t + 160$.
Antidifferentiating, we get $s(t) = -16t^2 + 160t + s_0$. $s_0 = 0$, so $s(t) = -16t^2 + 160t$. At $t = 5$, $s(t) = -400 + 800 = 400$ ft.

37. (a) Using $g = -32$ ft/sec^2, we have

TABLE 6.2

t (sec)	0	1	2	3	4	5
$v(t)$ (ft/sec)	80	48	16	−16	−48	−80

(b) The object reaches its highest point when $v = 0$, which appears to be at $t = 2.5$ seconds. By symmetry, the object should hit the ground again at $t = 5$ seconds.

(c) Left sum: $80(1) + 48(1) + 16(\frac{1}{2}) = 136$ ft.

Right sum: $48(1) + 16(1) + (-16)\frac{1}{2} = 56$ ft.

The left sum is an overestimate, the right sum an underestimate.

(d) We have $v(t) = 80 - 32t$, so antidifferentiation yields $s(t) = 80t - 16t^2 + s_0$.

But $s_0 = 0$, so $s(t) = 80t - 16t^2$.

At $t = 2.5$, $s(t) = 100$ ft., so 100 ft. is the highest point.

38. The velocity of the car decreases at a constant rate, so we can write: $dv/dt = -a$. Integrating this gives $v = -at + C$. The constant of integration C is the velocity when $t = 0$ so $C = 60$ mph $= 88$ ft/sec, so that $v = -at + 88$. From this equation we can see the car comes to rest at time $t = 88/a$.

Integrating the expression for velocity we get $s = -\frac{a}{2}t^2 + 88t + C$, where C is the initial position, so $C = 0$. We can use fact that the car comes to rest at time $t = 88/a$ after traveling 200 feet, to find the acceleration:

$$s = -\frac{a}{2}t^2 + 88t.$$

Substituting $t = 88/a$ and $s = 200$, we get

$$200 = -\frac{a}{2}\left(\frac{88}{a}\right)^2 + 88\left(\frac{88}{a}\right) = \frac{88^2}{2a}$$

$$a = \frac{88^2}{2(200)} = 19.36 \text{ ft/sec}^2$$

39. From the equation $v = -at + v_0$ we can see that the time at which the car comes to rest (i.e. when $v = 0$) is $t = v_0/a$. At this time the car has traveled a distance D. Putting these into the equation of motion $s = -\frac{a}{2}t^2 + v_0 t$, we get

$$D = -\frac{a}{2}\left(\frac{v_0}{a}\right)^2 + v_0\left(\frac{v_0}{a}\right) = \frac{v_0^2}{2a}.$$

40. (a) $F = -\dfrac{dV}{dr}$, so $\int F\, dr = -V + C$. Therefore,

$$V = -\int\left(-\frac{A}{r^7} + \frac{B}{r^{13}}\right) dr + C$$

$$= -\left(\frac{A}{6r^6} - \frac{B}{12r^{12}}\right) + C.$$

But as $r \to \infty$, $V \to 0$. Therefore, C must equal 0. So,

$$V = -\frac{A}{6r^6} + \frac{B}{12r^{12}}$$

(b)

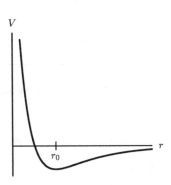

(c) r_0 represents the equilibrium separation distance between the molecules, since $F = 0$ at $r = r_0$. The equilibrium is stable since r_0 is a minimum for the potential energy.

41. (a) In the beginning, both birth and death rates are small; this is consistent with a very small population. Both rates begin climbing, the birth rate faster than the death rate, which is consistent with a growing population. The death rate is then high, but it begins to decrease as the population decreases.

(b)

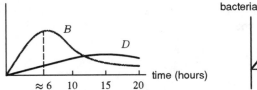

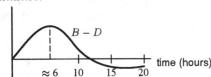

Figure 6.19: Difference between B and D is greatest at $t \approx 6$

The bacteria population is growing most quickly when $B-D$, the rate of change of population, is maximal; that happens when B is farthest above D, which is at a point where the slopes of both graphs are equal. The point on this graph satisfying that criterion is $t \approx 6$, so the greatest rate of increase occurs about 6 hours after things have begun.

(c)   Total number born by time t is the area under the B graph from $t = 0$ up to time t.

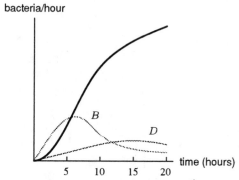

Figure 6.20: Number born by time t is $\int_0^t B(x)\,dx$

Total number alive at time t is the number born minus the number died, which is the area under the B graph up to the time t, minus the area under the D graph up to time t.

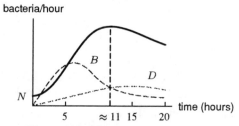

Figure 6.21: Number alive at time t is
$\int_0^t (B(x) - D(x))\,dx$

From Figure 6.21, we see that the population is at a maximum when $B = D$, that is, after about 11 hours. This stands to reason, because $B - D$ is the rate of change of population, so population is maximized when $B - D = 0$, that is, when $B = D$.

42.

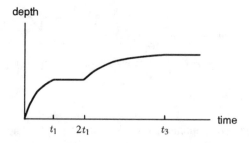

Suppose t_1 is the time to fill the left side to the top of the middle ridge. Since the container gets wider as you go up, the rate $\frac{dH}{dt}$ decreases with time. Therefore, for $0 \le t \le t_1$, graph is concave down.

At $t = t_1$, water starts to spill over to right side and so depth of left side doesn't alter. It takes as long for the right side to fill to the ridge as the left side, namely t_1. Thus the graph is horizontal for $t_1 \leq t \leq 2t_1$.

For $t \geq 2t_1$, water level is above the central ridge. The graph is climbing because the depth is increasing, but at a slower rate than for $t \leq t_1$ because the container is wider. The graph is concave down because width is increasing with depth. Time t_3 represents the time when container is full.

43. (a)

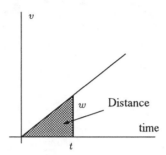

Since the acceleration — the rate of change of velocity — is constant, velocity grows at a constant rate. Hence, the graph of velocity versus time is a straight line.

(b)   Distance is the integral of velocity over time. Therefore, the distance moved by time t is the area under the graph of v between 0 and t: the area of the shaded triangle.

(c)

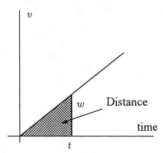

The area of the shaded triangle is $s = bh/2 = tw/2$. This conforms to $s = \frac{0+w}{2}t$, confirming the student's rule if $u = 0$.

(d)

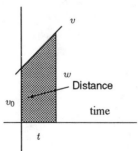

If the initial velocity is positive, then the distance traveled is the area under a line segment between the points $(0, v_0)$ and (t, w). That line has equation $y = x(w - v_0)/t + v_0$. So the area under the line between $x = 0$ and $x = t$ is

$$\int_0^t \left(\frac{x(w - v_0)}{t} + v_0 \right) \, dx$$

$$= \left(\frac{x^2(w - v_0)}{2t} + v_0 x \right) \Bigg|_0^t$$

$$= \frac{t^2(w - v_0)}{2t} + v_0 t$$

$$= \frac{w - v_0}{2} t + v_0 t$$

$$= \frac{w + v_0}{2} t.$$

One can also see this by noting that the area in question is a trapezoid with bases w and v and height t, and using the formula $A = \frac{b_1 + b_2}{2} h$ for the area of a trapezoid.

(e) Air resistance slows down any moving object, and acts more strongly on fast-moving objects, as you may know if you have ever ridden a bicycle. Therefore, the acceleration on the body decreases as its velocity decreases, so the graph of the velocity is concave down. Hence, the trapezoid is now below the curve, so $s \geq \frac{u+w}{2} t$.

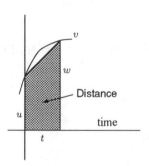

44. (a) $a(T) = \frac{1}{T} \int_0^T \sin t \, dt = \frac{1}{T}(1 - \cos T).$

(b)

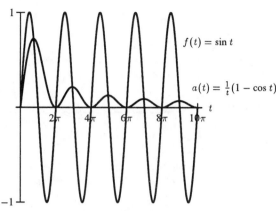

Figure 6.22

$$a'(T) = \frac{d}{dT}\left(\frac{1}{T}\int_0^T f(t)\,dt\right)$$

$$= \frac{d}{dT}\left(\frac{1}{T}\right)\int_0^T f(t)\,dt + \frac{1}{T}\frac{d}{dT}\left(\int_0^T f(t)\,dt\right).$$

Using the Fundamental Theorem of Calculus,

$$= -\frac{1}{T^2}\int_0^T f(t)\,dt + \frac{1}{T}f(T)$$

$$= -\frac{a(T)}{T} + \frac{f(T)}{T}.$$

So $a'(T) > 0$ (a is increasing) if $a(T) < f(T)$, and $a'(T) < 0$ (a is decreasing) if $a(T) > f(T)$. Thus $a(T)$ is maximum or minimum when $a(T) = f(t)$.

45. (a) We integrate by parts. Let $u = t$, so $u' = 1$, and let $v' = \sin t$, so that $v = -\cos t$. We obtain

$$a(T) = \frac{1}{T}\int_0^T t\sin t\,dt = \frac{1}{T}\left[(-t\cos t)\Big|_0^T + \int_0^T \cos t\,dt\right] = -\cos T + \frac{\sin T}{T}.$$

(b) As in Problem 44, we know that $a(t)$ is increasing when $a(t) < f(t)$ and decreasing when $a(t) > f(t)$. We also know that $a(t)$ is maximal or minimal when $a(t) = f(t)$.

So we really only need to know where the graphs of a and f cross. Looking at the graph tells us that they cross just a little before each multiple of π. One could find the actual points by computing where $a'(t) = 0$.

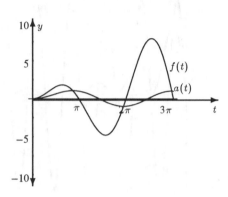

46. We know that $a(T) = \frac{1}{T} \int_0^T f(t)\, dt$. Suppose now that $a(T_0)$ is a local maximum or minimum of $a(T)$. Then $\frac{d}{dT}[a(T)]\Big|_{T=T_0} = 0$. By the Fundamental Theorem of Calculus we know that $\frac{d}{dT}\left(\int_0^T f(t)\, dt\right) = f(T)$, so by the product rule:

$$\frac{d}{dT} a(T) = \frac{1}{T}\frac{d}{dT}\left(\int_0^T f(t)\, dt\right) + \left(\int_0^T f(t)\, dt\right)\frac{d}{dT}\left(\frac{1}{T}\right)$$

$$= \frac{1}{T}f(T) + \left(\int_0^T f(t)\, dt\right)\left(-\frac{1}{T^2}\right)$$

$$= \frac{1}{T}\left(f(T) - \frac{1}{T}\int_0^T f(t)\, dt\right)$$

$$= \frac{1}{T}\left(f(T) - a(T)\right).$$

So, $\frac{d}{dT}[a(T)]\Big|_{T=T_0} = 0$ implies that $\frac{1}{T_0}\left(f(T_0) - a(T_0)\right) = 0$. This means that $f(T_0) = a(T_0)$, i.e. $f(T)$ and $a(T)$ intersect at $T = T_0$. Thus when $a(T)$ is a local maximum or minimum, the graphs of $a(T)$ and $f(T)$ intersect.

47. (a) If the poorest $p\%$ of the population has exactly $p\%$ of the goods, then $F(x) = x$.

(b) Any such F is increasing. For example, the poorest 50% of the population includes the poorest 40%, and so the poorest 50% must own more than the poorest 40%. Thus $F(0.4) \leq F(0.5)$, and so, in general, F is increasing. In addition, it is clear that $F(0) = 0$ and $F(1) = 1$.

The graph of F is concave up by the following argument. Suppose the poorest 40% own 4% of the resource. Then someone in this group owns at least $\frac{1}{10}\%$ of the resource. The next 10% of the population must own at least 1% of the resource (otherwise someone in this group would be poorer than the person from the 40% who owned at least $\frac{1}{10}$% of the resource). Thus the poorest 50% must own at least 5% of the resource and perhaps more. Suppose they own 6%. What about the next 10%? They must own at least 2% (or they'd be poorer than some of the previous 10%). Thus the poorest 60% must own at least 8% and perhaps more. Suppose they own 9%. Then the increase in wealth from 50% to 60% (in this example, 3%) is at least as great as the increase from 40% to 50% (here 2%). Notice that in this example we have decided that $F(0.4) = 0.04$, $F(0.5) = 0.06$, $F(0.6) = 0.09$, so the increases in $F(x)$ are increasing. A similar argument shows that, in general, the increases in $F(x)$ must increase with x, so the graph of F is concave up.

(c) G is twice the shaded area below. If the resource is distributed evenly, then G is zero. The larger G is, the more unevenly the resource is distributed.

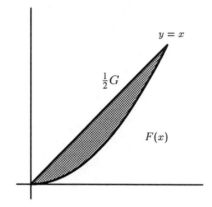

48.   (a)   The velocity $v(t)$ is given by

$$v(t) = v(0) + \int_0^t 30 \sin x \, dx$$

$$= 30 - 30 \cos x \Big|_0^t$$

$$= 30 - 30 \cos t + 30 \cos 0$$

$$= 60 - 30 \cos t.$$

(b)   The distance $d(t)$ that the car travels between $t = 0$ and $t = 3\pi$ is given by the Fundamental Theorem

$$d(3\pi) - d(0) = \int_0^{3\pi} (60 - 30 \cos t) \, dt$$

$$= 60t - 30 \sin t \Big|_0^{3\pi}$$

$$= 60(3\pi - 0) + 30(0 - 0)$$

$$= 180\pi \approx 565 \text{ feet}$$

(c) The driver is driving erratically. Note the velocity of the car oscillates between 60 ft/sec and 30 ft/sec with a period of $2\pi \approx 6.28$ seconds, i.e. every 6.28 seconds, the speed changes from 60 ft/sec to 30 ft/sec and back again. One isn't supposed to change speed all the time while driving on the highway, but more importantly, the car is going at dangerously low speeds: 60 ft/sec $\approx$ 41 mph and 30 ft/sec $\approx$ 21 mph.

(d) From part (c), one sees that the car was not speeding.

CHAPTER SEVEN

7.1 SOLUTIONS

1. $f(x) = 3$, so $F(x) = 3x + C$. $F(0) = 0$ implies that $3 \cdot 0 + C = 0$, so $C = 0$. Thus $F(x) = 3x$ is the only possibility.

2. $f(x) = 2x$, so $F(x) = x^2 + C$. $F(0) = 0$ implies that $0^2 + C = 0$, so $C = 0$. Thus $F(x) = x^2$ is the only possibility.

3. $f(x) = -7x$, so $F(x) = \frac{-7x^2}{2} + C$. $F(0) = 0$ implies that $-\frac{7}{2} \cdot 0^2 + C = 0$, so $C = 0$. Thus $F(x) = -7x^2/2$ is the only possibility.

4. $f(x) = \frac{1}{4}x$, so $F(x) = \frac{x^2}{8} + C$. $F(0) = 0$ implies that $\frac{1}{8} \cdot 0^2 + C = 0$, so $C = 0$. Thus $F(x) = x^2/8$ is the only possibility.

5. $f(x) = x^2$, so $F(x) = \frac{x^3}{3} + C$. $F(0) = 0$ implies that $\frac{0^3}{3} + C = 0$, so $C = 0$. Thus $F(x) = \frac{x^3}{3}$ is the only possibility.

6. $f(x) = x^{1/2}$, so $F(x) = \frac{2}{3}x^{3/2} + C$. $F(0) = 0$ implies that $\frac{2}{3} \cdot 0^{3/2} + C = 0$, so $C = 0$. Thus $F(x) = \frac{2}{3}x^{3/2}$ is the only possibility.

7. $f(x) = 2 + 4x + 5x^2$, so $F(x) = 2x + 2x^2 + \frac{5}{3}x^3 + C$. $F(0) = 0$ implies that $C = 0$. Thus $F(x) = 2x + 2x^2 + \frac{5}{3}x^3$ is the only possibility.

8. $f(x) = 5 - \frac{x^6}{6} - x^7$, so $F(x) = 5x - \frac{x^7}{42} - \frac{x^8}{8} + C$. $F(0) = 0$ implies that $C = 0$. Thus $F(x) = 5x - \frac{x^7}{42} - \frac{x^8}{8}$ is the only possibility.

9. $f(x) = \sin x$, so $F(x) = -\cos x + C$. $F(0) = 0$ implies that $-\cos 0 + C = 0$, so $C = 1$. Thus $F(x) = -\cos x + 1$ is the only possibility.

10. One antiderivative is $2x^{\frac{1}{2}}$. The general form for all antiderivatives is $2x^{\frac{1}{2}} + C$.

11. One antiderivative is $\frac{1}{4}x^4 + \frac{10}{3}x^{\frac{3}{2}} + 2x^{-1}$. The general form for all antiderivatives is $\frac{1}{4}x^4 + \frac{10}{3}x^{\frac{3}{2}} + 2x^{-1} + C$.

12. One antiderivative is $\frac{2}{5}x^{\frac{5}{2}} - 2x^{-\frac{1}{2}}$. The general form for all antiderivatives is $\frac{2}{5}x^{\frac{5}{2}} - 2x^{-\frac{1}{2}} + C$.

13. One antiderivative is $7t - \frac{t^9}{72} + \ln|t|$. The general form for all antiderivatives is $7t - \frac{t^9}{72} + \ln|t| + C$.

14. First write $h(y) = \frac{y^2+1}{y}$ as $h(y) = y + \frac{1}{y}$. Then we can find an antiderivative such as $\frac{1}{2}y^2 + \ln|y|$. The general form for all antiderivatives is $\frac{1}{2}y^2 + \ln|y| + C$.

15. One antiderivative is $\sin\theta - \cos\theta$. The general form for all antiderivatives is $\sin\theta - \cos\theta + C$.

16. $f(x) = e^x$, so $F(x) = e^x + C$. $0 = F(1) = e + C$, so $C = -e$. Thus $F(x) = e^x - e$ is the only possibility.

17. Let $F(x) = \frac{x^2 \sin x}{2}$. Then by the product rule $F'(x) = x \sin x + \frac{x^2 \cos x}{2} \neq x \cos x$. Thus $F(x)$ is not an antiderivative of $x \cos x$.

18. (a) Let $F(x) = (\frac{x^2}{2} + 6x)/(\frac{x^3}{3}) = \frac{3}{2x} + \frac{18}{x^2}$. $F'(x) = -\frac{3}{2x^2} - \frac{36}{x^3} \neq \frac{x+6}{x^2}$. Thus $(\frac{x^2}{2} + 6x)/(\frac{x^3}{3})$ is not an antiderivative of $\frac{x+6}{x^2}$.

   (b) $\frac{x+6}{x^2} = \frac{1}{x} + \frac{6}{x^2}$. $\ln|x| - \frac{6}{x}$ is one antiderivative. The general form for all antiderivatives of $\frac{x+6}{x^2}$ is $\ln|x| - \frac{6}{x} + C$.

19. Let $F(y) = \arctan 2y$. $F'(y) = \frac{1}{1+(2y)^2} \cdot 2 = \frac{2}{1+4y^2}$, so $\arctan 2y$ is an antiderivative of $\frac{2}{1+4y^2}$.

20. $\frac{5}{2}x^2 + 7x + C$

21. $3 \ln|t| + \dfrac{2}{t} + C$

22. $3 \sin \psi + 2\psi^{\frac{3}{2}} + C$

23. $\frac{2}{5}x^{\frac{5}{2}} + \frac{2}{15}x^{\frac{3}{2}} - 2 \ln|x| + C$

24. Since $f(x) = \frac{x+1}{x} = 1 + \frac{1}{x}$, the indefinite integral is $x + \ln|x| + C$

25. Since $f(x) = x + 1 + \frac{1}{x}$, the indefinite integral is $\frac{1}{2}x^2 + x + \ln|x| + C$

26. $e^x + 5x + C$

27. $3 \sin x + 7 \cos x + C$

28. $\frac{x^2}{2} + 2 \ln|x| - \pi \cos x + C$

29. $2e^x - 8 \sin x + C$

30. $\tan x + C$

31. $\frac{1}{\ln 2}2^x + C$, since $\frac{d}{dx}(2^x) = (\ln 2) \cdot 2^x$

32. $\int (x+1)^2 \, dx = \frac{(x+1)^3}{3} + C$.

   Another way to work the problem is to expand $(x+1)^2$ to $x^2 + 2x + 1$ as follows:

   $$\int (x+1)^2 \, dx = \int (x^2 + 2x + 1) \, dx = \frac{x^3}{3} + x^2 + x + C.$$

   These two answers are the same, since $\dfrac{(x+1)^3}{3} = \dfrac{x^3 + 3x^2 + 3x + 1}{3} = \dfrac{x^3}{3} + x^2 + x + \dfrac{1}{3}$, which is $\dfrac{x^3}{3} + x^2 + x$, plus a constant.

33. $\int (x+1)^3 \, dx = \frac{(x+1)^4}{4} + C$.

   Another way to work the problem is to expand $(x+1)^3$ to $x^3 + 3x^2 + 3x + 1$:

   $$\int (x+1)^3 \, dx = \int (x^3 + 3x^2 + 3x + 1) \, dx = \frac{x^4}{4} + x^3 + \frac{3}{2}x^2 + x + C.$$

   It can be shown that these answers are the same by expanding $\frac{(x+1)^4}{4}$.

34. $\frac{1}{10}(x+1)^{10} + C$

35. $\ln|x+1| + C$

36. $\frac{1}{2}\ln|2x-1| + C$, since $\frac{d}{dx}\ln|2x-1| = 2(\frac{1}{2x-1}) = 2f(x)$.

37. $e^{5+x} + \frac{1}{5}e^{5x} + C$, since $\frac{d}{dx}(e^{5x}) = 5e^{5x}$.

38. $\frac{1}{2}\sin 2x + 2\cos x + C$, since $\frac{d}{dx}(\sin 2x) = 2\cos 2x$.

39. (a) $\frac{1}{2}e^{2t}$ (b) $-\frac{1}{3}e^{-3\theta}$

40. $f(x) = x^3$, so $F(x) = \frac{x^4}{4} + C$.

If $F(0) = 0$, then $F(x) = \frac{x^4}{4}$.

If $F(0) = 1$, then $F(x) = \frac{x^4}{4} + 1$.

If $F(0) = -1$, then $F(x) = \frac{x^4}{4} - 1$.

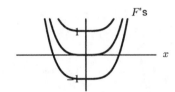

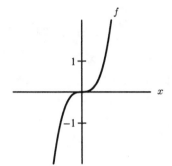

41. $\displaystyle\int_2^5 (x^3 - \pi x^2)\, dx = \left(\frac{x^4}{4} - \frac{\pi x^3}{3}\right)\Big|_2^5 = \frac{609}{4} - 39\pi \approx 29.728.$

42. $\displaystyle\int_0^1 \sin\theta\, d\theta = -\cos\theta\Big|_0^1 = 1 - \cos 1 \approx 0.460.$

43. Since $\dfrac{1+y^2}{y} = \dfrac{1}{y} + y$,

$$\int_1^2 \frac{1+y^2}{y}\, dy = \left(\ln|y| + \frac{y^2}{2}\right)\Big|_1^2 = \ln 2 + \frac{3}{2} \approx 2.193.$$

44. $\displaystyle\int_0^2 \left(\frac{x^3}{3} + 2x\right) dx = \left(\frac{x^4}{12} + x^2\right)\Big|_0^2 = \frac{4}{3} + 4 = 16/3 \approx 5.333.$

45. $\displaystyle\int_0^{\pi/4} (\sin t + \cos t)\, dt = (-\cos t + \sin t)\Big|_0^{\pi/4} = \left(-\frac{\sqrt{2}}{2} + 1 + \frac{\sqrt{2}}{2}\right) = 1.$

46. $\displaystyle\int_{-3}^{-1} \frac{2}{r^3}\, dr = -r^{-2}\Big|_{-3}^{-1} = -1 + \frac{1}{9} = -8/9 \approx -0.888.$

47. $\int_0^1 2e^x \, dx = 2e^x \Big|_0^1 = 2e - 2 \approx 3.437.$

48. Since $(\tan x)' = \dfrac{1}{\cos^2 x}$,

$$\int_0^{\frac{\pi}{4}} \frac{1}{\cos^2 x} \, dx = \tan x \Big|_0^{\frac{\pi}{4}} = \tan \frac{\pi}{4} - \tan 0 = 1.$$

49. $\int 2^x \, dx = \dfrac{1}{\ln 2} 2^x + C$, since $\dfrac{d}{dx} 2^x = \ln 2 \cdot 2^x$, so

$$\int_{-1}^1 2^x \, dx = \frac{1}{\ln 2} \left[2^x \Big|_{-1}^1 \right] = \frac{3}{2 \ln 2} \approx 2.164.$$

50. Since $\dfrac{d}{dx} \sin 2x = 2 \cos 2x$,

$$
\begin{aligned}
\int_0^{\frac{\pi}{6}} (\sin x + \cos 2x) \, dx &= \left(-\cos x + \frac{1}{2} \sin 2x \right) \Big|_0^{\frac{\pi}{6}} \\
&= \left(-\cos \frac{\pi}{6} + \frac{1}{2} \sin \frac{\pi}{3} \right) - \left(-\cos 0 + \frac{1}{2} \sin 0 \right) \\
&= 1 + \frac{1}{2} \sin \frac{\pi}{3} - \cos \frac{\pi}{6} \\
&= 1 + \frac{\sqrt{3}}{4} - \frac{\sqrt{3}}{2} \\
&= 1 - \frac{\sqrt{3}}{4} \\
&\approx 0.567.
\end{aligned}
$$

51. (a) (i) $\dfrac{d}{dx} \sin 5x = 5 \cos 5x$

   (ii) $\dfrac{d}{dx} \cos x^2 = -2x \sin x^2$

   (iii) $\dfrac{d}{dx} e^{\sin x} = (\cos x) e^{\sin x}$

   (iv) $\dfrac{d}{dx} \sin(\cos x) = -\cos(\cos x)(-\sin x) = -\sin x \cos(\cos x)$

   (v) $\dfrac{d}{dx} \ln(\cos x) = \dfrac{1}{\cos x}(-\sin x) = -\tan x$

   (vi) $\dfrac{d}{dx} \ln(\cos x^4) = \dfrac{1}{\cos x^4}(-\sin x^4)(4x^3) = -4x^3 \tan x^4$

   (b) (i) $\int \cos 5x \, dx = \dfrac{1}{5} \sin 5x + C$

(ii) $\displaystyle\int x \sin x^2\, dx = -\frac{1}{2}\cos x^2 + C$

(iii) $\displaystyle\int \cos x\, e^{\sin x}\, dx = e^{\sin x} + C$

(iv) $\displaystyle\int \sin x \cos(\cos x)\, dx = -\sin(\cos x) + C$

(v) $\displaystyle\int \tan x\, dx = -\ln(|\cos x|) + C$

(vi) $\displaystyle\int x^3 \tan x^4\, dx = -\frac{1}{4}\ln(|\cos x^4|) + C$

(c) We use the chain rule in part (a) and obtain derivatives which we recognize as integrands in part (b), up to a constant multiple. Therefore, we suspect there may be some sort of "chain rule in reverse" rule for integration.

52. (a) (i)
$$\frac{d}{dx}(\ln(1+x) - \ln(2+x)) = \frac{1}{1+x} - \frac{1}{2+x}$$
$$= \frac{(2+x)-(1+x)}{(1+x)(2+x)}$$
$$= \frac{1}{(1+x)(2+x)}$$

(ii) $\dfrac{d}{dx}\ln(\cos x) = \dfrac{1}{\cos x}\cdot(-\sin x) = -\tan x$ (iii) $\dfrac{d}{dx}e^{x^2} = 2xe^{x^2}$ (iv) $\dfrac{d}{dx}(1+x^2)^{15} = 15(1+x^2)^{14}\cdot 2x = 30x(1+x^2)^{14}$

(b) (i) $\displaystyle\int \tan 2x\, dx = \int \left(\frac{1}{\cos x}\right)\sin x\, dx = -\ln|\cos x| + C$

(ii) $\displaystyle\int x e^{x^2/2}\, dx = e^{x^2/2} + C$

(iii) $\displaystyle\int x(1+x^2)^{14}\, dx = \frac{1}{30}(1+x^2)^{15} + C$

(iv) $\displaystyle\int \frac{1}{(1+x)(2+x)}\, dx = \ln|1+x| - \ln|2+x| + C$

(v) $\displaystyle\int x(1+x^2)^{12}\, dx = \frac{1}{26}(1+x^2)^{13} + C$ (This is analogous to iii.)

(vi) Since $\dfrac{1}{(1+x)(3+x)} = \dfrac{1}{2}\left(\dfrac{1}{1+x} - \dfrac{1}{3+x}\right)$,

$\displaystyle\int \frac{1}{(1+x)(3+x)}\, dx = \frac{1}{2}[\ln|1+x| - \ln|3+x|] + C$ (Analogous to (iv))

53. The average value of $v(x)$ on the interval $1 \le x \le c]$ is

$$\frac{1}{c-1}\int_1^c \frac{6}{x^2}\, dx = \frac{1}{c-1}\left(-\frac{6}{x}\right)\Big|_1^c = \frac{1}{c-1}\left(\frac{-6}{c} + 6\right) = \frac{6}{c}.$$

Since $\dfrac{1}{c-1}\displaystyle\int_1^c \dfrac{6}{x^2}\,dx = 1$, $\dfrac{6}{c} = 1$, so $c = 6$.

54. (a) The average value of $f(t) = \sin t$ over $0 \le t \le 2\pi$ is given by the formula

$$\text{Average} = \frac{1}{2\pi - 0}\int_0^{2\pi} \sin t\,dt$$

$$= \frac{1}{2\pi}(-\cos t)\Big|_0^{2\pi}$$

$$= \frac{1}{2\pi}(-\cos 2\pi - (-\cos 0))$$

$$= 0.$$

We can check this answer by looking at the graph of $\sin t$. The area below the curve and above the t-axis over the interval $0 \le t \le \pi$, A_1, is the same as the area above the curve but below the t-axis over the interval $\pi \le t \le 2\pi$, A_2. When we take the integral of $\sin t$ over the entire interval $0 \le t \le 2\pi$, we get $A_1 - A_2 = 0$.

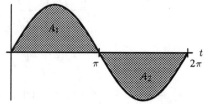

Figure 7.1

(b)

$$\int_0^{\pi} \sin t\,dt = -\cos t\Big|_0^{\pi} = -\cos \pi - (-\cos 0)$$

$$= -(-1) - (-1) = 2,$$

so the average value of $\sin t$ on $0 \le t \le \pi$ is $\frac{1}{\pi}\int_0^{\pi} \sin t\,dt = \frac{2}{\pi}$.

55. The curves intersect at $(0,0)$ and $(\pi, 0)$. At any x-coordinate the "height" between the two curves is $\sin x - x(x - \pi)$.

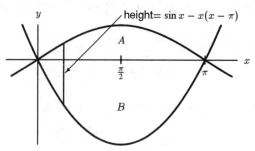

Figure 7.2

Thus the total area is

$$\int_0^\pi [\sin x - x(x - \pi)]\,dx == \int_0^\pi (\sin x - x^2 + \pi x)\,dx$$

$$= \left(-\cos x - \frac{x^3}{3} + \frac{\pi x^2}{2} \right) \Big|_0^\pi$$

$$= \left(1 - \frac{\pi^3}{3} + \frac{\pi^3}{2} \right) - (-1)$$

$$= 2 + \frac{\pi^3}{6} \approx 7.16771.$$

Another approach is to notice that the area between the two curves is (area A) + (area B).

$$\text{area A} = -\int_0^\pi x(x - \pi)\,dx \text{ since the function is negative on } 0 \le x \le \pi$$

$$= -\left(\frac{x^3}{3} - \frac{\pi x^2}{2} \right) \Big|_0^\pi$$

$$= \frac{\pi^3}{2} - \frac{\pi^3}{3} = \frac{\pi^3}{6};$$

$$\text{area B} = \int_0^\pi \sin x\,dx = -\cos x \Big|_0^\pi = 2.$$

Thus the area is $2 + \dfrac{\pi^3}{6}$.

56. Since $C'(x) = 4000 + 10x$ we want to evaluate the indefinite integral

$$\int (4000 + 10x)\,dx = 4000x + 5x^2 + K$$

where K is a constant. Thus $C(x) = 5x^2 + 4000x + K$, and the fixed cost of 1,000,000 Riyal means that $C(0) = 1,000,000 = K$. Therefore, the total cost is

$$C(x) = 5x^2 + 4000x + 1,000,000.$$

Since $C(x)$ depends on x^2, the square of the depth drilled, costs will increase dramatically as soon as $5x^2$ grows large compared to 1,000,000; i.e., after about $\sqrt{200,000} \approx 450$ meters.

57. (a)

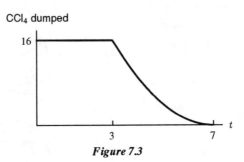

CCl$_4$ dumped

Figure 7.3

(b)   7 years, because $t^2 - 14t + 49 = (t - 7)^2$ indicates that the rate of flow was zero after 7 years.

(c)

$$\text{Area under the curve} = 3(16) + \int_3^7 (t^2 - 14t + 49)\, dt$$

$$= 48 + \left(\frac{1}{3}t^3 - 7t^2 + 49t \right)\Big|_3^7$$

$$= 48 + \frac{343}{3} - 343 + 343 - 9 + 63 - 147$$

$$= \frac{208}{3} = 69\frac{1}{3}.$$

7.2 SOLUTIONS

1. (a) $\frac{d}{dx} \sin(x^2 + 1) = 2x \cos(x^2 + 1);$ $\frac{d}{dx} \sin(x^3 + 1) = 3x^2 \cos(x^3 + 1)$

    (b) (i) $\frac{1}{2} \sin(x^2 + 1) + C$ (ii) $\frac{1}{3} \sin(x^3 + 1) + C$

    (c) (i) $-\frac{1}{2} \cos(x^2 + 1) + C$ (ii) $-\frac{1}{3} \cos(x^3 + 1) + C$

2. Make the substitution $w = x^2$, $dw = 2x\, dx$. We have
    $$\int 2x \cos(x^2)\, dx = \int \cos w\, dw = \sin w + C = \sin x^2 + C.$$

3. Make the substitution $w = 3x$, $dw = 3\, dx$. We have
    $$\int \sin 3x\, dx = \frac{1}{3} \int \sin w\, dw = \frac{1}{3}(-\cos w) + C = -\frac{1}{3} \cos 3x + C.$$

4. Make the substitution $w = 2 - 5x$, then $dw = -5dx$. We have
    $$\int \sin(2 - 5x)dx = \int \sin w \left(-\frac{1}{5} \right) dw = -\frac{1}{5}(-\cos w) + C = \frac{1}{5} \cos(2 - 5x) + C.$$

5. Make the substitution $w = \sin x$, $dw = \cos x\, dx$. We have
    $$\int e^{\sin x} \cos x\, dx = \int e^w\, dw = e^w + C = e^{\sin x} + C.$$

6. Make the substitution $w = x^2 + 1$, $dw = 2x\,dx$. We have
$$\int \frac{x}{x^2 + 1}\,dx = \frac{1}{2}\int \frac{dw}{w} = \frac{1}{2}\ln|w| + C = \frac{1}{2}\ln(x^2 + 1) + C.$$
(Notice that since $x^2 + 1 \geq 0$, $|x^2 + 1| = x^2 + 1$.)

7. Make the substitution $w = 2x$, the $dw = 2dx$. We have
$$\int \frac{1}{3\cos^2 2x}\,dx = \frac{1}{3}\int \frac{1}{\cos^2 w}\left(\frac{1}{2}\right)dw$$
$$= \frac{1}{6}\int \frac{1}{\cos^2 w}\,dw = \frac{1}{6}\tan w + C = \frac{1}{6}\tan 2x + C.$$

8. Let $w = 2 + 3\cos x$, so $dw = -3\sin x\,dx$ giving $-\frac{dw}{3} = \sin x\,dx$. Then
$$\int \sin x\left(\sqrt{2 + 3\cos x}\right)dx = \int \sqrt{w}\left(-\frac{dw}{3}\right) = -\frac{1}{3}\int\sqrt{w}\,dw$$
$$= \left(-\frac{1}{3}\right)\frac{w^{\frac{3}{2}}}{\frac{3}{2}} + C = -\frac{2}{9}(2 + 3\cos x)^{\frac{3}{2}} + C.$$

9. For Problem 12 we use the substitution $w = -x^2$, $dw = -2x\,dx$.
   For Problem 13 we use the substitution $w = y^2 + 5$, $dw = 2y\,dy$.
   For Problem 14 we use the substitution $w = t^3 - 3$, $dw = 3t^2\,dt$.
   For Problem 15 we use the substitution $w = x^2 - 4$, $dw = 2x\,dx$.
   For Problem 16 we use the substitution $w = y + 5$, $dw = dy$.
   For Problem 17 we use the substitution $w = 2t - 7$, $dw = 2\,dt$.
   For Problem 18 we use the substitution $w = x^2 + 3$, $dw = 2x\,dx$.
   For Problem 19 it would be easier if we just multiply out $(x^2 + 3)^2$ and then integrate.
   For Problem 20 use the substitution $w = 4 - x$, $dw = -dx$.
   For Problem 21 use the substitution $w = \cos\theta + 5$, $dw = -\sin\theta\,d\theta$.
   For Problem 22 use the substitution $w = x^3 + 1$, $dw = 3x^2\,dx$.
   For Problem 23 use the substitution $w = \sin\alpha$, $dw = \cos\alpha\,d\alpha$.

10. For Problem 24 use the substitution $w = \cos 3t$, $dw = -3\sin 3t\,dt$.
    For Problem 25 use the substitution $w = \ln z$, $dw = \frac{1}{z}\,dz$.
    For Problem 26 use the substitution $w = \sin\theta$, $dw = \cos\theta\,d\theta$.
    For Problem 27 use the substitution $w = \sin 5\theta$, $dw = 5\cos 5\theta\,d\theta$.
    For Problem 28 use the substitution $w = \sqrt{x}$, $dw = \frac{1}{2\sqrt{x}}\,dx$.
    For Problem 29 use the substitution $w = e^t + t$, $dw = (e^t + 1)\,dt$.
    For Problem 30 use the substitution $w = x + e^x$, $dw = (1 + e^x)\,dx$.
    For Problem 31 use the substitution $w = y^2 + 4$, $dw = 2y\,dy$.
    For Problem 32 use the substitution $w = 2 + e^x$, $dw = e^x\,dx$.
    For Problem 33 use the substitution $w = \sqrt{y}$, $dw = \frac{1}{2\sqrt{y}}\,dy$.

11. For Problem 34 use $w = \cos 2x$, $dw = -2\sin 2x\,dx$.

    For Problem 35 use $w = x^2 + 2x + 19$, $dw = 2(x + 1)\,dx$.

    For Problem 36 use $w = \sin(x^2)$, $dw = 2x\cos(x^2)\,dx$.

    For Problem 37 use $w = 1 + 2x^3$, $dw = 6x^2\,dx$.

    For Problem 38 it would be easier to multiply out and then integrate.

    For Problem 39 use $w = 1 + 3t^2$, $dw = 6t\,dt$.

    For Problem 40 it would be easier not to substitute.

12. We use the substitution $w = -x^2$, $dw = -2x\,dx$.

$$\int xe^{-x^2}\,dx = -\frac{1}{2}\int e^{-x^2}(-2x\,dx) = -\frac{1}{2}\int e^w\,dw$$

$$= -\frac{1}{2}e^w + C = -\frac{1}{2}e^{-x^2} + C.$$

Check: $\frac{d}{dx}\left(-\frac{1}{2}e^{-x^2} + C\right) = (-2x)\left(-\frac{1}{2}e^{-x^2}\right) = xe^{-x^2}$.

13. We use the substitution $w = y^2 + 5$, $dw = 2y\,dy$.

$$\int y(y^2 + 5)^8\,dy = \frac{1}{2}\int (y^2 + 5)^8 (2y\,dy)$$

$$= \frac{1}{2}\int w^8\,dw = \frac{1}{2}\frac{w^9}{9} + C$$

$$= \frac{1}{18}(y^2 + 5)^9 + C.$$

Check: $\frac{d}{dy}\left(\frac{1}{18}(y^2 + 5)^9 + C\right) = \frac{1}{18}[9(y^2 + 5)^8(2y)] = y(y^2 + 5)^8$.

14. We use the substitution $w = t^3 - 3$, $dw = 3t^2\,dt$.

$$\int t^2(t^3 - 3)^{10}\,dt = \frac{1}{3}\int (t^3 - 3)^{10}(3t^2\,dt) = \int w^{10}\left(\frac{1}{3}\,dw\right)$$

$$= \frac{1}{3}\frac{w^{11}}{11} + C = \frac{1}{33}(t^3 - 3)^{11} + C.$$

Check: $\frac{d}{dt}\left[\frac{1}{33}(t^3 - 3)^{11} + C\right] = \frac{1}{3}(t^3 - 3)^{10}(3t^2) = t^2(t^3 - 3)^{10}$.

15. We use the substitution $w = x^2 - 4$, $dw = 2x\,dx$.

$$\int x(x^2 - 4)^{\frac{7}{2}}\,dx = \frac{1}{2}\int (x^2 - 4)^{\frac{7}{2}}(2x\,dx) = \frac{1}{2}\int w^{\frac{7}{2}}\,dw$$

$$= \frac{1}{2}\left(\frac{2}{9}w^{\frac{9}{2}}\right) + C = \frac{1}{9}(x^2 - 4)^{\frac{9}{2}} + C.$$

Check: $\dfrac{d}{dx}[\dfrac{1}{9}(x^2-4)^{\frac{9}{2}}+C] = \dfrac{1}{9}\left[\dfrac{9}{2}(x^2-4)^{\frac{7}{2}}\right]2x = x(x^2-4)^{\frac{7}{2}}.$

16. We use the substitution $w = y + 5$, $dw = dy$, to get

$$\int \frac{dy}{y+5} = \int \frac{dw}{w} = \ln|w| + C = \ln|y+5| + C.$$

Check: $\dfrac{d}{dy}(\ln|y+5|+C) = \dfrac{1}{y+5}.$

17. We use the substitution $w = 2t - 7$, $dw = 2\,dt$.

$$\int (2t-7)^{73}\,dt = \frac{1}{2}\int w^{73}\,dw = \frac{1}{(2)(74)}w^{74} + C = \frac{1}{148}(2t-7)^{74} + C.$$

Check: $\dfrac{d}{dt}\left[\dfrac{1}{148}(2t-7)^{74}+C\right] = \dfrac{74}{148}(2t-7)^{73}(2) = (2t-7)^{73}.$

18. We use the substitution $w = x^2 + 3$, $dw = 2x\,dx$.

$$\int x(x^2+3)^2\,dx = \int w^2(\frac{1}{2}\,dw) = \frac{1}{2}\frac{w^3}{3} + C = \frac{1}{6}(x^2+3)^3 + C.$$

Check: $\dfrac{d}{dx}\left[\dfrac{1}{6}(x^2+3)^3+C\right] = \dfrac{1}{6}\left[3(x^2+3)^2(2x)\right] = x(x^2+3)^2.$

19. In this case, it seems easier not to substitute.

$$\int (x^2+3)^2\,dx = \int (x^4+6x^2+9)\,dx = \frac{x^5}{5} + 2x^3 + 9x + C.$$

Check: $\dfrac{d}{dx}\left[\dfrac{x^5}{5}+2x^3+9x+C\right] = x^4+6x^2+9 = (x^2+3)^2.$

20. We use the substitution $w = 4 - x$, $dw = -dx$.

$$\int \frac{1}{\sqrt{4-x}}\,dx = -\int \frac{1}{\sqrt{w}}\,dw = -2\sqrt{w} + C = -2\sqrt{4-x} + C.$$

Check: $\dfrac{d}{dx}(-2\sqrt{4-x}+C) = -2\cdot\dfrac{1}{2}\cdot\dfrac{1}{\sqrt{4-x}}\cdot -1 = \dfrac{1}{\sqrt{4-x}}.$

21. We use the substitution $w = \cos\theta + 5$, $dw = -\sin\theta\,d\theta$.

$$\int \sin\theta(\cos\theta+5)^7\,d\theta = -\int w^7\,dw = -\frac{1}{8}w^8 + C$$

$$= -\frac{1}{8}(\cos\theta+5)^8 + C.$$

Check:

$$\frac{d}{d\theta}\left[-\frac{1}{8}(\cos\theta+5)^8+C\right]=-\frac{1}{8}\cdot 8(\cos\theta+5)^7\cdot(-\sin\theta)$$
$$=\sin\theta(\cos\theta+5)^7$$

22. We use the substitution $w=x^3+1$, $dw=3x^2\,dx$, to get

$$\int x^2 e^{x^3+1}\,dx=\frac{1}{3}\int e^w\,dw=\frac{1}{3}e^w+C=\frac{1}{3}e^{x^3+1}+C.$$

Check: $\dfrac{d}{dx}\left(\dfrac{1}{3}e^{x^3+1}+C\right)=\dfrac{1}{3}e^{x^3+1}\cdot 3x^2=x^2 e^{x^3+1}.$

23. We use the substitution $w=\sin\alpha$, $dw=\cos\alpha\,d\alpha$.

$$\int \sin^3\alpha\cos\alpha\,d\alpha=\int w^3\,dw=\frac{w^4}{4}+C=\frac{\sin^4\alpha}{4}+C.$$

Check: $\dfrac{d}{d\alpha}\left(\dfrac{\sin^4\alpha}{4}+C\right)=\dfrac{1}{4}\cdot 4\sin^3\alpha\cdot\cos\alpha=\sin^3\alpha\cos\alpha.$

24. We use the substitution $w=\cos 3t$, $dw=-3\sin 3t\,dt$.

$$\int \sqrt{\cos 3t}\,\sin 3t\,dt=-\frac{1}{3}\int\sqrt{w}\,dw$$
$$=-\frac{1}{3}\cdot\frac{2}{3}w^{\frac{3}{2}}+C=-\frac{2}{9}(\cos 3t)^{\frac{3}{2}}+C.$$

Check:

$$\frac{d}{dt}\left[-\frac{2}{9}(\cos 3t)^{\frac{3}{2}}+C\right]=-\frac{2}{9}\cdot\frac{3}{2}(\cos 3t)^{\frac{1}{2}}\cdot(-\sin 3t)\cdot 3$$
$$=\sqrt{\cos 3t}\,\sin 3t.$$

25. We use the substitution $w=\ln z$, $dw=\frac{1}{z}\,dz$.

$$\int\frac{(\ln z)^2}{z}\,dz=\int w^2\,dw=\frac{w^3}{3}+C=\frac{(\ln z)^3}{3}+C.$$

Check: $\dfrac{d}{dz}\left[\dfrac{(\ln z)^3}{3}+C\right]=3\cdot\dfrac{1}{3}(\ln z)^2\cdot\dfrac{1}{z}=\dfrac{(\ln z)^2}{z}.$

26. We use the substitution $w = \sin\theta$, $dw = \cos\theta\, d\theta$.

$$\int \sin^6\theta \cos\theta\, d\theta = \int w^6\, dw = \frac{w^7}{7} + C = \frac{\sin^7\theta}{7} + C.$$

Check: $\dfrac{d}{d\theta}\left[\dfrac{\sin 7\theta}{7} + C\right] = \sin^6\theta \cos\theta.$

27. We use the substitution $w = \sin 5\theta$, $dw = 5\cos 5\theta\, d\theta$.

$$\int \sin^6 5\theta \cos 5\theta\, d\theta = \frac{1}{5}\int w^6\, dw = \frac{1}{5}\left(\frac{w^7}{7}\right) + C = \frac{1}{35}\sin^7 5\theta + C.$$

Check: $\dfrac{d}{d\theta}\left(\dfrac{1}{35}\sin^7 5\theta + C\right) = \dfrac{1}{35}[7\sin^6 5\theta](5\cos 5\theta) = \sin^6 5\theta \cos 5\theta.$

Note that we could also use Problem 26 to solve this problem, substituting $w = 5\theta$ and $dw = 5\, d\theta$ to get:

$$\int \sin^6 5\theta \cos 5\theta\, d\theta = \frac{1}{5}\int \sin^6 w \cos w\, dw$$

$$= \frac{1}{5}\left(\frac{\sin^7 w}{7}\right) + C = \frac{1}{35}\sin^7 5\theta + C.$$

28. We use the substitution $w = \sqrt{x}$, $dw = \frac{1}{2\sqrt{x}}\, dx$.

$$\int \frac{\cos\sqrt{x}}{\sqrt{x}}\, dx = \int \cos w(2\, dw) = 2\sin w + C = 2\sin\sqrt{x} + C.$$

Check: $\dfrac{d}{dx}(2\sin\sqrt{x} + C) = 2\cos\sqrt{x}\left(\dfrac{1}{2\sqrt{x}}\right) = \dfrac{\cos\sqrt{x}}{\sqrt{x}}.$

29. We use the substitution $w = e^t + t$, $dw = (e^t + 1)\, dt$.

$$\int \frac{e^t + 1}{e^t + t}\, dt = \int \frac{1}{w}\, dw = \ln|w| + C = \ln|e^t + t| + C.$$

Check: $\dfrac{d}{dt}(\ln|e^t + t| + C) = \dfrac{e^t + 1}{e^t + t}.$

30. We use the substitution $w = x + e^x$, $dw = (1 + e^x)\, dx$.

$$\int \frac{1 + e^x}{\sqrt{x + e^x}}\, dx = \int \frac{dw}{\sqrt{w}} = 2\sqrt{w} + C = 2\sqrt{x + e^x} + C.$$

Check: $\dfrac{d}{dx}(2\sqrt{x + e^x} + C) = 2 \cdot \dfrac{1}{2}(x + e^x)^{-\frac{1}{2}} \cdot (1 + e^x) = \dfrac{1 + e^x}{\sqrt{x + e^x}}.$

31. We use the substitution $w = y^2 + 4$, $dw = 2y\,dy$.

$$\int \frac{y}{y^2+4}\,dy = \frac{1}{2}\int \frac{dw}{w} = \frac{1}{2}\ln|w| + C = \frac{1}{2}\ln(y^2+4) + C.$$

(We can drop the absolute value signs since $y^2 + 4 \geq 0$ for all y.)

Check: $\dfrac{d}{dy}\left[\dfrac{1}{2}\ln(y^2+4) + C\right] = \dfrac{1}{2}\cdot\dfrac{1}{y^2+4}\cdot 2y = \dfrac{y}{y^2+4}.$

32. We use the substitution $w = 2 + e^x$, $dw = e^x\,dx$.

$$\int \frac{e^x}{2+e^x}\,dx = \int \frac{dw}{w} = \ln|w| + C = \ln(2+e^x) + C.$$

(We can drop the absolute value signs since $2 + e^x \geq 0$ for all x.)

Check: $\dfrac{d}{dx}[\ln(2+e^x) + C] = \dfrac{1}{2+e^x}\cdot e^x = \dfrac{e^x}{2+e^x}.$

33. We use the substitution $w = \sqrt{y}$, $dw = \dfrac{1}{2\sqrt{y}}\,dy$.

$$\int \frac{e^{\sqrt{y}}}{\sqrt{y}}\,dy = 2\int e^w\,dw = 2e^w + C = 2e^{\sqrt{y}} + C.$$

Check: $\dfrac{d}{dy}(2e^{\sqrt{y}} + C) = 2e^{\sqrt{y}}\cdot\dfrac{1}{2\sqrt{y}} = \dfrac{e^{\sqrt{y}}}{\sqrt{y}}.$

34. We use the substitution $w = \cos 2x$, $dw = -2\sin 2x\,dx$.

$$\int \tan 2x\,dx = \int \frac{\sin 2x}{\cos 2x}\,dx = -\frac{1}{2}\int \frac{dw}{w}$$

$$= -\frac{1}{2}\ln|w| + C = -\frac{1}{2}\ln|\cos 2x| + C.$$

Check:

$$\frac{d}{dx}\left[-\frac{1}{2}\ln|\cos 2x| + C\right] = -\frac{1}{2}\cdot\frac{1}{\cos 2x}\cdot -2\sin 2x$$

$$= \frac{\sin 2x}{\cos 2x} = \tan 2x.$$

35. We use the substitution $w = x^2 + 2x + 19$, $dw = 2(x+1)dx$.

$$\int \frac{(x+1)dx}{x^2+2x+19} = \frac{1}{2}\int \frac{dw}{w} = \frac{1}{2}\ln|w| + C = \frac{1}{2}\ln(x^2+2x+19) + C.$$

(We can drop the absolute value signs, since $x^2 + 2x + 19 = (x+1)^2 + 18 > 0$ for all x.)

Check: $\dfrac{1}{dx}[\dfrac{1}{2}\ln(x^2+2x+19)] = \dfrac{1}{2}\dfrac{1}{x^2+2x+19}(2x+2) = \dfrac{x+1}{x^2+2x+19}.$

36. We use the substitution $w = \sin(x^2)$, $dw = 2x \cos(x^2)\,dx$.

$$\int \frac{x \cos(x^2)}{\sqrt{\sin(x^2)}}\,dx = \frac{1}{2}\int w^{-\frac{1}{2}}\,dw = \frac{1}{2}(2w^{\frac{1}{2}}) + C = \sqrt{\sin(x^2)} + C.$$

Check: $\dfrac{d}{dx}(\sqrt{\sin(x^2)} + C) = \dfrac{1}{2\sqrt{\sin(x^2)}}[\cos(x^2)]2x = \dfrac{x\cos(x^2)}{\sqrt{\sin(x^2)}}.$

37. We use the substitution $w = 1 + 2x^3$, $dw = 6x^2\,dx$.

$$\int x^2(1 + 2x^3)^2\,dx = \int w^2(\frac{1}{6}\,dw) = \frac{1}{6}(\frac{w^3}{3}) + C = \frac{1}{18}(1 + 2x^3)^3 + C.$$

Check: $\dfrac{d}{dx}\left[\dfrac{1}{18}(1 + 2x^2)^3 + C\right] = \dfrac{1}{18}[3(1 + 2x^3)^2(6x^2)] = x^2(1 + 2x^3)^2.$

38. In this case, it seems easier not to substitute.

$$\int y^2(1 + y)^2\,dy = \int y^2(y^2 + 2y + 1)\,dy = \int (y^4 + 2y^3 + y^2)\,dy$$
$$= \frac{y^5}{5} + \frac{y^4}{2} + \frac{y^3}{3} + C.$$

Check: $\dfrac{d}{dy}\left(\dfrac{y^5}{5} + \dfrac{y^4}{2} + \dfrac{y^3}{3} + C\right) = y^4 + 2y^3 + y^2 = y^2(y + 1)^2.$

39. We use the substitution $w = 1 + 3t^2$, $dw = 6t\,dt$.

$$\int \frac{t}{1 + 3t^2}\,dt = \int \frac{1}{w}(\frac{1}{6}\,dw) = \frac{1}{6}\ln|w| + C = \frac{1}{6}\ln(1 + 3t^2) + C.$$

(We can drop the absolute value signs since $1 + 3t^2 > 0$ for all t).

Check: $\dfrac{d}{dt}\left[\dfrac{1}{6}\ln(1 + 3t^2) + C\right] = \dfrac{1}{6}\dfrac{1}{1 + 3t^2}(6t) = \dfrac{t}{1 + 3t^2}.$

40. It seems easier not to substitute.

$$\int \frac{(t + 1)^2}{t^2}\,dt = \int \frac{(t^2 + 2t + 1)}{t^2}\,dt$$
$$= \int \left(1 + \frac{2}{t} + \frac{1}{t^2}\right)\,dt = t + 2\ln|t| - \frac{1}{t} + C.$$

Check: $\dfrac{d}{dt}(t + 2\ln|t| - \dfrac{1}{t} + C) = 1 + \dfrac{2}{t} + \dfrac{1}{t^2} = \dfrac{(t + 1)^2}{t^2}.$

41. We use the substitution $w = e^x + e^{-x}$, $dw = (e^x - e^{-x})\,dx$.

$$\int \frac{e^x - e^{-x}}{e^x + e^{-x}}\,dx = \int \frac{dw}{w} = \ln|w| + C = \ln(e^x + e^{-x}) + C.$$

(We can drop the absolute value signs since $e^x + e^{-x} > 0$ for all x).

Check: $\dfrac{d}{dx}[\ln(e^x + e^{-x}) + C] = \dfrac{1}{e^x + e^{-x}}(e^x - e^{-x})$.

42. We use the substitution $w = x^2 + x$, $dw = (2x + 1)\,dx$.

$$\int (2x + 1)e^{x^2} e^x\,dx = \int (2x + 1)e^{x^2 + x}\,dx = \int e^w\,dw$$
$$= e^w + C = e^{x^2 + x} + C.$$

Check: $\dfrac{d}{dx}(e^{x^2 + x} + C) = e^{x^2 + x} \cdot (2x + 1) = (2x + 1)e^{x^2} e^x$.

43. (a) $\displaystyle\int 4x(x^2 + 1)\,dx = \int (4x^3 + 4x)\,dx = x^4 + 2x^2 + C.$

(b) If $w = x^2 + 1$, then $dw = 2x\,dx$.

$$\int 4x(x^2 + 1)\,dx = \int 2w\,dw = w^2 + C = (x^2 + 1)^2 + C.$$

(c) The expressions from parts (a) and (b) look different, but they are both correct. Note that $(x^2 + 1)^2 + C = x^4 + 2x^2 + 1 + C$. In other words, the expressions from parts (a) and (b) differ only by a constant, so they are both correct antiderivatives.

44. (a) $E(t) = 1.4e^{0.07t}$

(b)

$$\text{Average Yearly Consumption} = \frac{\text{Total Consumption for the Century}}{100 \text{ years}}$$
$$= \frac{1}{100} \int_0^{100} 1.4e^{0.07t}\,dt$$
$$= (0.014)\left[\frac{1}{0.07}e^{0.07t}\Big|_0^{100}\right]$$
$$= (0.014)\left[\frac{1}{0.07}(e^7 - e^0)\right]$$
$$= 0.2(e^7 - 1) \approx 219 \text{ million megawatt-hours.}$$

(c) We are looking for t such that $E(t) = 219$:

$$1.4e^{0.07t} \approx 219$$
$$e^{0.07t} = 156.4.$$

Taking natural logs,

$$0.07t = \ln 156.4$$

$$t \approx \frac{5.05}{0.07} \approx 72.18.$$

Thus, consumption was closest to the average during 1972.

(d) Between the years 1900 and 2000 the graph of $E(t)$ looks like

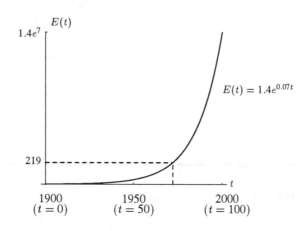

From the graph, we can see the t value such that $E(t) = 219$. It lies to the right of $t = 50$, and is thus in the second half of the century.

45. Since $v = \dfrac{dh}{dt}$, it follows that $h(t) = \displaystyle\int v(t)\, dt$ and $h(0) = h_0$. Since

$$v(t) = \frac{mg}{k}\left(1 - e^{-\frac{k}{m}t}\right) = \frac{mg}{k} - \frac{mg}{k}e^{-\frac{k}{m}t},$$

we have

$$h(t) = \int v(t)\, dt = \frac{mg}{k}\int dt - \frac{mg}{k}\int e^{-\frac{k}{m}t}\, dt.$$

The first integral is simply $\dfrac{mg}{k}t + C$. To evaluate the second integral, make the substitution $w = -\frac{k}{m}t$.
Then

$$dw = -\frac{k}{m}\, dt,$$

so

$$\int e^{-\frac{k}{m}t}\, dt = \int e^{w}\left(-\frac{m}{k}\right) dw = -\frac{m}{k}e^{w} + C = -\frac{m}{k}e^{-\frac{k}{m}t} + C.$$

Thus

$$h(t) = \int v \, dt = \frac{mg}{k} t - \frac{mg}{k} \left(-\frac{m}{k} e^{-\frac{k}{m}t} \right) + C$$

$$= \frac{mg}{k} t + \frac{m^2 g}{k^2} e^{-\frac{k}{m}t} + C.$$

Since $h(0) = h_0$,

$$h_0 = \frac{mg}{k} \cdot 0 + \frac{m^2 g}{k^2} e^0 + C;$$

$$C = h_0 - \frac{m^2 g}{k^2}.$$

Thus

$$h(t) = \frac{mg}{k} t + \frac{m^2 g}{k^2} e^{-\frac{k}{m}t} - \frac{m^2 g}{k^2} + h_0$$

$$h(t) = \frac{mg}{k} t - \frac{m^2 g}{k^2} \left(1 - e^{-\frac{k}{m}t} \right) + h_0.$$

7.3 SOLUTIONS

1. (a) We substitute $w = 1 + x^2$, $dw = 2x \, dx$.

$$\int_{x=0}^{x=1} \frac{x}{1+x^2} \, dx = \frac{1}{2} \int_{w=1}^{w=2} \frac{1}{w} \, dw = \frac{1}{2} \ln |w| \Big|_1^2 = \frac{1}{2} \ln 2.$$

   (b) We substitute $w = \cos x$, $dw = -\sin x \, dx$.

$$\int_{x=0}^{x=\frac{\pi}{4}} \frac{\sin x}{\cos x} \, dx = -\int_{w=1}^{w=\sqrt{2}/2} \frac{1}{w} \, dw$$

$$= -\ln |w| \Big|_1^{\sqrt{2}/2} = -\ln \frac{\sqrt{2}}{2} = \frac{1}{2} \ln 2.$$

2. We substitute $w = \pi x$. Then $dw = \pi \, dx$.

$$\int_{x=0}^{x=\frac{1}{2}} \cos \pi x \, dx = \int_{w=0}^{w=\pi/2} \cos w \left(\frac{1}{\pi} \, dw \right) = \frac{1}{\pi} (\sin w) \Big|_0^{\pi/2} = \frac{1}{\pi} \approx 0.318$$

3. We substitute $w = \sqrt[3]{x} = x^{\frac{1}{3}}$. Then $dw = \frac{1}{3} x^{-\frac{2}{3}} \, dx = \frac{1}{3\sqrt[3]{x^2}} \, dx$.

$$\int_1^8 \frac{e^{\sqrt[3]{x}}}{\sqrt[3]{x^2}} \, dx = \int_{x=1}^{x=8} e^w (3 \, dw) = 3e^w \Big|_{x=1}^{x=8} = 3e^{\sqrt[3]{x}} \Big|_1^8 = 3(e^2 - e) \approx 14.01.$$

4. We substitute $w = 1 + x^2$. Then $dw = 2x\,dx$.

$$\int_{x=0}^{x=2} \frac{x}{(1+x^2)^2}\,dx = \int_{w=1}^{w=5} \frac{1}{w^2}\left(\frac{1}{2}\,dw\right) = -\frac{1}{2}\left(\frac{1}{w}\right)\bigg|_1^5 = \frac{2}{5}.$$

5. We substitute $w = t + 2$, so $dw = dt$.

$$\int_{t=-1}^{t=e-2} \frac{1}{t+2}\,dt = \int_{w=1}^{w=e} \frac{dw}{w} = \ln|w|\bigg|_1^e = \ln e - \ln 1 = 1.$$

6. We substitute $w = \sqrt{x}$. Then $dw = \frac{1}{2}x^{-1/2}dx$.

$$\int_{x=1}^{x=4} \frac{\cos\sqrt{x}}{\sqrt{x}}\,dx = \int_{w=1}^{w=2} \cos w(2\,dw)$$

$$= 2(\sin w)\bigg|_1^2 = 2(\sin 2 - \sin 1) \approx 0.136.$$

7. No immediate substitution is apparent, so we must try to modify the integral in some way. First, we put the integral into a more convenient form by using the fact that $\sin^2\theta = 1 - \cos^2\theta$. Thus:

$$\int_{-\frac{\pi}{4}}^{\frac{\pi}{4}} \cos^2\theta\sin^5\theta\,d\theta = \int_{-\frac{\pi}{4}}^{\frac{\pi}{4}} \cos^2\theta(1 - \cos^2\theta)^2\sin\theta\,d\theta.$$

Now, we can make a substitution which helps. We let $w = \cos\theta$, so $dw = -\sin\theta\,d\theta$.

Note that $w = \frac{\sqrt{2}}{2}$ when $\theta = -\frac{\pi}{4}$ and when $\theta = \frac{\pi}{4}$. Thus after our substitution, we get

$$-\int_{w=\frac{\pi}{4}}^{w=\frac{\pi}{4}} w^2(1 - w^2)^2\,dw.$$

Since the upper and lower limits of integration are the same, this definite integral must equal 0. Notice that we could have deduced this fact immediately, since $\cos^2\theta$ is even and $\sin^5\theta$ is odd, so $\cos^2\theta\sin^5\theta$ is odd.

Thus $\int_{-\frac{\pi}{4}}^{0} \cos^2\theta\sin^5\theta\,d\theta = -\int_0^{\frac{\pi}{4}} \cos^2\theta\sin^5\theta\,d\theta$, and the given integral must evaluate to 0.

8. $\int_1^3 \frac{1}{x}\,dx = \ln x\bigg|_1^3 = \ln 3 \approx 1.099.$

9.

$$\int_{-1}^3 (x^3 + 5x)\,dx = \frac{x^4}{4}\bigg|_{-1}^3 + \frac{5x^2}{2}\bigg|_{-1}^3 = 40.$$

10. It turns out that $\dfrac{\sin x}{x}$ cannot be integrated using elementary methods. However, the function is decreasing on [1,2]. One way to see this is to graph the function on a calculator or computer, as has been done below:

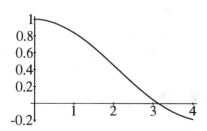

So since our function is monotonic, the error for our left- and right-hand sums is less than or equal to $\left|\dfrac{\sin 2}{2} - \dfrac{\sin 1}{1}\right| \Delta t \approx 0.61\Delta t$. So with 13 intervals, our error will be less than 0.05. With $n = 13$, the left sum is about 0.674, and the right sum is about 0.644. For more accurate sums, with $n = 100$ the left sum is about 0.6613 and the right sum is about 0.6574. The actual integral is about 0.6593.

11. We substitute $w = \cos\theta + 5$, $dw = -\sin\theta\,d\theta$. Then

$$\int_{\theta=0}^{\theta=\pi} \sin\theta\,d\theta(\cos\theta + 5)^7 = -\int_{w=6}^{w=4} w^7\,dw = \int_{w=4}^{w=6} w^7\,dw = \left.\frac{w^8}{8}\right|_4^6 = 201{,}760.$$

12. $\displaystyle\int_{-1}^{1} \frac{1}{1+y^2}\,dy = \left.\tan^{-1} y\right|_{-1}^{1} = \frac{\pi}{2}.$

13. Substitute $w = 1 + x^2$, $dw = 2x\,dx$. Then $x\,dx = \dfrac{1}{2}\,dw$, and

$$\int_{x=0}^{x=1} x(1 + x^2)^{20}\,dx = \frac{1}{2}\int_{w=1}^{w=2} w^{20}\,dw = \left.\frac{w^{21}}{42}\right|_1^2 = \frac{299593}{6} = 49932\frac{1}{6}.$$

14. Let $w = 1 + 5x^2$, $dw = 10x\,dx$ so $\dfrac{dw}{10} = x\,dx$.
    When $x = 0$, $w = 1$. When $x = 1$, $w = 6$.

$$\frac{x\,dx}{1 + 5x^2} = \int_1^6 \frac{\frac{1}{10}\,dw}{w} = \frac{1}{10}\int_1^6 \frac{dw}{w} = \left.\frac{1}{10}\ln|w|\right|_1^6$$

$$= \frac{1}{10}(\ln 6 - \ln 1) = \frac{\ln 6}{10} = 0.17918.$$

15. Substitute $w = 3\alpha$, $dw = 3\, d\alpha$. Then $d\alpha = \dfrac{1}{3}\, dw$. We have

$$\int_{\alpha=0}^{\alpha=\frac{\pi}{12}} \sin 3\alpha \, d\alpha = \frac{1}{3} \int_{w=0}^{w=\frac{\pi}{4}} \sin w \, dw$$

$$= -\frac{1}{3} \cos w \bigg|_{0}^{\frac{\pi}{4}}$$

$$= -\frac{1}{3}\left(\frac{\sqrt{2}}{2} - 1\right) = \frac{1}{3}\left(1 - \frac{\sqrt{2}}{2}\right) = 0.0976.$$

16.

$$\int_{1}^{2} \frac{x^2 + 1}{x}\, dx = \int_{1}^{2}\left(x + \frac{1}{x}\right)dx = \left(\frac{x^2}{2} + \ln|x|\right)\bigg|_{1}^{2} = \frac{3}{2} + \ln 2 = 2.193$$

17. Substitute $w = x^2 + 4$, $dw = 2x\, dx$. Then,

$$\int_{x=4}^{x=1} x\sqrt{x^2 + 4}\, dx = \frac{1}{2} \int_{w=20}^{w=5} w^{\frac{1}{2}}\, dw = \frac{1}{3} w^{\frac{3}{2}} \bigg|_{20}^{5}$$

$$= \frac{1}{3}\left(5^{\frac{3}{2}} - 8 \cdot 5^{\frac{3}{2}}\right) = -\frac{7}{3} \cdot 5^{\frac{3}{2}} = -\frac{7}{3}\sqrt{125} = -26.087.$$

18. $\displaystyle \int_{0}^{1} \frac{1}{x^2 + 2x + 1}\, dx = \int_{0}^{1} \frac{1}{(x+1)^2}\, dx.$

We substitute $w = x + 1$, so $dw = dx$. Note that when $x = 1$, we have $w = 2$, and when $x = 0$, we have $w = 1$.

$$\int_{x=0}^{x=1} \frac{1}{(x+1)^2}\, dx = \int_{w=1}^{w=2} \frac{1}{w^2}\, dw = -\frac{1}{w}\bigg|_{w=1}^{w=2} = -\frac{1}{2} + 1 = \frac{1}{2} = 0.5.$$

19. Let $w = x^2$, $dw = 2x\, dx$. When $x = 0$, $w = 0$, and when $x = \frac{1}{\sqrt{2}}$, $w = \frac{1}{2}$. Then

$$\int_{0}^{\frac{1}{\sqrt{2}}} \frac{x\, dx}{\sqrt{1 - x^4}} = \int_{0}^{\frac{1}{2}} \frac{\frac{1}{2}\, dw}{\sqrt{1 - w^2}} = \frac{1}{2}\arcsin w \bigg|_{0}^{\frac{1}{2}} = \frac{1}{2}\left(\arcsin\frac{1}{2} - \arcsin 0\right) = \frac{\pi}{12} = 0.261.$$

20. We substitute $w = x^2 + 4x + 5$, so $dw = (2x + 4)\, dx$. Notice that when $x = -2$, $w = 1$, and when $x = 0$, $w = 5$.

$$\int_{x=-2}^{x=0} \frac{2x + 4}{x^2 + 4x + 5}\, dx = \int_{w=1}^{w=5} \frac{1}{w}\, dw = \ln|w|\bigg|_{w=1}^{w=5} = \ln 5 = 1.609.$$

21. $f(t) = \sin \frac{1}{t}$ has no elementary antiderivative, so we will have to use left and right sums. With $n = 100$, left sum = 0.5462 and right sum = 0.5582. However, since f is not monotonic on $[1/4, 1]$ (see figure), we cannot be sure that the integral is between these values.

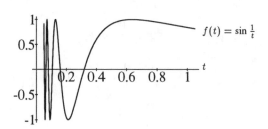

To get an upper and lower bound for this integral, divide the interval $[1/4, 1]$ into subintervals in such a way that f is monotonic on each one. Since $f'(t) = -\frac{1}{t^2} \cos \frac{1}{t} = 0$ when $\frac{1}{t} = \frac{\pi}{2}$ or $t = \frac{2}{\pi}$ (and this is the only point in $[1/4, 1]$ where $f'(t) = 0$), we will write

$$\int_{1/4}^{1} \sin \frac{1}{t} \, dt = \int_{1/4}^{2/\pi} \sin \frac{1}{t} \, dt + \int_{2/\pi}^{1} \sin \frac{1}{t} \, dt$$

Now, using $n = 100$, we find $0.209 < \int_{1/4}^{2/\pi} \sin \frac{1}{t} \, dt < 0.216$ (left sum = 0.209, right sum = 0.216, f is increasing), and $0.339 < \int_{2/\pi}^{1} \sin \frac{1}{t} \, dt < 0.340$ (here left sum = 0.340, right sum = 0.339 because f is decreasing). Thus

$$0.548 < \int_{1/4}^{1} \sin \frac{1}{t} \, dt < 0.556.$$

22. After the substitution $w = e^x$ and $dw = e^x \, dx$, the first integral becomes

$$\frac{1}{2} \int \frac{1}{1 + w^2} \, dw,$$

while after the substitution $w = \sin x$ and $dw = \cos x \, dx$, the second integral becomes

$$\int \frac{1}{1 + w^2} \, dw.$$

23. The substitution $w = \ln x$, $dw = \frac{1}{x} \, dx$ transforms the first integral into $\int w \, dw$, which is just a respelling of the integral $\int x \, dx$.

24. For the first integral, let $w = x + 1$, $dw = dx$. Then

$$\int \sqrt{x + 1} \, dx = \int \sqrt{w} \, dw.$$

For the second integral, let $w = 1 + \sqrt{x}$, $dw = \frac{1}{2}x^{-\frac{1}{2}}\,dx = \frac{1}{2\sqrt{x}}\,dx$. Then, $\frac{dx}{\sqrt{x}} = 2\,dw$, and

$$\int \frac{\sqrt{1 + \sqrt{x}}}{\sqrt{x}}\,dx = \int \sqrt{1 + \sqrt{x}}\left(\frac{dx}{\sqrt{x}}\right) = 2\int \sqrt{w}\,dw.$$

25. For the first integral, let $w = \sin x$, $dw = \cos x\,dx$. Then

$$\int e^{\sin x} \cos x\,dx = \int e^w\,dw.$$

For the second integral, let $w = \arcsin x$, $dw = \frac{1}{\sqrt{1-x^2}}\,dx$. Then

$$\int \frac{e^{\arcsin x}}{\sqrt{1 - x^2}}\,dx = \int e^w\,dw.$$

26. The substitutions $w = \sin x$, $dw = \cos w$ and $w = x^3 + 1$, $dw = 3x^2\,dx$ transform the integrals into

$$\int w^3\,dw \quad \text{and} \quad \frac{1}{3}\int w^3\,dw.$$

27.
$$\int \frac{dx}{x^2 + 4x + 5} = \int \frac{dx}{(x + 2)^2 + 1}.$$

We make the substitution $\tan \theta = x + 2$. Then $dx = \frac{1}{\cos^2 \theta}\,d\theta$.

$$\int \frac{dx}{(x + 2)^2 + 1} = \int \frac{d\theta}{\cos^2 \theta(\tan^2 \theta + 1)}$$
$$= \int \frac{d\theta}{\cos^2 \theta(\frac{\sin^2 \theta}{\cos^2 \theta} + 1)}$$
$$= \int \frac{d\theta}{\sin^2 \theta + \cos^2 \theta}$$
$$= \int d\theta = \theta + C$$

But since $\tan \theta = x + 2$, $\theta = \arctan(x + 2)$, and so $\theta + C = \arctan(x + 2) + C$.

28. (a) $2\sqrt{x} + C$
    (b) $2\sqrt{x + 1} + C$
    (c) To get this last result, we make the substitution $w = \sqrt{x}$. Normally we would like to substitute $dw = \frac{1}{2\sqrt{x}}\,dx$, but in this case we cannot since there are no spare $\frac{1}{\sqrt{x}}$ terms around. Instead, we

note $w^2 = x$, so $2w\,dw = dx$. Then

$$\int \frac{1}{\sqrt{x}+1}\,dx = \int \frac{2w}{w+1}\,dw$$

$$= 2\int \frac{(w+1)-1}{w+1}\,dw$$

$$= 2\int \left(1 - \frac{1}{w+1}\right)\,dw$$

$$= 2(w - \ln|w+1|) + C$$

$$= 2\sqrt{x} - 2\ln(\sqrt{x}+1) + C.$$

We also note that we can drop the absolute value signs, since $\sqrt{x}+1 \geq 0$ for all x.

29. To find the area under the graph of $f(x) = xe^{x^2}$, we need to evaluate the definite integral

$$\int_0^2 xe^{x^2}\,dx.$$

This is done in Example 1, Section 7.3, using the substitution $w = x^2$, the result being

$$\int_0^2 xe^{x^2}\,dx = \frac{1}{2}(e^4 - 1) \approx 26.7991.$$

30. If $f(x) = \dfrac{1}{x+1}$, the average value of f on the interval $0 \leq x \leq 2$ is defined to be

$$\frac{1}{2-0}\int_0^2 f(x)\,dx = \frac{1}{2}\int_0^2 \frac{dx}{x+1}.$$

We'll integrate by substitution. Let $w = x + 1$; then $dw = dx$, and we have

$$\int_{x=0}^{x=2} \frac{dx}{x+1} = \int_{w=1}^{w=3} \frac{dw}{w}$$

$$= \ln w\Big|_1^3 = \ln 3 - \ln 1 = \ln 3.$$

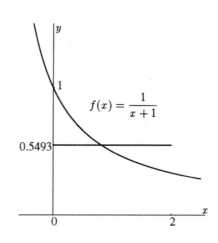

Thus, the average value of $f(x)$ on $0 \leq x \leq 2$ is $\frac{1}{2}\ln 3 \approx 0.5493$. See the graph to the right.

31. (a) We first try the substitution $w = \sin\theta$, $dw = \cos\theta\,d\theta$. Then

$$\int \sin\theta\cos\theta\,d\theta = \int w\,dw = \frac{w^2}{2} + C = \frac{\sin^2\theta}{2} + C.$$

(b) If we instead try the substitution $w = \cos\theta$, $dw = -\sin\theta\,d\theta$, we get
$$\int \sin\theta\cos\theta\,d\theta = -\int w\,dw = -\frac{w^2}{2} + C = -\frac{\cos^2\theta}{2} + C.$$

(c) Once we note that $\sin 2\theta = 2\sin\theta\cos\theta$, we can also say
$$\int \sin\theta\cos\theta\,d\theta = \frac{1}{2}\int \sin 2\theta\,d\theta.$$
Substituting $w = 2\theta$, $dw = 2\,d\theta$, the above equals
$$\frac{1}{4}\int \sin w\,dw = -\frac{\cos w}{4} + C = -\frac{\cos 2\theta}{4} + C.$$

(d) All these answers are correct. Although they have different forms, they differ from each other only in terms of a constant, and thus they are all acceptable antiderivatives. For example, $1 - \cos^2\theta = \sin^2\theta$, so $\frac{\sin^2\theta}{2} = -\frac{\cos^2\theta}{2} + \frac{1}{2}$. Thus the first two expressions differ only by a constant C. Similarly, $\cos 2\theta = \cos^2\theta - \sin^2\theta = 2\cos^2\theta - 1$, so $-\frac{\cos 2\theta}{4} = -\frac{\cos^2\theta}{2} + \frac{1}{4}$, and thus the second and third expressions differ only by a constant. Of course, if the first two expressions and the last two expressions differ only in the constant C, then the first and last only differ in the constant as well.

32. Since v is given as the velocity of a falling body, the height h is decreasing, so $v = -\frac{dh}{dt}$, and it follows that $h(t) = -\int v(t)\,dt$ and $h(0) = h_0$. Let $w = e^{t\sqrt{gk}} + e^{-t\sqrt{gk}}$. Then

$$dw = \sqrt{gk}\left(e^{t\sqrt{gk}} - e^{-t\sqrt{gk}}\right)dt,$$

so $\dfrac{dw}{\sqrt{gk}} = \left(e^{t\sqrt{gk}} - e^{-t\sqrt{gk}}\right)dt$. Therefore,

$$
\begin{aligned}
-\int v(t)dt &= -\int \sqrt{\frac{g}{k}}\left(\frac{e^{t\sqrt{gk}} - e^{-t\sqrt{gk}}}{e^{t\sqrt{gk}} + e^{-t\sqrt{gk}}}\right)dt \\
&= -\sqrt{\frac{g}{k}}\int \frac{1}{e^{t\sqrt{gk}} + e^{-t\sqrt{gk}}}\left(e^{t\sqrt{gk}} - e^{-t\sqrt{gk}}\right)dt \\
&= -\sqrt{\frac{g}{k}}\int \left(\frac{1}{w}\right)\frac{dw}{\sqrt{gk}} \\
&= -\sqrt{\frac{g}{gk^2}}\ln|w| + C \\
&= -\frac{1}{k}\ln\left(e^{t\sqrt{gk}} + e^{-t\sqrt{gk}}\right) + C.
\end{aligned}
$$

Since

$$h(0) = -\frac{1}{k}\ln(e^0 + e^0) + C = -\frac{\ln 2}{k} + C = h_0,$$

we have $C = h_0 + \dfrac{\ln 2}{k}$. Thus,

$$h(t) = -\frac{1}{k} \ln \left(e^{t\sqrt{gk}} + e^{-t\sqrt{gk}} \right) + \frac{\ln 2}{k} + h_0 = -\frac{1}{k} \ln \left(\frac{e^{t\sqrt{gk}} + e^{-t\sqrt{gk}}}{2} \right) + h_0.$$

33. (a) Amount of water entering tank in a short period of time $=$ rate$\times$time $= r(t)\Delta t$.
    (b)

$$\begin{array}{l}\text{Amount of water entering the tank} \\ \text{between } t = 0 \text{ and } t = 5\end{array} \quad \approx \sum_{i=0}^{n-1} r(t_i)\Delta t, \qquad \text{where } \Delta t = 5/n.$$

$$\begin{array}{l}\text{Amount of water entering the tank} \\ \text{between } t = 0 \text{ and } t = 5\end{array} \quad = \int_0^5 r(t)\, dt.$$

(c) If $Q(t)$ is the amount of water in the tank at time t, then $Q'(t) = r(t)$. We want to calculate $Q(5) - Q(0)$. By the Fundamental Theorem,

$$\begin{array}{l}\text{Amount which has} \\ \text{entered tank}\end{array} = Q(5) - Q(0) = \int_0^5 r(t)\, dt = \int_0^5 20 e^{0.02t}\, dt = \frac{20}{0.02} e^{0.02t} \bigg|_0^5$$

$$= 1000(e^{0.02(5)} - 1) \approx 105.17 \text{ gallons.}$$

(d) By the Fundamental Theorem again,

$$\begin{array}{l}\text{Amount which has} \\ \text{entered tank}\end{array} = Q(t) - Q(0) = \int_0^t r(t)\, dt$$

$$Q(t) - 3000 = \int_0^t 20 e^{0.02t}\, dt$$

so

$$Q(t) = 3000 + \int_0^t 20 e^{0.02t}\, dt = 3000 + \frac{20}{0.02} e^{0.02t} \bigg|_0^t$$

$$= 3000 + 1000(e^{0.02t} - 1)$$

$$= 1000 e^{0.02t} + 2000.$$

7.4 SOLUTIONS

1. (a) (i) $-x \sin x + \cos x$
       (ii) $-2 \sin 2x$

(iii) $-x^2 \sin x + 2x \cos x$

(iv) $1 + \ln x$

(b) (i) Since $(x \ln x)' = 1 + \ln x$, it follows that $(x \ln x - x)' = 1 + \ln x - 1 = \ln x$. Therefore, $\int \ln x \, dx = x \ln x - x + C$.

(ii) Since $(\cos 2x)' = -2 \sin 2x$, it follows that $(-\frac{1}{2} \cos 2x)' = \sin 2x$. Therefore, $\int \sin 2x \, dx = -\frac{1}{2} \cos 2x + C$.

(iii) Since $(x \cos x)' = -x \sin x + \cos x$, it follows that $(-x \cos x + \sin x)' = x \sin x - \cos x + \cos x = x \sin x$. Therefore, $\int x \sin x \, dx = -x \cos x + \sin x + C$.

(iv) Since $(x^2 \cos x)' = -x^2 \sin x + 2x \cos x$, and since $(2x \sin x)' = 2x \cos x + 2 \sin x$, it follows that

$$(-x^2 \cos x + 2x \sin x + 2 \cos x)' = x^2 \sin x - 2x \cos x + 2x \cos x + 2 \sin x - 2 \sin x$$
$$= x^2 \sin x.$$

Therefore, $\int x^2 \sin x \, dx = -x^2 \cos x + 2x \sin x + 2 \cos x + C$.

2. Let $u = \arctan x$, $v' = 1$. Then $v = x$ and $u' = \dfrac{1}{1 + x^2}$. Integrating by parts, we get:

$$\int 1 \cdot \arctan x \, dx = x \cdot \arctan x - \int x \cdot \frac{1}{1 + x^2} \, dx.$$

To compute the second integral use the substitution, $z = 1 + x^2$.

$$\int \frac{x}{1 + x^2} \, dx = \frac{1}{2} \int \frac{dz}{z} = \frac{1}{2} \ln |z| + C = \frac{1}{2} \ln(1 + x^2) + C.$$

Thus,

$$\int \arctan x \, dx = x \cdot \arctan x - \frac{1}{2} \ln(1 + x^2) + C.$$

3. Let $u = t$ and $v' = e^{5t}$, so $u' = 1$ and $v = \frac{1}{5} e^{5t}$.

Then $\int t e^{5t} \, dt = \frac{1}{5} t e^{5t} - \int \frac{1}{5} e^{5t} \, dt = \frac{1}{5} t e^{5t} - \frac{1}{25} e^{5t} + C$.

4. Let $u = t^2$ and $v' = e^{5t}$, so $u' = 2t$ and $v = \frac{1}{5} e^{5t}$.

Then $\int t^2 e^{5t} \, dt = \frac{1}{5} t^2 e^{5t} - \frac{2}{5} \int t e^{5t} \, dt$.

Using Problem 3, we have $\int t^2 e^{5t} \, dt = \frac{1}{5} t^2 e^{5t} - \frac{2}{5} (\frac{1}{5} t e^{5t} - \frac{1}{25} e^{5t}) + C$
$= \frac{1}{5} t^2 e^{5t} - \frac{2}{25} t e^{5t} + \frac{2}{125} e^{5t} + C$.

5. Let $u = p$ and $v' = e^{(-0.1)p}$, $u' = 1$. Thus, $v = \int e^{(-0.1)p} \, dp = -10 e^{(-0.1)p}$. With this choice of u and v, integration by parts gives:

$$\int p e^{(-0.1)p} \, dp = p(-10 e^{(-0.1)p}) - \int (-10 e^{(-0.1)p}) \, dp$$

$$= -10 p e^{(-0.1)p} + 10 \int e^{(-0.1)p} \, dp$$

$$= -10 p e^{(-0.1)p} - 100 e^{(-0.1)p} + C.$$

6. Let $u = \ln y$, $v' = y$. Then, $v = \frac{1}{2}y^2$ and $u' = \frac{1}{y}$. Integrating by parts, we get:

$$\int y \ln y \, dy = \frac{1}{2}y^2 \ln y - \int \frac{1}{2}y^2 \cdot \frac{1}{y} \, dy$$

$$= \frac{1}{2}y^2 \ln y - \frac{1}{2}\int y \, dy$$

$$= \frac{1}{2}y^2 \ln y - \frac{1}{4}y^2 + C.$$

7. Let $u = \ln x$ and $v' = x^3$, so $u' = \frac{1}{x}$ and $v = \frac{x^4}{4}$.
    Then

$$\int x^3 \ln x \, dx = \frac{x^4}{4} \ln x - \int \frac{x^3}{4} \, dx = \frac{x^4}{4} \ln x - \frac{x^4}{16} + C.$$

8. Let $u = t$, $v' = \sin t$. Thus, $v = -\cos t$ and $u' = 1$. With this choice of u and v, integration by parts gives:

$$\int t \sin t \, dt = -t \cos t - \int (-\cos t) \, dt$$

$$= -t \cos t + \sin t + C.$$

9. Let $u = t^2$, $v' = \sin t$ implying $v = -\cos t$ and $u' = 2t$. Integrating by parts, we get:

$$\int t^2 \sin t \, dt = -t^2 \cos t - \int 2t(-\cos t) \, dt.$$

Again, applying integration by parts with $u = t$, $v' = \cos t$, we have:

$$\int t \cos t \, dt = t \sin t + \cos t + C.$$

Thus

$$\int t^2 \sin t \, dt = -t^2 \cos t + 2t \sin t + 2 \cos t + C.$$

10. Let $u = \theta^2$ and $v' = \cos 3\theta$, so $u' = 2\theta$ and $v = \frac{1}{3}\sin 3\theta$.
    Then $\int \theta^2 \cos 3\theta \, d\theta = \frac{1}{3}\theta^2 \sin 3\theta - \frac{2}{3}\int \theta \sin 3\theta \, d\theta$. The integral on the right hand side is simpler than our original integral, but to evaluate it we need to again use integration by parts.
    To find $\int \theta \sin 3\theta \, d\theta$, let $u = \theta$ and $v' = \sin 3\theta$, so $u' = 1$ and $v = -\frac{1}{3}\cos 3\theta$.
    This gives

$$\int \theta \sin 3\theta \, d\theta = -\frac{1}{3}\theta \cos 3\theta + \frac{1}{3}\int \cos 3\theta \, d\theta = -\frac{1}{3}\theta \cos 3\theta + \frac{1}{9}\sin 3\theta + C.$$

Thus,

$$\int \theta^2 \cos 3\theta\, d\theta = \frac{1}{3}\theta^2 \sin 3\theta + \frac{2}{9}\theta \cos 3\theta - \frac{2}{27}\sin 3\theta + C.$$

11.   Let $u = z + 1$, $v' = e^{2z}$. Thus, $v = \frac{1}{2}e^{2z}$ and $u' = 1$. Integrating by parts, we get:

$$\int (z + 1)e^{2z}\, dz = (z + 1) \cdot \frac{1}{2}e^{2z} - \int \frac{1}{2}e^{2z}\, dz$$
$$= \frac{1}{2}(z + 1)e^{2z} - \frac{1}{4}e^{2z} + C$$
$$= \frac{1}{4}(2z + 1)e^{2z} + C.$$

12.   Let $u = z$, $v' = e^{-z}$. Thus $v = -e^{-z}$ and $u' = 1$. Integration by parts gives:

$$\int ze^{-z}\, dz = -ze^{-z} - \int (-e^{-z})\, dz$$
$$= -ze^{-z} - e^{-z} + C$$
$$= -(z + 1)e^{-z} + C.$$

13.   Let $u = \theta + 1$ and $v' = \sin(\theta + 1)$, so $u' = 1$ and $v = -\cos(\theta + 1)$.

$$\int (\theta + 1)\sin(\theta + 1)\, d\theta = -(\theta + 1)\cos(\theta + 1) + \int \cos(\theta + 1)\, d\theta$$
$$= -(\theta + 1)\cos(\theta + 1) + \sin(\theta + 1) + C.$$

14.   Let $u = \sin\theta$ and $v' = \sin\theta$, so $u' = \cos\theta$ and $v = -\cos\theta$. Then

$$\int \sin^2\theta\, d\theta = -\sin\theta\cos\theta + \int \cos^2\theta\, d\theta$$
$$= -\sin\theta\cos\theta + \int (1 - \sin^2\theta)\, d\theta$$
$$= -\sin\theta\cos\theta + \int 1\, d\theta - \int \sin^2\theta\, d\theta.$$

By adding $\int \sin^2\theta\, d\theta$ to both sides of the above equation, we find that $2\int \sin^2\theta\, d\theta = -\sin\theta\cos\theta + \theta + C$, so $\int \sin^2\theta\, d\theta = -\frac{1}{2}\sin\theta\cos\theta + \frac{\theta}{2} + C'$.

15. Let $u = \cos(3\alpha + 1)$ and $v' = \cos(3\alpha + 1)$, so $u' = -3\sin(3\alpha + 1)$, and $v = \frac{1}{3}\sin(3\alpha + 1)$. Then

$$
\begin{aligned}
\int \cos^2(3\alpha + 1)\, d\alpha &= \int (\cos(3\alpha + 1))\cos(3\alpha + 1)\, d\alpha \\
&= \frac{1}{3}\cos(3\alpha + 1)\sin(3\alpha + 1) + \int \sin^2(3\alpha + 1)\, d\alpha \\
&= \frac{1}{3}\cos(3\alpha + 1)\sin(3\alpha + 1) + \int (1 - \cos^2(3\alpha + 1))\, d\alpha \\
&= \frac{1}{3}\cos(3\alpha + 1)\sin(3\alpha + 1) + \alpha - \int \cos^2(3\alpha + 1)\, d\alpha.
\end{aligned}
$$

By adding $\int \cos^2(3\alpha + 1)\, d\alpha$ to both sides of the above equation, we find that

$$
2\int \cos^2(3\alpha + 1)\, d\alpha = \frac{1}{3}\cos(3\alpha + 1)\sin(3\alpha + 1) + \alpha + C,
$$

which gives

$$
\int \cos^2(3\alpha + 1)\, d\alpha = \frac{1}{6}\cos(3\alpha + 1)\sin(3\alpha + 1) + \frac{\alpha}{2} + C.
$$

16. Let $u = \ln 5q$, $v' = q^5$. Then $v = \frac{1}{6}q^6$ and $u' = \dfrac{1}{q}$. Integrating by parts, we get:

$$
\begin{aligned}
\int q^5 \ln 5q\, dq &= \frac{1}{6}q^6 \ln 5q - \int \left(5 \cdot \frac{1}{5q}\right) \cdot \frac{1}{6}q^6\, dq \\
&= \frac{1}{6}q^6 \ln 5q - \frac{1}{36}q^6 + C.
\end{aligned}
$$

17. Let $u = \ln x$, $v' = x^{-2}$. Then $v = -x^{-1}$ and $u' = x^{-1}$. Integrating by parts, we get:

$$
\begin{aligned}
\int x^{-2} \ln x\, dx &= -x^{-1} \ln x - \int (-x^{-1}) \cdot x^{-1}\, dx \\
&= -x^{-1} \ln x - x^{-1} + C.
\end{aligned}
$$

18. Let $u = y$ and $v' = (y + 3)^{1/2}$, so $u' = 1$ and $v = \frac{2}{3}(y + 3)^{3/2}$.
$\int y\sqrt{y + 3}\, dy = \frac{2}{3}y(y + 3)^{3/2} - \int \frac{2}{3}(y + 3)^{3/2}\, dy = \frac{2}{3}y(y + 3)^{3/2} - \frac{4}{15}(y + 3)^{5/2} + C.$

19. Let $u = y$ and $v' = \dfrac{1}{\sqrt{5 - y}}$, so $u' = 1$ and $v = -2(5 - y)^{1/2}$.

$$
\int \frac{y}{\sqrt{5 - y}}\, dy = -2y(5 - y)^{1/2} + 2\int (5 - y)^{1/2}\, dy = -2y(5 - y)^{1/2} - \frac{4}{3}(5 - y)^{3/2} + C.
$$

20. Let $u = t + 2$ and $v' = \sqrt{2 + 3t}$, so $u' = 1$ and $v = \frac{2}{9}(2 + 3t)^{3/2}$. Then

$$\int (t + 2)\sqrt{2 + 3t}\, dt = \frac{2}{9}(t + 2)(2 + 3t)^{3/2} - \frac{2}{9}\int (2 + 3t)^{3/2}\, dt$$

$$= \frac{2}{9}(t + 2)(2 + 3t)^{3/2} - \frac{4}{135}(2 + 3t)^{5/2} + C.$$

21. $\displaystyle \int \frac{t + 7}{\sqrt{5 - t}}\, dt = \int \frac{t}{\sqrt{5 - t}}\, dt + 7\int (5 - t)^{-1/2}\, dt.$

To calculate the first integral, we use integration by parts. Let $u = t$ and $v' = \frac{1}{\sqrt{5-t}}$, so $u' = 1$ and $v = -2(5 - t)^{1/2}$. Then

$$\int \frac{t}{\sqrt{5 - t}}\, dt = -2t(5 - t)^{1/2} + 2\int (5 - t)^{1/2}\, dt = -2t(5 - t)^{1/2} - \frac{4}{3}(5 - t)^{3/2} + C.$$

We can calculate the second integral directly: $7\displaystyle\int (5 - t)^{-1/2} = -14(5 - t)^{1/2} + C_1$. Thus

$$\int \frac{t + 7}{\sqrt{5 - t}}\, dt = -2t(5 - t)^{1/2} - \frac{4}{3}(5 - t)^{3/2} - 14(5 - t)^{1/2} + C_2.$$

22. Let $u = (\ln t)^2$ and $v' = 1$, so $u' = \dfrac{2\ln t}{t}$ and $v = t$. Then

$$\int (\ln t)^2\, dt = t(\ln t)^2 - 2\int \ln t\, dt = t(\ln t)^2 - 2t\ln t + 2t + C.$$

(We use the fact that $\displaystyle\int \ln x\, dx = x\ln x - x + C$, a result which can be derived using integration by parts.)

23. Let $u = (\ln x)^4$ and $v' = x$, so $u' = \frac{4(\ln x)^3}{x}$ and $v = \frac{x^2}{2}$. Then

$$\int x(\ln x)^4\, dx = \frac{x^2(\ln x)^4}{2} - 2\int x(\ln x)^3\, dx.$$

$\int x(\ln x)^3\, dx$ is somewhat less complicated than $\int x(\ln x)^4\, dx$. To calculate it, we again try integration by parts, this time letting $u = (\ln x)^3$ (instead of $(\ln x)^4$) and $v' = x$. We find

$$\int x(\ln x)^3\, dx = \frac{x^2}{2}(\ln x)^3 - \frac{3}{2}\int x(\ln x)^2\, dx.$$

Once again, express the given integral in terms of a less-complicated one. Using integration by parts two more times, we find that

$$\int x(\ln x)^2\, dx = \frac{x^2}{2}(\ln x)^2 - \int x(\ln x)\, dx$$

and that

$$\int x \ln x \, dx = \frac{x^2}{2} \ln x - \frac{x^2}{4} + C.$$

Putting this all together, we have

$$\int x (\ln x)^4 \, dx = \frac{x^2}{2}(\ln x)^4 - x^2(\ln x)^3 + \frac{3}{2}x^2(\ln x)^2 - \frac{3}{2}x^2 \ln x + \frac{3}{4}x^2 + C.$$

24. Let $u = \arctan 7z$ and $v' = 1$, so $u' = \frac{7}{1+49z^2}$ and $v = z$. Now $\int \frac{7z \, dz}{1+49z^2}$ can be evaluated by the substitution $w = 1 + 49z^2$, $dw = 98z \, dz$, so

$$\int \frac{7z \, dz}{1+49z^2} = 7 \int \frac{\frac{1}{98} \, dw}{w} = \frac{1}{14} \int \frac{dw}{w} = \frac{1}{14} \ln |w| + C = \frac{1}{14} \ln(1 + 49z^2) + C$$

So

$$\int \arctan 7z \, dz = z \arctan 7z - \frac{1}{14} \ln(1 + 49z^2) + C.$$

25. This integral can first be simplified by making the substitution $w = x^2$, $dw = 2x \, dx$. Then

$$\int x \arctan x^2 \, dx = \frac{1}{2} \int \arctan w \, dw.$$

To evaluate $\int \arctan w \, dw$, we'll use integration by parts. Let $u = \arctan w$ and $v' = 1$, so $u' = \frac{1}{1+w^2}$ and $v = w$. Then

$$\int \arctan w \, dw = w \arctan w - \int \frac{w}{1+w^2} \, dw = w \arctan w - \frac{1}{2} \ln |1 + w^2| + C.$$

Since $1 + w^2$ is never negative, we can drop the absolute value signs. Thus, we have

$$\int x \arctan x^2 \, dx = \frac{1}{2} \left(x^2 \arctan x^2 - \frac{1}{2} \ln(1 + (x^2)^2) + C \right)$$

$$= \frac{1}{2}x^2 \arctan x^2 - \frac{1}{4} \ln(1 + x^4) + C.$$

26. Let $u = \arcsin w$ and $v' = 1$, so $u' = \frac{1}{\sqrt{1-w^2}}$ and $v = w$. Then

$$\int \arcsin w \, dw = w \arcsin w - \int \frac{w}{\sqrt{1 - w^2}} \, dw = w \arcsin w + \sqrt{1 - w^2} + C.$$

27. Let $u = x^2$ and $v' = xe^{x^2}$, so $u' = 2x$ and $v = \frac{1}{2}e^{x^2}$. Then

$$\int x^3 e^{x^2} \, dx = \frac{1}{2}x^2 e^{x^2} - \int xe^{x^2} \, dx = \frac{1}{2}x^2 e^{x^2} - \frac{1}{2}e^{x^2} + C.$$

Note that we can also do this problem by substitution and integration by parts. If we let $w = x^2$, so $dw = 2x \, dx$, then $\int x^3 e^{x^2} \, dx = \frac{1}{2}\int we^w \, dw$. We could then perform integration by parts on this integral to get the same result.

28. To simplify matters, let us try the substitution $w = x^3$, $dw = 3x^2 \, dx$. Then

$$\int x^5 \cos x^3 \, dx = \frac{1}{3}\int w \cos w \, dw.$$

Now we integrate by parts. Let $u = w$ and $v' = \cos w$, so $u' = 1$ and $v = \sin w$. Then

$$\frac{1}{3}\int w \cos w \, dw = \frac{1}{3}[w \sin w - \int \sin w \, dw]$$

$$= \frac{1}{3}[w \sin w + \cos w] + C$$

$$= \frac{1}{3}x^3 \sin x^3 + \frac{1}{3}\cos x^3 + C$$

29. From integration by parts in Problem 14, we obtain

$$\int \sin^2 \theta \, d\theta = -\frac{1}{2}\sin \theta \cos \theta + \frac{1}{2}\theta + C.$$

Using the identity given in the book, we have

$$\int \sin^2 \theta \, d\theta = \int \frac{1 - \cos 2\theta}{2} \, d\theta = \frac{1}{2}\theta - \frac{1}{4}\sin 2\theta + C.$$

Although the answers differ in form, they are really the same, since (by one of the standard double angle formulas) $-\frac{1}{4}\sin 2\theta = -\frac{1}{4}(2 \sin \theta \cos \theta) = -\frac{1}{2}\sin \theta \cos \theta.$

30. Integration by parts: let $u = \cos \theta$ and $v' = \cos \theta$, so $u' = -\sin \theta$ and $v = \sin \theta$.

$$\int \cos^2 \theta \, d\theta = \sin \theta \cos \theta - \int (-\sin \theta)(\sin \theta) \, d\theta$$

$$= \sin \theta \cos \theta + \int \sin^2 \theta \, d\theta.$$

Now use $\sin^2 \theta = 1 - \cos^2 \theta.$

$$\int \cos^2 \theta \, d\theta = \sin \theta \cos \theta + \int (1 - \cos^2 \theta) \, d\theta$$

$$= \sin \theta \cos \theta + \int d\theta - \int \cos^2 \theta \, d\theta.$$

Adding $\int \cos^2 \theta \, d\theta$ to both sides, we have

$$2 \int \cos^2 \theta \, d\theta = \sin \theta \cos \theta + \theta + C$$

$$\int \cos^2 \theta \, d\theta = \frac{1}{2} \sin \theta \cos \theta + \frac{1}{2} \theta + C'.$$

Use the identity $\cos^2 \theta = \frac{1 + \cos 2\theta}{2}$.

$$\int \cos^2 \theta \, d\theta = \int \frac{1 + \cos 2\theta}{2} \, d\theta = \frac{1}{2} \theta + \frac{1}{4} \sin 2\theta + C.$$

The only difference is in the two terms $\frac{1}{2} \sin \theta \cos \theta$ and $\frac{1}{4} \sin 2\theta$, but since $\sin 2\theta = 2 \sin \theta \cos \theta$, we have $\frac{1}{4} \sin 2\theta = \frac{1}{4}(2 \sin \theta \cos \theta) = \frac{1}{2} \sin \theta \cos \theta$, so there is no real difference between the formulas.

31. First, let $u = e^x$ and $v' = \sin x$, so $u' = e^x$ and $v = -\cos x$.
Thus $\int e^x \sin x \, dx = -e^x \cos x + \int e^x \cos x \, dx$. To calculate $\int e^x \cos x \, dx$, we again need to use integration by parts. Let $u = e^x$ and $v' = \cos x$, so $u' = e^x$ and $v = \sin x$.
Thus

$$\int e^x \cos x \, dx = e^x \sin x - \int e^x \sin x \, dx.$$

This gives

$$\int e^x \sin x \, dx = e^x \sin x - e^x \cos x - \int e^x \sin x \, dx.$$

By adding $\int e^x \sin x \, dx$ to both sides, we obtain

$$2 \int e^x \sin x \, dx = e^x (\sin x - \cos x) + C.$$

$$\text{Thus} \int e^x \sin x \, dx = \frac{1}{2} e^x (\sin x - \cos x) + C.$$

This problem could also be done in other ways; for example, we could have started with $u = \sin x$ and $v' = e^x$ as well.

32. Let $u = e^\theta$ and $v' = \cos \theta$, so $u' = e^\theta$ and $v = \sin \theta$. Then $\int e^\theta \cos \theta \, d\theta = e^\theta \sin \theta - \int e^\theta \sin \theta \, d\theta$.
In Problem 31 we found that $\int e^x \sin x \, dx = \frac{1}{2} e^x (\sin x - \cos x) + C$.

$$\int e^\theta \cos \theta \, d\theta = e^\theta \sin \theta - \left[\frac{1}{2} e^\theta (\sin \theta - \cos \theta) \right] + C$$

$$= \frac{1}{2} e^\theta (\sin \theta + \cos \theta) + C.$$

33. We integrate by parts. Since in Problem 31 we found that $\int e^x \sin x \, dx = \frac{1}{2}e^x(\sin x - \cos x)$, we let $u = x$ and $v' = e^x \sin x$, so $u' = 1$ and $v = \frac{1}{2}e^x(\sin x - \cos x)$.

Then $\displaystyle \int x e^x \sin x \, dx = \frac{1}{2}x e^x(\sin x - \cos x) - \frac{1}{2}\int e^x(\sin x - \cos x) \, dx$

$$= \frac{1}{2}x e^x(\sin x - \cos x) - \frac{1}{2}\int e^x \sin x \, dx + \frac{1}{2}\int e^x \cos x \, dx.$$

Using Problems 31 and 32, we see that this equals

$$\frac{1}{2}x e^x(\sin x - \cos x) - \frac{1}{4}e^x(\sin x - \cos x) + \frac{1}{4}e^x(\sin x + \cos x) + C$$

$$= \frac{1}{2}x e^x(\sin x - \cos x) + \frac{1}{2}e^x \cos x + C.$$

34. Again we use Problems 31 and 32. Integrate by parts, letting $u = \theta$ and $v' = e^\theta \cos \theta$, so $u' = 1$ and $v = \frac{1}{2}e^\theta(\sin \theta + \cos \theta)$. Then

$$\int \theta e^\theta \cos \theta \, d\theta = \frac{1}{2}\theta e^\theta(\sin \theta + \cos \theta) - \frac{1}{2}\int e^\theta(\sin \theta + \cos \theta) \, d\theta$$

$$= \frac{1}{2}\theta e^\theta(\sin \theta + \cos \theta) - \frac{1}{2}\int e^\theta \sin \theta \, d\theta - \frac{1}{2}\int e^\theta \cos \theta \, d\theta$$

$$= \frac{1}{2}\theta e^\theta(\sin \theta + \cos \theta) - \frac{1}{4}e^\theta(\sin \theta - \cos \theta) - \frac{1}{4}(\sin \theta + \cos \theta) + C$$

$$= \frac{1}{2}\theta e^\theta(\sin \theta + \cos \theta) - \frac{1}{2}e^\theta \sin \theta + C.$$

35. We integrate by parts. Since we know what the answer is supposed to be, it's easier to choose u and v'. Let $u = x^n$ and $v' = e^x$, so $u' = nx^{n-1}$ and $v = e^x$. Then

$$\int x^n e^x \, dx = x^n e^x - n \int x^{n-1} e^x \, dx.$$

36. We integrate by parts. Let $u = x^n$ and $v' = \sin ax$, so $u' = nx^{n-1}$ and $v = -\frac{1}{a}\cos ax$.

Then $\displaystyle \int x^n \sin ax \, dx = -\frac{1}{a}x^n \cos ax - \int (nx^{n-1})(-\frac{1}{a}\cos ax) \, dx$

$$= -\frac{1}{a}x^n \cos ax + \frac{n}{a}\int x^{n-1} \cos ax \, dx.$$

37. We integrate by parts. Let $u = x^n$ and $v' = \cos ax$, so $u' = nx^{n-1}$ and $v = \frac{1}{a} \sin ax$. Then

$$\int x^n \cos ax \, dx = \frac{1}{a} x^n \sin ax - \int (nx^{n-1})(\frac{1}{a} \sin ax) \, dx$$
$$= \frac{1}{a} x^n \sin ax - \frac{n}{a} \int x^{n-1} \sin ax \, dx.$$

38. We integrate by parts. Since we know what the answer is supposed to be, it's easier to choose u and v'. Let $u = \cos^{n-1} x$ and $v' = \cos x$, so $u' = (n-1) \cos^{n-2} x(-\sin x)$ and $v = \sin x$.
    Then

$$\int \cos^n x \, dx = \cos^{n-1} x \sin x + (n-1) \int \cos^{n-2} x \sin^2 x \, dx$$
$$= \cos^{n-1} x \sin x + (n-1) \int \cos^{n-2} x(1 - \cos^2 x) \, dx$$
$$= \cos^{n-1} x \sin x - (n-1) \int \cos^n x \, dx + (n-1) \int \cos^{n-2} x \, dx.$$

Thus, by adding $(n-1) \int \cos^n x \, dx$ to both sides of the equation, we find

$$n \int \cos^n x \, dx = \cos^{n-1} x \sin x + (n-1) \int \cos^{n-2} x \, dx,$$
$$\text{so} \int \cos^n \, dx = \frac{1}{n} \cos^{n-1} x \sin x + \frac{n-1}{n} \int \cos^{n-2} x \, dx.$$

39. $\int_1^5 \ln t \, dt = (t \ln t - t) \Big|_1^5 = 5 \ln 5 - 4 \approx 4.047$

40. We use integration by parts. Let $u = z$ and $v' = e^{-z}$, so $u' = 1$ and $v = -e^{-z}$.

$$\text{Then} \int_0^{10} ze^{-z} \, dz = -ze^{-z} \Big|_0^{10} + \int_0^{10} e^{-z} \, dz$$
$$= -10e^{-10} + (-e^{-z}) \Big|_0^{10}$$
$$= -11e^{-10} + 1$$
$$\approx 0.9995.$$

41. $\displaystyle\int_3^5 x\cos x\,dx = (\cos x + x\sin x)\Big|_3^5 = \cos 5 + 5\sin 5 - \cos 3 - 3\sin 3 \approx -3.944.$

42. $\displaystyle\int_1^3 t\ln t\,dt = \left(\frac{1}{2}t^2\ln t - \frac{1}{2}t\right)\Big|_1^3 = \frac{9}{2}\ln 3 - 2 \approx 2.944.$

43. $\displaystyle\int_0^5 \ln(1+t)\,dt = ((1+t)\ln(1+t) - (1+t))\Big|_0^5 = 6\ln 6 - 5 \approx 5.751.$

44. We use integration by parts. Let $u = \arctan y$ and $v' = 1$, so $u' = \frac{1}{1+y^2}$ and $v = y$. Thus

$$\int_0^1 \arctan y\,dy = (\arctan y)y\Big|_0^1 - \int_0^1 \frac{y}{1+y^2}\,dy$$

$$= \frac{\pi}{4} - \frac{1}{2}\ln|1+y^2|\Big|_0^1$$

$$= \frac{\pi}{4} - \frac{1}{2}\ln 2 \approx 0.439.$$

45. First we make the substitution $y = x^2$, so $dy = 2x\,dx$. Thus

$$\int_{x=0}^{x=1} x\arctan x^2\,dx = \frac{1}{2}\int_{y=0}^{y=1}\arctan y\,dy.$$

From Problem 44, we know that

$$\int_0^1 \arctan y\,dy = \frac{\pi}{4} - \frac{\ln 2}{2}.$$

Thus

$$\int_0^1 x\arctan x^2\,dx = \frac{1}{2}\left(\frac{\pi}{4} - \frac{1}{2}\ln 2\right) \approx 0.219.$$

46. We use integration by parts. Let $u = \arcsin z$ and $v' = 1$, so $u' = \dfrac{1}{\sqrt{1-z^2}}$ and $v = z$. Then

$$\int_0^1 \arcsin z\,dz = z\arcsin z\Big|_0^1 - \int_0^1 \frac{z}{\sqrt{1-z^2}}\,dz = \frac{\pi}{2} - \int_0^1 \frac{z}{\sqrt{1-z^2}}\,dz.$$

To find $\displaystyle\int_0^1 \frac{z}{\sqrt{1-z^2}}\,dz$, we substitute $w = 1 - z^2$, so $dw = -2z\,dz$.
Then

$$\int_{z=0}^{z=1} \frac{z}{\sqrt{1-z^2}}\,dz = -\frac{1}{2}\int_{w=1}^{w=0} w^{-\frac{1}{2}}\,dw = \frac{1}{2}\int_{w=0}^{w=1} w^{-\frac{1}{2}}\,dw = w^{\frac{1}{2}}\Big|_0^1 = 1.$$

Thus our final answer is $\frac{\pi}{2} - 1 \approx 0.571.$

47. To simplify the integral, we first make the substitution $z = u^2$, so $dz = 2u\,du$. Then

$$\int_{u=0}^{u=1} u \arcsin u^2\, du = \frac{1}{2} \int_{z=0}^{z=1} \arcsin z\, dz.$$

From Problem 46, we know that $\int_0^1 \arcsin z\, dz = \frac{\pi}{2} - 1$. Thus,

$$\int_0^1 u \arcsin u^2\, du = \frac{1}{2}\left(\frac{\pi}{2} - 1\right) \approx 0.285.$$

48. Since $\ln x$ is monotonically increasing between 1 and 2, we know that the value of the integral should be between the left sum and right sum approximations. We find $\text{LEFT}(100) \approx 0.3828$, $\text{RIGHT}(100) \approx 0.3898$. Using the Fundamental Theorem of Calculus,

$$\int_1^2 \ln x\, dx = (x \ln x - x)\Big|_1^2 = 2 \ln 2 - 1 \approx 0.3863.$$

The value from the Fundamental Theorem does indeed fall within the boundaries of the left and right sums; it will do so no matter how many subdivisions we use.

49. (a) One way to avoid integrating by parts is to take the derivative of the right hand side instead. Since $\int e^{ax} \sin bx\, dx$ is the antiderivative of $e^{ax} \sin bx$,

$$\begin{aligned}
e^{ax} \sin bx &= \frac{d}{dx}\left[e^{ax}(A \sin bx + B \cos bx) + C\right] \\
&= ae^{ax}(A \sin bx + B \cos bx) + e^{ax}(Ab \cos bx - Bb \sin bx) \\
&= e^{ax}[(aA - bB) \sin bx + (aB + bA) \cos bx].
\end{aligned}$$

Thus $aA - bB = 1$ and $aB + bA = 0$. Solving for A and B in terms of a and b, we get

$$A = \frac{a}{a^2 + b^2}, \quad B = -\frac{b}{a^2 + b^2}.$$

Thus

$$\int e^{ax} \sin bx = e^{ax}\left(\frac{a}{a^2 + b^2} \sin bx - \frac{b}{a^2 + b^2} \cos bx\right) + C.$$

(b) If we go through the same process, we find

$$ae^{ax}[(aA - bB) \sin bx + (aB + bA) \cos bx] = e^{ax} \cos bx.$$

Thus $aA - bB = 0$, and $aB + bA = 1$. In this case, solving for A and B yields

$$A = \frac{b}{a^2 + b^2}, \quad B = \frac{a}{a^2 + b^2}.$$

Thus $\int e^{ax} \cos bx = e^{ax}\left(\frac{b}{a^2+b^2} \sin bx + \frac{a}{a^2+b^2} \cos bx\right) + C$.

50. (a) We know that $\dfrac{dE}{dt} = r$, so the total energy E used in the first T hours is given by $E = \displaystyle\int_0^T te^{-at}\, dt$.

   We use integration by parts. Let $u = t$, $v' = e^{-at}$. Then $u' = 1$, $v = -\frac{1}{a}e^{-at}$.

$$E = \int_0^T te^{-at}\, dt$$

$$= -\frac{t}{a}e^{-at}\Big|_0^T - \int_0^T \left(-\frac{1}{a}e^{-at}\right) dt$$

$$= -\frac{1}{a}Te^{-aT} + \frac{1}{a}\int_0^T e^{-at}\, dt$$

$$= -\frac{1}{a}Te^{-aT} + \frac{1}{a^2}(1 - e^{-aT}).$$

   (b)

$$\lim_{T\to\infty} E = -\frac{1}{a}\lim_{T\to\infty}\left(\frac{T}{e^{aT}}\right) + \frac{1}{a^2}\left(1 - \lim_{T\to\infty}\frac{1}{e^{aT}}\right).$$

   Since $a > 0$, the second limit on the right hand side in the above expression is 0. In the first limit, although both the numerator and the denominator go to infinity, the denominator e^{aT} goes to infinity more quickly than T does. So in the end the denominator e^{aT} is much greater than the numerator T. Hence $\displaystyle\lim_{T\to\infty}\frac{T}{e^{aT}} = 0$. (You can check this by graphing $y = \dfrac{T}{e^{aT}}$ on a calculator or computer for some values of a.) Thus $\displaystyle\lim_{T\to\infty} E = \frac{1}{a^2}$.

7.5 SOLUTIONS

1. See the solutions to Problems 5–13. Answers may vary, as there may be more than one way to approach a problem.

2. See the solutions to Problems 14–25.

3. See the solutions to Problems 26–38.

4. See the solutions to Problems 39–50.

5. $\left(\dfrac{1}{2}x^3 - \dfrac{3}{4}x^2 + \dfrac{3}{4}x - \dfrac{3}{8}\right)e^{2x} + C.$
   (Let $a = 2$, $p(x) = x^3$ in III-14.)

6. $\dfrac{5}{16}\sin 3\theta \sin 5\theta + \dfrac{3}{16}\cos 3\theta \cos 5\theta + C.$
   (Let $a = 3$, $b = 5$ in II-12.)

7. $\dfrac{3}{16}\cos 3\theta \sin 5\theta - \dfrac{5}{16}\sin 3\theta \cos 5\theta + C.$
   (Let $a = 3$, $b = 5$ in II-10.)

8. $\frac{1}{10}e^{(-3\theta)}(-3\cos\theta + \sin\theta) + C$.
   (Let $a = -3, b = 1$ in II-9.)

9. $\frac{1}{6}x^6 \ln x - \frac{1}{36}x^6 + C$. (Let $n = 5$ in III-13.)

10. $-\frac{1}{5}\cos^5 w + C$
    (Let $x = \cos w$, as suggested in IV-23. Then $-\sin w\,dw = dx$, and $\int \sin w \cos^4 w\,dw = -\int x^4\,dx$.)

11. Let $m = 3$ in IV-21.

$$\int \frac{1}{\cos^3 x}\,dx = \frac{1}{2}\frac{\sin x}{\cos^2 x} + \frac{1}{2}\int \frac{1}{\cos x}\,dx$$
$$= \frac{1}{2}\frac{\sin x}{\cos^2 x} + \frac{1}{4}\ln\left|\frac{\sin x + 1}{\sin x - 1}\right| + C \text{ by IV-22.}$$

12. $-\frac{1}{4}\sin^3 x \cos x - \frac{3}{8}\sin x \cos x + \frac{3}{8}x + C$.
    (Use IV-17.)

13. $\frac{1}{\sqrt{3}}\arctan\frac{y}{\sqrt{3}} + C$.
    (Let $a = \sqrt{3}$ in V-24).

14. $\left(\frac{1}{3}x^2 - \frac{2}{9}x + \frac{2}{27}\right)e^{3x} + C$.
    (Let $a = 3, p(x) = x^2$ in III-14.)

15. $\left(\frac{1}{3}x^4 - \frac{4}{9}x^3 + \frac{4}{9}x^2 - \frac{8}{27}x + \frac{8}{81}\right)e^{3x} + C$.
    (Let $a = 3, p(x) = x^4$ in III-14.)

16. $\frac{1}{3}e^{x^3} + C$.
    (Substitute $w = x^3$, $dw = 3x^2\,dx$. It isn't necessary to use the table.)

17.

$$\int y^2 \sin 2y\,dy = -\frac{1}{2}y^2 \cos 2y + \frac{1}{4}(2y)\sin 2y + \frac{1}{8}(2)\cos 2y + C$$
$$= -\frac{1}{2}y^2 \cos 2y + \frac{1}{2}y \sin 2y + \frac{1}{4}\cos 2y + C.$$

(Use $a = 2, p(y) = y^2$ in III-15.)

18. $\frac{1}{45}(7\cos 2y \sin 7y - 2\sin 2y \cos 7y) + C$.
    (Let $a = 2, b = 7$ in II-11.)

19. $\dfrac{1}{34}e^{5x}(5\sin 3x - 3\cos 3x) + C.$
    (Let $a = 5, b = 3$ in II-8.)

20. Substitute $w = x^2$, $dw = 2x\,dx$. Then $\displaystyle\int x^3 \sin x^2\,dx = \dfrac{1}{2}\int w \sin w\,dw$. By III-15, we have

$$\int w \sin w\,dw = -\frac{1}{2}w\cos w + \frac{1}{2}\sin w + C = -\frac{1}{2}x^2 \cos x^2 + \frac{1}{2}\sin x^2 + C.$$

21. If we make the substitution $w = 2z^2$ then $dw = 4z\,dz$, and the integral becomes:

$$\int ze^{2z^2}\cos(2z^2)\,dz = \frac{1}{4}\int e^w \cos w\,dw$$

Now we can use Formula 9 from the table of integrals to get:

$$\frac{1}{4}\int e^w \cos w\,dw = \frac{1}{4}\left[\frac{1}{2}e^w(\cos w + \sin w) + C\right]$$

$$= \frac{1}{8}e^w(\cos w + \sin w) + C$$

$$= \frac{1}{8}e^{2z^2}(\cos 2z^2 + \sin 2z^2) + C$$

22. Substitute $w = 5u$, $dw = 5\,du$. Then

$$\int u^5 \ln(5u)\,du = \frac{1}{5^6}\int w^5 \ln w\,dw$$

$$= \frac{1}{5^6}(\frac{1}{6}w^6 \ln w - \frac{1}{36}w^6 + C)$$

$$= \frac{1}{6}u^6 \ln 5u - \frac{1}{36}u^6 + C.$$

Or use $\ln 5u = \ln 5 + \ln u$.

$$\int u^5 \ln 5u\,du = \ln 5 \int u^5\,du + \int u^5 \ln u\,du$$

$$= \frac{u^6}{6}\ln 5 + \frac{1}{6}u^6 \ln u - \frac{1}{36}u^6 + C \quad \text{(using III-13)}$$

$$= \frac{u^6}{6}\ln 5u - \frac{1}{36}u^6 + C.$$

23. Since $\ln y^3 = 3 \ln y$,

$$\int y^7 \ln(y^3)\, dy = 3 \int y^7 \ln y\, dy$$

$$= 3 \left(\frac{1}{8} y^8 \ln y - \frac{1}{64} y^8 \right) + C \quad \text{(using III-13)}$$

$$= \frac{3}{8} y^8 \ln y - \frac{3}{64} y^8 + C.$$

24. Substitute $w = 3y$, $dw = 3\, dy$. Then use IV-18.

$$\int \cos^4 3y\, dy = \frac{1}{3} \int \cos^4 w\, dw = \frac{1}{3} \left[\frac{1}{4} \cos^3 w \sin w + \frac{3}{4} \int \cos^2 w\, dw \right]$$

$$= \frac{1}{12} \cos^3 w \sin w + \frac{1}{4} \int \cos^2 w\, dw.$$

Using Formula IV-18 again, $\frac{1}{4} \int \cos^2 w\, dw = \frac{1}{4} \left(\frac{1}{2} \cos w \sin w + \frac{1}{2} w \right) + C$.
Thus,

$$\int \cos^4 3y\, dy = \frac{1}{12} \cos^3 w \sin w + \frac{1}{8} \cos w \sin w + \frac{1}{8} w + C$$

$$= \frac{1}{12} \cos^3 3y \sin 3y + \frac{1}{8} \cos 3y \sin 3y + \frac{3}{8} y + C.$$

25. Substitute $w = z^2$, $dw = 2z\, dz$. Using IV-17,

$$\int z \sin^3(z^2)\, dz = \frac{1}{2} \int \sin^3 w\, dw = \frac{1}{2} [-\frac{1}{3} \sin^2 w \cos w + \frac{2}{3} \int \sin w\, dw]$$

$$= -\frac{1}{6} \sin^2 w \cos w - \frac{1}{3} \cos w + C$$

$$= -\frac{1}{6} \sin^2(z^2) \cos(z^2) - \frac{1}{3} \cos(z^2) + C.$$

26. $\arcsin \dfrac{x}{\sqrt{2}} + C.$
    (Let $a = \sqrt{2}$ in VI-28.)

27.

$$\int \frac{1}{\sqrt{1 - 9x^2}}\, dx = \frac{1}{3} \int \frac{1}{\sqrt{\frac{1}{9} - x^2}}\, dx = \frac{1}{3} \arcsin 3x + C.$$

(Let $a = \frac{1}{3}$ in VI-28.)

28.

$$\int \frac{1}{1+4x^2}\,dx = \frac{1}{4}\int \frac{1}{\frac{1}{4}+x^2}\,dx = \frac{1}{2}\arctan 2x + C.$$

(Let $a = \frac{1}{2}$ in V-24.)

29. Substitute $w = 2\theta$, $dw = 2\,d\theta$. Then use IV-19, letting $m = 2$.

$$\int \frac{1}{\sin^2 2\theta}\,d\theta = \frac{1}{2}\int \frac{1}{\sin^2 w}\,dw = \frac{1}{2}\left(-\frac{\cos w}{\sin w}\right) + C = -\frac{1}{2\tan w} + C = -\frac{1}{2\tan 2\theta} + C.$$

30. Substitute $w = 3\theta$, $dw = 3\,d\theta$. Then use IV-19, letting $m = 3$.

$$\begin{aligned}
\int \frac{1}{\sin^3 3\theta}\,d\theta &= \frac{1}{3}\int \frac{1}{\sin^3 w}\,dw = \frac{1}{3}\left[-\frac{1}{2}\frac{\cos w}{\sin^2 w} + \frac{1}{2}\int \frac{1}{\sin w}\,dw\right] \\
&= -\frac{1}{6}\frac{\cos w}{\sin^2 w} + \frac{1}{6}\left[\frac{1}{2}\ln\left|\frac{\cos(w)-1}{\cos(w)+1}\right| + C\right] \text{ by IV-20} \\
&= -\frac{1}{6}\frac{\cos 3\theta}{\sin^2 3\theta} + \frac{1}{12}\ln\left|\frac{\cos(3\theta)-1}{\cos(3\theta)+1}\right| + C.
\end{aligned}$$

31. Substitute $w = 7x$, $dw = 7\,dx$. Then use IV-21.

$$\begin{aligned}
\int \frac{1}{\cos^4 7x}\,dx &= \frac{1}{7}\int \frac{1}{\cos^4 w}\,dw = \frac{1}{7}\left[\frac{1}{3}\frac{\sin w}{\cos^3 w} + \frac{2}{3}\int \frac{1}{\cos^2 w}\,dw\right] \\
&= \frac{1}{21}\frac{\sin w}{\cos^3 w} + \frac{2}{21}\left[\frac{\sin w}{\cos w} + C\right] \\
&= \frac{1}{21}\frac{\tan w}{\cos^2 w} + \frac{2}{21}\tan w + C \\
&= \frac{1}{21}\frac{\tan 7x}{\cos^2 7x} + \frac{2}{21}\tan 7x + C.
\end{aligned}$$

32. Since

$$\frac{1}{\sqrt{9-4x^2}} = \frac{1}{\sqrt{4(\frac{9}{4}-x^2)}} = \frac{1}{2}\frac{1}{\sqrt{\frac{9}{4}-x^2}} = \frac{1}{2}\frac{1}{\sqrt{(\frac{3}{2})^2-x^2}},$$

let $a = \frac{3}{2}$ in VI-28. Then

$$\int \frac{1}{\sqrt{9-4x^2}} = \frac{1}{2}\arcsin\frac{2x}{3} + C.$$

33. $-\dfrac{1}{4}(9-4x^2)^{\frac{1}{2}} + C.$

(Substitute $w = 9 - 4x^2$, $dw = -8x\,dx$. You need not use the table.)

34. Following the advice given in IV-23, since $n = m = 2$ are both even, we convert everything to cosines:

$$\int \cos^2 \theta \sin^2 \theta \, d\theta = \int \cos^2 \theta (1 - \cos^2 \theta) \, d\theta$$

$$= \int (\cos^2 \theta - \cos^4 \theta) \, d\theta$$

$$= \int \cos^2 \theta \, d\theta - \int \cos^4 \theta \, d\theta.$$

Using Formula IV-18:

$$\int \cos^2 \theta \, d\theta = \frac{1}{2} \cos \theta \sin \theta + \frac{1}{2} \theta + C$$

$$\int \cos^4 \theta \, d\theta = \frac{1}{4} \cos^3 \theta \sin \theta + \frac{3}{4} \int \cos^2 \theta \, d\theta.$$

So

$$\int \cos^2 \theta \, d\theta - \int \cos^4 \theta \, d\theta = \frac{1}{4} \int \cos^2 \theta \, d\theta - \frac{1}{4} \cos^3 \theta \sin \theta$$

$$= \frac{1}{8} \cos \theta \sin \theta + \frac{1}{8} \theta - \frac{1}{4} \cos^3 \theta \sin \theta + C.$$

35.

$$\int \sin^3 3\theta \cos^2 3\theta \, d\theta = \int (\sin 3\theta)(\cos^2 3\theta)(1 - \cos^2 3\theta) \, d\theta$$

$$= \int \sin 3\theta (\cos^2 3\theta - \cos^4 3\theta) \, d\theta.$$

Using an extension of the tip given in rule IV-23, we let $w = \cos 3\theta$, $dw = -3 \sin 3\theta \, d\theta$.

$$\int \sin 3\theta (\cos^2 3\theta - \cos^4 3\theta) \, d\theta = -\frac{1}{3} \int (w^2 - w^4) \, dw$$

$$= -\frac{1}{3} \left(\frac{w^3}{3} - \frac{w^5}{5} \right) + C$$

$$= -\frac{1}{9} (\cos^3 3\theta) + \frac{1}{15} (\cos^5 3\theta) + C.$$

36. Using the advice in IV-23, since both m and n are even and since n is negative, we convert everything to cosines, since $\cos x$ is in the denominator.

$$\int \tan^4 x \, dx = \int \frac{\sin^4 x}{\cos^4 x} \, dx$$

$$= \int \frac{(1 - \cos^2 x)^2}{\cos^4 x} \, dx$$

$$= \int \frac{1}{\cos^4 x} \, dx - 2 \int \frac{1}{\cos^2 x} \, dx + \int 1 \, dx.$$

By IV-21

$$\int \frac{1}{\cos^4 x} \, dx = \frac{1}{3} \frac{\sin x}{\cos^3 x} + \frac{2}{3} \int \frac{1}{\cos^2 x} \, dx,$$

$$\int \frac{1}{\cos^2 x} \, dx = \frac{\sin x}{\cos x} + C.$$

Substituting back in, we get

$$\int \tan^4 x \, dx = \frac{1}{3} \frac{\sin x}{\cos^3 x} - \frac{4}{3} \frac{\sin x}{\cos x} + x + C.$$

37.
$$\int \frac{dz}{z(z - 3)} = -\frac{1}{3} (\ln |z| - \ln |z - 3|) + C.$$

(Let $a = 0, b = 3$ in V-26.)

38.
$$\int \frac{dy}{4 - y^2} = -\int \frac{dy}{(y + 2)(y - 2)} = -\frac{1}{4} (\ln |y - 2| - \ln |y + 2|) + C.$$

(Let $a = 2, b = -2$ in V-26.)

39. $\arctan(z + 2) + C.$
(Substitute $w = z + 2$ and use V-24, letting $a = 1$.)

40. Substitute $w = y + 1$, $dw = dy$ and use VI-29, letting $a = 2$.

$$\int \frac{dy}{\sqrt{4 + (1 + y)^2}} = \int \frac{dw}{\sqrt{4 + w^2}} = \ln |w + \sqrt{w^2 + 4}| + C = \ln |y + 1 + \sqrt{(y + 1)^2 + 4}| + C.$$

41.
$$\arcsin \frac{x + 1}{\sqrt{2}} + C.$$

(Substitute $w = x + 1$, and then apply VI-28 with $a = \sqrt{2}$).

42.
$$\int \frac{1}{x^2 + 4x + 3} \, dx = \int \frac{1}{(x + 1)(x + 3)} \, dx = \frac{1}{2} (\ln |x + 1| - \ln |x + 3|) + C.$$

(Let $a = -1$ and $b = -3$ in V-26).

43.

$$\int \frac{1}{x^2 + 4x + 4} \, dx = \int \frac{1}{(x+2)^2} \, dx = -\frac{1}{x+2} + C.$$

You need not use the table.

44.

$$\int \frac{1}{y^2 + 4y + 5} \, dy = \int \frac{1}{1 + (y+2)^2} \, dy = \arctan(y+2) + C.$$

(Substitute $w = y + 2$, and let $a = 1$ in V-24).

45. Using long division, we find that

$$\frac{x^3 + 3}{x^2 - 3x + 2} = x + 3 + \frac{7x - 3}{x^2 - 3x + 2}.$$

Thus

$$\int \frac{x^3 + 3}{x^2 - 3x + 2} \, dx = \int \left(x + 3 + \frac{7x - 3}{x^2 - 3x + 2} \right) \, dx$$

$$= \int (x + 3) \, dx + \int \frac{7x - 3}{(x-1)(x-2)} \, dx.$$

Using V-27 (with $a = 1, b = 2, c = 7$, and $d = -3$) we have

$$\int \frac{7x - 3}{(x-1)(x-2)} \, dx = -4 \ln|x - 1| + 11 \ln|x - 2| + C.$$

Thus

$$\int \frac{x^3 + 3}{x^2 - 3x + 2} \, dx = \frac{x^2}{2} + 3x - 4 \ln|x - 1| + 11 \ln|x - 2| + C.$$

46. Using long division, we find that

$$\int \frac{x^2}{x^2 + 6x + 13} \, dx = \int \left(1 - \frac{6x + 13}{x^2 + 6x + 13} \right) \, dx$$

$$= \int dx - \int \frac{6x + 13}{x^2 + 6x + 13} \, dx$$

$$= x - \int \frac{6x + 13}{x^2 + 6x + 13} \, dx.$$

Completing the square in the denominator and substituting $w = x + 3$ yields

$$\int \frac{6x + 13}{(x+3)^2 + 4} \, dx.$$

Let $w = x + 3$. Then $x = w - 3$, and $6x + 13 = 6w - 5$. Thus

$$\int \frac{6x + 13}{x^2 + 6x + 13} \, dx = \int \frac{6w - 5}{w^2 + 4} \, dw = 6 \int \frac{w}{w^2 + 4} \, dw - 5 \int \frac{1}{w^2 + 4} \, dw$$

$$= 3 \ln |w^2 + 4| - \frac{5}{2} \arctan \frac{w}{2} + C.$$

We find the second integral in the expression by letting $a = 2$ in V-24. Note also that $w^2 + 4 \geq 0$ always, so we may drop the absolute value signs. Thus

$$\int \frac{x^2}{x^2 + 6x + 13} \, dx = x - 3 \ln(x^2 + 6x + 13) - \frac{5}{2} \arctan \frac{x + 3}{2} + C.$$

47. Completing the square, we find that $x^2 + 8x + 7 = (x + 4)^2 - 9$. Substitute $w = x + 4$ and $dw = dx$.

$$\int \sqrt{x^2 + 8x + 7} \, dx = \int \sqrt{(x + 4)^2 - 9} \, dx = \int \sqrt{w^2 - 9} \, dw.$$

Now using VI-31 and VI-29 with $a = 3$:

$$\int \sqrt{w^2 - 9} \, dw = \frac{1}{2} (w \sqrt{w^2 - 9} - 9 \int \frac{1}{\sqrt{w^2 - 9}} \, dw) + C$$

$$= \frac{1}{2} w \sqrt{w^2 - 9} - \frac{9}{2} \ln |w + \sqrt{w^2 - 9}| + C$$

$$= \frac{1}{2} (x + 4) \sqrt{x^2 + 8x + 7} - \frac{9}{2} \ln |x + 4 + \sqrt{x^2 + 8x + 7}| + C.$$

48. We note that

$$\int \frac{4y + 9}{y^2 + 3y} \, dy = \int \frac{4y + 9}{y(y + 3)} \, dy.$$

Let $a = 0, b = -3, c = 4$, and $d = 9$ in V-27.

$$\int \frac{4y + 9}{y(y + 3)} \, dy = \frac{1}{3} [9 \ln |y| - (-3) \ln |y + 3|] + C = 3 \ln |y| + \ln |y + 3| + C.$$

49.

$$\int \frac{5z - 13}{z^2 - 5z + 6} \, dz = \int \frac{5z - 13}{(z - 3)(z - 2)} \, dz.$$

Let $a = 3, b = 2, c = 5$, and $d = -13$ in V-27.

$$\int \frac{5z - 13}{(z - 3)(z - 2)} \, dz = 2 \ln |z - 3| + 3 \ln |z - 2| + C.$$

50. Use long division to reorganize the integral:

$$\int \frac{t^2+1}{t^2-1}\,dt = \int \left(1+\frac{2}{t^2-1}\right)\,dt = \int dt + \int \frac{2}{(t-1)(t+1)}\,dt.$$

To get this second integral, let $a = 1, b = -1$ in V-26, so

$$\int \frac{t^2+1}{t^2-1}\,dt = t + \ln|t-1| - \ln|t+1| + C.$$

51.

$$\int_0^2 \frac{1}{4+x^2}\,dx = \frac{1}{2}\arctan\frac{x}{2}\Big|_0^2 \quad \text{using V-24}$$

$$= \frac{1}{2}\arctan 1 - \frac{1}{2}\arctan 0 = \frac{\pi}{8} \approx 0.3927.$$

Since $\frac{1}{4+x^2}$ is monotonically decreasing on $0 \le x \le 2$, we expect the integral to be between the left- and right-hand sums. Using 100 subintervals, we find that

$$0.3939 > \int_0^2 \frac{1}{4+x^2}\,dx > 0.3914$$

so our answer checks.

52. Let $a = 3$ and $p(y) = y^2 + 3$ in III-16.
Then

$$\int_\pi^{2\pi} (y^2+3)\cos 3y\,dy = \left(\frac{1}{3}(y^2+3)\sin 3y + \frac{2}{9}y\cos 3y - \frac{2}{27}\sin 3y\right)\Big|_\pi^{2\pi} = \frac{2}{3}\pi \approx 2.0944.$$

$(y^2+3)\cos 3y$ is not monotonic, over $\pi \le y \le 2\pi$, but the average of the left- and right-hand sums is close to our answer. Using 250 intervals,

$$\text{left sum} \approx 1.7469$$
$$\text{right sum} \approx 2.4424$$
$$\text{average} \approx 2.0946.$$

53.

$$\int_0^1 \frac{dx}{x^2+2x+5} = \;=\; \int_0^1 \frac{dx}{(x+1)^2+4}$$

$$= \frac{1}{2}\arctan\frac{x+1}{2}\Big|_0^1 = \frac{1}{2}\arctan 1 - \frac{1}{2}\arctan\frac{1}{2} \approx 0.1609.$$

(Substitute $w = x + 1$ and use V-24).

$\dfrac{1}{x^2 + 2x + 5}$ is monotonic over $0 \leq x \leq 1$, so we expect the value of the integral to be between the left- and right-hand sums. Using 100 subintervals, we find

$$0.1605 < \int_0^1 \frac{dx}{x^2 + 2x + 5} < 0.1613$$

which matches our result.

54. Using IV-19 with $m = 3$, followed by IV-20, we find that

$$\int_{\frac{\pi}{4}}^{\frac{\pi}{3}} \frac{dx}{\sin^3 x} = -\frac{1}{2}\frac{\cos x}{\sin^2 x} + \frac{1}{4}\ln\left|\frac{\cos x - 1}{\cos x + 1}\right|\Big|_{\frac{\pi}{4}}^{\frac{\pi}{3}} \approx 0.5398.$$

Since $\frac{1}{\sin^3 x}$ is monotonic over the interval, we expect the value of the integral to be between the left- and right-hand sums. Using 100 subintervals, we find $0.5381 < \int_{\frac{\pi}{4}}^{\frac{\pi}{3}} \dfrac{dx}{\sin^3 x} < 0.5415$, which matches our result.

55.

$$\int_{-3}^{-1} \frac{dx}{\sqrt{x^2 + 6x + 10}} = \int_{-3}^{-1} \frac{dx}{\sqrt{(x+3)^2 + 1}} = \ln\left|x + 3 + \sqrt{x^2 + 6x + 10}\right|\Big|_{-3}^{-1}.$$

(Substitute $w = x + 3$ and then use VI-29)

$$= \ln\left|2 + \sqrt{5}\right| \approx 1.4436.$$

$\dfrac{1}{\sqrt{x^2+6x+10}}$ is monotonic over $-3 \leq x \leq -1$, so we expect the value of the integral to be between the left- and right-hand sums. Using 100 subintervals, we find that

$$1.4381 < \int_{-3}^{-1} \frac{dx}{\sqrt{x^2 + 6x + 10}} < 1.4492$$

which matches our result.

56.

$$\frac{1}{2}\ln|x^2 + 2| + \frac{1}{\sqrt{2}}\arctan\frac{x}{\sqrt{2}}\Big|_0^3 = \frac{1}{2}\ln 11 + \frac{1}{\sqrt{2}}\arctan\frac{3}{\sqrt{2}} - \frac{1}{2}\ln 2 \approx 1.652.$$

(Let $a = \sqrt{2}, b = 1, c = 1$ in V-25.)
$\frac{1+x}{2+x^2}$ is not monotonic over the given interval; it is increasing near 0 and decreasing for larger x values. The left- and right-hand sums, however, are both close to our value of the integral. Using 100 subdivisions, the left-hand sum ≈ 1.654, the right-hand sum ≈ 1.650, and the average ≈ 1.652.

57. Use $\sin 2\theta = 2\sin\theta\cos\theta$. Then

$$\int_0^2 \cos\theta\sin 2\theta\, d\theta = 2\int_0^2 \cos^2\theta\sin\theta\, d\theta = (-2)\frac{\cos^3\theta}{3}\Big|_0^2 \approx 0.7147.$$

$\cos\theta\sin 2\theta$ is not monotonic over the interval $0 \le \theta \le 2$, but we find using 100 subintervals that the left-hand sum ≈ 0.7115, the right-hand sum ≈ 0.7178, and the average ≈ 0.7147, so these results match our answer very well.

58. Let $a = 5$ and $b = 6$ in II-12. Then

$$\int_{-\pi}^{\pi} \sin 5x\cos 6x\, dx = \frac{1}{11}(6\sin 5x\sin 6x + 5\cos 5x\cos 6x)\Big|_{-\pi}^{\pi} = 0.$$

This also makes sense since $\sin 5x\cos 6x$ is odd, so its integral over any interval $-a \le x \le a$ should be 0. This can also be checked numerically.

59. Use $\sin 2x = 2\sin x\cos x$. Then

$$\int_{-\pi}^{\pi} \sin 5x\cos 5x\, dx = \frac{1}{2}\int_{-\pi}^{\pi} \sin 10x\, dx = -\frac{1}{20}\cos 10x\Big|_{-\pi}^{\pi} = 0.$$

This makes sense because $\sin 5x\cos 5x$ is odd. This can also be checked numerically.

60.

$$\int_1^2 (x - 2x^3)\ln x\, dx = \int_1^2 x\ln x\, dx - 2\int_1^2 x^3\ln x\, dx$$

$$= (\frac{1}{2}x^2\ln x - \frac{1}{4}x^2)\Big|_1^2 - (\frac{1}{2}x^4\ln x - \frac{1}{8}x^4)\Big|_1^2 \text{ using III-13}$$

$$= 2\ln 2 - \frac{3}{4} - (8\ln 2 - \frac{15}{8})$$

$$= \frac{9}{8} - 6\ln 2 \approx -3.034.$$

Since $x - 2x^3$ is decreasing and negative, and $\ln x$ is increasing, we see that the function is decreasing. Thus, using 100 subintervals, we expect that

$$-3.083 < \int_1^2 (x - 2x^3)\ln x\, dx < -2.986$$

which matches our result.

61. $$\int_0^1 \sqrt{3 - x^2}\, dx = (\frac{1}{2}x\sqrt{3 - x^2} + \frac{3}{2}\arcsin\frac{x}{\sqrt{3}})\Big|_0^1 \approx 1.630.$$

(Let $a = \sqrt{3}$ in VI-30 and VI-28).

Again, $\sqrt{3 - x^2}$ is monotonic on $0 \le x \le 1$, and using 100 subintervals, we find $1.629 < \int_0^1 \sqrt{3 - x^2}\, dx < 1.632$, which matches our result.

62.   We use VI-30 and VI-28:

$$\int_0^1 \sqrt{4-x^2}\, dx = \frac{1}{2}(x\sqrt{4-x^2})\Big|_0^1 + \frac{1}{2}(2^2)\int_0^1 \frac{1}{\sqrt{4-x^2}}\, dx$$

$$= \frac{1}{2}\sqrt{3} + 2\arcsin\frac{x}{2}\Big|_0^1$$

$$\approx 1.913.$$

Since $\sqrt{4-x^2}$ is monotonically decreasing, we expect the value of the integral to fall between the left- and right-hand sums. Using 100 intervals, we find $1.912 < \int_0^1 \sqrt{4-x^2}\, dx < 1.915$, which matches our result.

63.   In the interval of $0 \le x \le 2$, $y = \sqrt{4-x^2}$ is the equation of one quadrant of the radius 2 circle centered at the origin. Interpreting the integral as an area gives the answer π. When we check numerically using 100 subintervals, we find that the left-hand sum ≈ 3.16, the right-hand sum ≈ 3.12, and the average ≈ 3.14, so our result checks.

64.   (a)

$$\frac{1}{1-0}\int_0^1 V_0\cos(120\pi t)dt = \frac{V_0}{120\pi}\sin(120\pi t)\Big|_0^1$$

$$= \frac{V_0}{120\pi}[\sin(120\pi) - \sin(0)]$$

$$= \frac{V_0}{120\pi}[0-0] = 0.$$

   (b)   Let's find the average of V^2 first.

$$\overline{V^2} = \text{Average of } V^2 = \frac{1}{1-0}\int_0^1 V^2 dt$$

$$= \frac{1}{1-0}\int_0^1 (V_0\cos(120\pi t))^2 dt$$

$$= V_0^2\int_0^1 \cos^2(120\pi t)dt$$

Now, let $120\pi t = x$, and $dt = \dfrac{dx}{120\pi}$. So

$$\overline{V^2} = \frac{V_0^2}{120\pi}\int_0^{120\pi} \cos^2 x\, dx.$$

$$= \frac{V_0^2}{120\pi}\left(\frac{1}{2}\cos x \sin x + \frac{1}{2}x\right)\Big|_0^{120\pi} \qquad \text{II-18}$$

$$= \frac{V_0^2}{120\pi}60\pi = \frac{V_0^2}{2}.$$

So, the average of V^2 is $\dfrac{V_0^2}{2}$ and $\overline{V} = \sqrt{\text{average of } V^2} = \dfrac{V_0}{\sqrt{2}}$.

(c)　$V_0 = \sqrt{2} \cdot \overline{V} = 110\sqrt{2} \approx 156$ volts.

65.　(a)　Since $R(T)$ is the rate or production, we find the total production by integrating:

$$\int_0^N R(t)\,dt = \int_0^N (A + Be^{-t}\sin(2\pi t))\,dt$$

$$= NA + B\int_0^N e^{-t}\sin(2\pi t)\,dt.$$

Let $a = -1$ and $b = 2\pi$ in II-8.

$$= NA + \frac{B}{1 + 4\pi^2}e^{-t}(-\sin(2\pi t) - 2\pi\cos(2\pi t))\Big|_0^N.$$

Since N is an integer (so $\sin 2\pi N = 0$ and $\cos 2\pi N = 1$),

$$\int_0^N R(t)\,dt = NA + B\frac{2\pi}{1 + 4\pi^2}(1 - e^{-N}).$$

Thus the total production is $NA + \frac{2\pi B}{1+4\pi^2}(1 - e^{-N})$ over the first N years.

(b)　The average production over the first N years is

$$\int_0^N \frac{R(t)\,dt}{N} = A + \frac{2\pi B}{1 + 4\pi^2}\left(\frac{1 - e^{-N}}{N}\right).$$

(c)　As $N \to \infty$, $A + \frac{2\pi B}{1+4\pi^2}\frac{1-e^{-N}}{N} \to A$, since the second term in the sum goes to 0. This is why A is called the average!

(d)　When t gets large, the term $Be^{-t}\sin(2\pi t)$ gets very small. Thus, $R(t) \approx A$ for most t, so it makes sense that the average of $\int_0^N R(t)\,dt$ is A as $N \to \infty$.

(e)　This model is not reasonable for long periods of time, since an oil well has finite capacity and will eventually "run dry." Thus, we cannot expect average production to be close to constant over a long period of time.

66.　(a)　$\displaystyle\int \frac{1}{x^2 - x}\,dx = \int \left(\frac{1}{x-1} - \frac{1}{x}\right)dx = \ln|x-1| - \ln|x| + C.$

(b)　$\displaystyle\int \frac{1}{x^2 - x}\,dx = \int \frac{1}{(x-1)(x)}\,dx.$ Using $a = 1$ and $b = 0$ in V-26, we get $\ln|x-1| - \ln|x| + C.$

67.　(a)　$\dfrac{2}{x} + \dfrac{1}{x+3} = \dfrac{2(x+3)}{x(x+3)} + \dfrac{x}{x(x+3)} = \dfrac{3x+6}{x^2+3x}$. Thus

$$\int \frac{3x+6}{x^2+3x}\,dx = \int \left(\frac{2}{x} + \frac{1}{x+3}\right)dx = 2\ln|x| + \ln|x+3| + C.$$

(b)   Let $a = 0, b = -3, c = 3$, and $d = 6$ in V-27.

$$\int \frac{3x + 6}{x^2 + 3x}\, dx = \int \frac{3x + 6}{x(x + 3)}\, dx$$

$$= \frac{1}{3}(6 \ln |x| + 3 \ln |x + 3|) + C = 2 \ln |x| + \ln |x + 3| + C.$$

68.   Split the integrand into partial fractions, giving

$$\frac{1}{x(L - x)} = \frac{A}{x} + \frac{B}{L - x}$$

$$1 = A(L - x) + Bx = (B - A)x + AL.$$

We have $B - A = 0$ and $AL = 1$, so $A = B = 1/L$. Thus,

$$\int \frac{1}{x(L - x)}\, dx = \int \frac{1}{L}\left(\frac{1}{x} + \frac{1}{L - x}\right)\, dx = \frac{1}{L}\left(\ln |x| - \ln |L - x|\right) + C.$$

69.   (a)   Let $y = a \ln x + b \ln (1 + x) + \dfrac{c}{1 + x}$. Then

$$\frac{dy}{dx} = \frac{a}{x} + \frac{b}{1 + x} - \frac{c}{(1 + x)^2} = \frac{a(1 + x)^2 + bx(1 + x) - cx}{x(1 + x)^2}.$$

(b)   The denominator of $\frac{dy}{dx}$ is the same as that of the integrand. The numerator of $\frac{dy}{dx}$ is a polynomial in x of the same degree as that of the integrand:

$$\begin{aligned} \text{Numerator} &= a(1 + x)^2 + bx(1 + x) - cx \\ &= ax^2 + 2ax + a + bx^2 + bx - cx \\ &= (a + b)x^2 + (2a + b - c)x + a \end{aligned}$$

Set the numerator $= 1 + x^2$:

$$1 + x^2 = (a + b)x^2 + (2a + b - c)x + a.$$

Then the coefficients of the polynomial are given by

$$\begin{aligned} a + b &= 1, \\ 2a + b - c &= 0, \\ a &= 1 \end{aligned}$$

which implies that $a = 1$, $b = 0$, and $c = 2$. So, plugging in the values of a, b, and c to the equation

$$y = a \ln x + b \ln (1 + x) + \frac{c}{1 + x},$$

we get

$$\ln x + \frac{2}{1+x} = \int \frac{1+x^2}{x(1+x)^2}\, dx.$$

Thus

$$\int_1^2 \frac{1+x^2}{x(1+x)^2}\, dx = \left(\ln x + \frac{2}{1+x}\right)\Big|_1^2 = \ln 2 - \frac{1}{3}.$$

70. Using II-10 in the integral table, if $m \neq \pm n$, then

$$
\begin{aligned}
\int_{-\pi}^{\pi} \sin m\theta \sin n\theta\, d\theta &= \frac{1}{n^2 - m^2}[m\cos m\theta \sin n\theta - n\sin m\theta \cos n\theta]\Big|_{-\pi}^{\pi} \\
&= \frac{1}{n^2 - m^2}[(m\cos m\pi \sin n\pi - n\sin m\pi \cos n\pi) - \\
&\qquad (m\cos(-m\pi)\sin(-n\pi) - n\sin(-m\pi)\cos(-n\pi))]
\end{aligned}
$$

But $\sin k\pi = 0$ for all integers k, so each term reduces to 0, making the whole integral reduce to 0.

71. Using formula II-11, if $m \neq \pm n$, then

$$\int_{-\pi}^{\pi} \cos m\theta \cos n\theta\, d\theta = \frac{1}{n^2 - m^2}(n\cos m\theta \sin n\theta - m\sin m\theta \cos n\theta)\Big|_{-\pi}^{\pi}.$$

We see that in the evaluation, each term will have a $\sin k\pi$ term, so the expression reduces to 0.

7.6 SOLUTIONS

1.

TABLE 7.1

n	1	2	4
LEFT	40	40.7846	41.7116
RIGHT	51.2250	46.3971	44.5179
TRAP	45.6125	43.5909	43.1147
MID	41.5692	42.6386	42.8795

2.

TABLE 7.2

N	Left Sum	Right Sum	Trapezoid	Midpoint
10	0.06017	0.07677	0.06847	0.06821
100	0.06747	0.06913	0.06830	0.06829
1000	0.06821	0.06838	0.06829	0.06829

If $g(\theta) = (\sin\theta)^{\frac{3}{2}}$, then $g'(\theta) = \frac{3}{2}(\sin\theta)^{\frac{1}{2}} \cdot \cos\theta$, and

$$g''(\theta) = \frac{3}{4}(\sin\theta)^{-\frac{1}{2}} \cdot (\cos\theta)^2 + \frac{3}{2}(\sin\theta)^{\frac{1}{2}} \cdot (-\sin\theta)$$

$$= \frac{3}{4\sqrt{\sin\theta}}\left(\cos^2\theta - 2\sin^2\theta\right).$$

The curve is increasing and concave up on the interval $0 \le \theta \le \frac{1}{2}$, so left sums and midpoint sums give underestimates and right sums and trapezoid sums give overestimates.

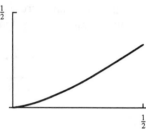

3. $g(x) = \sqrt{x}\, e^x \implies g'(x) = e^x\left(\sqrt{x} + \frac{1}{2\sqrt{x}}\right) \implies g''(x) = e^x\left(\sqrt{x} + \frac{1}{\sqrt{x}} - \frac{1}{4\sqrt{x^3}}\right)$

The first and second derivatives are positive for $1 \le x \le 2$, so g is increasing and concave up on this interval. Hence, the left sum and the midpoint sum underestimate the integral, and the right sum and the trapezoid sum overestimate the integral:

TABLE 7.3

N	Left Sum	Right Sum	Trapezoid	Midpoint
10	5.47115	6.24429	5.85772	5.84649
100	5.81165	5.88896	5.85031	5.85023
1000	5.84637	5.85410	5.85023	5.85023

4.

TABLE 7.4

N	Left Sum	Right Sum	Trapezoid	Midpoint
10	3.01320	2.97111	2.99215	2.99304
100	2.99484	2.99064	2.992740	2.992749
1000	2.99296	2.99254	2.9927459	2.9927460

The function is decreasing over the interval $0 \le \theta \le \frac{\pi}{2}$, so left sums give an overestimate and right sums give an underestimate. It is concave down over the interval, so the trapezoid sum gives an underestimate and the midpoint sum gives an overestimate.

5.

TABLE 7.5

N	Left Sum	Right Sum	Trapezoid	Midpoint
10	0.14047	0.18842	0.16445	0.16335
100	0.16132	0.16612	0.16372	0.16371
1000	0.16347	0.16395	0.16371	0.16371

The function is increasing on the interval $0 \leq \theta \leq 1$, so left sums give an underestimate and right sums an overestimate. It is concave down on all of the interval, so the trapezoid sum gives an underestimate and the midpoint sum gives an overestimate.

6.

TABLE 7.6

N	Left Sum	Right Sum	Trapezoid	Midpoint
10	0.92479	0.82549	0.87514	0.87206
100	0.87807	0.86814	0.87310	0.87307
1000	0.87358	0.87259	0.87308	0.87308

The function is decreasing on the interval $0 \leq x \leq \frac{\pi}{2}$, so left sums give an overestimate and right sums an underestimate. It is concave up on all of the interval, so the trapezoid sum gives an overestimate and the midpoint sum gives an underestimate.

7.

TABLE 7.7

N	Left Sum	Right Sum	Trapezoid	Midpoint
10	6.71685	8.00430	7.36058	7.33181
100	7.27723	7.40597	7.34160	7.34131
1000	7.33497	7.34785	7.34141	7.34141

The function is increasing on the interval $0 \leq x \leq 3$, so left sums give an underestimate and right sums an overestimate. It is concave up on all of the interval, so the trapezoid sum gives an overestimate and the midpoint sum gives an underestimate.

8. (a) (i) Let $f(x) = \frac{1}{1+x^2}$. The left-hand Riemann sum is

$$\frac{1}{8}\left(f(0) + f\left(\frac{1}{8}\right) + f\left(\frac{2}{8}\right) + \cdots + f\left(\frac{7}{8}\right)\right)$$

$$= \frac{1}{8}\left(\frac{64}{64} + \frac{64}{65} + \frac{64}{68} + \frac{64}{73} + \frac{64}{80} + \frac{64}{89} + \frac{64}{100} + \frac{64}{113}\right)$$

$$\approx 8(0.1020) = 0.8160.$$

(ii) Let $f(x) = \frac{1}{1+x^2}$. The right-hand Riemann sum is

$$\frac{1}{8}\left(f\left(\frac{1}{8}\right) + f\left(\frac{2}{8}\right) + f\left(\frac{3}{8}\right) + \cdots + f(1)\right)$$

$$= \frac{1}{8} \left(\frac{64}{65} + \frac{64}{68} + \frac{64}{73} + \frac{64}{80} + \frac{64}{89} + \frac{64}{100} + \frac{64}{113} + \frac{64}{128} \right)$$

$$\approx 0.8160 - \frac{1}{128} = 0.7535.$$

(iii)   The trapezoid rule gives us that

$$\text{TRAP}(8) = \frac{\text{LEFT}(8) + \text{RIGHT}(8)}{2} \approx 0.7847.$$

(b)   Since $1 + x^2$ is increasing for $x > 0$, so $\dfrac{1}{1 + x^2}$ is decreasing over the interval. Thus

$$\text{RIGHT}(8) < \int_0^1 \frac{1}{1 + x^2}\, dx < \text{LEFT}(8)$$

$$0.7535 < \frac{\pi}{4} < 0.8160$$

$$3.014 < \pi < 3.264.$$

9.   (a)   (i) $\text{LEFT}(32) = 13.6961, \text{RIGHT}(32) = 14.3437, \text{TRAP}(32) = 14.0199$

Exact value $= (x \ln x - x) \Big|_1^{10} \approx 14.02585093$

(ii) $\text{LEFT}(32) = 50.3180, \text{RIGHT}(32) = 57.0178, \text{TRAP}(32) = 53.6679$

Exact value $= e^x \Big|_0^4 \approx 53.59815003$

(b)   Both $\ln x$ and e^x are increasing, so the left sum underestimates and the right sum overestimates.

(i) $\text{LEFT}(32) \leq \text{TRAP}(32) \leq \text{Actual value} \leq \text{RIGHT}(32)$

(ii) $\text{LEFT}(32) \leq \text{Actual value} \leq \text{TRAP}(32) \leq \text{RIGHT}(32)$

The trapezoid rule is an overestimate if f is concave up, and an underestimate if it is concave down.

Since $\ln x$ is concave down, the trapezoidal estimate is too small. Since e^x is concave up, the trapezoidal estimate is too large. In each case, however, the trapezoidal estimate should be better than the left- or right-hand sums, since it is the average of the two.

10.   For a decreasing function whose curve is concave up, the diagrams below show that RIGHT < MID < TRAP < LEFT. Thus,

(a) $0.664 = \text{LEFT}, 0.633 = \text{TRAP}, 0.632 = \text{MID}$, and $0.601 = \text{RIGHT}$, and

(b) $0.632 < \text{true value} < 0.633$.

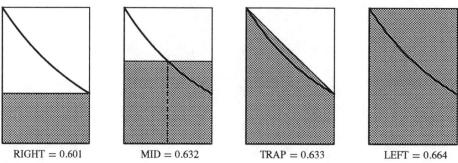

RIGHT = 0.601   MID = 0.632   TRAP = 0.633   LEFT = 0.664

Figure 7.4

11. Let $s(t)$ be the distance traveled at time t and $v(t)$ be the velocity at time t. Then the distance traveled during the interval $0 \le t \le 6$ is

$$s(6) - s(0) = s(t)\Big|_0^6$$

$$= \int_0^6 s'(t)\, dt \quad \text{(by the Fundamental Theorem)}$$

$$= \int_0^6 v(t)\, dt.$$

We estimate the distance by estimating this integral.

From the table, we find: LEFT(6) = 31, RIGHT(6) = 39, TRAP(6) = 35.

12. (a)

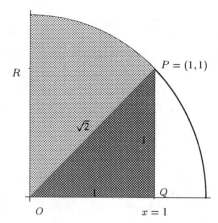

The graph of $y = \sqrt{2 - x^2}$ is the upper half of a circle of radius $\sqrt{2}$ centered at the origin. The integral represents the area under this curve between the lines $x = 0$ and $x = 1$. From the picture, we see that this area can be split into 2 parts, A_1 and A_2. Notice since $OQ = QP = 1$,

$\triangle OQP$ is isosceles. Thus $\angle POQ = \angle ROP = \frac{\pi}{4}$, and A_1 is exactly $\frac{1}{8}$ of the entire circle. Thus the total area is

$$\text{Area} = A_1 + A_2 = \frac{1}{8}\pi(\sqrt{2})^2 + \frac{1 \cdot 1}{2} = \frac{\pi}{4} + \frac{1}{2}.$$

(b) LEFT(5) $\approx$ 1.32350, RIGHT(5) $\approx$ 1.24066,
TRAP(5) $\approx$ 1.28208, MID(5) $\approx$ 1.28705

Exact value $\approx$ 1.285398163

Left-hand error $\approx$ +0.03810, Right-hand error $\approx$ −0.04474, Trapezoidal error $\approx$ −0.00332, Midpoint error $\approx$ +0.001656

Thus right-hand error < trapezoidal error < 0 < midpoint error < left-hand error, and |midpt error| < |trap error| < |left-error| < |right-error|.

13. (a) $\displaystyle\int_0^{2\pi} \sin\theta \, d\theta = -\cos\theta \Big|_0^{2\pi} = 0.$

(b) MID(1) is 0 since the midpoint of 0 and 2π is π, and $\sin\pi = 0$. Thus MID(1) $= 2\pi(\sin\pi) = 0$.
MID(2) is 0 since the midpoints we use are $\pi/2$ and $3\pi/2$, and $\sin(\pi/2) = -\sin(3\pi/2)$. So MID(2) $= \pi\sin(\pi/2) + \pi\sin(3\pi/2) = 0$.

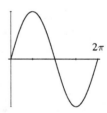

(c) MID(3) = 0.
In general, MID(n) = 0 for all n, even though your calculator (because of round-off error) might not return it as such. The reason is that $\sin(x) = -\sin(2\pi - x)$. If we use MID($n$), we will always take sums where we are adding pairs of the form $\sin(x)$ and $\sin(2\pi - x)$, so the sum will cancel to 0. (If n is odd, we will get a $\sin\pi$ in the sum which doesn't pair up with anything — but $\sin\pi$ is already 0!)

14. (a)

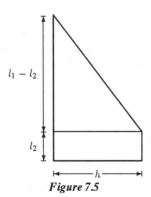

Figure 7.5

The area can be obtained by breaking the trapezoid into a rectangle of height l_2, base h and a triangle of height $(l_1 - l_2)$, base h. So

$$\begin{aligned}\text{Area} &= \text{area of rectangle} + \text{area of triangle}\\ &= h \cdot l_2 \qquad\quad + \frac{1}{2} \cdot h \cdot (l_1 - l_2)\\ &= h \cdot \frac{l_1 + l_2}{2}\end{aligned}$$

The formula suggests that the area of a trapezoid equals the base times the average of l_1 and l_2.

(b)

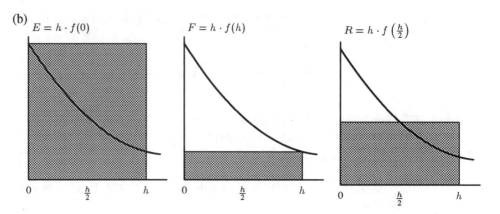

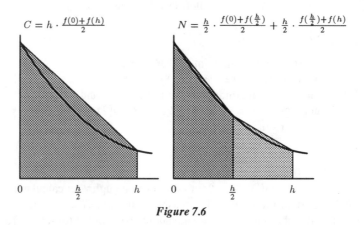

Figure 7.6

(c) Since the region F is inside the region A, $F < A$. (We abuse the notation by labeling the regions with the same letters that denote their areas.) Similarly, $A < N < C < E$ by the inclusion relations among the corresponding regions. Since $N = \frac{R+C}{2}$ is the average of R and C, it lies halfway between R and C. Thus, $R < N < C < E$. To determine the relationship of R and A, notice that the following statements are equivalent:

$R < A$

$h \cdot f(\frac{h}{2}) < \int_0^h f(t)\, dt$,

$f(\frac{h}{2}) < \frac{1}{h} \int_0^h f(t)\, dt$,

$f(\frac{h}{2}) <$ Average value of f in the interval $[0, h]$.

If we construct the tangent line to the graph of f at the point $(\frac{1}{2}h, f(\frac{1}{2}h))$ and call it g, we see that the tangent line g lies below the graph of f, because f is evidently concave up.

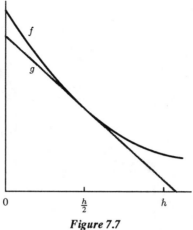

Figure 7.7

Thus the average value of f is greater than the average value of g. Moreover, $f(h/2)$ is clearly the average value of g in the interval $[0, h]$, so

$$f(h/2) = \text{(average value of } g) < \text{(average value of } f),$$

and so $R < A$. The region F is included in the region R, so we have $F < R$. Putting everything together:

$$F < R < A < N < C < E.$$

(d) Visually, F is better. Since $C = \frac{E+F}{2}$, and $A < C$, the average of E and F, A must be closer to the *smaller* of E and F, so F is the better estimate.

(e) If we mark off R and C on a number line, N marks the midpoint of $\overline{RC}$ because N is the average of R and C. Since $R < A < N$, A lies closer to R than it does to C, so R is the better estimate.

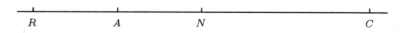

15.

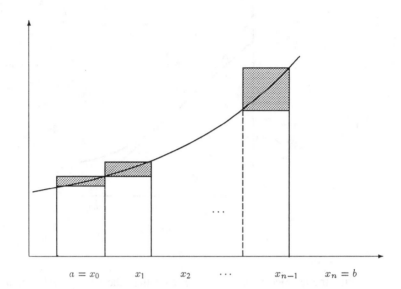

From the diagram, the difference between RIGHT(n) and LEFT(n) is the area of the shaded rectangles.

$$\text{RIGHT}(n) = f(x_1)\Delta x + f(x_2)\Delta x + \cdots + f(x_n)\Delta x$$
$$\text{LEFT}(n) = f(x_0)\Delta x + f(x_1)\Delta x + \cdots + f(x_{n-1})\Delta x$$

Notice that the terms in these two sums are the same, except that RIGHT(n) contains $f(x_n)\Delta x$ ($= f(b)\Delta x$), and LEFT(n) contains $f(x_0)\Delta x$ ($= f(a)\Delta x$). Thus

$$\text{RIGHT}(n) = \text{LEFT}(n) + f(x_n)\Delta x - f(x_0)\Delta x$$
$$= \text{LEFT}(n) + f(b)\Delta x - f(a)\Delta x$$

16.

$$\text{TRAP}(n) = \frac{\text{LEFT}(n) + \text{RIGHT}(n)}{2}$$
$$= \frac{\text{LEFT}(n) + \text{LEFT}(n) + f(b)\Delta x - f(a)\Delta x}{2}$$
$$= \text{LEFT}(n) + \frac{1}{2}(f(b) - f(a))\Delta x$$

17.

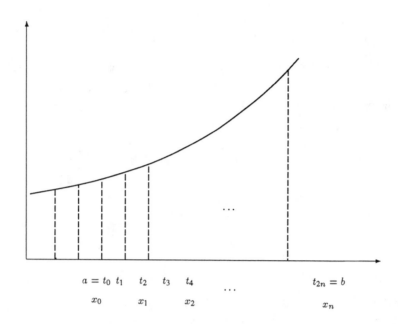

Divide the interval $[a, b]$ into n pieces, by $x_0, x_1, x_2, \ldots, x_n$, and also into $2n$ pieces, by $t_0, t_1, t_2, \ldots, t_{2n}$. Then the x's coincide with the even t's, so $x_0 = t_0$, $x_1 = t_2$, $x_2 = t_4$, $\ldots$, $x_n = t_{2n}$ and $\Delta t = \frac{1}{2}\Delta x$.

$$\text{LEFT}(n) = f(x_0)\Delta x + f(x_1)\Delta x + \cdots + f(x_{n-1})\Delta x$$

Since $\text{MID}(n)$ is obtained by evaluating f at the midpoints $t_1, t_3, t_5, \ldots$ of the x intervals, we get

$$\text{MID}(n) = f(t_1)\Delta x + f(t_3)\Delta x + \cdots + f(t_{2n-1})\Delta x$$

Now

$$\text{LEFT}(2n) = f(t_0)\Delta t + f(t_1)\Delta t + f(t_2)\Delta t + \cdots + f(t_{2n-1})\Delta t.$$

Regroup terms, putting all the even t's first, the odd t's last:

$$\text{LEFT}(2n) = f(t_0)\Delta t + f(t_2)\Delta t + \cdots + f(t_{2n-2})\Delta t + f(t_1)\Delta t + f(t_3)\Delta t + \cdots + f(t_{2n-1})\Delta t$$

$$= \underbrace{f(x_0)\frac{\Delta x}{2} + f(x_1)\frac{\Delta x}{2} + \cdots + f(x_{n-1})\frac{\Delta x}{2}}_{\text{LEFT}(n)/2} + \underbrace{f(t_1)\frac{\Delta x}{2} + f(t_3)\frac{\Delta x}{2} + \cdots + f(t_{2n-1})\frac{\Delta x}{2}}_{\text{MID}(n)/2}$$

So

$$\text{LEFT}(2n) = \frac{1}{2}(\text{LEFT}(n) + \text{MID}(n))$$

18. When $n = 10$, we have $a = 1; b = 2; \Delta x = \frac{1}{10}; f(a) = 1; f(b) = \frac{1}{2}$.
    $\text{LEFT}(10) \approx 0.71877, \text{RIGHT}(10) \approx 0.66877, \text{TRAP}(10) \approx 0.69377$
    We have
    $\text{RIGHT}(10) = \text{LEFT}(10) + f(b)\Delta x - f(a)\Delta x = 0.71877 + \frac{1}{10}(\frac{1}{2}) - \frac{1}{10}(1) = 0.66877,$ and $\text{TRAP}(10) =$
    $\text{LEFT}(10) + \frac{\Delta x}{2}(f(b) - f(a)) = 0.71877 + \frac{1}{10}\frac{1}{2}(\frac{1}{2} - 1) = 0.69377,$
    so the equations are verified.

19. First, we compute:

$$(f(b) - f(a))\Delta x = (f(b) - f(a))\left(\frac{b - a}{n}\right)$$
$$= (f(5) - f(2))\left(\frac{3}{n}\right)$$
$$= (21 - 13)\left(\frac{3}{n}\right)$$
$$= \frac{24}{n}$$

$\text{RIGHT}(10) = \text{LEFT}(10) + 24 = 3.156 + 2.4 = 5.556.$
$\text{TRAP}(10) = \text{LEFT}(10) + \frac{1}{2}(2.4) = 3.156 + 1.2 = 4.356.$
$\text{LEFT}(20) = \frac{1}{2}(\text{LEFT}(10) + \text{MID}(10)) = \frac{1}{2}(3.156 + 3.242) = 3.199.$
$\text{RIGHT}(20) = \text{LEFT}(20) + 2.4 = 3.199 + 1.2 = 4.399.$
$\text{TRAP}(20) = \text{LEFT}(20) + \frac{1}{2}(1.2) = 3.199 + 0.6 = 3.799.$

20. We approximate the area of the playing field by using Riemann sums. From the data provided,

$$\text{LEFT}(10) = \text{RIGHT}(10) = \text{TRAP}(10) = 89,000 \text{ square feet.}$$

Thus approximately
$$\frac{89,000 \text{ sq. ft.}}{200 \text{ sq. ft./lb.}} = 445 \text{ lbs. of fertilizer}$$

should be necessary.

21. Approximate $\int_1^{100001} \frac{1}{x} \, dx$, by rectangles, using $n = 100,000$ so $\Delta x = 1$.

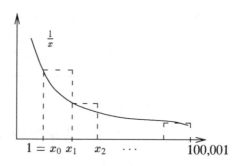

Then

$$\text{LEFT}(100,000) = f(1) \cdot 1 + f(2) \cdot 1 + \cdots + f(100,000) \cdot 1$$

$$= \frac{1}{1} + \frac{1}{2} + \cdots + \frac{1}{100,000} = \sum_{k=1}^{100{,}000} \frac{1}{k}$$

Since the left sum is an overestimate,

$$\int_1^{100001} \frac{1}{x}\, dx < \text{LEFT}(100{,}000),$$

and since

$$\int_1^{100001} \frac{1}{x}\, dx = \ln(100{,}001) - \ln 1 = \ln(100{,}001),$$

so

$$\ln 100001 < \sum_{k=1}^{100000} \frac{1}{k}.$$

Now imagine all the rectangles moved one unit to the left; they are the right sum approximation to

$$\int_1^{100000} \frac{1}{x}\, dx + \text{area of first rectangle}$$

and this time they give an underestimate.

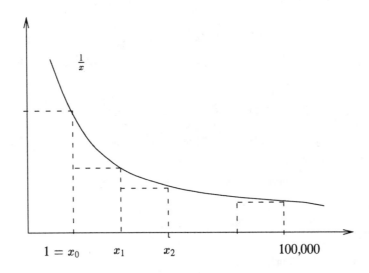

The area of the rectangles is our sum, so

$$\sum_{k=1}^{100000} \frac{1}{k} < \int_{1}^{100000} \frac{1}{x}\, dx + \text{area of first rectangle}$$

So

$$\sum_{k=1}^{100000} \frac{1}{k} < (\ln 100000) + 1$$

Thus

$$\ln(100001) < \sum_{k=1}^{100000} \frac{1}{k} < (\ln 100{,}000) + 1$$

$$11.5 < \sum_{k=1}^{100000} \frac{1}{k} < 12.5 \quad \text{so} \quad \sum_{k=1}^{100000} \frac{1}{k} \approx 12.$$

7.7 SOLUTIONS

1.
$$\text{SIMP} = \frac{1}{3}\left(2\,\text{MID} + \text{TRAP}\right) = \frac{1}{3}\left(2\,\text{MID} + \frac{\text{LEFT} + \text{RIGHT}}{2}\right)$$
$$= \frac{1}{3}\left(2 \cdot 0.6857 + \frac{0.8333 + 0.5833}{2}\right)$$
$$\approx 0.6932$$

The actual value is $\ln 2 \approx 0.6932$.

2. For $\int_{1}^{2} \frac{1}{x}\, dx$ with $n = 10$, $\text{SIMP}(10) \approx 0.6931474$ and true value $= \ln 2 \approx 0.6931472$, so the error is about 2×10^{-7}.

3. $\text{SIMP}(10) \approx 0.23182$. When we do $n = 10$ intervals and $n = 20$ intervals, these digits match, so they are probably correct digits since Simpson's rule will improve the number of digits of accuracy when we double the number of intervals. This reason also holds true for Problems 4-10.

4. 4.2365. ($n = 10$ intervals, or more).

5. 1.5699. ($n = 10$ intervals, or more)

6. 1.4301. ($n = 10$ intervals, or more)

7. 1.0894. ($n = 10$ intervals, or more)

8. 29.09346. ($n = 20$ intervals, or more)

9. 0.904524. ($n = 10$ intervals, or more)

10. 0.6593299. ($n = 10$ intervals, or more)

11. (a) $\displaystyle\int_0^1 7x^6 \, dx = x^7 \Big|_0^1 = 1.$

    (b)

	LEFT(5)	RIGHT(5)	TRAP(5)	MID(5)	SIMP(5)
VALUE	0.438144	1.838144	1.138144	0.931623	1.0004633
ERROR	−0.561856	0.838144	0.138144	−0.068377	0.0004633

    (c)

	LEFT(10)	RIGHT(10)	TRAP(10)	MID(10)	SIMP(10)
VALUE	0.6848835	1.3848835	1.0348835	0.9826019	1.000029115
ERROR	−0.3151165	0.3848835	0.0348835	−0.0173981	0.000029115

    (d) ratios:
    LEFT $= 1.78$, RIGHT $= 2.18$, TRAP $= 3.96$, MID $= 3.93$, SIMP $= 15.91$
    The values are about what we would expect, in that the LEFT and RIGHT approximations improve by about the same factor, the TRAP and MID approximations improve by the square of this factor, and the SIMP approximation improves by the fourth power of this factor. This is what the discussion in the book predicts.

12. (a) $\displaystyle\int_0^2 (x^3 + 3x^2) \, dx = \left(\frac{x^4}{4} + x^3 \right) \Big|_0^2 = 12.$

    (b) SIMP(2) $= 12$.
    SIMP(4) $= 12$.
    SIMP(100) $= 12$.
    SIMP(n) $= 12$ for all n. Simpson's rule always gives the exact answer if the integrand is a polynomial of degree less than 4.

13. (a) For the left-hand rule, error is approximately proportional to $\frac{1}{n}$. If we let n_p be the number of subdivisions needed for accuracy to p places, then there is a constant k such that

$$5 \times 10^{-5} = \frac{1}{2} \times 10^{-4} \approx \frac{k}{n_4}$$

$$5 \times 10^{-9} = \frac{1}{2} \times 10^{-8} \approx \frac{k}{n_8}$$

$$5 \times 10^{-13} = \frac{1}{2} \times 10^{-12} \approx \frac{k}{n_{12}}$$

$$5 \times 10^{-21} = \frac{1}{2} \times 10^{-20} \approx \frac{k}{n_{20}}$$

Thus the ratios $n_4 : n_8 : n_{12} : n_{20} \approx 1 : 10^4 : 10^8 : 10^{16}$, and assuming the computer time necessary is proportional to n_p, the computer times are approximately

4 places:	2 seconds	
8 places:	2×10^4 seconds	≈ 7 hours
12 places:	2×10^8 seconds	≈ 6 years
20 places:	2×10^{16} seconds	≈ 600 million years

(b)   For the trapezoidal rule, error is approximately proportional to $\frac{1}{n^2}$. If we let N_p be the number of subdivisions needed for accuracy to p places, then there is a constant C such that

$$5 \times 10^{-5} = \frac{1}{2} \times 10^{-4} \approx \frac{C}{N_4{}^2}$$

$$5 \times 10^{-9} = \frac{1}{2} \times 10^{-8} \approx \frac{C}{N_8{}^2}$$

$$5 \times 10^{-13} = \frac{1}{2} \times 10^{-12} \approx \frac{C}{N_{12}{}^2}$$

$$5 \times 10^{-21} = \frac{1}{2} \times 10^{-20} \approx \frac{C}{N_{20}{}^2}$$

Thus the ratios $N_4{}^2 : N_8{}^2 : N_{12}{}^2 : N_{20}{}^2 \approx 1 : 10^4 : 10^8 : 10^{16}$, and the ratios $N_4 : N_8 : N_{12} : N_{20} \approx 1 : 10^2 : 10^4 : 10^8$. So the computer times are approximately

4 places:	2 seconds	
8 places:	2×10^2 seconds	≈ 3 minutes
12 places:	2×10^4 seconds	≈ 7 hours
20 places:	2×10^8 seconds	≈ 6 years

14.   We assume that the error is of the same sign for both LEFT(10) and LEFT(20); that is, they are both underestimates or overestimates. Since LEFT(20) < LEFT(10), and LEFT(20) is more accurate, they must both be overestimates.

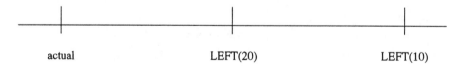

We assume that LEFT(10) is twice as far from the actual value as LEFT(20). Thus

$$\text{LEFT}(20) - \text{actual} = \text{LEFT}(10) - \text{LEFT}(20)$$
$$\text{actual} = 2\,\text{LEFT}(20) - \text{LEFT}(10)$$
$$= 0.34289.$$

Thus the error for LEFT(10) is 0.04186.

15. Since the midpoint rule is sensitive to f'', the simplifying assumption should be that f'' does not change sign in the interval of integration. Thus MID(10) and MID(20) will both be overestimates or will both be underestimates. Since the larger number, MID(10) is less accurate than the smaller number, they must both be overestimates. Then the information that ERROR(10) $= 4 \times$ ERROR(20) means that the the value of the integral and the two sums are arranged as follows:

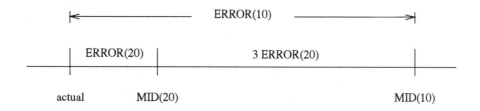

Thus
$$3 \times \text{ERROR}(20) = \text{MID}(10) - \text{MID}(20) = 35.619 - 35.415 = 0.204,$$
so ERROR(20) $= 0.068$ and ERROR(10) $= 4 \times$ ERROR(20) $= 0.272$.

16. True. $y^2 - 1$ is concave up, and the midpoint rule always underestimates for a function that is concave up.

17. False. If the function $f(x)$ is a line, then the trapezoid rule gives the exact answer to $\int_a^b f(x)\,dx$.

18. False. Suppose f is the following:

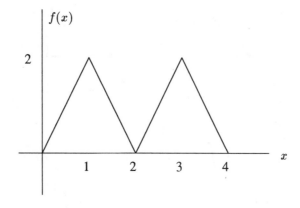

Then LEFT(2) $= 0$, LEFT(4) $= 4$, and
$$\int_a^b f(x)\,dx = 4.$$

19. True. Since f' and g' are greater than 0, all left rectangles give underestimates. The bigger the derivative, the bigger the underestimate, so the bigger the error. (Note: if we didn't have $0 < f' < g'$, but instead just had $f' < g'$, the statement wouldn't necessarily be true. This is because some left rectangles could be overestimates and some could be underestimates–so, for example, it could be that the error in approximating g is 0! If $0 < f' < g'$, however, this can't happen.

20. (a) If $f(x) = 1$, then

$$\int_a^b f(x)\, dx = (b - a).$$

Also,

$$\frac{h}{3}\left(\frac{f(a)}{2} + 2f(m) + \frac{f(b)}{2}\right) = \frac{b-a}{3}\left(\frac{1}{2} + 2 + \frac{1}{2}\right) = (b - a).$$

So the equation holds for $f(x) = 1$.
   If $f(x) = x$, then

$$\int_a^b f(x)\, dx = \frac{x^2}{2}\Big|_a^b = \frac{b^2 - a^2}{2}.$$

Also,

$$\frac{h}{3}\left(\frac{f(a)}{2} + 2f(m) + \frac{f(b)}{2}\right) = \frac{b-a}{3}\left(\frac{a}{2} + 2\frac{a+b}{2} + \frac{b}{2}\right)$$

$$= \frac{b-a}{3}\left(\frac{a}{2} + a + b + \frac{b}{2}\right)$$

$$= \frac{b-a}{3}\left(\frac{3}{2}b + \frac{3}{2}a\right)$$

$$= \frac{(b-a)(b+a)}{2}$$

$$= \frac{b^2 - a^2}{2}.$$

So the equation holds for $f(x) = x$.
   If $f(x) = x^2$, then $\displaystyle\int_a^b f(x)\, dx = \frac{x^3}{3}\Big|_a^b = \frac{b^3 - a^3}{3}$. Also,

$$\frac{h}{3}\left(\frac{f(a)}{2} + 2f(m) + \frac{f(b)}{2}\right) = \frac{b-a}{3}\left(\frac{a^2}{2} + 2\left(\frac{a+b}{2}\right)^2 + \frac{b^2}{2}\right)$$

$$= \frac{b-a}{3}\left(\frac{a^2}{2} + \frac{a^2 + 2ab + b^2}{2} + \frac{b^2}{2}\right)$$

$$= \frac{b-a}{3}\left(\frac{2a^2 + 2ab + 2b^2}{2}\right)$$

$$= \frac{b-a}{3}\left(a^2 + ab + b^2\right)$$

$$= \frac{b^3 - a^3}{3}.$$

So the equation holds for $f(x) = x^2$.

(b) For any quadratic function, $f(x) = Ax^2 + Bx + C$, the "Facts about Sums and Constant Multiples of Integrands" give us:

$$\int_a^b f(x)\,dx = \int_a^b (Ax^2 + Bx + C)\,dx = A\int_a^b x^2\,dx + B\int_a^b x\,dx + C\int_a^b 1\,dx.$$

Now we use the results of part (a) to get:

$$\int_a^b f(x)\,dx = A\frac{h}{3}\left(\frac{a^2}{2} + 2m^2 + \frac{b^2}{2}\right) + B\frac{h}{3}\left(\frac{a}{2} + 2m + \frac{b}{2}\right) + C\frac{h}{3}\left(\frac{1}{2} + 2\cdot 1 + \frac{1}{2}\right)$$

$$= \frac{h}{3}\left(\frac{Aa^2 + Ba + C}{2} + 2(Am^2 + Bm + C) + \frac{Ab^2 + Bb + C}{2}\right)$$

$$= \frac{h}{3}\left(\frac{f(a)}{2} + 2f(m) + \frac{f(b)}{2}\right)$$

21. (a) Suppose $q_i(x)$ is the quadratic function approximating $f(x)$ on the subinterval $[x_i, x_{i+1}]$, and m_i is the midpoint of the interval, $m_i = (x_i + x_{i+1})/2$. Then, using the equation in Problem 20, with $a = x_i$ and $b = x_{i+1}$ and $h = \Delta x = x_{i+1} - x_i$:

$$\int_{x_i}^{x_{i+1}} f(x)\,dx \approx \int_{x_i}^{x_{i+1}} q_i(x)\,dx = \frac{\Delta x}{3}\left(\frac{q_i(x_i)}{2} + 2q_i(m_i) + \frac{q_i(x_{i+1})}{2}\right).$$

(b) Summing over all subintervals gives

$$\int_a^b f(x)\,dx \approx \sum_{i=0}^{n-1}\int_{x_i}^{x_{i+1}} q_i(x)\,dx = \sum_{i=0}^{n-1}\frac{\Delta x}{3}\left(\frac{q_i(x_i)}{2} + 2q_i(m_i) + \frac{q_i(x_{i+1})}{2}\right).$$

Splitting the sum into two parts:

$$= \frac{2}{3}\sum_{i=0}^{n-1} q_i(m_i)\Delta x + \frac{1}{3}\sum_{i=0}^{n-1}\frac{q_i(x_i) + q_i(x_{i+1})}{2}\Delta x$$

$$= \frac{2}{3}\,\text{MID}(n) + \frac{1}{3}\,\text{TRAP}(n)$$

$$= \text{SIMP}(n).$$

7.8 SOLUTIONS

1.

$$\int_1^\infty e^{-2x}\, dx = \lim_{b\to\infty} \int_1^b e^{-2x}\, dx = \lim_{b\to\infty} -\frac{e^{-2x}}{2}\Big|_1^b$$

$$= \lim_{b\to\infty} (-e^{-2b}/2 + e^{-2}/2) = 0 + e^{-2}/2 = e^{-2}/2,$$

where the first limit is 0 because $\lim_{x\to\infty} e^{-x} = 0$.

2.

$$\int_1^\infty \frac{x}{4+x^2} = \lim_{b\to\infty} \int_1^b \frac{x}{4+x^2}\, dx = \lim_{b\to\infty} \frac{1}{2}\ln|4+x^2|\Big|_1^b = \lim_{b\to\infty} \frac{1}{2}\ln|4+b^2| - \frac{1}{2}\ln 5.$$

As $b \to \infty$, $\ln|4+b^2| \to \infty$, so the limit diverges.

3. Using integration by parts with $u = x$ and $v' = e^{-x}$, we find that

$$\int xe^{-x}\, dx = -xe^{-x} - \int -e^{-x}dx = -(1+x)e^{-x}$$

so

$$\int_0^\infty \frac{x}{e^x}\, dx = \lim_{b\to\infty} \int_0^b \frac{x}{e^x}\, dx$$

$$= \lim_{b\to\infty} -1(1+x)e^{-x}\Big|_0^b$$

$$= \lim_{b\to\infty} \left[1 - (1+b)e^{-b}\right]$$

$$= 1.$$

4.

$$\int_{-\infty}^0 \frac{e^x}{1+e^x}\, dx = \lim_{b\to-\infty} \int_b^0 \frac{e^x}{1+e^x}\, dx$$

$$= \lim_{b\to-\infty} \ln|1+e^x|\Big|_b^0$$

$$= \lim_{b\to-\infty} \left[\ln|1+e^0| - \ln|1+e^b|\right]$$

$$= \ln(1+1) - \ln(1+0) = \ln 2.$$

5.

$$\int_{\pi}^{\infty} \sin y \, dy = \lim_{b \to \infty} \int_{\pi}^{b} \sin y \, dy$$

$$= \lim_{b \to \infty} (-\cos y) \Big|_{\pi}^{b}$$

$$= \lim_{b \to \infty} [-\cos b - (-\cos \pi)].$$

As $b \to \infty$, $-\cos b$ fluctuates between -1 and 1, so the limit fails to exist: the integral diverges. (This doesn't follow right from the fact that $\sin y$ fluctuates between -1 and 1!)

6. First, we note that $1/(z^2 + 25)$ is an even function. Therefore,

$$\int_{-\infty}^{\infty} \frac{dz}{z^2 + 25} = \int_{-\infty}^{0} \frac{dz}{z^2 + 25} + \int_{0}^{\infty} \frac{dz}{z^2 + 25} = 2 \int_{0}^{\infty} \frac{dz}{z^2 + 25}.$$

We'll now evaluate this improper integral by using a limit:

$$\int_{0}^{\infty} \frac{dz}{z^2 + 25} = \lim_{b \to \infty} \left(\frac{1}{5} \arctan(b/5) - \frac{1}{5} \arctan(0) \right) = \frac{1}{5} \cdot \frac{\pi}{2} = \frac{\pi}{10}.$$

So the original integral is twice that, namely $\pi/5$.

7.

$$\int_{\pi/4}^{\pi/2} \frac{\sin x}{\sqrt{\cos x}} \, dx = \lim_{b \to \pi/2^-} \int_{\pi/4}^{b} \frac{\sin x}{\sqrt{\cos x}} \, dx$$

$$= \lim_{b \to \pi/2^-} - \int_{\pi/4}^{b} (\cos x)^{-1/2} (-\sin x) \, dx$$

$$= \lim_{b \to \pi/2^-} -2(\cos x)^{1/2} \Big|_{\pi/4}^{b}$$

$$= \lim_{b \to \pi/2^-} [-2(\cos b)^{1/2} + 2(\cos \pi/4)^{1/2}]$$

$$= 2 \left(\frac{\sqrt{2}}{2} \right)^{\frac{1}{2}} = 2^{\frac{3}{4}}.$$

8. This is an improper integral because $\sqrt{16 - x^2} = 0$ at $x = 4$. So

$$\int_{0}^{4} \frac{dx}{\sqrt{16 - x^2}} = \lim_{b \to 4^-} \int_{0}^{b} \frac{dx}{\sqrt{16 - x^2}}$$

$$= \lim_{b \to 4^-} (\arcsin x/4) \Big|_{0}^{b}$$

$$= \lim_{b \to 4^-} [\arcsin(b/4) - \arcsin(0)] = \pi/2 - 0 = \pi/2.$$

9. This integral is improper because $1/v$ blows up at $v = 0$. To evaluate it, we must split the region of integration up into two pieces, from 0 to 1 and from -1 to 0. But notice,

$$\int_0^1 \frac{1}{v} \, dv = \lim_{b \to 0+} \int_b^1 \frac{1}{v} \, dv = \lim_{b \to 0+} \left(\ln v \Big|_b^1 \right) = -\ln b.$$

As $b \to 0^+$, this goes to infinity and the integral diverges, so our original integral also diverges.

10.

$$\int_1^\infty \frac{1}{x^2 + 1} \, dx = \lim_{b \to \infty} \int_1^b \frac{1}{x^2 + 1} \, dx$$

$$= \lim_{b \to \infty} \arctan(x) \Big|_1^b$$

$$= \lim_{b \to \infty} [\arctan(b) - \arctan(1)]$$

$$= \pi/2 - \pi/4 = \pi/4.$$

11.

$$\int_1^\infty \frac{1}{\sqrt{x^2 + 1}} \, dx = \lim_{b \to \infty} \int_1^b \frac{1}{\sqrt{x^2 + 1}} \, dx$$

$$= \lim_{b \to \infty} \ln |x + \sqrt{x^2 + 1}| \Big|_1^b$$

$$= \lim_{b \to \infty} \ln(b + \sqrt{b^2 + 1}) - \ln(1 + \sqrt{2}).$$

As $b \to \infty$, this limit does not exist, so the integral diverges.

12.

$$\lim_{a \to 0+} \int_a^1 \frac{x^4 + 1}{x} \, dx = \lim_{a \to 0+} \left(\frac{x^4}{4} + \ln x \right) \Big|_a^1 = \lim_{a \to 0+} [1/4 - (a^4/4 + \ln a)],$$

which diverges as $a \to 0$, since $\ln a \to -\infty$.

13.

$$\int_1^\infty \frac{y}{y^4 + 1} \, dy = \lim_{b \to \infty} \frac{1}{2} \int_1^b \frac{2y}{(y^2)^2 + 1} \, dy$$

$$= \lim_{b \to \infty} \frac{1}{2} \arctan(y^2) \Big|_1^b$$

$$= \lim_{b \to \infty} \frac{1}{2} [\arctan(b^2) - \arctan 1]$$

$$= (1/2)[\pi/2 - \pi/4] = \pi/8.$$

14. This is a proper integral; use V- 26 in the integral table with $a = 4$ and $b = -4$.

$$\int_{16}^{20} \frac{1}{y^2 - 16} \, dy = \int_{16}^{20} \frac{1}{(y-4)(y+4)} \, dy$$

$$= \frac{\ln|y-4| - \ln|y+4|}{8} \Big|_{16}^{20}$$

$$= \frac{\ln 16 - \ln 24 - (\ln 12 - \ln 20)}{8}$$

$$= \frac{\ln 320 - \ln 288}{8} = \frac{1}{8} \ln(10/9) = 0.01317.$$

15. We use V-26 with $a = 4$ and $b = -4$:

$$\int_0^4 \frac{1}{u^2 - 16} \, du = \lim_{b \to 4^-} \int_0^b \frac{1}{u^2 - 16} \, du$$

$$= \lim_{b \to 4^-} \int_0^b \frac{1}{(u-4)(u+4)} \, du$$

$$= \lim_{b \to 4^-} \frac{(\ln|u-4| - \ln|u+4|)}{8} \Big|_0^b$$

$$= \lim_{b \to 4^-} \frac{1}{8} \left(\ln|b-4| + \ln 4 - \ln|b+4| - \ln 4 \right).$$

As $b \to 4^-$, $\ln|b-4| \to -\infty$, so the limit does not exist and the integral diverges.

16. With the substitution $w = \ln x$, $dw = \frac{1}{x} dx$,

$$\int \frac{\ln x}{x} \, dx = \int w \, dw = \frac{1}{2} w^2 + C = \frac{1}{2} (\ln x)^2 + C$$

so

$$\int_0^1 \frac{\ln x}{x} \, dx = \lim_{a \to 0^+} \int_a^1 \frac{\ln x}{x} \, dx = \lim_{a \to 0^+} \frac{1}{2} [\ln(x)]^2 \Big|_a^1 = \lim_{a \to 0^+} -\frac{1}{2} [\ln(a)]^2.$$

As $a \to 0^+$, $\ln a \to -\infty$, so the integral diverges.

17. With the substitution $w = \ln x$, $dw = \frac{1}{x} dx$,

$$\int \frac{dx}{x \ln x} = \int \frac{1}{w} \, dw = \ln|w| + C = \ln|\ln x| + C$$

so

$$\int_2^\infty \frac{dx}{x \ln x} = \lim_{b \to \infty} \int_2^b \frac{dx}{x \ln x}$$

$$= \lim_{b \to \infty} \ln |\ln x| \Big|_2^b$$

$$= \lim_{b \to \infty} [\ln |\ln b| - \ln |\ln 2|].$$

As $b \to \infty$, the limit goes to ∞ and hence the integral diverges.

18.

$$\int_0^2 \frac{1}{\sqrt{4 - x^2}} \, dx = \lim_{b \to 2^-} \int_0^b \frac{1}{\sqrt{4 - x^2}} \, dx$$

$$= \lim_{b \to 2^-} \arcsin \frac{x}{2} \Big|_0^b$$

$$= \lim_{b \to 2^-} \arcsin \frac{b}{2}$$

$$= \arcsin 1$$

$$= \frac{\pi}{2}.$$

19. Using the substitution $w = -x^{\frac{1}{2}}$, $-2dw = x^{-\frac{1}{2}} \, dx$,

$$\int e^{-x^{\frac{1}{2}}} x^{-\frac{1}{2}} \, dx = -2 \int e^w \, dw = -2e^{-x^{\frac{1}{2}}} + C.$$

So

$$\int_0^\pi \frac{1}{\sqrt{x}} e^{-\sqrt{x}} \, dx = \lim_{b \to 0^+} \int_b^\pi \frac{1}{\sqrt{x}} e^{-\sqrt{x}} \, dx$$

$$= \lim_{b \to 0^+} -2e^{-\sqrt{x}} \Big|_b^\pi$$

$$= 2 - 2e^{-\sqrt{\pi}}.$$

20. Letting $w = \ln x$, $dw = \frac{1}{x} dx$,

$$\int \frac{dx}{x(\ln x)^2} = \int w^{-2} dw = -w^{-1} + C = -\frac{1}{\ln x} + C,$$

so

$$\int_3^\infty \frac{dx}{x(\ln x)^2} = \lim_{b \to \infty} \int_3^b \frac{dx}{x(\ln x)^2}$$

$$= \lim_{b \to \infty} \left(-\frac{1}{\ln b} + \frac{1}{\ln 3} \right)$$

$$= \frac{1}{\ln 3}.$$

21. As in Problem 17, $\displaystyle\int \frac{dx}{x \ln x} = \ln|\ln x| + C$, so

$$\int_1^2 \frac{dx}{x \ln x} = \lim_{b \to 1+} \int_b^2 \frac{dx}{x \ln x}$$

$$= \lim_{b \to 1+} \ln|\ln x| \Big|_b^2$$

$$= \lim_{b \to 1+} \ln(\ln 2) - \ln(\ln b).$$

As $b \to 1^+$, $\ln(\ln b) \to -\infty$, so the integral diverges.

22.

$$\int_7^\infty \frac{dy}{\sqrt{y-5}} = \lim_{b \to \infty} \int_7^b \frac{dy}{\sqrt{y-5}}$$

$$= \lim_{b \to \infty} 2\sqrt{y-5} \Big|_7^b$$

$$= \lim_{b \to \infty} (2\sqrt{b-5} - 2\sqrt{2}).$$

As $b \to \infty$, this limit goes to ∞, so the integral diverges.

23. $\displaystyle\int \frac{dx}{x^2 - 1} = \int \frac{dx}{(x-1)(x+1)} = \frac{1}{2}(\ln|x-1| - \ln|x+1|) + C = \frac{1}{2}\left(\ln\frac{|x-1|}{|x+1|}\right) + C$, so

$$\int_4^\infty \frac{dx}{x^2 - 1} = \lim_{b \to \infty} \int_4^b \frac{dx}{x^2 - 1}$$

$$= \lim_{b \to \infty} \frac{1}{2}\left(\ln\frac{|x-1|}{|x+1|}\right) \Big|_4^b$$

$$= \lim_{b \to \infty} \left[\frac{1}{2}\ln\left(\frac{b-1}{b+1}\right) - \frac{1}{2}\ln\frac{3}{5}\right]$$

$$= -\frac{1}{2}\ln\frac{3}{5} = \frac{1}{2}\ln\frac{5}{3}.$$

24.

$$\int_4^\infty \frac{dx}{(x-1)^2} = \lim_{b \to \infty} \int_4^b \frac{dx}{(x-1)^2} = \lim_{b \to \infty} -\frac{1}{(x-1)} \Big|_4^b = \lim_{b \to \infty} \left[-\frac{1}{b-1} + \frac{1}{3}\right] = \frac{1}{3}.$$

25. The curve has an asymptote at $t = \frac{\pi}{2}$, and so the area integral is improper there.

$$\text{Area} = \int_0^{\frac{\pi}{2}} \frac{dt}{\cos^2 t} = \lim_{b \to \frac{\pi}{2}} \int_0^b \frac{dt}{\cos^2 t} = \lim_{b \to \frac{\pi}{2}} \tan t \Big|_0^b,$$

which diverges. Therefore the area is infinite.

26.   (a)

$$\int_0^\infty h(x)\,dx = \int_0^4 h(x)\,dx + \int_4^\infty h(x)\,dx$$

$$\int_4^\infty h(x)\,dx = \int_4^\infty x^{-2}\,dx$$

$$= \lim_{b\to\infty} \int_4^b x^{-2}\,dx$$

$$= \lim_{b\to\infty} \left. [-x^{-1}]\right|_4^b$$

$$= \lim_{b\to\infty} [\frac{1}{4} - \frac{1}{b}]$$

$$= \frac{1}{4}.$$

$$\int_0^4 h(x)\,dx = \int_0^4 (x^{-\frac{3}{2}} - \frac{1}{16})\,dx$$

$$= \int_0^4 x^{-\frac{3}{2}}\,dx - \int_0^4 \frac{1}{16}\,dx$$

$$= \lim_{b\to 0+} \int_b^4 x^{-\frac{3}{2}}\,dx - \frac{1}{4}$$

$$= \lim_{b\to 0+} \left. -2x^{-\frac{1}{2}}\right|_b^4 - \frac{1}{4}$$

$$= \lim_{b\to 0+} \left(\frac{2}{\sqrt{b}} - 1\right) - \frac{1}{4}.$$

As $b \to 0^+$, this limit diverges, so the entire integral must diverge.

(b)   Since h is differentiable for $0 < x < 4$ and for $x > 4$, the question is whether the slope to the left of $x = 4$ is the same as the slope to the right of $x = 4$. If so, h is differentiable. For $0 < x < 4$, $h'(x) = -\frac{3}{2}x^{-5/2}$ so $\lim_{x\to 4-} h'(x) = -\frac{3}{2}(4)^{-5/2} = -\frac{3}{64}$. For $x > 4$, $h'(x) = -\frac{2}{x^3}$ so $\lim_{x\to 4+} h'(x) = -\frac{2}{4^3} = -\frac{1}{32}$. This shows that, to the left of $x = 4$, the slope is $-\frac{3}{64}$ and to the right of $x = 4$, the slope is $-\frac{1}{32}$. Since the slope is not the same on either side of $x = 4$, the curve is not smooth there. If magnified you would see a "corner" at this point, so h is not differentiable there.

27.   (a)

$$\int \frac{1}{z^2 - z}\,dz = \int \frac{1}{(z-1)z}\,dz = \ln|z-1| - \ln|z| + C$$

by V-26 of the integral table.

(b)

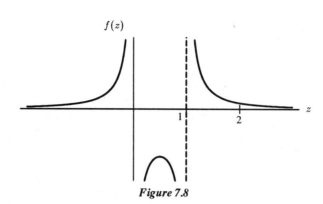

Figure 7.8

The function is undefined at $z = 0$ and $z = 1$.

(c)

$$\int_3^\infty \frac{1}{z^2 - z}\, dz = \lim_{b \to \infty} \int_3^b \frac{1}{z^2 - z}\, dz = \lim_{b \to \infty} \left(\ln|z - 1| - \ln|z| \right) \Big|_3^b$$

$$= \lim_{b \to \infty} \left[\ln \frac{|b - 1|}{|b|} - \ln \frac{2}{3} \right] = -\ln \frac{2}{3} = \ln \frac{3}{2}.$$

(d)

$$\int_1^3 \frac{1}{z^2 - z}\, dz = \lim_{b \to 1^+} \int_b^3 \frac{1}{z^2 - z}\, dz = \lim_{b \to 1^+} \ln \frac{|z - 1|}{|z|} \Big|_b^3 = \lim_{b \to 1^+} \left(\ln \frac{2}{3} - \ln \frac{b - 1}{b} \right).$$

As $b \to 1^+$, $\ln \frac{b-1}{b} \to -\infty$, so the limit and the integral diverge.

(e) If $\int_a^x \frac{dz}{z^2 - z}$ is proper, then

$$\int_a^x \frac{dz}{z^2 - z} = \left(\ln|z - 1| - \ln|z| \right) \Big|_a^x$$

$$= \ln|x - 1| - \ln|x| - \left(\ln|a - 1| - \ln|a| \right)$$

$$= \ln \frac{|x - 1||a|}{|x||a - 1|}.$$

This formula won't work if the integral is improper. In fact, if 0 or 1 is between a and x, the integral diverges, as it did in (d). Thus we must have $a, x < 0, 0 < a, x < 1$, or $a, x > 1$ for the formula to work. (We assume that a and x are numbers, not $\pm\infty$.)

28. (a)

$$\Gamma(1) = \int_0^\infty e^{-t}\, dt$$

$$= \lim_{b \to \infty} \int_0^b e^{-t} \, dt$$

$$= \lim_{b \to \infty} -e^{-t} \Big|_0^b$$

$$= \lim_{b \to \infty} [1 - e^{-b}]$$

$$= 1.$$

Using Problem 3,

$$\Gamma(2) = \int_0^\infty te^{-t} \, dt$$

$$= 1.$$

(b)   We integrate by parts. Let $u = t^n$, $v' = e^{-t}$. Then $u' = nt^{n-1}$ and $v = -e^{-t}$, so

$$\int t^n e^{-t} \, dt = -t^n e^{-t} + n \int t^{n-1} e^{-t} \, dt.$$

So

$$\Gamma(n+1) = \int_0^\infty t^n e^{-t} \, dt$$

$$= \lim_{b \to \infty} \int_0^b t^n e^{-t} \, dt$$

$$= \lim_{b \to \infty} \left[-t^n e^{-t} \Big|_0^b + n \int_0^b t^{n-1} e^{-t} \, dt \right]$$

$$= \lim_{b \to \infty} -b^n e^{-b} + \lim_{b \to \infty} n \int_0^b t^{n-1} e^{-t} \, dt$$

$$= 0 + n \int_0^\infty t^{n-1} e^{-t} \, dt$$

$$= n\Gamma(n).$$

(c)   We already have $\Gamma(1) = 1$ and $\Gamma(2) = 1$. Using $\Gamma(n+1) = n\Gamma(n)$ we can get

$$\Gamma(3) = 2\Gamma(2) = 2$$
$$\Gamma(4) = 3\Gamma(3) = 3 \cdot 2$$
$$\Gamma(5) = 4\Gamma(4) = 4 \cdot 3 \cdot 2.$$

So it appears that $\Gamma(n)$ is just the first $n - 1$ numbers multiplied together, so $\Gamma(n) = (n-1)!$.

29. The energy required is

$$E = \int_1^\infty \frac{kq_1q_2}{r^2}\, dr = kq_1q_2 \lim_{b \to \infty} \left. -\frac{1}{r} \right|_1^b$$
$$= (9 \times 10^9)(1)(1)(1) = 9 \times 10^9 \text{ joules}$$

30. (a) Using a calculator or a computer, the graph is:

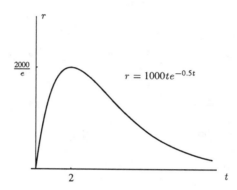

(b) People are getting sick fastest when the rate of infection is highest, i.e. when r is at its maximum. Since

$$r' = 1000e^{-0.5t} - 1000(0.5)te^{-0.5t}$$
$$= 500e^{-0.5t}(2 - t)$$

this must occur at $t = 2$.

(c) The total number of sick people $= \int_0^\infty 1000te^{-0.5t}\, dt$.

Using integration by parts, with $u = t$, $v' = e^{-0.5t}$:

$$\text{Total} = \lim_{b \to \infty} 1000 \left(\left. \frac{-t}{0.5} e^{-0.5t} \right|_0^b - \int_0^b \frac{-1}{0.5} e^{-0.5t}\, dt \right)$$

$$= \lim_{b \to \infty} 1000 \left. \left(-2be^{-0.5b} - \frac{2}{0.5} e^{-0.5b} \right) \right|_0^b$$

$$= \lim_{b \to \infty} 1000 \left(-2be^{-0.5b} - 4e^{-0.5b} + 4 \right)$$

$$= 4000 \text{ people.}$$

31. The factor $\ln x$ grows slowly enough not to change the convergence or divergence of the integral, although it will change what it converges or diverges to.

Integrating by parts or using the table of integrals, we get

$$
\int_e^\infty x^p \ln x \, dx = \lim_{b \to \infty} \int_e^b x^p \ln x \, dx
$$

$$
= \lim_{b \to \infty} \left[\frac{1}{p+1} x^{p+1} \ln x - \frac{1}{(p+1)^2} x^{p+1} \right] \Big|_e^b
$$

$$
= \lim_{b \to \infty} \left[\left(\frac{1}{p+1} b^{p+1} \ln b - \frac{1}{(p+1)^2} b^{p+1} \right) \right.
$$

$$
\left. - \left(\frac{1}{p+1} e^{p+1} - \frac{1}{(p+1)^2} e^{p+1} \right) \right].
$$

If $p > -1$, then $(p+1)$ is positive and the limit does not exist since b^{p+1} and $\ln b$ both approach ∞ as b does.

If $p < -1$, then $(p+1)$ is negative and both b^{p+1} and $b^{p+1} \ln b$ approach 0 as $b \to \infty$. (This follows by looking at graphs of $x^{p+1} \ln x$ (for different values of p), or by noting that $\ln x$ grows more slowly than x^{p+1} tends to 0.) So the value of the integral is $-pe^{p+1}/(p+1)^2$.

The case $p = -1$ has to be handled separately. For $p = -1$,

$$
\int_e^\infty \frac{\ln x}{x} \, dx = \lim_{b \to \infty} \int_e^b \frac{\ln x}{x} \, dx = \lim_{b \to \infty} \frac{(\ln x)^2}{2} \Big|_e^b = \lim_{b \to \infty} \left(\frac{(\ln b)^2 - 1}{2} \right).
$$

As $b \to \infty$, this limit does not exist, so the integral diverges if $p = -1$.

To summarize, $\int_e^\infty x^p \ln x \, dx$ converges for $p < -1$ to the value $-pe^{p+1}/(p+1)^2$.

32. The factor $\ln x$ grows slowly enough (as $x \to 0^+$) not to change the convergence or divergence of the integral, although it will change what it converges or diverges to.

The integral is always improper, because $\ln x$ is not defined for $x = 0$. Integrating by parts (or, alternatively, the integral table) yields

$$
\int_0^e x^p \ln x \, dx = \lim_{a \to 0^+} \int_a^e x^p \ln x \, dx
$$

$$
= \lim_{a \to 0^+} \left(\frac{1}{p+1} x^{p+1} \ln x - \frac{1}{(p+1)^2} x^{p+1} \right) \Big|_a^e
$$

$$
= \lim_{a \to 0^+} \left[\left(\frac{1}{p+1} e^{p+1} - \frac{1}{(p+1)^2} e^{p+1} \right) \right.
$$

$$
\left. - \left(\frac{1}{p+1} a^{p+1} \ln a - \frac{1}{(p+1)^2} a^{p+1} \right) \right].
$$

If $p < -1$, then $(p+1)$ is negative, so as $a \to 0^+$, $a^{p+1} \to \infty$ and $\ln a \to -\infty$, and therefore the limit does not exist.

If $p > -1$, then $(p + 1)$ is positive and it's easy to see that $a^{p+1} \to 0$ as $a \to 0$. Looking at graphs of $x^{p+1} \ln x$ (for different values of p) shows that $a^{p+1} \ln a \to 0$ as $a \to 0$. This isn't so easy to see analytically. It's true because if we let $t = \frac{1}{a}$ then

$$\lim_{a \to 0^+} a^{p+1} \ln a = \lim_{t \to \infty} \left(\frac{1}{t}\right)^{p+1} \ln\left(\frac{1}{t}\right) = \lim_{t \to \infty} -\frac{\ln t}{t^{p+1}}.$$

This last limit is zero because $\ln t$ grows very slowly, much more slowly than t^{p+1}. So if $p > -1$, the integral converges and equals $e^{p+1}[1/(p+1) - 1/(p+1)^2] = pe^{p+1}/(p+1)^2$.

What happens if $p = -1$? Then we get

$$\int_0^e \frac{\ln x}{x} \, dx = \lim_{a \to 0^+} \int_a^e \frac{\ln x}{x} \, dx$$

$$= \lim_{a \to 0^+} \left.\frac{(\ln x)^2}{2}\right|_a^e$$

$$= \lim_{a \to 0^+} \left(\frac{1 - (\ln a)^2}{2}\right).$$

Since $\ln a \to -\infty$ as $a \to 0^+$, this limit does not exist.

To summarize, $\int_0^e x^p \ln x$ converges for $p > -1$ to the value $pe^{p+1}/(p+1)^2$.

7.9 SOLUTIONS

1. It converges:

$$\int_{50}^\infty \frac{dz}{z^3} = \lim_{b \to \infty} \int_{50}^b \frac{dz}{z^3} = \lim_{b \to \infty} \left(\left.-\frac{1}{2}z^{-2}\right|_{50}^b\right) = \frac{1}{2} \lim_{b \to \infty} \left(\frac{1}{50^2} - \frac{1}{b^2}\right) = \frac{1}{5000}$$

2. The integral converges.

$$\int_{0.5}^1 \frac{1}{x^{(19/20)}} \, dx = \left.20(x^{1/20})\right|_{0.5}^1$$

$$= 20 \left(1 - (0.5)^{1/20}\right) \approx 0.681.$$

3. If $x \geq 1$, we know that $\dfrac{1}{x^3 + 1} \leq \dfrac{1}{x^3}$, and since $\displaystyle\int_1^\infty \frac{dx}{x^3}$ converges, the improper integral $\displaystyle\int_1^\infty \frac{dx}{x^3 + 1}$ converges.

4. For $\theta \geq 2$, we have $\dfrac{1}{\sqrt{\theta^3 + 1}} \leq \dfrac{1}{\sqrt{\theta^3}} = \dfrac{1}{\theta^{\frac{3}{2}}}$, and $\displaystyle\int_2^\infty \frac{d\theta}{\theta^{3/2}}$ converges (check by integration), so $\displaystyle\int_2^\infty \frac{d\theta}{\sqrt{\theta^3 + 1}}$ converges.

5. Since $\dfrac{1}{1+x} \geq \dfrac{1}{2x}$ and $\dfrac{1}{2}\displaystyle\int_0^\infty \dfrac{1}{x}\,dx$ diverges, we have that $\displaystyle\int_1^\infty \dfrac{dx}{1+x}$ diverges.

6. Since $\dfrac{1}{1+e^y} \leq \dfrac{1}{e^y} = e^{-y}$ and $\displaystyle\int_0^\infty e^{-y}\,dy$ converges, the integral $\displaystyle\int_0^\infty \dfrac{dy}{1+e^y}$ converges.

7. This integral diverges. To see this, substitute $t+1 = w$, $dt = dw$. So,

$$\int_{t=-1}^{t=5} \frac{dt}{(t+1)^2} = \int_{w=0}^{w=6} \frac{dw}{w^2},$$

which diverges.

8. This integral is convergent because, for $\phi \geq 1$,

$$\frac{2 + \cos\phi}{\phi^2} \leq \frac{3}{\phi^2},$$

and $\displaystyle\int_1^\infty \dfrac{3}{\phi^2}\,d\phi = 3\displaystyle\int_1^\infty \dfrac{1}{\phi^2}\,d\phi$ converges.

9. Since $\dfrac{1}{e^z + 2^z} < \dfrac{1}{e^z} = e^{-z}$ for $z \geq 0$, and $\displaystyle\int_0^\infty e^{-z}\,dz$ converges, $\displaystyle\int_0^\infty \dfrac{dz}{e^z + 2^z}$ converges.

10. Since $\dfrac{1}{\phi^2} \leq \dfrac{2 - \sin\phi}{\phi^2}$ for $0 < \phi \leq \pi$, and since $\displaystyle\int_0^\pi \dfrac{1}{\phi^2}\,d\phi$ diverges, $\displaystyle\int_0^\pi \dfrac{2 - \sin\phi}{\phi^2}\,d\phi$ must diverge.

11. Since we know the antiderivative of $\dfrac{1}{1 + u^2}$, we can use the Fundamental Theorem of Calculus to evaluate the integral. Since the integrand is even, we write

$$\int_{-\infty}^\infty \frac{du}{1 + u^2} = 2\int_0^\infty \frac{du}{1 + u^2} = 2\lim_{b\to\infty} \int_0^b \frac{du}{1 + u^2}$$

$$= 2\lim_{b\to\infty} \arctan b = 2\left(\frac{\pi}{2}\right) = \pi.$$

Thus, the integral converges to π.

12. Since $\dfrac{1}{u + u^2} < \dfrac{1}{u^2}$ for $u \geq 1$, and since $\displaystyle\int_1^\infty \dfrac{du}{u^2}$ converges, $\displaystyle\int_1^\infty \dfrac{du}{u + u^2}$ converges.

13. Since $\dfrac{3 + \sin\alpha}{\alpha} \geq \dfrac{2}{\alpha}$ for $\alpha \geq 4$, and since $\displaystyle\int_4^\infty \dfrac{2}{\alpha}\,d\alpha$ diverges, then $\displaystyle\int_4^\infty \dfrac{3 + \sin\alpha}{\alpha}\,d\alpha$ diverges.

14. This improper integral diverges. We expect this because, for large θ, $\dfrac{1}{\sqrt{\theta^2 + 1}} \approx \dfrac{1}{\sqrt{\theta^2}} = \dfrac{1}{\theta}$ and $\displaystyle\int_1^\infty \dfrac{d\theta}{\theta}$ diverges. More precisely, for $\theta \geq 1$

$$\frac{1}{\sqrt{\theta^2 + 1}} \geq \frac{1}{\sqrt{\theta^2 + \theta^2}} = \frac{1}{\sqrt{2}\sqrt{\theta^2}} = \frac{1}{\sqrt{2}} \cdot \frac{1}{\theta}$$

and $\int_1^\infty \frac{d\theta}{\theta}$ diverges. (The factor $\frac{1}{\sqrt{2}}$ doesn't affect the divergence.)

15. This integral is improper at $\theta = 0$. For $0 \leq \theta \leq 1$, we have $\frac{1}{\sqrt{\theta^3 + \theta}} \leq \frac{1}{\sqrt{\theta}}$, and since $\int_0^1 \frac{1}{\sqrt{\theta}} d\theta$

   converges, $\int_0^1 \frac{d\theta}{\sqrt{\theta^3 + \theta}}$ converges.

16. The integral diverges. Since $e^{-x} \leq x$ for $x \geq 1$, we have $\frac{x}{e^{-x} + x} \geq \frac{1}{2}$. So

$$\int_1^\infty \frac{x}{e^{-x} + x} \, dx \geq \int_1^\infty \frac{1}{2} \, dx$$

   Thus the integral does not converge, since $\int_1^\infty \frac{1}{2} \, dx$ diverges.

17. If we integrate e^{-x^2} from 1 to 10, we get 0.139. This answer doesn't change noticeably if you extend the region of integration to from 1 to 11, say, or even up to 1000. There's a reason for this; and the reason is that the tail, $\int_{10}^\infty e^{-x^2} \, dx$, is very small indeed. In fact

$$\int_{10}^\infty e^{-x^2} \, dx \leq \int_{10}^\infty e^{-x} \, dx = e^{-10},$$

   which is very small. (In fact, the tail integral is less than $e^{-100}/10$. Can you prove that? [Hint: $e^{-x^2} \leq e^{-10x}$ for $x \geq 10$.])

18. Approximating the integral by $\int_0^{10} e^{-x^2} \cos^2 x \, dx$ yields 0.606 to two decimal places. This is a good approximation to the improper integral because the "tail" is small:

$$\int_{10}^\infty e^{-x^2} \cos^2 x \, dx \leq \int_{10}^\infty e^{-x} \, dx = e^{-10},$$

   which is very small.

19. To find a, we first calculate $\int_0^{10} e^{-\frac{x^2}{2}} \, dx$. Since $\frac{x^2}{2} \geq x$ for $x \geq 10$, this will differ from $\int_0^\infty e^{-\frac{x^2}{2}} \, dx$ by at most

$$\int_{10}^\infty e^{-\frac{x^2}{2}} \, dx \leq \int_{10}^\infty e^{-x} \, dx = e^{-10},$$

   which is very small. Using Simpson's rule with 100 intervals (well more than necessary), we find $\int_0^{10} e^{-\frac{x^2}{2}} \, dx \approx 1.253314137$. Thus, since $e^{-\frac{x^2}{2}}$ is even, $\int_{-10}^{10} e^{-\frac{x^2}{2}} \, dx \approx 2.506628274$, and this is extremely close to $\int_{-\infty}^\infty e^{-\frac{x^2}{2}} \, dx$.

   To find a, we need $\int_{-\infty}^\infty a e^{-\frac{x^2}{2}} \, dx = 1$.

$$a = \frac{1}{\int_{-\infty}^\infty e^{-\frac{x^2}{2}} \, dx} \approx 0.399 \text{ to three decimal places.}$$

20. (a) If we substitute $w = x - k$ and $dw = dx$, we find

$$\int_{-\infty}^{\infty} ae^{-\frac{(x-k)^2}{2}} \, dx = \int_{-\infty}^{\infty} ae^{-\frac{w^2}{2}} \, dw.$$

This integral is the same as the integral in Problem 19, so the value of a will be the same, namely 0.399.

(b) The answer is the same because $g(x)$ is the same as $f(x)$ in Problem 19 except that it is shifted by k to the right. Since we are integrating from $-\infty$ to ∞, however, this shift doesn't mean anything for the integral.

21. (a) Since $e^{-x^2} \leq e^{-3x}$ for $x \geq 3$,

$$\int_3^{\infty} e^{-x^2} \, dx \leq \int_3^{\infty} e^{-3x} \, dx$$

Now

$$\int_3^{\infty} e^{-3x} \, dx = \lim_{b \to \infty} \int_3^b e^{-3x} \, dx = \lim_{b \to \infty} -\frac{1}{3} e^{-3x} \Big|_3^b$$

$$= \lim_{b \to \infty} \frac{e^{-9}}{3} - \frac{e^{-3b}}{3} = \frac{e^{-9}}{3}.$$

Thus

$$\int_3^{\infty} e^{-x^2} \, dx \leq \frac{e^{-9}}{3}.$$

(b) By reasoning similar to part (a),

$$\int_n^{\infty} e^{-x^2} \, dx \leq \int_n^{\infty} e^{-nx} \, dx,$$

and

$$\int_n^{\infty} e^{-nx} \, dx = \frac{1}{n} e^{-n^2},$$

so

$$\int_n^{\infty} e^{-x^2} \, dx \leq \frac{1}{n} e^{-n^2}.$$

22. (a) For large x,

$$\frac{2x^2 + 1}{4x^4 + 4x^2 - 2} \approx \frac{2x^2}{4x^4} = \frac{1}{2x^2},$$

and since $\int_1^{\infty} \frac{dx}{2x^2}$ converges, we expect the original integral to converge also. More precisely, we can say that for $x \geq 1$, $2x^2 + 1 \leq 3x^2$ and $4x^4 + 4x^2 - 2 \geq 4x^4$, so

$$\int_1^{\infty} \frac{2x^2 + 1}{4x^4 + 4x^2 - 2} \, dx \leq \int_1^{\infty} \frac{3x^2}{4x^4} \, dx = \frac{3}{4}$$

(b) For large x,

$$\left(\frac{2x^4 + 1}{4x^4 + 4x^2 - 2}\right)^{\frac{1}{4}} \approx \left(\frac{2x^2}{4x^4}\right)^{\frac{1}{4}} = \frac{1}{2^{\frac{1}{4}}x^{\frac{1}{2}}},$$

and since $\displaystyle\int_1^\infty \frac{dx}{2^{\frac{1}{4}}x^{\frac{1}{2}}}$ diverges, we expect the original integral will diverge. To show this, notice that for $x \geq 1$, $2x^2 + 1 \geq 2x^2$ and $4x^4 + 4x^2 - 2 \leq 4x^4 + 4x^4 = 8x^4$, so

$$\int_1^\infty \left(\frac{2x^2 + 1}{4x^4 + 4x^2 - 2}\right)^{\frac{1}{4}} dx \geq \int_1^\infty \left(\frac{2x^2}{8x^4}\right)^{\frac{1}{4}} dx = \frac{1}{\sqrt{2}}\int_1^\infty \frac{dx}{\sqrt{x}}$$

So the original integral diverges.

23. First let's calculate the indefinite integral $\displaystyle\int \frac{dx}{x(\ln x)^p}$. Let $\ln x = w$, then $\dfrac{dx}{x} = dw$. So

$$\int \frac{dx}{x(\ln x)^p} = \int \frac{dw}{w^p}$$

$$= \begin{cases} \ln|w| + C, & \text{if } p = 1 \\ \frac{1}{1-p}w^{1-p} + C, & \text{if } p \neq 1 \end{cases}$$

$$= \begin{cases} \ln|\ln x| + C, & \text{if } p = 1 \\ \frac{1}{1-p}(\ln x)^{1-p} + C, & \text{if } p \neq 1. \end{cases}$$

Notice that $\displaystyle\lim_{x \to \infty} \ln x = +\infty$.

(a) $p = 1$:

$$\int_2^\infty \frac{dx}{x \ln x} = \lim_{b \to \infty}\left(\ln|\ln b| - \ln|\ln 2|\right) = +\infty.$$

(b) $p < 1$:

$$\int_2^\infty \frac{dx}{x(\ln x)^p} = \frac{1}{1-p}\left(\lim_{b \to \infty}(\ln b)^{1-p} - (\ln 2)^{1-p}\right) = +\infty.$$

(c) $p > 1$:

$$\int_2^\infty \frac{dx}{x(\ln x)^p} = \frac{1}{1-p}\left(\lim_{b \to \infty}(\ln b)^{1-p} - (\ln 2)^{1-p}\right)$$

$$= \frac{1}{1-p}\left(\lim_{b \to \infty}\frac{1}{(\ln b)^{p-1}} - (\ln 2)^{1-p}\right)$$

$$= -\frac{1}{1-p}(\ln 2)^{1-p}.$$

Thus, $\displaystyle\int_2^\infty \frac{dx}{x(\ln x)^p}$ is convergent for $p > 1$, divergent for $p \leq 1$.

24. The indefinite integral $\int \dfrac{dx}{x(\ln x)^p}$ is computed in Problem 23. Let $\ln x = w$, then $\dfrac{dx}{x} = dw$. Notice that $\lim\limits_{x \to 1} \ln x = 0$, and $\lim\limits_{x \to 0^+} \ln x = -\infty$.

For this integral notice that $\ln 1 = 0$, so the integrand blows up at $x = 1$.

(a) $p = 1$:

$$\int_1^2 \frac{dx}{x \ln x} = \lim_{a \to 1+} \left(\ln|\ln 2| - \ln|\ln a| \right)$$

Since $\ln a \to 0$ as $a \to 1$, $\ln|\ln a| \to -\infty$ as $b \to 1$. So the integral is divergent.

(b) $p < 1$:

$$\int_1^2 \frac{dx}{x(\ln x)^p} = \frac{1}{1-p} \lim_{a \to 1+} \left((\ln 2)^{1-p} - (\ln a)^{1-p} \right)$$

$$= \frac{1}{1-p}(\ln 2)^{1-p}.$$

(c) $p > 1$:

$$\int_1^2 \frac{dx}{x(\ln x)^p} = \frac{1}{1-p} \lim_{a \to 1+} \left((\ln 2)^{1-p} - (\ln a)^{1-p} \right)$$

As $\lim\limits_{a \to 1+} (\ln a)^{1-p} = \lim\limits_{a \to 1+} \dfrac{1}{(\ln a)^{p-1}} = +\infty$, the integral diverges.

Thus, $\int_1^2 \dfrac{dx}{x(\ln x)^p}$ is convergent for $p < 1$, divergent for $p \geq 1$.

25. (a) The tangent line to e^t has slope $(e^t)' = e^t$. Thus at $t = 0$, the slope is $e^0 = 1$. The line passes through $(0, e^0) = (0, 1)$. Thus the equation of the tangent line is $y = 1 + t$. Since e^t is everywhere concave up, its graph is always above the graph of any of its tangent lines; in particular, e^t is always above the line $y = 1 + t$. This is tantamount to saying

$$1 + t \leq e^t,$$

with equality holding only at the point of tangency, $t = 0$.

(b) If $t = \dfrac{1}{x}$, then the above inequality becomes

$$1 + \frac{1}{x} \leq e^{1/x}, \text{ or } e^{1/x} - 1 \geq \frac{1}{x}.$$

Since $t = \dfrac{1}{x}$, t is never zero. Therefore, the inequality is strict, and we write

$$e^{1/x} - 1 > \frac{1}{x}.$$

(c)   Since $e^{1/x} - 1 > \dfrac{1}{x}$,

$$\frac{1}{x^5 \left(e^{1/x} - 1\right)} < \frac{1}{x^5 \left(\frac{1}{x}\right)} = \frac{1}{x^4}.$$

Since $\displaystyle\int_1^\infty \frac{dx}{x^4}$ converges, $\displaystyle\int_1^\infty \frac{dx}{x^5 \left(e^{1/x} - 1\right)}$ converges.

26.   (a)

$$b = 3: \quad \begin{array}{lll} n = 20 & \text{gives} & 0.3941 \\ n = 50 & \text{gives} & 0.3943 \\ n = 100 & \text{gives} & 0.3943 \\ n = 200 & \text{gives} & 0.3943 \end{array}$$

So $\displaystyle\int_1^3 e^{-x^2/2}\, dx \approx 0.3943.$

$$b = 4: \quad \begin{array}{lll} n = 200 & \text{gives} & 0.3976 \\ n = 500 & \text{gives} & 0.3976 \end{array}$$

So $\displaystyle\int_1^4 e^{-x^2/2}\, dx \approx 0.3976.$

$$b = 5: \quad \begin{array}{lll} n = 200 & \text{gives} & 0.3977 \\ n = 500 & \text{gives} & 0.3977 \end{array}$$

So $\displaystyle\int_1^5 e^{-x^2/2}\, dx \approx 0.3977.$

$$b = 6: \quad \begin{array}{lll} n = 200 & \text{gives} & 0.3977 \\ n = 500 & \text{gives} & 0.3977 \end{array}$$

So $\displaystyle\int_1^6 e^{-x^2/2}\, dx \approx 0.3977.$
Thus we conclude that

$$\int_1^\infty e^{-x^2/2}\, dx \approx 0.3977.$$

(b)

$$n = 20: \quad \begin{array}{lll} b = 3 & \text{gives} & 0.3941 \\ b = 4 & \text{gives} & 0.3970 \\ b = 5 & \text{gives} & 0.3967 \\ b = 6 & \text{gives} & 0.3961 \\ b = 10 & \text{gives} & 0.3925 \\ b = 100 & \text{gives} & 0.0118 \\ b = 500 & \text{gives} & 9.3 \times 10^{-39} \\ b = 1000 & \text{gives} & 0 \end{array}$$

The result is zero.

(c) The value of $e^{-x^2/2}$ approaches zero very rapidly. Thus, if b is large (in reality, if $b > 5$), $\int_1^b e^{-x^2/2}\, dx$ is almost the same as $\int_1^\infty e^{-x^2/2}\, dx$ since the tail end of the curve contributes almost nothing to the total area. So, by fixing b and letting n grow large (as you did in part a), you were estimating with increasing accuracy areas which approximated the integral $\int_1^\infty e^{-x^2/2}\, dx$.

Now consider what happens when you fix n and let b grow large (as you did in part b). When $n = 20$, you are approximating the curve by 20 rectangles of equal width. The larger the value of b, the larger the width of each rectangle and the smaller the height (because we're using the midpoint approximation and the integrand is decreasing). The rectangles get shorter so much faster than they get wide that their area approaches zero. Thus, the limit is 0, instead of the value of the integral.

7.10 SOLUTIONS

1.

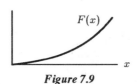

Figure 7.9

By the Fundamental Theorem of Calculus, $f(x) = F'(x)$. Since f is positive and increasing, F is increasing and concave up. Notice that since $F(0) = \int_0^0 f(t)dt = 0$, the graph of F must start from the origin.

2.

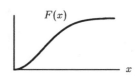

Since f is always positive, F is always increasing. F has an inflection point where $f' = 0$. Since $F(0) = \int_0^0 f(t)dt = 0$, F goes through the origin.

3.

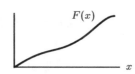

Since f is always non-negative, F is increasing. F is concave up where f is increasing and concave down where f is decreasing; F has inflection points at the critical points of f. Since $F(0) = \int_0^0 f(t)dt = 0$, the graph of F goes through the origin.

4.

TABLE 7.8

x	0	0.5	1	1.5	2
$I(x)$	0	0.50	1.09	2.03	3.65

5. (a) Again using 0.00001 as the lower limit, because the integral is improper, gives Si(4) = 1.76, Si(5) = 1.55.

(b) Si(x) decreases when the integrand is negative, which occurs when $\pi < x < 2\pi$.

6. I–(b). II–(e). III–(c). IV–(a). V–(d). VI–(f).

7. See the following figures:

(I)
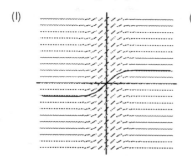

(II)
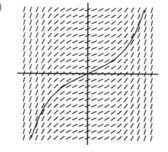

(III)
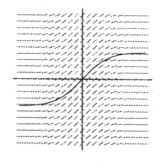

(IV)
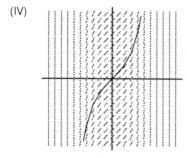

(V)
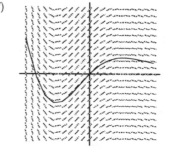

(VI)
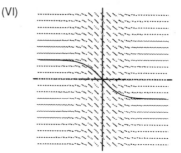

8. $\sqrt{3 + \cos(x^2)}$.

9. $(1 + x)^{200}$.

10. $\arctan(x^2)$.

11. $\dfrac{d}{dt} \displaystyle\int_t^\pi \cos(z^3)\, dz = \dfrac{d}{dt}\left(-\int_\pi^t \cos(z^3)\, dz\right) = -\cos(t^3)$.

12. $\frac{d}{dx}\int_x^1 \ln t\, dt = \frac{d}{dx}\left(-\int_1^x \ln t\, dt\right) = -\ln x$.

13. $\dfrac{d}{dx}\left[\text{Si}(x^2)\right] = 2x\dfrac{\sin(x^2)}{x^2} = \dfrac{2\sin x^2}{x}$.

14.

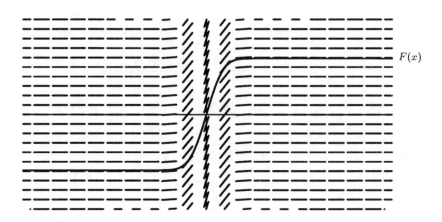

$F(x)$ is an antiderivative of e^{-x^2}; since $F(0) = 0$, we have

$$F(x) = \int_0^x e^{-t^2}\, dt.$$

Thus $\displaystyle\lim_{x \to \infty} F(x) = \lim_{x \to \infty} \int_0^x e^{-t^2}\, dt$. Estimating $\int_0^x e^{-t^2}\, dt$ for large x using Simpson's Rule, we find that $\displaystyle\lim_{x \to \infty} \int_0^x e^{-t^2}\, dt \approx 0.8862269$, or $\displaystyle\lim_{x \to \infty} F(x) \approx 0.8862269$.

15. (a)

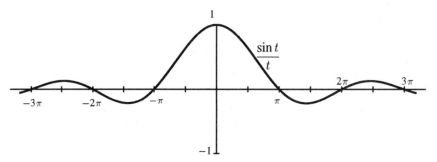

(b) Si(x) neither always decreases nor always increases, since its derivative, $x^{-1}\sin x$, attains both positive and negative values for $x > 0$. For positive x, Si(x) represents the area under the curve $\sin t/t$ between 0 and x. Looking at the graph above, one can see that this number is going to always be positive.

(c)

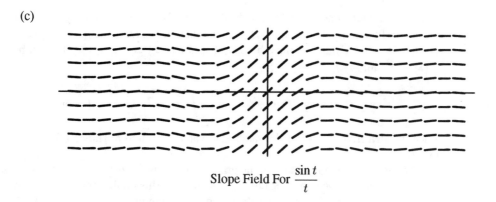

Slope Field For $\dfrac{\sin t}{t}$

It seems that the limit exists: the curve drawn in the slope field, which approximates $\text{Si}(x)$, seems to approach some limiting height as $x \to \infty$. (In fact, the limiting height is $\pi/2$, an interesting result.)

16.

(a)

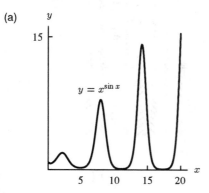

(b)

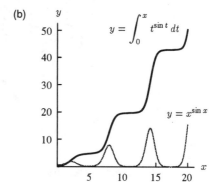

(c)

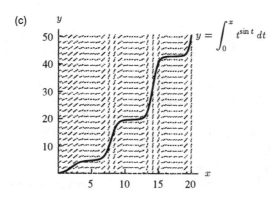

17. (a) The most obvious feature of the graph of $y = \sin(x^2)$ is its symmetry about the y-axis. This means the function $g(x) = \sin(x^2)$ is an even function, i.e. for all x, $g(x) = g(-x)$. Since $\sin(x^2)$ is even, its antiderivative F must be odd, that is $F(-x) = -F(-x)$. This can be seen since if $F(t) = \int_0^t \sin(x^2)\, dx$,

$$F(-t) = \int_0^{-t} \sin(x^2)\, dx = -\int_{-t}^0 \sin(x^2)\, dx = -\int_0^t \sin(x^2)\, dx,$$

since the area from $-t$ to 0 is the same as the area from 0 to t. Thus $F(t) = -F(-t)$ and F is odd.

The second obvious feature of the graph of $y = \sin(x^2)$ is that it oscillates between -1 and 1 with a "period" which goes to zero as $|x|$ increases. This implies that $F'(x)$ alternates between intervals where it is positive or negative, and increasing or decreasing, with frequency growing arbitrarily large as $|x|$ increases. Thus $F(x)$ itself similarly alternates between intervals where it is increasing or decreasing, and concave up or concave down.

Finally, since $y = \sin(x^2) = F'(x)$ passes through $(0, 0)$, and $F(0) = 0$, F is tangent to the x−axis at the origin.

(b)

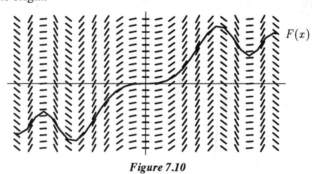

$F(x)$

Figure 7.10

F never crosses the x-axis in the region $x > 0$, and $\lim_{x \to \infty} F(x)$ exists. One way to see these facts is to note that by the Construction Theorem,

$$F(x) = F(x) - F(0) = \int_0^x F'(t)\, dt.$$

So $F(x)$ is just the area under the curve $y = \sin(t^2)$ for $0 \le t \le x$. Now looking at the graph of curve, we see that this area will include alternating pieces above and below the x−axis. We can also see that the area of these pieces is approaching 0 as we go further out. So we add a piece, take a piece away, add another piece, take another piece away, and so on. It turns out that this means that the sums of the pieces converge. To see this, think of walking from point A to point B. If you walk almost to B, then go a smaller distance toward A, then a yet smaller distance back toward B, and so on, you will eventually approach some point between A and B. So we can see that $\lim_{x \to \infty} F(x)$ exists. Also, since we always subtract a smaller piece than we just added, and the first piece is added instead of subtracted, we see that we never get a negative sum; thus $F(x)$ is never negative in the region $x > 0$, so $F(x)$ never crosses the x-axis there.

18. (a) By the integral table (or repeated integration by parts) we obtain

$$F(x) = \int_1^x (t+1)^2 \cos 2t \, dt$$

$$= \frac{1}{2}(t+1)^2 \sin 2t + \frac{1}{4}2(t+1) \cos 2t - \frac{1}{8}2 \sin 2t \Big|_1^x$$

$$= \left(\frac{2x^2 + 4x + 1}{4}\right) \sin 2x + \frac{x+1}{2} \cos 2x - \frac{7 \sin 2 + 4 \cos 2}{4}.$$

(b)

$$F'(x) = (x+1)\sin 2x + 2\left(\frac{2x^2 + 4x + 1}{4}\right)\cos 2x + \frac{\cos 2x}{2} - 2\left(\frac{x+1}{2}\right)\sin 2x$$

$$= (x+1)^2 \cos 2x.$$

Therefore $F(x)$ is an antiderivative of $(x+1)^2 \cos 2x$.

19.

$$\frac{d}{dx}[x\,\mathrm{erf}(x)] = \mathrm{erf}(x)\frac{d}{dx}(x) + x\frac{d}{dx}[\mathrm{erf}(x)]$$

$$= \mathrm{erf}(x) + x\frac{d}{dx}\left(\frac{2}{\sqrt{\pi}}\int_0^x e^{-t^2}\,dt\right)$$

$$= \mathrm{erf}(x) + \frac{2}{\sqrt{\pi}}xe^{-x^2}.$$

20. If we let $f(x) = \mathrm{erf}(x)$ and $g(x) = \sqrt{x}$, then we are looking for $\frac{d}{dx}[f(g(x))]$. By the chain rule, this is the same as $g'(x)f'(g(x))$. Since by the Construction Theorem

$$f'(x) = \frac{d}{dx}\left(\frac{2}{\sqrt{\pi}}\int_0^x e^{-t^2}\,dt\right)$$

$$= \frac{2}{\sqrt{\pi}}e^{-x^2}$$

and $g'(x) = \frac{1}{2\sqrt{x}}$, we have

$$f'(g(x)) = \frac{2}{\sqrt{\pi}}e^{-x}$$

and so

$$\frac{d}{dx}[\mathrm{erf}(\sqrt{x})] = \frac{1}{2\sqrt{x}}\frac{2}{\sqrt{\pi}}e^{-x}$$

$$= \frac{1}{\sqrt{\pi x}}e^{-x}.$$

21. Let $w^2 = \dfrac{t^2}{2}$ and $w = \dfrac{1}{\sqrt{2}}t.$ Then $dt = \sqrt{2}\,dw,$ and $w = \dfrac{x}{\sqrt{2}}$ when $t = x.$

Therefore $\sqrt{\dfrac{2}{\pi}}\displaystyle\int_0^x e^{-\frac{t^2}{2}}\,dt = \sqrt{\dfrac{2}{\pi}}\cdot\sqrt{2}\displaystyle\int_0^{x/\sqrt{2}} e^{-w^2}\,dw = \mathrm{erf}\left(\dfrac{x}{\sqrt{2}}\right).$

22. Let $w^2 = \frac{t^2}{2}$ and $w = \frac{1}{\sqrt{2}}t.$ Then $dt = \sqrt{2}dw,$ and $w = \frac{x_i}{\sqrt{2}}$ when $t = x_i,$ for $i = 1$ or $2.$ Therefore

$$\sqrt{\dfrac{2}{\pi}}\int_{x_1}^{x_2} e^{-\frac{t^2}{2}}\,dt = \sqrt{\dfrac{2}{\pi}}\int_0^{x_2} e^{-\frac{t^2}{2}}\,dt - \sqrt{\dfrac{2}{\pi}}\int_0^{x_1} e^{-\frac{t^2}{2}}\,dt$$

$$= \sqrt{\dfrac{2}{\pi}}\cdot\sqrt{2}\int_0^{x_2/\sqrt{2}} e^{-w^2}\,dw - \sqrt{\dfrac{2}{\pi}}\cdot\sqrt{2}\int_0^{x_1/\sqrt{2}} e^{-w^2}\,dw$$

$$= \mathrm{erf}\left(\dfrac{x_2}{\sqrt{2}}\right) - \mathrm{erf}\left(\dfrac{x_1}{\sqrt{2}}\right).$$

SOLUTIONS TO REVIEW PROBLEMS FOR CHAPTER SEVEN

1. The limits of integration are 0 and $b,$ and the rectangle represents the region under the curve $f(x) = h$ between these limits. Thus,

$$\text{Area of rectangle} = \int_0^b h\,dx = hx\Big|_0^b = hb.$$

2. Name the slanted line $y = f(x).$ Then the triangle is the region under the line $y = f(x)$ and between the lines $y = 0$ and $x = b.$ Thus,

$$\text{Area of triangle} = \int_0^b f(x)\,dx.$$

Since $f(x)$ is a line of slope h/b which passes through the origin, its equation is $f(x) = hx/b.$ Thus,

$$\text{Area of triangle} = \int_0^b \dfrac{hx}{b}\,dx = \dfrac{hx^2}{2b}\Big|_0^b = \dfrac{hb^2}{2b} = \dfrac{hb}{2}.$$

3. The circle $x^2 + y^2 = r^2$ cannot be expressed as a function $y = f(x),$ since for every x with $-r < x < r,$ there are two corresponding y values on the circle. However, if we consider the top half of the circle only, we have $x^2 + y^2 = r^2,$ or $y^2 = r^2 - x^2,$ and taking the positive square root, we have that $y = \sqrt{r^2 - x^2}$ is the equation of the top semicircle.

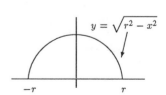

Then

$$\text{Area of Circle} = 2(\text{Area of semicircle})$$
$$= 2 \int_{-r}^{r} \sqrt{r^2 - x^2}\, dx$$

We evaluate this using integral table formula 30.

$$2 \int_{x=-r}^{x=r} \sqrt{r^2 - x^2}\, dx = 2 \left[\frac{1}{2} \left(x\sqrt{r^2 - x^2} + r^2 \arcsin \frac{x}{r} \right) \right] \Big|_{-r}^{r}$$
$$= r^2 (\arcsin 1 - \arcsin(-1))$$
$$= r^2 \left(\frac{\pi}{2} - \left(-\frac{\pi}{2} \right) \right) = \pi r^2.$$

4. (a) Let $w = 2x$, so $w^2 = 4x^2$ and $dw = 2\, dx$.

$$\int \frac{dx}{\sqrt{1 - 4x^2}} = \frac{1}{2} \int \frac{dw}{\sqrt{1 - w^2}} = \frac{1}{2} \arcsin w + C \text{ by VI-28}$$
$$= \frac{1}{2} \arcsin 2x + C.$$

(b)

$$\int_0^{\frac{\pi}{8}} \frac{dx}{\sqrt{1 - 4x^2}} = \frac{1}{2} \arcsin 2x \Big|_0^{\frac{\pi}{8}} \approx 0.45167.$$

(c) Simpson's rule with 100 intervals also yields ≈ 0.45167.

5. (a) Recall that $x = e^{\ln x}$. Thus $x^x = (e^{\ln x})^x = e^{x \ln x}$.

(b)
$$\frac{d}{dx}(x^x) = \frac{d}{dx}(e^{x \ln x}) = e^{x \ln x} \frac{d}{dx}(x \ln x) \text{ by the chain rule}$$
$$= e^{x \ln x}(\ln x + 1)$$
$$= x^x(\ln x + 1).$$

(c) By the Fundamental Theorem of Calculus and part (b),

$$\int x^x (1 + \ln x)\, dx = x^x + C.$$

(d) By the Fundamental Theorem of Calculus,

$$\int_1^2 x^x (1 + \ln x)\, dx = x^x \Big|_1^2$$
$$= 2^2 - 1^1$$
$$= 3.$$

Using a calculator, we can check our answer numerically. With 50 subdivisions, the left-hand sum ≈ 2.943 and the right-hand sum ≈ 3.058. With 100 subdivisions, the left-hand sum ≈ 2.971 and the right-hand sum ≈ 3.029.

6. Since the definition of f is different on $0 \leq t \leq 1$ than it is on $1 \leq t \leq 2$, break the definite integral at $t = 1$.

$$
\begin{aligned}
\int_0^2 f(t)\,dt &= \int_0^1 f(t)\,dt + \int_1^2 f(t)\,dt \\
&= \int_0^1 t^2\,dt + \int_1^2 (2-t)\,dt \\
&= \left. \frac{t^3}{3} \right|_0^1 + \left. \left(2t - \frac{t^2}{2} \right) \right|_1^2 \\
&= 1/3 + 1/2 \\
&= 5/6 \approx 0.833
\end{aligned}
$$

7. Substitute $w = t^2$, so $dw = 2t\,dt$.

$$
\int t e^{t^2}\,dt = \frac{1}{2} \int e^{t^2} 2t\,dt = \frac{1}{2} \int e^w\,dw = \frac{1}{2} e^w + C = \frac{1}{2} e^{t^2} + C.
$$

Check:

$$
\frac{d}{dt} \left(\frac{1}{2} e^{t^2} + C \right) = 2t \left(\frac{1}{2} e^{t^2} \right) = t e^{t^2}.
$$

8. $x \sin x + \cos x + C$.

(Integrate by parts: $u = x, v' = \cos x$, or use III-16 with $p(x) = x$ and $a = 1$ in the integral table.)

9. Let $w = 2 + 3\cos x$, so $dw = -3\sin x\,dx$, giving $-\dfrac{1}{3}\,dw = \sin x\,dx$. Then

$$
\begin{aligned}
\int \sin x \left(\sqrt{2 + 3\cos x} \right) dx &= \int \sqrt{w} \left(-\frac{1}{3} \right) dw = -\frac{1}{3} \int \sqrt{w}\,dw \\
&= \left(-\frac{1}{3} \right) \frac{w^{\frac{3}{2}}}{\frac{3}{2}} + C = -\frac{2}{9} (2 + 3\cos x)^{\frac{3}{2}} + C.
\end{aligned}
$$

10. $(\frac{1}{2} x^2 - \frac{1}{2} x + \frac{1}{4}) e^{2x} + C$.

(Integrate by parts twice, or use the integral table, III-14 with $p(x) = x^2$ and $a = 1$)

11. $\frac{2}{5}(1 - x)^{\frac{5}{2}} - \frac{2}{3}(1 - x)^{\frac{3}{2}} + C$.

(Let $w = 1 - x$.)

12. $\frac{1}{2} x^2 \ln x - \frac{1}{4} x^2 + C$.

(Integrate by parts: $u = \ln x, v' = x$, or use III–13 with $n = 1$ in the integral table.)

13. We integrate by parts, with $u = y$, $v' = \sin y$. We have $u' = 1$, $v = -\cos y$, and

$$\int y \sin y \, dy = -y \cos y - \int (-\cos y) \, dy = -y \cos y + \sin y + C.$$

Check:

$$\frac{d}{dy}(-y \cos y + \sin y + C) = -\cos y + y \sin y + \cos y = y \sin y.$$

14.

$$\int \frac{dz}{z^2 + z} = \int \frac{dz}{z(z+1)} = \int \left(\frac{1}{z} - \frac{1}{z+1} \right) dz = \ln|z| - \ln|z+1| + C.$$

(This is formula V–26 in the integral table.)
Check:

$$\frac{d}{dz} \left(\ln|z| - \ln|z+1| + C \right) = \frac{1}{z} - \frac{1}{z+1} = \frac{1}{z^2 + z}.$$

15. Substitute $w = \sqrt{y}$, $dw = 1/(2\sqrt{y}) \, dy$. Then

$$\int \frac{\cos \sqrt{y}}{\sqrt{y}} \, dy = 2 \int \cos w \, dw = 2 \sin w + C = 2 \sin \sqrt{y} + C.$$

Check:

$$\frac{d}{dy} 2 \sin \sqrt{y} + C = \frac{2 \cos \sqrt{y}}{2 \sqrt{y}} = \frac{\cos \sqrt{y}}{\sqrt{y}}.$$

16. We integrate by parts, using $u = (\ln x)^2$ and $v' = 1$. Then $u' = 2\frac{\ln x}{x}$ and $v = x$, so

$$\int (\ln x)^2 \, dx = x(\ln x)^2 - 2 \int \ln x \, dx.$$

But, by the integral table, $\int \ln x \, dx = x \ln x - x + C$. Therefore,

$$\int (\ln x)^2 \, dx = x(\ln x)^2 - 2x \ln x + 2x + C.$$

Check:

$$\frac{d}{dx} \left[x(\ln x)^2 - 2x \ln x + 2x + C \right] = (\ln x)^2 + x\frac{2 \ln x}{x} - 2 \ln x - 2x\frac{1}{x} + 2 = (\ln x)^2.$$

17. Remember that $\ln(x^2) = 2 \ln x$. Therefore,

$$\int \ln(x^2) \, dx = 2 \int \ln x \, dx = 2x \ln x - 2x + C.$$

Check:

$$\frac{d}{dx}(2x\ln x - 2x + C) = 2\ln x + \frac{2x}{x} - 2 = 2\ln x = \ln(x^2).$$

18.

$$\int e^{0.5-0.3t}\,dt = e^{0.5}\int e^{-0.3t}\,dt = -\frac{e^{0.5}}{0.3}e^{-0.3t} + C.$$

19. Let $w = \cos 2\theta$. Then $dw = -2\sin 2\theta\,d\theta$, whence

$$\int \cos^3 2\theta \sin 2\theta\,d\theta = -\frac{1}{2}\int w^3\,dw = -\frac{w^4}{8} + C = -\frac{\cos^4 2\theta}{8} + C.$$

Check:

$$\frac{d}{d\theta}\left(-\frac{\cos^4 2\theta}{8}\right) = -\frac{(4\cos^3 2\theta)(-\sin 2\theta)(2)}{8} = \cos^3 2\theta \sin 2\theta.$$

20. The integral table yields

$$\int \frac{5x+6}{x^2+4}\,dx = \frac{5}{2}\ln|x^2+4| + \frac{6}{2}\arctan\frac{x}{2} + C$$

$$= \frac{5}{2}\ln|x^2+4| + 3\arctan\frac{x}{2} + C.$$

Check:

$$\frac{d}{dx}\left(\frac{5}{2}\ln|x^2+4| + \frac{6}{2}\arctan\frac{x}{2} + C\right) = \frac{5}{2}\left(\frac{1}{x^2+4}(2x) + 3\frac{1}{1+(x/2)^2}\frac{1}{2}\right)$$

$$= \frac{5x}{x^2+4} + \frac{6}{x^2+4} = \frac{5x+6}{x^2+4}.$$

21. Substitute $w = 4 - x^2$, $dw = -2x\,dx$:

$$\int x\sqrt{4-x^2}\,dx = -\frac{1}{2}\int \sqrt{w}\,dw = -\frac{1}{3}w^{3/2} + C = -\frac{1}{3}(4-x^2)^{3/2} + C.$$

Check

$$\frac{d}{dx}\left[-\frac{1}{3}(4-x^2)^{3/2} + C\right] = -\frac{1}{3}\left[\frac{3}{2}(4-x^2)^{1/2}(-2x)\right] = x\sqrt{4-x^2}.$$

22. By VI-30 in the table of integrals, we have

$$\int \sqrt{4-x^2}\,dx = \frac{x\sqrt{4-x^2}}{2} + 2\int \frac{1}{\sqrt{4-x^2}}\,dx.$$

The same table informs us in formula VI-28 that

$$\int \frac{1}{\sqrt{4-x^2}}\,dx = \arcsin\frac{x}{2} + C.$$

Thus

$$\int \sqrt{4-x^2}\,dx = \frac{x\sqrt{4-x^2}}{2} + 2\arcsin\frac{x}{2} + C.$$

23. By IV-21 in the table of integrals,

$$\int \frac{1}{\cos^2 z}\,dz = \frac{\sin z}{\cos z} + C = \tan z + C.$$

Check:

$$\frac{d}{dt}(\tan z + C) = \frac{d}{dt}\frac{\sin z}{\cos z} = \frac{(\cos z)(\cos z) - (\sin z)(-\sin z)}{\cos^2 z} = \frac{1}{\cos^2 z}.$$

24. Denote $\int \cos^2\theta\,d\theta$ by A. Let $u = \cos\theta$, $v' = \cos\theta$. Then, $v = \sin\theta$ and $u' = -\sin\theta$. Integrating by parts, we get:

$$A = \cos\theta\sin\theta - \int(-\sin\theta)\sin\theta\,d\theta.$$

Employing the identity $\sin^2\theta = 1 - \cos^2\theta$, the equation above becomes:

$$A = \cos\theta\sin\theta + \int d\theta - \int \cos^2\theta\,d\theta$$
$$= \cos\theta\sin\theta + \theta - A + C.$$

Solving this equation for A, and using the identity $\sin 2\theta = 2\cos\theta\sin\theta$ we get:

$$A = \int \cos^2\theta\,d\theta = \frac{1}{4}\sin 2\theta + \frac{1}{2}\theta + C.$$

[Note: An alternate solution would have been to use the identity $\cos^2\theta = \frac{1}{2}\cos 2\theta + \frac{1}{2}$.]

25.

$$\int \frac{(u+1)^3}{u^2}\,du = \int \frac{(u^3 + 3u^2 + 3u + 1)}{u^2}\,du$$
$$= \int \left(u + 3 + \frac{3}{u} + \frac{1}{u^2}\right)du$$
$$= \frac{u^2}{2} + 3u + 3\ln|u| - \frac{1}{u} + C.$$

Check:

$$\frac{d}{du}\left(\frac{u^2}{2} + 3u + 3\ln|u| - \frac{1}{u} + C\right) = u + 3 + 3/u + 1/u^2 = \frac{(u+1)^3}{u^2}.$$

26. Substitute $w = 2x - 6$. Then $dw = 2\,dx$ and

$$\int \tan(2x - 6)\,dx = \frac{1}{2}\int \tan w\,dw$$

$$= -\frac{1}{2}\ln|\cos w| + C \text{ by Formula I-7 of the integral table.}$$

$$= -\frac{1}{2}\ln|\cos(2x - 6)| + C.$$

27.

$$\int_1^3 \ln(x^3)\,dx = 3\int_1^3 \ln x\,dx$$

$$= 3(x\ln x - x)\Big|_1^3$$

$$= 9\ln 3 - 6 \approx 3.8875.$$

This matches the approximation given by Simpson's rule with 10 intervals.

28. In Problem 16, we found that

$$\int (\ln x)^2\,dx = x(\ln x)^2 - 2x\ln x + 2x + C.$$

Thus

$$\int_1^e (\ln x)^2\,dx = [x(\ln x)^2 - 2x\ln x + 2x]\Big|_1^e = e - 2 \approx 0.71828.$$

This matches the approximation given by Simpson's rule with 10 intervals.

29. $\int e^{2x}\sin 2x\,dx = \frac{1}{4}e^{2x}(\sin 2x - \cos 2x) + C$ by II-8 in the integral table.

Thus $\int_{-\pi}^{\pi} e^{2x}\sin 2x = [\frac{1}{4}e^{2x}(\sin 2x - \cos 2x)]\Big|_{-\pi}^{\pi} = \frac{1}{4}(e^{-2\pi} - e^{2\pi}) \approx -133.8724.$

We get -133.37 using Simpson's rule with 10 intervals. With 100 intervals, we get -133.8724. Thus our answer matches the approximation of Simpson's rule.

30. 0. This integral is 0 because the function $x^3\cos(x^4)$ is odd (meaning $f(-x) = -f(x)$), and so the negative contribution to the integral from $-\frac{\pi}{4} < x < 0$ exactly cancels the positive contribution from $0 < x < \frac{\pi}{4}$.

31. After the substitution $w = x + 2$, the first integral becomes

$$\int w^{-2}\, dw.$$

After the substitution $w = x^2 + 1$, the second integral becomes

$$\frac{1}{2}\int w^{-2}\, dw.$$

32. After the substitution $w = x^2$, the second integral becomes

$$\frac{1}{2}\int \frac{dw}{\sqrt{1 - w^2}}.$$

33. After the substitution $w = 1 - x^2$, the first integral becomes

$$-\frac{1}{2}\int w^{-1}\, dw.$$

After the substitution $w = \ln x$, the second integral becomes

$$\int w^{-1}\, dw.$$

34. *First solution*: After the substitution $w = x + 1$, the first integral becomes

$$\int \frac{w - 1}{w}\, dw = w - \int w^{-1}\, dw.$$

With this same substitution, the second integral becomes

$$\int w^{-1}\, dw.$$

Second solution: We note that the sum of the integrands is 1, so the sum of the integrals is x. Thus

$$\int \frac{x}{x + 1}\, dx = x - \int \frac{1}{x + 1}\, dx.$$

35. (a) $\ln(1 + e^x) + C$. (Let $w = 1 + e^x$.)

(b) $\arctan(e^x) + C$. (Let $w = e^x$, getting $\int \dfrac{dw}{1 + w^2}$, and use formula V-24 .)

(c) $x - \ln(1 + e^x) + C$.

[Note that $\dfrac{1}{1 + e^x} = 1 - \dfrac{e^x}{1 + e^x}$ and use part (a).]

36. (a) i. 0   ii. $\frac{2}{\pi}$ iii. $\frac{1}{2}$

(b) Average value of $f(t)$ < Average value of $k(t)$ < Average value of $g(t)$

We can look at the three functions in the range $-\frac{\pi}{2} \le x \le \frac{3\pi}{2}$, since they all have periods of 2π ($|\cos t|$ and $(\cos t)^2$ also have a period of π, but that doesn't hurt our calculation). It is clear from the graphs of the three functions that the average value for $\cos t$ is 0 (since the area above the x-axis is equal to the area below it), while the average values for the other two are positive (since they are everywhere positive, except where they are 0).

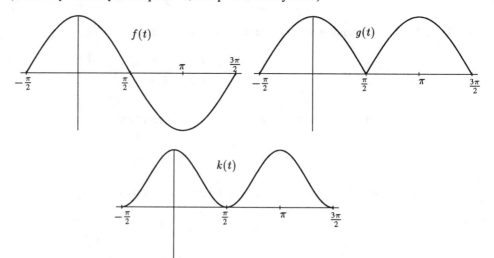

It is also fairly clear from the graphs that the average value of $g(t)$ is greater than the average value of $k(t)$; it is also possible to see this algebraically, since

$$(\cos t)^2 = |\cos t|^2 \leq |\cos t|$$

because $|\cos t| \leq 1$ (and both of these $\leq$'s are $<$'s at all the points where the functions are not 0 or 1).

37. If $I(t)$ is average per capita income t years after 1987, then $I'(t) = r(t)$.

(a) Since $t = 8$ in 1995, by the Fundamental Theorem,

$$I(8) - I(0) = \int_0^8 r(t)\, dt = \int_0^8 480(1.024)^t\, dt$$

$$= \frac{480(1.024)^t}{\ln(1.024)}\Bigg|_0^8 = 4228$$

so $I(8) = 26{,}000 + 4228 = 30{,}228$.

(b)

$$I(t) - I(0) = \int_0^t r(t)\, dt = \int_0^t 480(1.024)^t\, dt$$

$$= \frac{480(1.024)^t}{\ln(1.024)}\Bigg|_0^t$$

$$= \frac{480}{\ln(1.024)}\left((1.024)^t - 1\right)$$

$$= 20{,}239\left((1.024)^t - 1\right)$$

Thus, since $I(0) = 26{,}000$,

$$I(t) = 26{,}000 + 20{,}239(1.024^t - 1)$$

$$= 20{,}239(1.024)^t + 5761$$

38. Let $C(y)$ be the consumption of petroleum from 1991 through the year $1991 + y$. Let $a = 1.02$ and $K = 1.4 \times 10^{20}$. We are told that in the year $1990 + t$, the annual rate of consumption will be Ka^t joules/year. Thus

$$C(y) = \sum_{t=1}^y Ka^t.$$

Since $a > 1$, the function $u = Ka^t$ is increasing and $C(y)$ can be viewed as a right-hand Riemann sum overestimate for a definite integral

$$C(y) \geq \int_0^y Ka^t\, dt = \frac{K}{\ln a}(a^y - 1).$$

Thus we seek y such that

$$\frac{K}{\ln a}(a^y - 1) = 10^{22},$$

or

$$a^y = \frac{10^{22} \ln a}{K} + 1 \approx 2.414.$$

Taking logarithms, we get $y \ln a \approx \ln 2.414$, which gives $y \approx 45$. So in about 45 years, we will run out of petroleum!

39. (a) $f(t) = Q - \frac{Q}{A}t$

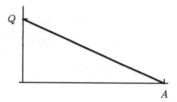

(b)

$$\text{Average level} = \frac{\int_0^A f(t)\, dt}{A}$$

$$= \frac{1}{A}\int_0^A \left(Q - \frac{Q}{A}t\right) dt$$

$$= \frac{1}{A}\left(Qt - \frac{Q}{2A}t^2\right)\bigg|_0^A = \frac{1}{A}\left(QA - \frac{QA}{2}\right) = \frac{1}{2}Q.$$

Graphically, the average will be the y coordinate of the midpoint of the line in the graph above. Thus, the answer should be $\frac{Q+0}{2} = \frac{Q}{2}$.

Common sense tells us that since the rate is constant, the average amount should equal the amount at the midpoint of the interval, which is indeed $\frac{Q}{2}$.

40. The point of intersection of the two curves $y = x^2$ and $y = 6 - x$ is at $(2,4)$. The average height of the shaded area is the average value of the difference between the functions:

$$\frac{1}{(2-0)}\int_0^2 ((6-x) - x^2)\, dx = \left(3x - \frac{x^2}{4} - \frac{x^3}{6}\right)\bigg|_0^2$$

$$= \frac{11}{3}.$$

41. The average width of the shaded area is the average value of the horizontal distance between the two functions. If we call this horizontal distance $h(y)$, then the average width is

$$\frac{1}{(6-0)} \int_0^6 h(y)\, dy.$$

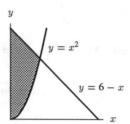

We could compute this integral if we wanted to, but we don't need to. We can simply note that the integral (without the $\frac{1}{6}$ term) is just the area of the shaded region; similarly, the integral in Problem 40 is *also* just the area of the shaded region. So they are the same. Now we know that our average width is just $\frac{1}{3}$ as much as the average height, since we divide by 6 instead of 2. So the answer is $\frac{11}{9}$.

42.

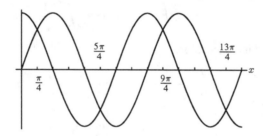

As is evident from the accompanying figure of the graphs of $y = \sin x$ and $y = \cos x$, the crossings occur at $x = \frac{\pi}{4}, \frac{5\pi}{4}, \frac{9\pi}{4}, \ldots$, and the regions bounded by any two consecutive crossings have the same area. So picking two consecutive crossings, we get an area of

$$\text{Area} = \int_{\frac{\pi}{4}}^{\frac{5\pi}{4}} (\sin x - \cos x)\, dx$$

$$= 2\sqrt{2}.$$

(Note that we integrated $\sin x - \cos x$ here because for $\frac{\pi}{4} \le x \le \frac{5\pi}{4}$, $\sin x \ge \cos x$.)

43. $\int_4^\infty \frac{dt}{t^{\frac{3}{2}}}$ should converge, since $\int_1^\infty \frac{dt}{t^n}$ converges for $n > 1$.
We calculate its value.

$$\int_4^\infty \frac{dt}{t^{\frac{3}{2}}} = \lim_{b \to \infty} \int_4^b t^{-\frac{3}{2}}\, dt = \lim_{b \to \infty} -2t^{-\frac{1}{2}} \Big|_4^b = \lim_{b \to \infty} \left(1 - \frac{2}{\sqrt{b}}\right) = 1.$$

44. To find $\int we^{-w}\, dw$, integrate by parts, with $u = w$ and $v' = e^{-w}$. Then $u' = 1$ and $v = -e^{-w}$. Then

$$\int we^{-w}\, dw = -we^{-w} + \int e^{-w}\, dw = -we^{-w} - e^{-w} + C.$$

Thus

$$\int_0^\infty we^{-w}\, dw = \lim_{b \to \infty} \int_0^b we^{-w}\, dw = \lim_{b \to \infty} \left(-we^{-w} - e^{-w} \right) \Big|_0^b = 1.$$

45. $\int \frac{dx}{x \ln x} = \ln |\ln x| + C.$ (Substitute $w = \ln x$, $dw = \frac{1}{x}\, dx$).
Thus

$$\int_{10}^\infty \frac{dx}{x \ln x} = \lim_{b \to \infty} \int_{10}^b \frac{dx}{x \ln x} = \lim_{b \to \infty} \ln |\ln x| \Big|_{10}^b = \lim_{b \to \infty} \ln(\ln b) - \ln(\ln 10).$$

As $b \to \infty$, $\ln(\ln b) \to \infty$, so this diverges.

46. It is easy to see that this integral converges, since

$$\frac{1}{4 + z^2} < \frac{1}{z^2}, \text{ so}$$

$$\int_2^\infty \frac{1}{4 + z^2}\, dz < \int_2^\infty \frac{1}{z^2}\, dz = 1/2.$$

We can also find its exact value.

$$\int_2^\infty \frac{1}{4 + z^2}\, dz = \lim_{b \to \infty} \int_2^b \frac{1}{4 + z^2}\, dz$$

$$= \lim_{b \to \infty} \left(\frac{1}{2} \arctan \frac{z}{2} \Big|_2^b \right)$$

$$= \lim_{b \to \infty} \left(\frac{1}{2} \arctan \frac{b}{2} - \frac{1}{2} \arctan 1 \right)$$

$$= \frac{1}{2}\frac{\pi}{2} - \frac{1}{2}\frac{\pi}{4} = \frac{\pi}{8}.$$

Note that $\frac{\pi}{8} < \frac{1}{2}$.

47. We find the exact value:

$$\int_{10}^\infty \frac{1}{z^2 - 4}\, dz = \int_{10}^\infty \frac{1}{(z + 2)(z - 2)}\, dz$$

$$= \lim_{b \to \infty} \int_{10}^b \frac{1}{(z + 2)(z - 2)}\, dz$$

$$= \lim_{b \to \infty} \frac{1}{4} \left(\ln |z - 2| - \ln |z + 2| \right) \Big|_{10}^b$$

$$= \frac{1}{4} \lim_{b \to \infty} [(\ln |b - 2| - \ln |b + 2|) - (\ln 8 - \ln 12)]$$

$$= \frac{1}{4} \lim_{b \to \infty} \left[\left(\ln \frac{b - 2}{b + 2} \right) + \ln \frac{3}{2} \right]$$

$$= \frac{1}{4} (\ln 1 + \ln 3/2) = \frac{\ln 3/2}{4} \approx 0.10.$$

48. The trouble spot is at $x = 0$, so we write

$$\int_{-1}^{1} \frac{1}{x^4} \, dx = \int_{-1}^{0} \frac{1}{x^4} \, dx + \int_{0}^{1} \frac{1}{x^4} \, dx.$$

However, both these integrals diverge. For example,

$$\int_{0}^{1} \frac{1}{x^4} \, dx = \lim_{a \to 0+} \int_{a}^{1} \frac{1}{x^4} \, dx = \lim_{a \to 0+} -\frac{x^{-3}}{3} \Big|_{a}^{1} = \lim_{a \to 0+} \left(\frac{1}{3a^3} - \frac{1}{3} \right).$$

Since this limit does not exist, $\int_{0}^{1} \frac{1}{x^4} \, dx$ diverges and so the original integral diverges.

49. Since the value of $\tan \theta$ is between -1 and 1 on the interval $-\pi/4 \leq \theta \leq \pi/4$, our integral is not improper and so converges. Moreover, since $\tan \theta$ is an odd function, we have

$$\int_{-\frac{\pi}{4}}^{\frac{\pi}{4}} \tan \theta \, d\theta = \int_{-\frac{\pi}{4}}^{0} \tan \theta \, d\theta + \int_{0}^{\frac{\pi}{4}} \tan \theta \, d\theta = - \int_{-\frac{\pi}{4}}^{0} \tan(-\theta) \, d\theta + \int_{0}^{\frac{\pi}{4}} \tan \theta \, d\theta$$

$$= - \int_{0}^{\frac{\pi}{4}} \tan \theta \, d\theta + \int_{0}^{\frac{\pi}{4}} \tan \theta \, d\theta = 0.$$

50. Since $\sin \phi < \phi$ for $\phi > 0$,

$$\int_{0}^{\frac{\pi}{2}} \frac{1}{\sin \phi} \, d\phi > \int_{0}^{\frac{\pi}{2}} \frac{1}{\phi} \, d\phi,$$

The integral on the right diverges, so the integral on the left must also. Alternatively, we use IV-20 in the integral table to get

$$\int_{0}^{\frac{\pi}{2}} \frac{1}{\sin \phi} \, d\phi = \lim_{b \to 0+} \int_{b}^{\frac{\pi}{2}} \frac{1}{\sin \phi} \, d\phi$$

$$= \lim_{b \to 0+} \frac{1}{2} \ln \left| \frac{\cos \phi - 1}{\cos \phi + 1} \right| \Big|_{b}^{\frac{\pi}{2}}$$

$$= -\frac{1}{2} \lim_{b \to 0+} \ln \left| \frac{\cos b - 1}{\cos b + 1} \right|.$$

As $b \to 0^+$, $\cos b - 1 \to 0$ and $\cos b + 1 \to 2$, so $\ln \left| \frac{\cos b - 1}{\cos b + 1} \right| \to -\infty$. Thus the integral diverges.

51. Substituting $w = t + 5$, we see that our integral is just $\int_0^{15} \frac{dw}{\sqrt{w}}$. This will converge, since $\int_0^b \frac{dw}{w^p}$ converges for $0 < p < 1$. We find its exact value:

$$\int_0^{15} \frac{dw}{\sqrt{w}} = \lim_{a \to 0^+} \int_a^{15} \frac{dw}{\sqrt{w}} = \lim_{a \to 0^+} 2w^{\frac{1}{2}} \Big|_a^{15} = 2\sqrt{15}.$$

52. Let $\phi = 2\theta$. Then $d\phi = 2 \, d\theta$, and

$$\int_0^{\frac{\pi}{4}} \tan 2\theta \, d\theta = \int_0^{\frac{\pi}{2}} 2 \tan \phi \, d\phi = \int_0^{\frac{\pi}{2}} 2 \frac{\sin \phi}{\cos \phi} \, d\phi$$

$$= \lim_{b \to (\pi/2)^-} \int_0^b 2 \frac{\sin \phi}{\cos \phi} \, d\phi = \lim_{b \to (\pi/2)^-} -2 \ln |\cos \phi| \, \Big|_0^b.$$

As $b \to \pi/2$, $\cos \phi \to 0$, so $\ln |\cos \phi| \to -\infty$. Thus the integral diverges.

One could also see this by noting that $\cos x \approx \pi/2 - x$ and $\sin x \approx 1$ for x close to $\pi/2$: therefore, $\tan x \approx 1/(\frac{\pi}{2} - x)$, the integral of which diverges.

53. This function is difficult to integrate, so instead we try to compare it with some other function. Since $\frac{\sin^2 \theta}{\theta^2 + 1} \geq 0$, we see that $\int_0^\infty \frac{\sin^2 \theta}{\theta^2 + 1} \, d\theta \geq 0$. Also, since $\sin^2 \theta \leq 1$,

$$\int_0^\infty \frac{\sin^2 \theta}{\theta^2 + 1} \, d\theta \leq \int_0^\infty \frac{1}{\theta^2 + 1} \, d\theta = \lim_{b \to \infty} \arctan \theta \, \Big|_0^b = \frac{\pi}{2}.$$

Thus $\int_0^\infty \frac{\sin^2 \theta}{\theta^2 + 1} \, d\theta$ converges, and its value is between 0 and $\frac{\pi}{2}$.

54. $\int_0^\pi \tan^2 \theta \, d\theta = \tan \theta - \theta + C$, by formula IV-23. The integrand blows up at $\theta = \frac{\pi}{2}$, so

$$\int_0^\pi \tan^2 \theta \, d\theta = \int_0^{\frac{\pi}{2}} \tan^2 \theta \, d\theta + \int_{\frac{\pi}{2}}^\pi \tan^2 \theta \, d\theta = \lim_{b \to \frac{\pi}{2}} [\tan \theta - \theta]_0^b + \lim_{a \to \frac{\pi}{2}} [\tan \theta - \theta]_a^\pi$$

which is undefined.

55. Since $0 \leq \sin x < 1$ for $0 \leq x \leq 1$, we have

$$(\sin x)^{\frac{3}{2}} < (\sin x)$$

$$\text{so} \quad \frac{1}{(\sin x)^{\frac{3}{2}}} > \frac{1}{(\sin x)}$$

$$\text{or} \quad (\sin x)^{-\frac{3}{2}} > (\sin x)^{-1}$$

Thus $\int_0^1 (\sin x)^{-1} \, dx = \lim_{a \to 0} \ln \left| \frac{1}{\sin x} - \frac{1}{\tan x} \right| \, \Big|_a^1$, which is infinite.

Hence, $\int_0^1 (\sin x)^{-\frac{3}{2}} \, dx$ is infinite.

56. The integrand $\dfrac{x}{x+1} \to 1$ as $x \to \infty$, so there's no way $\displaystyle\int_1^\infty \dfrac{x}{x+1}\, dx$ can converge.

57. (a) $\displaystyle\int_0^\infty \sqrt{x}\, e^{-x}\, dx \approx 0.8862269\ldots$ [It turns out that $\int_0^\infty \sqrt{x}\, e^{-x}\, dx = \frac{\sqrt{\pi}}{2}$]

   (b) $\displaystyle\int_1^\infty \ln\left(\dfrac{e^x+1}{e^x-1}\right) dx = 0.747402\ldots$

58. (a)   (i) $\displaystyle\int \ln x\, dx = x\ln x - x + C$. It is helpful to develop the following:

$$\text{(ii)} \int (\ln x)^n\, dx = x(\ln x)^n - n\int (\ln x)^{n-1}\, dx.$$

This comes from integrating by parts, with

$$u = (\ln x)^n, \qquad v' = 1, \qquad u' = \frac{n}{x}(\ln x)^{n-1}, \qquad v = x.$$

We will use this reduction formula to find each new integral.

$$\int (\ln x)^2\, dx = x(\ln x)^2 - 2\int \ln x\, dx$$
$$= x(\ln x)^2 - 2[x\ln x - x] + C$$
$$= x(\ln x)^2 - 2x\ln x + 2x + C$$

(iii)

$$\int (\ln x)^3\, dx = x(\ln x)^3 - 3\int (\ln x)^2\, dx$$
$$= x(\ln x)^3 - 3\left[x(\ln x)^2 - 2x\ln x + 2x\right] + C$$
$$= x(\ln x)^3 - 3x(\ln x)^2 + 6x\ln x - 6x + C$$

(iv)

$$\int (\ln x)^4\, dx = x(\ln x)^4 - 4\left[x(\ln x)^3 - 3x(\ln x)^2 + 6x\ln x - 6x\right] + C$$
$$= x(\ln x)^4 - 4x(\ln x)^3 + 12x(\ln x)^2 - 24x\ln x + 24x + C$$

(b) The integrals are all improper, because $\ln x \to -\infty$ as $x \to 0^+$. Note, however, that by letting $t = \frac{1}{x}$, we find that for any positive integer n,

$$\lim_{x\to 0^+} x^n \ln x = \lim_{t\to\infty} \frac{\ln\frac{1}{t}}{t^n} = \lim_{t\to\infty} -\frac{\ln t}{t^n} = 0,$$

since $\ln t$ grows so much more slowly than t^n.

(i)

$$\int_0^1 \ln x \, dx = \lim_{a \to 0+} \left[x \ln x - x \right]_a^1 = -1 - \lim_{a \to 0+} a \ln a = -1 - 0 = -1$$

(ii)

$$\int_0^1 (\ln x)^2 \, dx = \lim_{a \to 0+} \left[x(\ln x)^2 - 2x \ln x + 2x \right]_a^1 = 2 - \lim_{a \to 0+} \left(a(\ln a)^2 - 2a \ln a + 2a \right) = 2$$

Notice that in the rest of these, when you plug in $x = 1$, the $\ln x$ terms all drop out, and $\lim_{a \to 0+}$ (all terms) $= 0$, so

(iii) $\int_0^1 (\ln x)^3 \, dx = -6$,

(iv) $\int_0^1 (\ln x)^4 \, dx = 24$.

(c)   As you may have already guessed, $\int_0^1 (\ln x)^n \, dx = (-1)^n n!$, $n = 0, 1, 2, \ldots$

59.   It will be helpful to have the following:

$$\int x^n e^{-x} \, dx = -x^n e^{-x} + n \int x^{n-1} e^{-x} \, dx.$$

To show this, integrate by parts with $u = x^n$ and $v' = e^{-x}$, so $u' = nx^{n-1}$ and $v = -e^{-x}$. Then

$$\int x^n e^{-x} = x^n(-e^{-x}) - \int nx^{n-1}(-e^{-x}) \, dx$$

$$= -x^n e^{-x} + \int nx^{n-1} e^{-x} \, dx.$$

Thus

$$\int e^{-x} \, dx = -e^{-x} + C$$

$$\int xe^{-x} \, dx = -xe^{-x} - e^{-x} + C$$

$$\int x^2 e^{-x} \, dx = -x^2 e^{-x} - 2xe^{-x} - 2e^{-x} + C$$

$$\int x^3 e^{-x} \, dx = -x^3 e^{-x} - 3x^2 e^{-x} - 6xe^{-x} - 6e^{-x} + C.$$

Note that $\lim_{x \to \infty} \frac{x^n}{e^x} = 0$ for any positive integer n. We now calculate the improper integrals:

$$\int_0^\infty e^{-x}\,dx = \lim_{b \to \infty} \left[-e^{-x}\right]\Big|_0^b = 1.$$

$$\int_0^\infty xe^{-x}\,dx = \lim_{b \to \infty} \left[-xe^{-x} - e^{-x}\right]\Big|_0^b = 1.$$

$$\int_0^\infty x^2 e^{-x}\,dx = \lim_{b \to \infty} \left[-x^2 e^{-x} - 2xe^{-x} - 2e^{-x}\right]\Big|_0^b = 2.$$

$$\int_0^\infty x^3 e^{-x}\,dx = \lim_{b \to \infty} \left[-x^3 e^{-x} - 3x^2 e^{-x} - 6xe^{-x} - 6e^{-x}\right] = 6.$$

It seems that $\int_0^\infty x^n e^{-x}\,dx = n!$.

60. (a) $f(x) = 1 + e^{-x}$ is concave up for $0 \le x \le 0.5$, so trapezoids will overestimate $\int_0^{0.5} f(x)dx$, and the midpoint rule will underestimate.

(b) $f(x) = e^{-x^2}$ is concave down for $0 \le x \le 0.5$, so trapezoids will underestimate $\int_0^{0.5} f(x)dx$ and midpoint will overestimate the integral.

(c) Both the trapezoid rule and the midpoint rule will give the exact value of the integral. Note that upper and lower sums will not, unless the line is horizontal.

61. Let's assume that TRAP(10) and TRAP(50) are either both overestimates or both underestimates. Since TRAP(50) is more accurate, and it is bigger than TRAP(10), both are underestimates. Since TRAP(50) is 25 times more accurate, we have

$$I - \text{TRAP}(10) = 25(I - \text{TRAP}(50)),$$

where I is the value of the integral. Solving for I, we have

$$I \approx \frac{25\,\text{TRAP}(50) - \text{TRAP}(10)}{24} \approx 4.6969$$

Thus the error for TRAP(10) is approximately 0.0078.

62. Let us assume that SIMP(5) and (10) are both overestimates or both underestimates. Then since SIMP(10) is more accurate and bigger than SIMP(5), they are both underestimates. Since SIMP(10) is 16 times more accurate,

$$I - \text{SIMP}(5) = 16(I - \text{SIMP}(10)).$$

Solving for I, we have

$$I = \frac{16\text{SIMP}(10) - \text{SIMP}(5)}{15} \approx 7.4175.$$

63. (a) $F(\pi) = \displaystyle\int_0^{\pi} \sin 2t \, dt = -\frac{1}{2} \cos 2t \Big|_0^{\pi} = -\frac{1}{2}(1 - 1) = 0.$

(b) $F(\pi) = $ (area above t-axis) $-$ (area below t-axis) $= 0$. (The two areas are equal.)

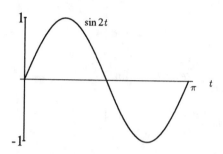

(c) $F(x) \geq 0$ everywhere. $F(x) = 0$ only at integer multiples of π. This can be seen for $x \geq 0$ since $F(x) = $ (area above t-axis) $-$ (area below t-axis), which is always non-negative and only equals zero when x is an integer multiple of π.
For $x > 0$

$$F(-x) = \int_0^{-x} \sin 2t \, dt$$

$$= -\int_{-x}^0 \sin 2t \, dt$$

$$= \int_0^x \sin 2t \, dt = F(x),$$

since the area from $-x$ to 0 is the negative of the area from 0 to x. So we have $F(x) \geq 0$ for all x.

64. (a) $F'(x) = \frac{1}{\ln x}$ by the Fundamental Construction Theorem.

(b) For $x \geq 2$, $F'(x) > 0$, so $F(x)$ is increasing. $F''(x) = -\frac{1}{x(\ln x)^2} < 0$ for $x \geq 2$, whence $F(x)$ is concave down.

(c) See graph:

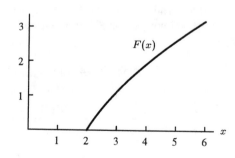

65.

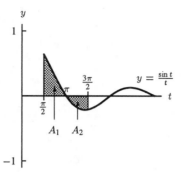

Figure 7.11

$F(x)$ represents the net area between $\frac{\sin t}{t}$ and the t-axis from $t = \frac{\pi}{2}$ to $t = x$, with area counted as negative for $\frac{\sin t}{t}$ below the t-axis. As long as the integrand is positive $F(x)$ is increasing. Therefore, the global maximum of $F(x)$ occurs at $x = \pi$ and is given by the area

$$A_1 = \int_{\pi/2}^{\pi} \frac{\sin t}{t} \, dt.$$

At $x = \pi/2$, $F(x) = 0$. Figure 7.11 shows that the area A_1 is larger than the area A_2. Thus $F(x) > 0$ for $\frac{\pi}{2} < x \le \frac{3\pi}{2}$. Therefore the global minimum is $F(\frac{\pi}{2}) = 0$.

66. If $e^t \ge 1 + t$, then

$$e^x = 1 + \int_0^x e^t \, dt$$

$$\ge 1 + \int_0^x (1 + t) \, dt$$

$$= 1 + x + \frac{1}{2}x^2.$$

Of course, we can keep going: since $e^t \ge 1 + t + \frac{1}{2}t^2$,

$$e^x = 1 + \int_0^x e^t \, dt$$

$$\ge 1 + \int_0^x (1 + t + \frac{1}{2}t^2) \, dt$$

$$= 1 + x + \frac{1}{2}x^2 + \frac{1}{6}x^3.$$

We notice that each term in our summation is of the form $\frac{x^n}{n!}$.

Furthermore, we see that if we have a sum $1 + x + \frac{x^2}{2} + \cdots + \frac{x^n}{n!}$ such that

$$e^x \ge 1 + x + \frac{x^2}{2} + \cdots + \frac{x^n}{n!},$$

then

$$e^x = 1 + \int_0^x e^t \, dt$$

$$\geq 1 + \int_0^x \left(1 + t + \frac{t^2}{2} + \cdots + \frac{t^n}{n!}\right) dt$$

$$= 1 + x + \frac{x^2}{2} + \frac{x^3}{6} + \cdots + \frac{x^{n+1}}{(n+1)!}.$$

Thus we can continue this process as far as we want, so

$$e^x \geq 1 + x + \frac{1}{2}x^2 + \cdots + \frac{1}{n!}x^n = \sum_{j=0}^n \frac{x^j}{j!} \text{ for any } n.$$

(In fact, it turns out that if you were to let n get larger and larger and keep adding up the terms, your values would approach exactly e^x.)

67. We note that $\sin x = \int_0^x \cos t \, dt$ and $\cos x = 1 - \int_0^x \sin t \, dt$. Thus, since $\cos t \leq 1$, we have

$$\sin x \leq \int_0^x 1 \, dt$$
$$= x.$$

Now using $\sin t \leq t$, we have

$$\cos x \leq 1 - \int_0^x t \, dt$$
$$= 1 - \frac{1}{2}x^2.$$

Then we just keep going:

$$\sin x \leq \int_0^x \left(1 - \frac{1}{2}t^2\right) dt$$
$$= x - \frac{1}{6}x^3.$$

Therefore

$$\cos x \leq 1 - \int_0^x \left(t - \frac{1}{6}t^3\right) dt = 1 - \frac{1}{2}x^2 + \frac{1}{24}x^4.$$

CHAPTER EIGHT

1. (a) Suppose we choose an x, $0 \leq x \leq 2$. If Δx is a small fraction of a meter, then the density of the rod is approximately $\rho(x)$ anywhere from x to $x + \Delta x$ meters from the left end of the rod. The mass of the rod from x to $x + \Delta x$ meters is therefore approximately $\rho(x)\Delta x$.

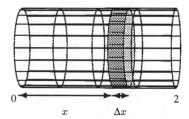

$$0 \xleftrightarrow{\hspace{3cm}} \hspace{0.5cm} 2$$

$$\hspace{1cm} x \hspace{2cm} \Delta x$$

   (b) The definite integral is

$$M = \int_0^2 \rho(x)\, dx = \int_0^2 (2 + 6x)\, dx = (2x + 3x^2)\Big|_0^2 = 16 \text{ grams}.$$

2. We have

$$\text{Moment} = \int_0^2 x\rho(x)\, dx = \int_0^2 x(2 + 6x)\, dx$$

$$= \int_0^2 (6x^2 + 2x)\, dx = (2x^3 + x^2)\Big|_0^2$$

$$= 20 \text{ gram-meters}.$$

Now, using this and Problem 1 (b), we have

$$\text{Center of Mass} = \frac{\text{moment}}{\text{total mass}} = \frac{20 \text{ gram-meters}}{16 \text{ grams}}$$

$$= \frac{5}{4} \text{ meters (from its left end)}.$$

3. (a)

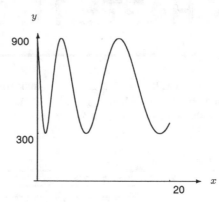

(b) Suppose we choose an x, $0 \le x \le 20$. We approximate the density of the number of the cars between x and $x + \Delta x$ miles as $p(x)$ cars per mile. Therefore the number of cars between x and $x + \Delta x$ is approximately $p(x)\Delta x$.

   If we slice the 20 mile strip into N slices, we get that the total number of cars is $C \approx \sum_{i=1}^{N} p(x_i)\Delta x = \sum_{i=1}^{N} \left[600 + 300 \sin(4\sqrt{x_i + 0.15})\right] \Delta x$, where $\Delta x = 20/N$. (This is a right-hand approximation; the corresponding left-hand approximation is $\sum_{i=0}^{N-1} p(x_i)\Delta x$.)

(c) As $N \to \infty$, the Riemann sum above approaches the integral

$$C = \int_0^{20} \left(600 + 300 \sin 4\sqrt{x + 0.15}\right) dx.$$

If we approximate the integral using one of our approximation methods (like Simpson's rule) we find $C \approx 11513$.

We can also find the integral exactly as follows:

$$C = \int_0^{20} \left(600 + 300 \sin 4\sqrt{x + 0.15}\right) dx$$

$$= \int_0^{20} 600 \, dx + \int_0^{20} 300 \sin 4\sqrt{x + 0.15} \, dx$$

$$= 12000 + 300 \int_0^{20} \sin 4\sqrt{x + 0.15} \, dx.$$

Let $w = \sqrt{x + 0.15}$, so $x = w^2 - 0.15$ and $dx = 2w \, dw$. Then

$$\int_{x=0}^{x=20} \sin 4\sqrt{x + 0.15} \, dx = 2 \int_{w=\sqrt{0.15}}^{w=\sqrt{20.15}} w \sin 4w \, dw,$$

using integral table formula 15

$$= 2 \left[-\frac{1}{4} w \cos 4w + \frac{1}{16} \sin 4w \right] \Bigg|_{\sqrt{0.15}}^{\sqrt{20.15}}$$

$$\approx -1.624$$

Using this, we have $C \approx 12000 + 300(-1.624) \approx 11513$, which matches our numerical approximation.

4. (a) We must find where the population density is zero. The density is given by the function

$$10{,}000(3 - r);$$

if $10{,}000(3 - r) = 0$, then we must have $r = 3$. We thus conclude that the radius of Circle City is 3 miles. (Note that for $r > 3$, $10{,}000(3 - r)$ becomes negative, so at that point, our function no longer gives a meaningful representation of population density.)

(b) We refer to Example 5 in this section, with $f(r) = 10{,}000(3 - r)$. The population is approximated by a sum

$$\sum 2\pi r \cdot 10{,}000(3 - r)\Delta r.$$

Since the city radius is 3 miles, r ranges from 0 to 3. Hence as $\Delta r \to 0$, the sum is given by the integral

$$\int_0^3 2\pi r \cdot 10{,}000(3 - r)\, dr.$$

This integral evaluates to $9\pi \cdot 10{,}000 \approx 282{,}743$. So we can say that the population of Circle City is approximately 282,743.

5. (a) Partition $0 \le r \le 8$ into eight subintervals of width $\Delta r = 1$ mile. Note that $r_i = i$. Let $y_i = \#$ of people living in the ith subinterval and $y = $ the total population. Then $y_i \approx \rho(r_i)A_i$, where $A_i = $ area in the ith subinterval. $A_i \approx 2\pi r_i \Delta r/2 = \pi r_i = \pi i$. So $y_i \approx \rho(i) \cdot \pi i$, and the total population will be approximately

$$y \approx \sum_{i=0}^{7} \pi i \rho(i) = \pi[0(75) + 1(75) + 2(67.5) + 3(60) + 4(52.5) + 5(45) + 6(37.5) + 7(30)]$$

$$\approx 3.96 \text{ million people.}$$

(b) We expect our estimate to be an underestimate for several reasons. First, intuitively, the fact that the first term in our sum is 0, when we know the population in the first mile is some positive number, leads us to believe we are underestimating. Second, $(\pi r\rho(r))$, the function we are approximating, although not increasing over the whole interval $0 \le r \le 8$, is mostly increasing. We thus expect our left-hand sum to be an underestimate. Finally, A_i is actually $\pi(i + \frac{1}{2})$, not πi. (Check this.) Our underestimate in the areas (the A_i's) also causes our result to be an underestimate.

(c) For r between 1 and 8, $\rho(r) = 75 - 7.5(r - 1) = 82.5 - 7.5r$. Assuming the population density is constant for $0 \le r \le 1$, the number of people living within the first mile is $\frac{\pi}{2}(75)$ thousand. In the next seven miles, the total population is approximately

$$\int_1^8 \pi r(82.5 - 7.5r)\,dr = \left[\frac{82.5\pi}{2}r^2 - \frac{7.5\pi}{3}r^3\right]_1^8 \approx 4.15 \text{ million.}$$

Then $y \approx \left(\dfrac{\pi}{2}\dfrac{(75)}{1000} + 4.15\right)$ million ≈ 4.27 million.

6. (a) Partition $[0, 10{,}000]$ into N subintervals of width Δr. The area in the ith subinterval is $\approx 2\pi r_i \Delta r$.
        So the total mass in the slick $= M \approx \sum_{i=1}^{N} 2\pi r_i \left(\frac{50}{1+r_i}\right) \Delta r$.

    (b) $M = \displaystyle\int_0^{10{,}000} 100\pi \frac{r}{1+r} dr$. We may rewrite $\frac{r}{1+r}$ as $\frac{1+r}{1+r} - \frac{1}{1+r} = 1 - \frac{1}{1+r}$, so that

    $$M = \int_0^{10{,}000} 100\pi\left(1 - \frac{1}{1+r}\right) dr = 100\pi \left(r - \ln|1+r|\Big|_0^{10{,}000}\right)$$

    $$= 100\pi(10{,}000 - \ln(10{,}001)) \approx 3.14 \times 10^6 \text{ kg}.$$

    (c) We wish to find an R such that

    $$\int_0^R 100\pi \frac{r}{1+r} dr = \frac{1}{2} \int_0^{10{,}000} 100\pi \frac{r}{1+r} dr \approx 1.57 \times 10^6.$$

    So $100\pi(R - \ln|R+1|) \approx 1.57 \times 10^6$; $R - \ln|R+1| \approx 5000$. By trial and error, we find $R \approx 5009$ meters.

7. (a) Orient the rectangle in the coordinate plane in such a way that the side referred to in the problem — call it S — lies on the y-axis from $y = 0$ to $y = 5$, as shown in the figure. We may subdivide the rectangle into strips of width Δx and length 5. If the left side of a given strip is a distance x away from S (i.e., the y-axis), its density 2 is $1/(1+x^4)$. If Δx is small enough, the density of the strip is approximately constant – i.e., the density of the whole strip is about $1/(1+x^4)$. The mass of the strip is just its density times its area, or $5\Delta x/(1+x^4)$. Thus the mass of the whole rectangle is approximated by the left Riemann sum

    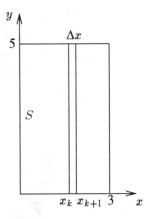

    $$\sum_{k=0}^{n-1} \frac{5\Delta x}{1+x_k^4},$$

    Figure 8.1: Slicing the Rectangle

        where $0 = x_0 < x_1 < x_2 < \ldots < x_{n-1} < x_n = 3$ and $\Delta x = x_k - x_{k-1}$. (Since the density function $1/(1+x^4)$ is strictly decreasing on the entire interval, the left Riemann sum overestimates the mass.) If we had used the right hand side of each strip in approximating its density, we would have obtained the right Riemann sum

    $$\sum_{k=1}^{n} \frac{5\Delta x}{1+x_k^4},$$

    which is an underestimate of the mass.

(b) The exact mass of the rectangle is obtained by letting $\Delta x \to 0$ in the Riemann sums above, giving us the integral

$$\int_0^3 \frac{5\,dx}{1 + x^4}.$$

Since it is not easy to find an antiderivative of $5/(1 + x^4)$, we evaluate this integral numerically. Because the integrand is decreasing, we know that the value of the integral is between the left and right hand sums. For $n = 256$, the right sum is 5.46 and the left sum is 5.52; since both of these quantities are 5.5 to one decimal place, then the exact mass must be 5.5 to one decimal place as well.

8. Partition $a \le x \le b$ into N subintervals of width $\Delta x = \dfrac{(b - a)}{N}$; $a = x_0 < x_1 < \ldots < x_N = b$. The mass of the strip on the ith subinterval is approximately $m_i = \rho(x_i)[f(x_i) - g(x_i)]\Delta x$. If we use a right-hand Riemann sum, the approximation for the total mass is

$$\sum_{i=1}^{N} \rho(x_i)[f(x_i) - g(x_i)]\Delta x, \text{ and the exact mass is } M = \int_a^b \rho(x)[f(x) - g(x)]dx.$$

9. First we rewrite the chart, listing the density with the corresponding distance from the center of the earth (x km below the surface is equivalent to $6370 - x$ km from the center):

This gives us spherical shells whose volumes are $\frac{4}{3}\pi(r_i^3 - r_{i+1}^3)$ for any two consecutive distances from the origin. We will assume that the density of the earth is increasing with depth. Therefore, the average density of the ith shell is between D_i and D_{i+1}, the densities at top and bottom of shell i. So $\frac{4}{3}\pi D_{i+1}(r_i^3 - r_{i+1}^3)$ and $\frac{4}{3}\pi D_i(r_i^3 - r_{i+1}^3)$ are upper and lower bounds for the mass of the shell.

TABLE 8.1

i	x_i	$r_i = 6370 - x_i$	D_i
0	0	6370	3.3
1	1000	5370	4.5
2	2000	4370	5.1
3	2900	3470	5.6
4	3000	3370	10.1
5	4000	2370	11.4
6	5000	1370	12.6
7	6000	370	13.0
8	6370	0	13.0

To get a rough approximation of the mass of the earth, we don't need to use all the data. Let's just use the densities at $x = 0, 2900, 5000$ and 6370 km. Calculating an upper bound on the mass,

$$M_U = \frac{4}{3}\pi[13.0(1370^3 - 0^3) + 12.6(3470^3 - 1370^3) + 5.6(6370^3 - 3470^3)] \cdot 10^{15} \approx 7.29 \times 10^{27} \text{ g}.$$

The factor of 10^{15} may appear unusual. Remember the radius is given in kilometers and the density is given in g/cm^3, so we must convert kilometers to centimeters: 1 km $= 10^5$ cm , so 1 km$^3 = 10^{15}$ cm^3.

The lower bound is

$$M_L = \frac{4}{3}\pi[12.6(1370^3 - 0^3) + 5.6(3470^3 - 1370^3) + 3.3(6370^3 - 3470^3)] \cdot 10^{15} \approx 4.05 \times 10^{27} \text{ g}.$$

Here, our upper bound is just under 2 times our lower bound.

Using all our data, we can find a more accurate estimate. The upper and lower bounds are

$$M_U = \frac{4}{3}\pi \sum_{i=0}^{7} D_{i+1}(r_i^3 - r_{i+1}^3) \cdot 10^{15} \text{ g}$$

and

$$M_L = \frac{4}{3}\pi \sum_{i=0}^{7} D_i(r_i^3 - r_{i+1}^3) \cdot 10^{15} \text{ g}.$$

We have

$$\begin{aligned}
M_U = \frac{4}{3}\pi[&4.5(6370^3 - 5370^3) + 5.1(5370^3 - 4370^3) + 5.6(4370^3 - 3470^3) \\
&+ 10.1(3470^3 - 3370^3) + 11.4(3370^3 - 2370^3) + 12.6(2370^3 - 1370^3) \\
&+ 13.0(1370^3 - 370^3) + 13.0(370^3 - 0^3)] \cdot 10^{15} \text{ g} \\
\approx\;& 6.50 \times 10^{27} \text{ g}.
\end{aligned}$$

and

$$\begin{aligned}
M_L = \frac{4}{3}\pi[&3.3(6370^3 - 5370^3) + 4.5(5370^3 - 4370^3) + 5.1(4370^3 - 3470^3) \\
&+ 5.6(3470^3 - 3370^3) + 10.1(3370^3 - 2370^3) + 11.4(2370^3 - 1370^3) \\
&+ 12.6(1370^3 - 370^3) + 13.0(370^3 - 0^3)] \cdot 10^{15} \text{ g} \\
\approx\;& 5.46 \times 10^{27} \text{ g}.
\end{aligned}$$

10. (a) Partition $0 \le h \le 100$ into N subintervals of width $\Delta h = \dfrac{100}{N}$. The density is taken to be approximately $\rho(h_i)$ on the ith spherical shell, and the volume is approximately the surface area of a sphere of radius $r_e + h_i$ meters times Δh, where $r_e = 6.37 \times 10^6$ meters is the radius of the earth. If the volume of the ith shell is V_i, then $V_i \approx 4\pi(r_e + h_i)^2\Delta h$, and a left-hand Riemann sum for the total mass is

$$M \approx \sum_{i=0}^{N-1} 4\pi(r_e + h_i)^2 \times 1.28e^{-0.000124h_i}\Delta h.$$

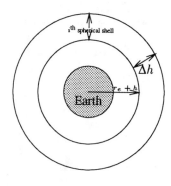

Figure 8.2

(b) This Riemann sum becomes the integral

$$M = 4\pi \int_0^{100} (r_e + h)^2 \times 1.28e^{-0.000124h}\, dh$$

$$= 4\pi \int_0^{100} (6.37 \times 10^6 + h)^2 \times 1.28e^{-0.000124h}\, dh.$$

Evaluating the integral using numerical methods gives $M = 6.48 \times 10^{16}$ kg.

11. We want to take a cross-section of the pipe and cut it up in such a way that the speed of the water is nearly uniform on each slice. We will use thin rings around the pipe's center; if a given ring is narrow enough, all points on it will be roughly equidistant from the center. Since the water speed is a function of the distance from the center, it will be nearly constant on the entire ring.

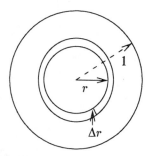

Let r be the distance from the center to the inner boundary of the ring, and let Δr be the width of the ring, as in the figure above. By straightening the ring into a thin rectangle, we find that its area is approximately given by the quantity $2\pi r\Delta r$. The speed across any part of the ring is roughly equal to the speed across the inner boundary, $10(1 - r^2)$ inches per second. The flow is defined as the speed times the area; thus on any given ring we have

$$\text{Flow} \approx 10(1 - r^2) \cdot 2\pi r\Delta r.$$

The total flow across the pipe cross-section is approximated by a Riemann sum incorporating all of the rings:

$$\text{Total Flow} \approx 20\pi \sum (1 - r^2)r\Delta r,$$

where r is in between 0 and 1. Letting $\Delta r \to 0$, we obtain the exact solution:

$$\text{Total Flow} = 20\pi \int_0^1 (1 - r^2)r\, dr = 20\pi \left(\frac{r^2}{2} - \frac{r^4}{4}\right)\bigg|_0^1 = 5\pi \text{ cubic inches/second.}$$

8.2 SOLUTIONS

1. Vertical slices are circular. Horizontal slices would be similar to ellipses in cross-section, or at least ovals (a word derived from *ovum*, the Latin word for egg).

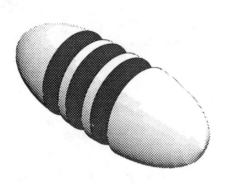

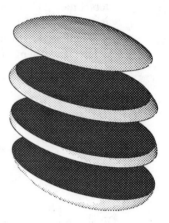

2.

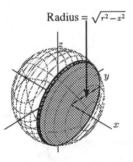

Radius $= \sqrt{r^2 - x^2}$

We slice up the sphere in planes perpendicular to the x-axis. Each slice is a circle, with radius $y = \sqrt{r^2 - x^2}$; that's the radius because $x^2 + y^2 = r^2$ when $z = 0$. Then the volume is

$$V \approx \sum \pi(y^2)\,\Delta x = \sum \pi(r^2 - x^2)\,\Delta x.$$

Therefore, as Δx tends to zero, we get

$$V = \int_{x=-r}^{x=r} \pi(r^2 - x^2)\,dx$$
$$= 2\int_{x=0}^{x=r} \pi(r^2 - x^2)\,dx$$
$$= 2\left(\pi r^2 x - \frac{\pi x^3}{3}\right)\Big|_0^r$$
$$= \frac{4\pi r^3}{3}.$$

3.

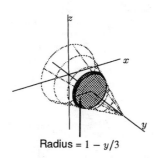

Radius $= 1 - y/3$

Slice parallel to the base of the cone, or, equivalently, rotate the line $x = (3 - y)/3$ about the y–axis. (One can also slice the other way.) The the volume V is given by

$$V = \int_{y=0}^{y=3} \pi x^2 \, dy = \int_0^3 \pi \left(\frac{3-y}{3} \right)^2 dy$$

$$= \int_0^3 \left(1 - \frac{2y}{3} + \frac{y^2}{9} \right) dy$$

$$= \pi \left(y - \frac{y^2}{3} + \frac{y^3}{27} \right) \bigg|_0^3 = \pi.$$

4.

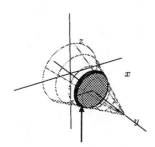

Radius $= \frac{r(h-y)}{h}$

This cone is what you get when you rotate the line $x = r(h - y)/h$ about the y–axis. So slicing perpendicular to the y–axis yields

$$V = \int_{y=0}^{y=h} \pi x^2 \, dy = \pi \int_0^h \left(\frac{(h-y)r}{h} \right)^2 dy$$

$$= \pi \frac{r^2}{h^2} \int_0^h (h^2 - 2hy + y^2) \, dy$$

$$= \frac{\pi r^2}{h^2} \left[h^2 y - hy^2 + \frac{y^3}{3} \right] \bigg|_0^h = \frac{\pi r^2 h}{3}.$$

5.

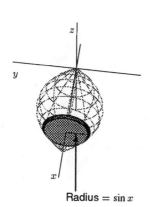

Radius $= \sin x$

We take slices perpendicular to the x–axis. The Riemann sum for approximating the volume is $\sum \pi \sin^2 x \Delta x$. The volume is the integral corresponding to that sum, namely

$$V = \int_0^\pi \pi \sin^2 x \, dx$$

$$= \pi \left[-\frac{1}{2} \sin x \cos x + \frac{1}{2} x \right] \bigg|_0^\pi = \frac{\pi^2}{2} \approx 4.935.$$

6.

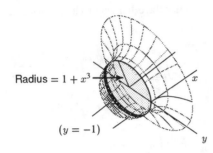

Radius = $1 + x^3$

($y = -1$)

We slice the region perpendicular to the x–axis. The Riemann sum we get is $\sum \pi(x^3+1)^2 \Delta x$. So the volume V is the integral

$$V = \int_{-1}^{1} \pi(x^3 + 1)^2\, dx$$

$$= \pi \int_{-1}^{1} (x^6 + 2x^3 + 1)\, dx$$

$$= \pi \left(\frac{x^7}{7} + \frac{x^4}{2} + x \right) \Big|_{-1}^{1}$$

$$= (16/7)\pi \approx 7.18.$$

7.

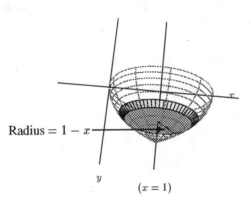

Radius = $1 - x$

($x = 1$)

We slice the region perpendicular to the y–axis. The Riemann sum we get is $\sum \pi(1 - x)^2 \Delta y = \sum \pi(1 - y^2)^2 \Delta y$. So the volume V is the integral

$$V = \int_{0}^{1} \pi(1 - y^2)^2\, dy$$

$$= \pi \int_{0}^{1} (1 - 2y^2 + y^4)\, dy$$

$$= \pi \left(y - \frac{2y^3}{3} + \frac{y^5}{5} \right) \Big|_{0}^{1}$$

$$= (8/15)\pi \approx 1.68.$$

8.

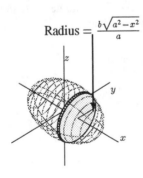

Radius = $\frac{b\sqrt{a^2 - x^2}}{a}$

$$y^2 = b^2 \left(1 - \frac{x^2}{a^2} \right).$$

$$V = \int_{-a}^{a} \pi y^2\, dx = \pi \int_{-a}^{a} b^2 \left(1 - \frac{x^2}{a^2} \right) dx$$

$$= 2\pi b^2 \int_{0}^{a} \left(1 - \frac{x^2}{a^2} \right) dx = 2\pi b^2 \left[x - \frac{x^3}{3a^2} \right]_{0}^{a}$$

$$= 2\pi b^2 \left(a - \frac{a^3}{3a^2} \right) = 2\pi b^2 \left(a - \frac{1}{3}a \right)$$

$$= \frac{4}{3}\pi ab^2.$$

9.

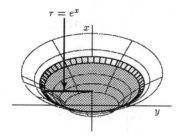

This is the volume of revolution gotten from the rotating the curve $y = e^x$. Take slices perpendicular to the x-axis. They will be circles with radius e^x, so

$$V = \int_{x=0}^{x=1} \pi y^2 \, dx = \pi \int_0^1 e^{2x} \, dx$$

$$= \left. \frac{\pi e^{2x}}{2} \right|_0^1 = \frac{\pi(e^2 - 1)}{2} \approx 10.036.$$

10.

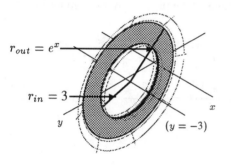

We slice the volume with planes perpendicular to the line $y = -3$. This divides the curve into thin washers, as in Example 5, whose volumes are

$$\pi r_{\text{out}}^2 dx - \pi r_{\text{in}}^2 dx = \pi(3 + y)^2 dx - \pi 3^2 dx.$$

So the integral we get from adding all these washers up is

$$V = \int_{x=0}^{x=1} [\pi(3 + y)^2 - \pi 3^2] \, dx$$

$$= \pi \int_0^1 [(3 + e^x)^2 - 9] \, dx$$

$$= \pi \int_0^1 [e^{2x} + 6e^x] \, dx = \pi[\frac{e^{2x}}{2} + 6e^x] \Big|_0^1$$

$$= \pi[(e^2/2 + 6e) - (1/2 + 6)] \approx 42.42.$$

11.

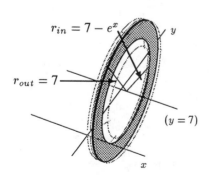

This problem can be done by slicing the volume into washers with planes perpendicular to the axis of rotation, $y = 7$, just like in Example 5. This time the outside radius of a washer is 7, and the inside radius is $7 - e^x$. Therefore, the volume V is

$$V = \int_{x=0}^{x=1} [\pi 7^2 - \pi(7 - e^x)^2] \, dx = \pi \int_0^1 (14e^x - e^{2x}) \, dx$$

$$= \pi \left[14e^x - \frac{1}{2} e^{2x} \right] \Big|_0^1 = \pi \left[14e - \frac{1}{2} e^2 - \left(14 - \frac{1}{2} \right) \right]$$

$$\approx 65.54.$$

12.

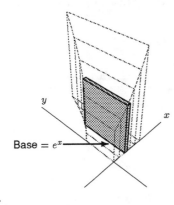

Base $= e^x$

We now slice perpendicular to the x-axis. As stated in the problem, the cross-sections obtained thereby will be squares, with base length e^x. The volume of one square slice is $(e^x)^2\, dx$. (Look at the picture.) Adding up the volumes of the slices yields

$$\text{Volume } = \int_{x=0}^{x=1} y^2\, dx = \int_0^1 e^{2x}\, dx$$

$$= \left. \frac{e^{2x}}{2} \right|_0^1 = \frac{e^2 - 1}{2} \approx 3.195.$$

13.

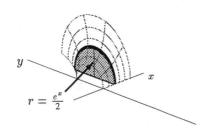

$r = \dfrac{e^x}{2}$

We slice perpendicular to the x-axis. As stated in the problem, the cross-sections obtained thereby will be semicircles, with radius $\frac{e^x}{2}$. The volume of one semicircular slice is $\frac{1}{2}\pi \left(\frac{e^x}{2}\right)^2\, dx$. (Look at the picture.) Adding up the volumes of the slices yields

$$\text{Volume } = \int_{x=0}^{x=1} \pi \frac{y^2}{2}\, dx = \frac{\pi}{8} \int_0^1 e^{2x}\, dx$$

$$= \left. \frac{\pi e^{2x}}{16} \right|_0^1 = \frac{\pi(e^2 - 1)}{16} \approx 1.25.$$

14. If $y = e^{-x^2/2}$, then $x = \sqrt{-2\ln y}$. (Note that since $0 < y \le 1$, $\ln y \le 0$.) A typical slice has thickness Δy and radius x.

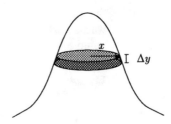

So

$$\text{Volume of slice } = \pi x^2\, \Delta y = -2\pi \ln y\, \Delta y.$$

Thus,

$$\text{Total volume} = -2\pi \int_0^1 \ln y \, dy.$$

Since $\ln y$ is not defined at $y = 0$, this is an improper integral:

$$\text{Total Volume} = -2\pi \int_0^1 \ln y \, dy = -2\pi \lim_{a \to 0} \int_a^1 \ln y \, dy$$

$$= -2\pi \lim_{a \to 0} (y \ln y - y) \Big|_a^1 = -2\pi \lim_{a \to 0} (-1 - a \ln a + a).$$

By looking at the graph of $x \ln x$ on a calculator, we see that $\lim_{a \to 0} a \ln a = 0$. Thus,

$$\text{Total volume} = -2\pi(-1) = 2\pi.$$

15. We want to approximate $\int_0^{120} A(h) \, dh$, where h is height, and $A(h)$ represents the cross-sectional area of the trunk at height h. Since $A = \pi r^2$ (circular cross-sections), and $c = 2\pi r$, where c is the circumference, we have $A = \pi r^2 = \pi[c/(2\pi)]^2 = c^2/(4\pi)$. We make a table of $A(h)$ based on this:

TABLE 8.2

height (feet)	0	20	40	60	80	100	120
Area (square feet)	53.79	38.52	28.73	15.60	2.865	0.716	0.080

We now form left & right sums using the chart:

$$\text{LEFT}(6) = 53.79 \cdot 20 + 38.52 \cdot 20 + 28.73 \cdot 20 + 15.60 \cdot 20 + 2.865 \cdot 20 + 0.716 \cdot 20$$
$$= 2804.42.$$
$$\text{RIGHT}(6) = 38.52 \cdot 20 + 28.73 \cdot 20 + 15.60 \cdot 20 + 2.865 \cdot 20 + 0.716 \cdot 20 + 0.080 \cdot 20$$
$$= 1730.22$$

So

$$\text{TRAP}(6) = \frac{\text{RIGHT}(6) + \text{LEFT}(6)}{2} = \frac{2804.42 + 1730.22}{2} = 2267.32 \text{ cubic feet.}$$

16. Although we could work this problem by using the formula for the volume of a right pyramid with a square base, we'll find the volume of the dump by using slices instead. The slices will be squares, and we'll start slicing at the base of the pyramid. The side of a square slice at the base is 100 yards; for every yard above the base, the side of the square slice decreases by 1 yard. Therefore, the side of a slice y yards above the base is $(100 - y)$, and the volume of the slice is $(100 - y)^2 \Delta y$.

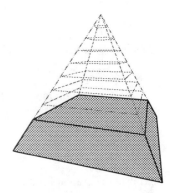

Figure 8.3: Garbage Dump

Thus, the volume of the dump is

$$V = \int_0^{20} (100 - y)^2 \, dy$$

$$= \int_0^{20} (100^2 - 200y + y^2) \, dy$$

$$= \left(10{,}000y - 100y^2 + \frac{y^3}{3} \right) \Big|_0^{20}$$

$$\approx 162{,}666.67 \text{ cubic yards.}$$

If 65 cubic yards arrive at the dump every day, then 365(65) cubic yards arrive each year. This means it will take approximately

$$\frac{162{,}667}{365(65)} \approx 6.87 \text{ years}$$

for the dump to fill up.

17. The problem appears complicated, because we are now working in three dimensions. However, if we take one dimension at a time, we will see that the solution is not too difficult. For example, let's just work at a constant depth, say 0. We apply the trapezoid rule to find the approximate area along the length of the boat. For example, by the trapezoid rule the approximate area at depth 0 from the front of the boat to 10 feet toward the back is $\frac{(2+8)\cdot 10}{2} = 50$. Overall, at depth 0 we have that the area for each length span is as follows:

TABLE 8.3

length span:	0–10	10–20	20–30	30–40	40–50	50–60
depth 0	50	105	145	165	165	130

We can fill in the whole chart the same way:

TABLE 8.4

length span:		0–10	10–20	20–30	30–40	40–50	50–60
	0	50	105	145	165	165	130
	2	25	60	90	105	105	90
depth	4	15	35	50	65	65	50
	6	5	15	25	35	35	25
	8	0	5	10	10	10	10

Now, to find the volume, we just apply the trapezoid rule to the depths and areas. For example, according to the trapezoid rule the approximate volume as the depth goes from 0 to 2 and the length goes from 0 to 10 is $\frac{(50+25)\cdot 2}{2} = 75$. Again, we fill in a chart:

TABLE 8.5

length span:		0–10	10–20	20–30	30–40	40–50	50–60
	0–2	75	165	235	270	270	220
depth	2–4	40	95	140	170	170	140
span	4–6	20	50	75	100	100	75
	6–8	5	20	35	45	45	35

Adding all this up, we find the volume is approximately 2595 cubic feet.

You might wonder what would have happened if we had done our trapezoids along the depth axis first instead of along the length axis. If you try this, you'd find that you come up with the same answers in the volume chart! For the trapezoid rule, it doesn't matter which axis you choose first.

18. This is a one-quarter of the circumference of a circle of radius 2. That circumference is $2 \cdot 2\pi = 4\pi$, so the length is $\frac{4\pi}{4} = \pi$.

19. Note that this function is actually $x^{3/2}$ in disguise. So

$$L = \int_0^2 \sqrt{1 + \left[\frac{3}{2}x^{\frac{1}{2}}\right]^2}\, dx = \int_{x=0}^{x=2} \sqrt{1 + \frac{9}{4}x}\, dx$$

$$= \frac{4}{9} \int_{w=1}^{w=\frac{11}{2}} w^{\frac{1}{2}}\, dw$$

$$= \frac{8}{27} w^{\frac{3}{2}}\Big|_1^{\frac{11}{2}} = \frac{8}{27}\left(\left(\frac{11}{2}\right)^{\frac{3}{2}} - 1\right) \approx 3.526,$$

where we set $w = 1 + \frac{9}{4}x$, so $dx = \frac{4}{9}dw$.

20. (a) The equation of a circle of radius r around the origin is $x^2 + y^2 = r^2$. This means that $y^2 = r^2 - x^2$, so $2y(dy/dx) = -2x$, and $dy/dx = -x/y$. Since the circle is symmetric about both axes, its arc length is 4 times the arc length in the first quadrant, namely

$$4 \int_0^r \sqrt{1 + \left(\frac{dy}{dx}\right)^2} \, dx = 4 \int_0^r \sqrt{1 + \left(-\frac{x}{y}\right)^2} \, dx.$$

(b) Evaluating this integral yields

$$4 \int_0^r \sqrt{1 + \left(-\frac{x}{y}\right)^2} \, dx = 4 \int_0^r \sqrt{1 + \frac{x^2}{r^2 - x^2}} \, dx = 4 \int_0^r \sqrt{\frac{r^2}{r^2 - x^2}} \, dx$$

$$= 4r \int_0^r \sqrt{\frac{1}{r^2 - x^2}} \, dx = 4r(\arcsin(x/r)) \Big|_0^r = 2\pi r.$$

This is the expected answer.

21. Since $y = (e^x + e^{-x})/2$, $y' = (e^x - e^{-x})/2$. The length of the catenary is

$$\int_{-1}^1 \sqrt{1 + (y')^2} \, dx = \int_{-1}^1 \sqrt{1 + \left[\frac{e^x - e^{-x}}{2}\right]^2} \, dx = \int_{-1}^1 \sqrt{1 + \frac{e^{2x}}{4} - \frac{1}{2} + \frac{e^{-2x}}{4}} \, dx$$

$$= \int_{-1}^1 \sqrt{\left[\frac{e^x + e^{-x}}{2}\right]^2} \, dx = \int_{-1}^1 \frac{e^x + e^{-x}}{2} \, dx$$

$$= \left[\frac{e^x - e^{-x}}{2}\right] \Big|_{-1}^1 = e - e^{-1} \approx 2.35.$$

22.

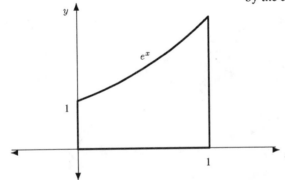

As you can see, the region has three straight sides and one curved o
The lengths of the straight sides are 1, 1, and e. The curved side is gi
by the equation $y = f(x) = e^x$. We can find its length by the formula

$$\int_0^1 \sqrt{1 + f'(x)^2} \, dx = \int_0^1 \sqrt{1 + (e^x)^2} \, dx$$

$$= \int_0^1 \sqrt{1 + e^{2x}} \, dx.$$

But this is hard to integrate, so we approximate. Using Simpson's rule with $n = 10$ and $n = 20$ intervals, we find the integral ≈ 2.003. We could also approximate the integral by noting the the second

derivative of $g(x) = \sqrt{1 + e^{2x}}$ is $g''(x) = \dfrac{e^{4x} + 2e^{2x}}{(1 + e^{2x})^{3/2}}$. Thus our integrand is concave up, so the trapezoid rule gives an overestimate and the midpoint rule gives an underestimate. TRAP(20) = 2.0038 ... and MID(10) = 2.0033 ..., so 2.003 is correct within 0.001. The total length, therefore, is about $1 + 1 + e + 2.003 \approx 6.7212$. (Note that we use e to 4 decimal places to ensure that the total roundoff error is less than 0.001.)

23. Since the ellipse is symmetric about its axes, we can just find its arc length in the first quadrant and multiply that by 4. To determine the arc length of this section, we first solve for y in terms of x: since $x^2/4 + y^2 = 1$ is the equation for the ellipse, we have $y^2 = 1 - x^2/4$, so $y = \sqrt{1 - x^2/4}$. We also need to find dy/dx; we can do this by differentiating $y^2 = 1 - x^2/4$ implicitly, obtaining $2y\,dy/dx = -x/2$, whence $dy/dx = -x/(4y)$. We now set up the integral:

$$\text{length} = \int_0^2 \sqrt{1 + \left(-\frac{x}{4y}\right)^2}\,dx = \int_0^2 \sqrt{1 + \frac{x^2}{16y^2}}\,dx$$

$$= \int_0^2 \sqrt{1 + \frac{x^2}{16 - 4x^2}}\,dx = \int_0^2 \sqrt{\frac{16 - 3x^2}{16 - 4x^2}}\,dx.$$

This is an improper integral, since $16 - 4x^2 = 0$ for $x = 2$. Hence, integrating it numerically is somewhat tricky. None of the methods we have studied will work in this case. However, what we *can* do is numerically integrate from 0 to 1.999, and then use a vertical line to approximate the last section. The upper point of the line is $(1.999, 0.016)$; the lower point is $(2, 0)$. The length of the line connecting these two points is $\sqrt{(2 - 1.999)^2 + (0 - 0.016)^2} \approx 0.016$. Approximating the integral from 0 to 1.999 gives 2.391; hence the total arc length of the first quadrant is approximately 2.391 + 0.016 = 2.407. So the arc length of the whole ellipse is about 9.63.

24. Here are many functions which "work".

- Any linear function $y = mx + b$ "works". This follows because $\frac{dy}{dx} = m$ is constant for such functions. So

$$\int_a^b \sqrt{1 + \left(\frac{dy}{dx}\right)^2}\,dx = \int_a^b \sqrt{1 + m^2}\,dx = (b - a)\sqrt{1 + m^2}.$$

- The function $y = \frac{x^4}{8} + \frac{1}{4x^2}$ "works": $\frac{dy}{dx} = \frac{1}{2}(x^3 - 1/x^3)$, and

$$\int \sqrt{1 + \left(\frac{dy}{dx}\right)^2}\,dx = \int \sqrt{1 + \frac{\left(x^3 - \frac{1}{x^3}\right)^2}{4}}\,dx = \int \sqrt{1 + \frac{x^6}{4} - \frac{1}{2} + \frac{1}{4x^6}}\,dx$$

$$= \int \sqrt{\frac{1}{4}\left(x^3 + \frac{1}{x^3}\right)^2}\,dx = \int \frac{1}{2}\left(x^3 + \frac{1}{x^3}\right)\,dx$$

$$= \left[\frac{x^4}{8} - \frac{1}{4x^2}\right] + C.$$

- One more function that "works" is $y = \ln(\cos x)$; we have $\frac{dy}{dx} = -\sin x / \cos x$. Hence

$$\int \sqrt{1 + \left(\frac{dy}{dx}\right)^2} \, dx. = \int \sqrt{1 + \left(\frac{-\sin x}{\cos x}\right)^2} \, dx = \int \sqrt{1 + \frac{\sin^2 x}{\cos^2 x}} \, dx$$

$$= \int \sqrt{\frac{\sin^2 x + \cos^2 x}{\cos^2 x}} \, dx = \int \sqrt{\frac{1}{\cos^2 x}} \, dx$$

$$= \int \frac{1}{\cos x} \, dx = \frac{1}{2} \ln \left| \frac{\sin x + 1}{\sin x - 1} \right| + C,$$

where the last integral comes from Formula 22 of the integral tables.

25. (a) If $f(x) = \int_0^x \sqrt{g'(t)^2 - 1} \, dt$, then, by the Fundamental Theorem of Calculus, $f'(x) = \sqrt{g'(x)^2 - 1}$. So the arc length of f from 0 to x is

$$\int_0^x \sqrt{1 + (f'(t))^2} \, dt = \int_0^x \sqrt{1 + (\sqrt{g'(t)^2 - 1})^2} \, dt$$

$$= \int_0^x \sqrt{1 + g'(t)^2 - 1} \, dt$$

$$= \int_0^x g'(t) \, dt = g(x) - g(0) = g(x).$$

(b) If g is the arc length of any function f, then by the Fundamental Theorem of Calculus, $g'(x) = \sqrt{1 + f'(x)^2} \geq 1$. So if $g'(x) < 1$, g cannot be the arc length of a function.

(c) We find a function f whose arc length from 0 to x is $g(x) = 2x$. Using part (a), we see that

$$f(x) = \int_0^x \sqrt{(g'(t))^2 - 1} \, dt = \int_0^x \sqrt{2^2 - 1} \, dt = \sqrt{3}x.$$

This is the equation of a line. Does it make sense to you that the arc length of a line segment depends linearly on its right endpoint?

8.3 SOLUTIONS

1. Let x be the distance measured from the bottom the
    tank. It follows that $0 \leq x \leq 10$. To pump a layer
    of water of thickness Δx at x feet from the bottom,
    the work needed is $62.4\pi6^2(20 - x)\Delta x$. Therefore, the
    total work is

    $$W = \int_0^{10} 36 \cdot 62.4\pi(20 - x)dx$$

    $$= 36 \cdot 62.4\pi(20x - \frac{1}{2}x^2)\Big|_0^{10}$$

    $$= 36 \cdot 62.4\pi(200 - 50)$$

    $$\approx 1,058,591.1 \text{ ft-lb.}$$

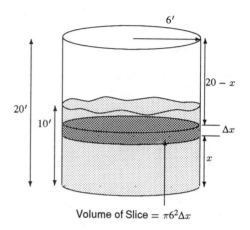

Volume of Slice $= \pi6^2\Delta x$

2. Let x be the distance from the bottom
    of the tank to the surface of the water.
    It follows that $0 \leq x \leq 20$. To pump
    a layer of water of thickness Δx at x
    feet from the bottom to 10 feet above
    the tank, the work done is $62.4\pi6^2(30 - x)\Delta x$. Thus the total work is

    $$\int_0^{20} 36 \cdot 62.4\pi(30 - x)dx$$

    $$= 36 \cdot 62.4\pi\left(30x - \frac{1}{2}x^2\right)\Big|_0^{20}$$

    $$= 36 \cdot 62.4\pi(30(20) - \frac{1}{2}20^2)$$

    $$\approx 2,822,909.50 \quad \text{ft-lb.}$$

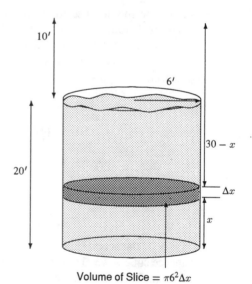

Volume of Slice $= \pi6^2\Delta x$

Figure 8.4

3. Consider lifting a rectangular slab of water h feet from the top up to the top. The area of such a slab is
    $(10)(20) = 200$ square feet; if the thickness is dh, then the volume of such a slab is $200\,dh$ cubic feet.
    This much water weighs 62.4 pounds per ft^3, so the weight of such a slab is $(200\,dh)(62.4) = 12480\,dh$
    pounds. To lift that much water h feet requires $12480h\,dh$ foot-pounds of work. To lift the whole tank,
    we lift one plate at a time; integrating over the slabs yields

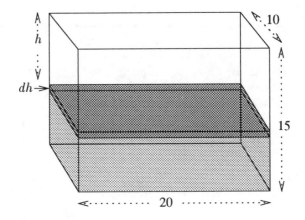

$$\int_0^{15} 12480h\, dh = \left.\frac{12480h^2}{2}\right|_0^{15} = \frac{12480 \cdot 15^2}{2} = 1{,}404{,}000 \text{ foot-pounds.}$$

4. Let x be the distance from ground to the bucket of cement. It follows that $0 \le x \le 30$. At height x, if the bucket is lifted by Δx, the work done is $500\Delta x + 5(75 - x)\Delta x$. The $500\Delta x$ term is due to the bucket of cement; the $5(75 - x)\Delta x$ term is due to the remaining cable. So the total work required to lift the bucket is

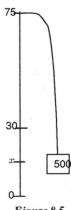

$$W = \int_0^{30} 500dx + \int_0^{30} 5(75 - x)dx$$

$$= (500)(30) + 5(75(30) - \frac{1}{2}30^2)$$

$$= 24000 \quad \text{ft-lb.}$$

Figure 8.5

5. Let x be the height (in feet) from ground to the cube of ice. It follows that $0 \le x \le 100$. At height x, the ice cube w weighs $2000 - 4x$ since it's being lifted at a rate 1 ft./min. and it's melting at a rate of 4 lb/min. To lift it Δx more the work required is $(2000 - 4x)\Delta x$. So the total work done is

$$W = \int_0^{100} (2000 - 4x)dx$$

$$= \left.(2000x - 2x^2)\right|_0^{100}$$

$$= 2000(100) - 2 \cdot (100)^2$$

$$= 180{,}000 \quad \text{ft-lb.}$$

6.

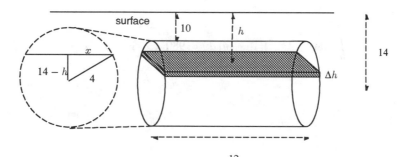

Figure 8.6

Let h represent distance below the surface in feet. We slice the tank up into horizontal slabs of thickness Δh. From looking at the figure, we can see that the slabs will be rectangular. The length of any slab is 12 feet. The width w of a slab h units below the ground will equal $2x$, where $(14-h)^2 + x^2 = 16$, so $w = 2\sqrt{4^2 - (14-h)^2}$. The volume of such a slab is therefore $12w\,\Delta h = 24\sqrt{16 - (14-h)^2}\,\Delta h$ cubic feet; the slab weighs $42 \cdot 24\sqrt{16 - (14-h)^2}\,\Delta h = 1008\sqrt{16 - (14-h)^2}\,\Delta h$ pounds. So the total work done in pumping out all the gasoline is

$$\int_{10}^{18} 1008h\sqrt{16 - (14-h)^2}\,dh = 1008\int_{10}^{18} h\sqrt{16 - (14-h)^2}\,dh.$$

Substitute $s = 14 - h$, $ds = -dh$. We get

$$1008\int_{10}^{18} h\sqrt{16 - (14-h)^2}\,dh = -1008\int_{4}^{-4} (14-s)\sqrt{16 - s^2}\,ds$$

$$= 1008 \cdot 14 \int_{-4}^{4} \sqrt{16 - s^2}\,ds - 1008\int_{-4}^{4} s\sqrt{16 - s^2}\,ds.$$

The first integral represents the area of a semicircle of radius 4, which is 8π. The second is the integral of an odd function, over the interval $-4 \le s \le 4$, and is therefore 0. Hence, the total work is $1008 \cdot 14 \cdot 8\pi \approx 354{,}673$ foot-pounds.

7. Cut the wine into horizontal pieces. Let y denote height above the top of the glass stem. In this case, each layer is a circular disc of thickness Δy and base area πx^2, where $x = y/2$ by the similar triangles in Figure 8.7. The volume of the disc is $\pi x^2\,\Delta y$, so the mass of the disc of wine is $1.2\pi x^2\,\Delta y$ grams. This means that the force due to gravity acting on this mass (i.e., its weight) is $980(1.2\pi x^2\Delta y)$ dynes.

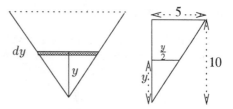

Figure 8.7: A Cold Look at Wine

To get that layer of liquid to the top of the straw, we must raise it a height of $15 - y$. Thus the total work is

$$\int_0^8 980(1.2\pi x^2)(15 - y)\,dy = 980(1.2\pi)\int_0^8 \frac{y^2}{4}(15 - y)\,dy$$

$$= 294\pi\int_0^8 (15y^2 - y^3)\,dy = 294\pi\left(5y^3 - \frac{y^4}{4}\right)\Big|_0^8$$

$$\approx 1{,}418{,}693 \text{ ergs (about 0.142 joules).}$$

8.   The force exerted on the satellite by the earth (and vice versa!) is GMm/r^2, where r is the distance from the center of the earth to the center of the satellite, m is the mass of the satellite, M is the mass of the earth, and G is the gravitational constant. So the total work done is

$$\int_{6.4\times10^6}^{8.4\times10^6} \frac{GMm}{r^2}\,dr = \left(\frac{-GMm}{r}\right)\Big|_{6.4\times10^6}^{8.4\times10^6} \approx 1.489\times10^{10} \text{ joules.}$$

9.   Setting the initial kinetic energy and escape work equal to each other gives

$$\frac{1}{2}mv^2 = \frac{GMm}{R}, \text{ or } v^2 = \frac{2GM}{R}.$$

Since the planet is assumed to be a sphere of radius R and density ρ, we have $M = \rho(\frac{4}{3}\pi)R^3$. Hence

$$v^2 = \frac{2G\rho(\frac{4}{3}\pi)R^3}{R}$$

and therefore

$$v = k\sqrt{\rho}R$$

where $k = \sqrt{\frac{8\pi G}{3}}$. That is, the escape velocity is proportional to R and $\sqrt{\rho}$.

10.   On page 441 of the text it is stated that:

$$v = \sqrt{\frac{2GM}{R}}$$

where M is the mass of the planet we're trying to leave—in this case, the Moon. Since the force on a mass m on the surface of the moon is $F = mg = GMm/R^2$, we have $GM/R = gR$. Therefore,

$$v = \sqrt{\frac{2GM}{R}} = \sqrt{2gR} = \sqrt{2(1.6)(1740\cdot10^3)} \approx 2360 \text{ m/sec.}$$

11. (a) Divide the wall into N horizontal strips, each of which is of height Δh. The area of each strip is $1000\Delta h$, and the pressure at depth h_i is $62.4h_i$, so we approximate the pressure on the strip as $1000(62.4h_i)\Delta h$.

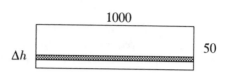

Therefore,

$$\text{Force on the Dam} \approx \sum_{i=0}^{N-1} 1000(62.4h_i)\Delta h.$$

(b) As $N \to \infty$, the Riemann sum becomes the integral, so the force on the dam is

$$\int_0^{50} (1000)(62.4h)\, dh = 62400\frac{h^2}{2}\bigg|_0^{50} = 78{,}000{,}000 \text{ pounds.}$$

12.

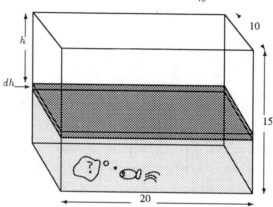

- Bottom: The bottom of the tank is at constant depth 15 feet, and therefore is under constant pressure, $15 \cdot 62.4 = 936 \text{ lb/ft}^2$. The area of the base is 200 ft^2 and so the total force is $200 \text{ ft}^2 \cdot 936 \text{ lb/ft}^2 = 187200 \text{ lb.}$

- 15×10 side: The area of a horizontal strip of width dh is $10\, dh$ square feet, and the pressure at height h is $62.4h$ pounds per square foot. Therefore, the force on such a strip is $62.4h(10\, dh)$ pounds. Hence, the total force on this side is

$$\int_0^{15} (62.4h)(10)\, dh = 624\frac{h^2}{2}\bigg|_0^{15} = 70200 \text{ lbs.}$$

- 15×20 side: Similarly, the total force on this side is

$$\int_0^{15} (62.4h)(20)\, dh = 1248\frac{h^2}{2}\bigg|_0^{15} = 140400 \text{ lbs.}$$

13.   We need to divide the disk up into circular rings of charge and integrate their contributions to the potential (at P) from 0 to a. These rings, however, are not uniformly distant from the point P. A ring of radius z is $\sqrt{R^2 + z^2}$ away from point P (See picture).

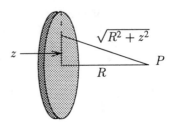

The ring has area $2\pi z\,\Delta z$, and charge $2\pi z\sigma\,\Delta z$. The potential of the ring is then $\dfrac{2\pi z\sigma\,\Delta z}{\sqrt{R^2 + z^2}}$ and the total potential at point P is

$$\int_0^a \frac{2\pi z\sigma\,dz}{\sqrt{R^2 + z^2}} = \pi\sigma \int_0^a \frac{2z\,dz}{\sqrt{R^2 + z^2}}.$$

We make the substitution $u = z^2$. Then $du = 2z\,dz$. We obtain

$$\pi\sigma \int_0^a \frac{2z\,dz}{\sqrt{R^2 + z^2}} = \pi\sigma \int_0^{a^2} \frac{du}{\sqrt{R^2 + u}} = \pi\sigma(2\sqrt{R^2 + u})\Big|_0^{a^2}$$

$$= \pi\sigma(2\sqrt{R^2 + z^2})\Big|_0^{a} = 2\pi\sigma(\sqrt{R^2 + a^2} - R).$$

(The substitution $u = R^2 + z^2$ or $\sqrt{R^2 + z^2}$ works also.)

14.   Pick a small interval of time Δt which takes place at time t. Fuel is consumed at a rate of $(25 + 0.1v)^{-1}$ gallons per mile. In the time Δt, the car moves $v\,\Delta t$ miles, so it consumes $v\,\Delta t/(25 + 0.1v)$ gallons during the instant Δt. Since $v = 50\frac{t}{t+1}$, the car consumes

$$\frac{v\,\Delta t}{25 + 0.1v} = \frac{50\frac{t}{t+1}\,\Delta t}{25 + 0.1\left(50\frac{t}{t+1}\right)} = \frac{50t\,\Delta t}{25(t+1) + 5t} = \frac{10t\,\Delta t}{6t + 5} = \left(\frac{5}{3} - \frac{25}{3(6t + 5)}\right)\Delta t$$

gallons of gas, in terms of the time t at which the instant occurs. To find the total gas consumed, sum up the instants in an integral:

$$\int_2^3 \left(\frac{5}{3} - \frac{25}{3(6t + 5)}\right)dt = \int_2^3 \frac{5}{3}\,dt - \int_2^3 \frac{25}{3(6t + 5)}\,dt$$

$$= \frac{5t}{3}\Big|_2^3 - \frac{25}{18}\ln|6t + 5|$$

$$= 5/3 - (25/18)(\ln 23 - \ln 17) \approx 1.25 \text{ gallons.}$$

15. The density of the rod is $10\text{ kg}/6\text{ m} = \frac{5}{3}\frac{\text{kg}}{\text{m}}$. A little piece, dx, of the rod thus has mass $5/3\,dx$. If this piece has an angular velocity of 2 rad/sec, then its actual velocity is $2|x|$ m/sec. This is because a radian angle sweeps out an arc length equal to the radius of the circle, and in this case the little piece moves in circles about the origin of radius $|x|$. The kinetic energy of the little piece is $mv^2/2 = (5/3\,dx)(2|x|)^2/2 = \frac{10}{3}x^2\,dx$.

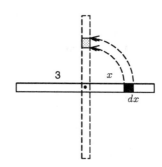

Therefore,

$$\text{Total Kinetic Energy} = \int_{-3}^{3}\frac{10x^2}{3}\,dx = \frac{20}{3}\left[\frac{x^3}{3}\right]\Big|_0^3 = 60\text{ kg}\cdot\text{m}^2/\text{sec}^2 = 60\text{ joules}.$$

16. We slice the record into rings in such a way that every point has approximately the same speed: use concentric circles around the hole. We assume the record is a flat disk of uniform density: since its mass is 50 grams, and has area $\pi(10\text{cm})^2 = 100\pi\text{ cm}^2$, the record has density $\frac{50}{100\pi} = \frac{1}{2\pi}\frac{\text{gram}}{\text{cm}^2}$. So a ring of width dr, having area about $2\pi r\,dr\text{ cm}^2$, has mass approximately $(2\pi r\,dr)(1/2\pi) = r\,dr$ gm. At radius r, the velocity of the ring is

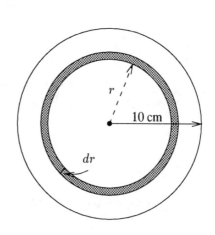

$$33\tfrac{1}{3}\frac{\text{rev}}{\text{min}}\cdot\frac{1\text{ min}}{60\text{ sec}}\cdot\frac{2\pi r\text{ cm}}{1\text{ rev}} = \frac{10\pi r}{9}\frac{\text{cm}}{\text{sec}}.$$

The kinetic energy of the ring is

$$\frac{1}{2}mv^2 = \frac{1}{2}(r\,dr\text{ grammes})\left(\frac{10\pi r}{9}\frac{\text{cm}}{\text{sec}}\right)^2 = \frac{50\pi^2 r^3\,dr}{81}\frac{\text{gram}\cdot\text{cm}^2}{\text{sec}^2}.$$

So the kinetic energy of the record, summing the energies of all these rings, is

$$\int_0^{10}\frac{50\pi^2 r^3\,dr}{81} = \frac{25\pi^2 r^4}{162}\Big|_0^{10} \approx 15231\frac{\text{gram}\cdot\text{cm}}{\text{sec}^2} = 15231\text{ ergs}.$$

17.

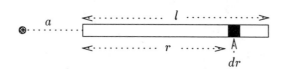

The density of the rod, in mass per unit length, is M/l. So a slice of size dr has mass $\frac{M\,dr}{l}$. It pulls the small mass m with force $Gm\frac{M\,dr}{l}/r^2 = \frac{GmM\,dr}{lr^2}$. So the total gravitational attraction between the rod and point is

$$\int_a^{a+l} \frac{GmM\,dr}{lr^2} = \frac{GmM}{l}\left(-\frac{1}{r}\right)\Big|_a^{a+l}$$

$$= \frac{GmM}{l}\left(\frac{1}{a}-\frac{1}{a+l}\right)$$

$$= \frac{GmM}{l}\frac{l}{a(a+l)} = \frac{GmM}{a(a+l)}.$$

18.

This time, let's split the second rod into small slices of length dr. Each slice is of mass $\frac{M_2}{l_2}\,dr$, since the density of the second rod is $\frac{M_2}{l_2}$. Since the slice is small, we can treat it as a particle at distance r away from the end of the first rod, as in Problem 17. By that problem, the force of attraction between the first rod and particle is

$$\frac{GM_1\frac{M_2}{l_2}\,dr}{(r)(r+l_1)}.$$

So the total force of attraction between the rods is

$$\int_a^{a+l_2} \frac{GM_1\frac{M_2}{l_2}\,dr}{(r)(r+l_1)} = \frac{GM_1M_2}{l_2}\int_a^{a+l_2}\frac{dr}{(r)(r+l_1)}$$

$$= \frac{GM_1M_2}{l_2}\int_a^{a+l_2}\frac{1}{l_1}\left(\frac{1}{r}-\frac{1}{r+l_1}\right)dr.$$

$$= \frac{GM_1M_2}{l_1l_2}\left(\ln|r|-\ln|r+l_1|\right)\Big|_a^{a+l_2}$$

$$= \frac{GM_1M_2}{l_1l_2}\left[\ln|a+l_2|-\ln|a+l_1+l_2|-\ln|a|+\ln|a+l_1|\right]$$

$$= \frac{GM_1M_2}{l_1l_2}\ln\left[\frac{(a+l_1)(a+l_2)}{a(a+l_1+l_2)}\right]$$

This result is symmetric: if you switch l_1 and l_2 or M_1 and M_2, you get the same answer. That means it's not important which rod is "first", and which is "second".

8.4 SOLUTIONS

1.

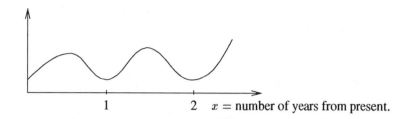

The graph reaches a peak each summer, and a trough each winter. The graph shows sunscreen sales increasing from cycle to cycle. This gradual increase may be due in part to inflation and to population growth.

2. Option 1:

$$\text{Future Value} = 5000e^{(.08)3} + 5000e^{(.08)2} + 5000e^{(.08)1} + 5000$$
$$\approx 6356.25 + 5867.55 + 5416.44 + 5000$$
$$= 22640.24$$

Option 2:

$$\text{Future Value} = 25000.$$

Choose Option 2.

However, other considerations include that the company might go bankrupt and so you should take as much as you can now. "A bird in the hand..."

3.

$$\text{Future Value} = \int_0^{15} 3000e^{0.06(15-t)}dt = 3000e^{0.9}\int_0^{15} e^{-0.06t}dt$$

$$= 3000e^{0.9}\left(\frac{1}{-0.06}e^{-0.06t}\right)\Bigg|_0^{15} = 3000e^{0.9}\left(\frac{1}{-0.06}e^{-0.9} + \frac{1}{0.06}e^0\right)$$

$$\approx \$72{,}980.16$$

$$\text{Present Value} = \int_0^{15} 3000e^{-0.06t}dt = 3000\left(-\frac{1}{0.06}\right)e^{-0.06t}\Bigg|_0^{15}$$

$$\approx \$29{,}671.52.$$

There's a quicker way to calculate the present value of the income stream, since the future value of the income stream is (as we've shown) $72,980.16, the present value of the income stream must be the present value of $72,980.16. Thus,

$$\text{Present Value} = \$72{,}980.16(e^{-.06 \cdot 15})$$
$$\approx \$29{,}671.52,$$

which is what we got before.

4.

$$\text{Present Value (after 10 years)} = \int_0^{10} (100 + 10t)e^{-.05t}\,dt$$

$$= 100 \int_0^{10} e^{-.05t}\,dt + 10 \int_0^{10} te^{-.05t}\,dt$$

$$= -\frac{100}{.05}\left(e^{-.05(10)} - 1\right) + 10\left(\frac{t}{-.05}e^{-.05t} - \frac{e^{-.05t}}{(-.05)^2}\right)\Big|_0^{10}$$

$$= 786.94 + 10(-363.92 + 400)$$

$$= \$1{,}147.75.$$

5. (a) Solve for $P(t) = P$.

$$100000 = \int_0^{10} Pe^{0.10(10-t)}\,dt = Pe \int_0^{10} e^{-0.10t}\,dt$$

$$= \frac{Pe}{-0.10}e^{-0.10t}\Big|_0^{10} = Pe(-3.678 + 10)$$

$$= P \cdot 17.183$$

So, $P \approx \$5820$ per year.

(b) To answer this, we'll calculate the present value of $100,000:

$$100000 = Pe^{0.10(10)}$$

$$P \approx \$36{,}787.94.$$

6. Price in future $= P(1 + 20\sqrt{t})$.

The present value V of price satisfies $V = P(1 + 20\sqrt{t})e^{-0.05t}$.

We want to maximize V. To do so, we find the critical points of $V(t)$ for $t \geq 0$. (Recall that $\sqrt{t}$ is nondifferentiable at $t = 0$.)

$$\frac{dV}{dt} = P\left[\frac{20}{2\sqrt{t}}e^{-0.05t} + (1 + 20\sqrt{t})(-0.05e^{-0.05t})\right]$$

$$= Pe^{-0.05t}\left[\frac{10}{\sqrt{t}} - 0.05 - \sqrt{t}\right].$$

Setting $\dfrac{dV}{dt} = 0$ gives $\dfrac{10}{\sqrt{t}} - 0.05 - \sqrt{t} = 0$. Using a calculator, we find $t_0 \approx 10$ years. Since $V'(t) > 0$ for $0 < x < 10$ and $V'(t) < 0$ for $x > 10$, we confirm that this is a maximum. Thus, the best time to sell the wine is in 10 years.

7. (a) Let L be the number of years for the balance to reach $10,000. Since our income stream is $1000 per year, the future value of this income stream should equal (in L years) $10,000. Thus

$$10000 = \int_0^L 1000e^{0.05(L-t)}dt = 1000e^{0.05L}\int_0^L e^{-0.05t}dt$$

$$= 1000e^{0.05L}\left(-\frac{1}{0.05}\right)e^{-0.05t}\Big|_0^L = 20000e^{0.05L}\left(1 - e^{-0.05L}\right)$$

$$= 20000e^{0.05L} - 20000$$

so $\quad e^{0.05L} = \frac{3}{2}$

$$L = 20\ln\left(\frac{3}{2}\right)$$

$$\approx 8.11 \text{ years.}$$

(b) We want

$$10000 = 2000e^{0.05L} + \int_0^L 1000e^{0.05(L-t)}dt$$

The first term on the right hand side is the future value of our initial balance. The second term is the future value of our income stream. We want this sum to equal $10,000 in L years. We solve for L:

$$10000 = 2000e^{0.05L} + 1000e^{0.05L}\int_0^L e^{-0.05t}dt$$

$$= 2000e^{0.05L} + 1000e^{0.05L}\left(\frac{1}{-0.05}\right)e^{-0.05t}\Big|_0^L$$

$$= 2000e^{0.05L} + 20000e^{0.05L}\left(1 - e^{-0.05L}\right)$$

$$= 2000e^{0.05L} + 20000e^{0.05L} - 20000$$

So,

$$22000e^{0.05L} = 30000$$

$$e^{0.05L} = \frac{30000}{22000}$$

$$L = 20\ln\frac{15}{11}$$

$$L \approx 6.203 \text{ years.}$$

8. (a) In the first case, we are given that $R_0 = 1000$ widgets/year. So we have $R = 1000e^{0.15t}$. To determine the total number sold, we need to integrate this rate over the time period from 0 to 10. So the total number of widgets sold is

$$\int_0^{10} 1000e^{0.15t}\,dt = \frac{1000}{0.15}e^{0.15t}\Big|_0^{10} = 6667(e^{1.5} - 1) = 23,211 \text{ widgets.}$$

In the second case, the total number of widgets sold is

$$\int_0^{10} 150,000,000 e^{0.15t}\, dt = 1,000,000,000 e^{0.15t}\Big|_0^{10} \approx 3.5 \text{ billion widgets.}$$

(b) We want to determine T such that

$$\int_0^T 1000 e^{0.15t}\, dt = \frac{23,211}{2}.$$

Evaluating both sides, we get

$$6667(e^{0.15T} - 1) = 11,606$$
$$6667 e^{0.15T} = 18273$$
$$e^{0.15T} = 2.740$$
$$0.15T = 1.01, \quad \text{so} \quad T = 6.7 \text{ years.}$$

Similarly, in the second case,

$$\int_0^T 150,000,000 e^{0.15t}\, dt = 3.5 \text{ billion.}$$

Evaluating both sides, we get

$$(1 \text{ billion})(e^{0.15T} - 1) = 1.75 \text{ billion}$$
$$e^{0.15T} = 2.75$$
$$T \approx 6.7 \text{ years}$$

So the half way mark is reached at the same time regardless of the initial rate.

(c) Since half the widgets are sold in the last $3\frac{1}{2}$ years of the decade, if each widget is expected to last $3\frac{1}{2}$ years, their claim could easily be true.

9. (a) Let's split the time interval into n parts, each of length Δt.

During the interval from t_i to t_{i+1}, profit is earned at a rate of approximately $(2 - 0.1t_i)$ thousand dollars per year, or $(2000 - 100t_i)$ dollars per year. Thus during this period, a total profit of $(2000 - 100t_i)\Delta t$ dollars is earned. Since this profit is earned t_i years in the future, its present value is $(2000 - 100t_i)\Delta t e^{-0.1t_i}$ dollars. Thus

$$\text{Total Present Value} \approx \sum_{i=0}^{n-1} (2000 - 100t_i)e^{-0.1t_i}\Delta t.$$

(b) The Riemann sum corresponds to the integral:

$$\int_0^T e^{-0.10t}(2000 - 100t)\, dt.$$

(c) To find where the present value is maximized, we take the derivative of

$$P(T) = \int_0^T e^{-0.10t}(2000 - 100t)\, dt,$$

and obtain

$$P'(T) = e^{-0.10T}(2000 - 100T).$$

This is 0 exactly when $2000 - 100T = 0$, that is, when $T = 20$ years. The value $T = 20$ maximizes $P(T)$, since $P'(T) > 0$ for $T < 20$, and $P'(T) < 0$ for $T > 20$. To determine what the maximum is, we evaluate the integral representation for $P(T)$ by formula III-14 in the integral table:

$$P(20) = \int_0^{20} e^{-0.10t}(2000 - 100t)\, dt$$

$$= \left[\frac{(2000 - 100t)}{-0.10}e^{-0.10t} + 10000e^{-0.10t} \right]\Big|_0^{20} \approx \$11353.35.$$

10. One good way to approach the problem is in terms of present values. In 1980, the present value of Germany's loan was 20 billion DM. Now let's figure out the rate that the Soviet Union would have to give money to Germany to pay off 10% interest on the loan by using the formula for the present value of a continuous stream. Since the Soviet Union sends gas at a constant rate, the rate of deposit, $P(t)$, is a constant c. Since they don't start sending the gas until after 5 years have passed, the present value of the loan is given by:

$$\text{Present Value} = \int_5^\infty P(t)e^{-rt}\, dt.$$

We want to find c so that

$$20{,}000{,}000{,}000 = \int_5^\infty ce^{-rt}\, dt = c\int_5^\infty e^{-rt}\, dt$$

$$= c\lim_{b\to\infty} (-10e^{-0.10t})\Big|_5^b = ce^{-0.10(5)} \approx 6.065c.$$

Dividing, we see that c should be about 3.3 billion DM per year. At 0.10 DM per m^3 of natural gas, the Soviet Union must deliver gas at the constant, continuous rate of about 33 billion m^3 per year.

11.

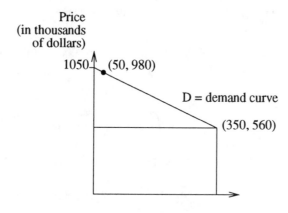

Quantity (number of cars)

Measuring money in thousands of dollars, the equation of the line representing the demand curve passes through (50, 980) and (350, 560). So the equation is $y - 560 = \frac{420}{-300}(x - 350)$, i.e. $y - 560 = -\frac{7}{5}x + 1050$.
The consumer surplus is thus

$$\int_0^{350} \left(-\frac{7}{5}x + 1050 \right) dx - (350)(560) = \left. -\frac{7}{10}x^2 + 1050x \right|_0^{350} - 196000$$

$$= 85750.$$

(Note that $85750 = \frac{1}{2} \cdot 490 \cdot 350$, the area of the triangle in the diagram. We thus could have avoided the formula for consumer surplus in solving the problem.)
Recalling that our unit measure for the price axis is $1000/car, the consumer surplus is $85,750,000.

12.

$$\int_0^{q^*} (p^* - S(q)) \, dq = \int_0^{q^*} p^* \, dq - \int_0^{q^*} S(q) \, dq$$

$$= p^* q^* - \int_0^{q^*} S(q) \, dq.$$

Using Problem 13, this integral is the extra amount consumers pay (i.e., suppliers earn over and above the minimum they would be willing to accept for supplying the good). It results from charging the equilibrium price.

13.

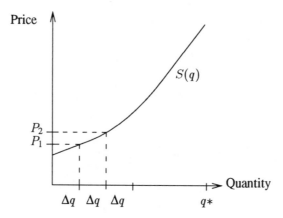

The supply curve, $S(q)$, represents the minimum price p per unit that the suppliers will be willing to supply some quantity q of the good for. If the suppliers have q^* of the good and q^* is divided into subintervals of size Δq, then if the consumers could offer the suppliers for each Δq a price increase just sufficient to induce the suppliers to sell an additional Δq of the good, the consumers' total expenditure on q^* goods would be

$$p_1 \Delta q + p_2 \Delta q + \cdots = \sum p_i \Delta q.$$

As $\Delta q \to 0$ the Riemann sum becomes the integral $\int_0^{q^*} S(q)\, dq$. Thus $\int_0^{q^*} S(q)\, dq$ is the amount the consumers would pay if suppliers could be forced to sell at the lowest price they would be willing to accept.

14. (a) $p^* q^* =$ the total amount paid for q^* of the good at equilibrium.

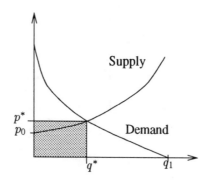

(b) $\int_0^{q^*} D(q)\, dq$ = the maximum consumers would be willing to pay if they had to pay the highest price acceptable to them for each additional unit of the good.

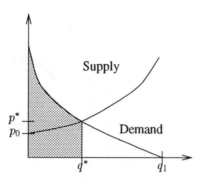

(c) $\int_0^{q^*} S(q)\, dq$ = the minimum suppliers would be willing to accept if they were paid the minimum price acceptable to them for each additional unit of the good.

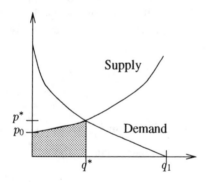

(d) $\int_0^{q^*} D(q)\, dq - p^* q^*$ = consumer surplus.

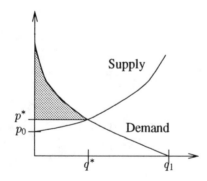

(e) $p^* q^* - \int_0^{q^*} S(q)\, dq$ = producer surplus.

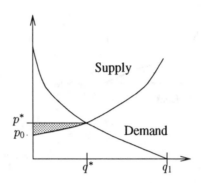

(f) $\int_0^{q^*} (D(q) - S(q))\, dq$ = producer surplus and consumer surplus.

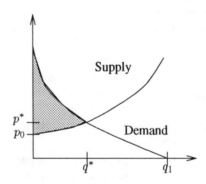

8.5   SOLUTIONS

1.

% of population
per dollar of income

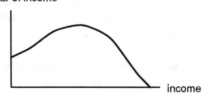

income

Figure 8.8: Density function

% of population having
at least this income

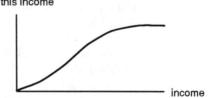

income

Figure 8.9: Cumulative distribution function

2.

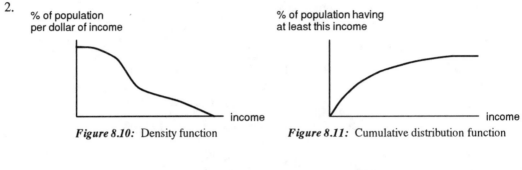

% of population
per dollar of income

% of population having
at least this income

Figure 8.10: Density function

Figure 8.11: Cumulative distribution function

3.

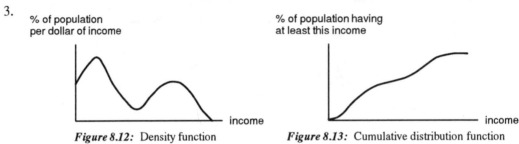

% of population
per dollar of income

% of population having
at least this income

Figure 8.12: Density function

Figure 8.13: Cumulative distribution function

4. No. Though the density function has its maximum value at 50, this does not mean that a large fraction of the population receives scores near 50. The value $p(50)$ can not be interpreted as a probability. Probability corresponds to *area* under the graph of a density function. Most of the area in this case is in the broad hump covering the range $0 \leq x \leq 40$, very little in the peak around $x = 50$. Most people score in the range $0 \leq x \leq 40$.

5. (a) Let $P(x)$ be the cumulative distribution function of the heights of the unfertilized plants. As do all cumulative distribution functions, $P(x)$ rises from 0 to 1 as x increases. The greatest number of plants will have heights in the range where $P(x)$ rises the most. The steepest rise appears to occur at about $x = 1$ m. Reading from the graph we see that $P(0.9) \approx 0.2$ and $P(1.1) \approx 0.8$, so that approximately $P(1.1) - P(0.9) = 0.8 - 0.2 = 0.6 = 60\%$ of the unfertilized plants grow to heights between 0.9 m and 1.1 m. Most of the plants grow to heights in the range 0.9 m to 1.1 m.

   (b) Let $P_A(x)$ be the cumulative distribution function of the plants that were fertilized with A. Since $P_A(x)$ rises the most in the range 0.7 m $\leq x \leq$ 0.9 m, many of the plants fertilized with A will have heights in the range 0.7 m to 0.9 m. Reading from the graph of P_A, we find that $P_A(0.7) \approx 0.2$ and $P_A(0.9) \approx 0.8$, so $P_A(0.9) - P_A(0.7) \approx 0.8 - 0.2 = 0.6 = 60\%$ of the plants fertilized with A have heights between 0.7 m and 0.9 m. Fertilizer A had the effect of stunting the growth of the plants.

   On the other hand, the cumulative distribution function $P_B(x)$ of the heights of the plants fertilized with B rises the most in the range 1.1 m $\leq x \leq$ 1.3 m, so most of these plants have heights in the range 1.1 m to 1.3 m. Fertilizer B caused the plants to grow about 0.2 m taller than they would have with no fertilizer.

6. (a) The percentage of calls lasting from 1 to 2 minutes is given by the integral

$$\int_1^2 p(x)\, dx = \int_1^2 0.4e^{-0.4x}\, dx = e^{-0.4} - e^{-0.8} \approx 22.1\%.$$

(b) A similar calculation (changing the limits of integration) gives the percentage of calls lasting 1 minute or less as

$$\int_0^1 p(x)\, dx = \int_0^1 0.4e^{-0.4x}\, dx = 1 - e^{-0.4} \approx 33.0\%.$$

(c) The percentage of calls lasting 3 minutes or more is given by the improper integral

$$\int_3^\infty p(x)\, dx = \lim_{b \to \infty} \int_3^b 0.4e^{-0.4x}\, dx = \lim_{b \to \infty} \left(e^{-1.2} - e^{-0.4b}\right) = e^{-1.2} \approx 30.1\%.$$

(d) The cumulative distribution function is the integral of the probability density; thus,

$$C(h) = \int_0^h p(x)\, dx = \int_0^h 0.4e^{-0.4x}\, dx = 1 - e^{-0.4h}.$$

7. (a)

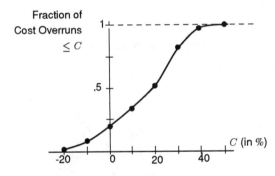

Fraction of Cost Overruns $\leq C$

This is a cumulative distribution function.

(b) The density function is the derivative of the cumulative distribution function.

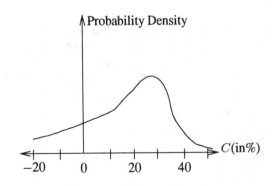

Probability Density

(c) Let's call the cumulative distribution function $F(C)$. The probability that there will be a cost overrun of more than 50% is $1 - F(50) = 0.01$, a 1% chance. The probability that it will between 20% and 50% is $F(50) - F(20) = 0.99 - 0.50 = 0.49$, or 49%. The most likely amount of cost overrun occurs when the slope of the tangent line to the cumulative distribution function is a maximum. This occurs at the inflection point of the cumulative distribution graph, at about $C = 28\%$.

8. (a)

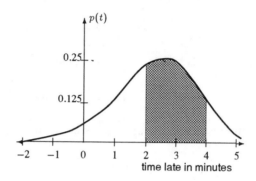

The shaded region represents the probability that the bus will be from 2 to 4 minutes late.

(b)

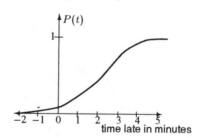

The probability that the bus will be 2 to 4 minutes late (the area shaded above) is $P(4) - P(2)$. The inflection point on the graph of $P(t)$ corresponds to where $p(t)$ is a maximum. To the left of the inflection point, P is increasing at an increasing rate, while to the right of the inflection point P is increasing at a decreasing rate. Thus, the inflection point marks where the rate at which P is increasing is a maximum (i.e. where the derivative of P, which is p, is a maximum).

9. (a) The fraction of students passing is given by the area under the curve from 2 to 4 divided by the total area under the curve. This appears to be about $\frac{2}{3}$.

(b) The fraction with honor grades corresponds to the area under the curve from 3 to 4 divided by the total area. This is about $\frac{1}{3}$.

(c) The peak around 2 probably exists because many students work to get just a passing grade.

(d)

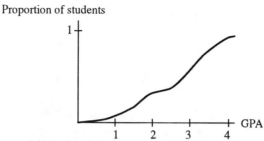

Proportion of students

10. (a) Most of the earth's surface is below sea level. Much of the earth's surface is either around 3 miles below sea level or exactly at sea level. It appears that essentially all of the surface is between 4 miles below sea level and 2 miles above sea level. Very little of the surface is around 1 mile below sea level.

(b) The fraction below sea level corresponds to the area under the curve from -4 to 0 divided by the total area under the curve. This appears to be about $\frac{3}{4}$.

11.

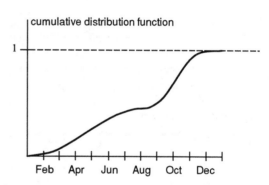

12. (a)

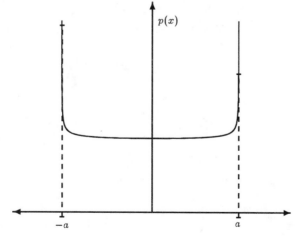

(b) The graphs should look similar.

(c)   We expect $\int_{-a}^{a} \dfrac{dx}{\pi\sqrt{a^2 - x^2}} = 1$, since

$$f(x) = \begin{cases} \frac{1}{\pi\sqrt{a^2 - x^2}} & -a < x < a; \\ 0 & |x| \geq a, \end{cases}$$

and thus $\int_{-a}^{a} \dfrac{dx}{\pi\sqrt{a^2 - x^2}} = 1$ by the definition of a probability density function.
Indeed,

$$\int_{-a}^{a} \frac{dx}{\pi\sqrt{a^2 - x^2}} = \frac{1}{\pi}\arcsin\frac{x}{a}\Big|_{-a}^{a}$$

$$= \frac{1}{\pi}(\arcsin 1 - \arcsin(-1))$$

$$= 1.$$

(d)   It does make sense, physically speaking. The fact that $f(x) \to \infty$ as $x \to a$ does not mean that the ball spends an infinite amount of time at a, but just that the ratio of the time spent near $-a$ and a to the time spent elsewhere goes to ∞. This makes sense—if we watch a pendulum, we note that more time is spent near the ends of its path (where its velocity is small) than in the middle of the path (where its velocity is largest).

8.6   SOLUTIONS

1.

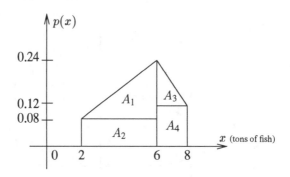

Splitting the figure into four pieces, we see that

$$\text{Area under the curve} = A_1 + A_2 + A_3 + A_4$$

$$= \frac{1}{2}(0.16)4 + 4(0.08) + \frac{1}{2}(0.12)2 + 2(0.12)$$

$$= 1.$$

We expect the area to be 1, since $\int_{-\infty}^{\infty} p(x)\,dx = 1$ for any probability density function, and $p(x)$ is 0 except when $2 \leq x \leq 8$.

2. Recall that the mean is $\int_{-\infty}^{\infty} xp(x)\,dx$. In the fishing example, $p(x) = 0$ except when $2 \leq x \leq 8$, so the mean is

$$\int_2^8 xp(x)\,dx.$$

Using the equation for $p(x)$ in the chapter,

$$\int_2^8 xp(x)\,dx = \int_2^6 xp(x)\,dx + \int_6^8 xp(x)\,dx$$

$$= \int_2^6 x(0.04x)\,dx + \int_6^8 x(-0.06x + 0.6)\,dx$$

$$= \left.\frac{0.04x^3}{3}\right|_2^6 + \left.(-0.02x^3 + 0.3x^2)\right|_6^8$$

$$\approx 5.253 \text{ tons.}$$

3. (a) Since $\mu = 100$ and $\sigma = 15$:

$$p(x) = \frac{1}{15\sqrt{2\pi}} e^{-\frac{1}{2}\left(\frac{x-100}{15}\right)^2}$$

(b) The fraction of the population with IQ scores between 115 and 120 is (integrating numerically)

$$\int_{115}^{120} p(x)\,dx = \int_{115}^{120} \frac{1}{15\sqrt{2\pi}} e^{-\frac{(x-100)^2}{450}}\,dx$$

$$= \frac{1}{15\sqrt{2\pi}} \int_{115}^{120} e^{-\frac{(x-100)^2}{450}}\,dx$$

$$\approx 0.067 = 6.7\% \text{ of the population.}$$

4. We try to find $\dfrac{1}{\sqrt{2\pi}} \int_{-\infty}^{\infty} e^{-\frac{(x-15)^2}{2}}\,dx.$

Since this has no elementary antiderivative, we must do it numerically. Note that this is a normal distribution with mean 15 and standard deviation 1. Almost all of the area under the graph will lie within 5 standard deviations of the mean, so we can try to find $\dfrac{1}{\sqrt{2\pi}} \int_{10}^{20} e^{-\frac{(x-15)^2}{2}}\,dx.$

Using Simpson's rule with 100 intervals, we get that the above integral is approximately 0.9999994267, which is indeed very close to 1. We can get even closer to 1 by choosing different limits of integration.

5. (a) i.   ii.

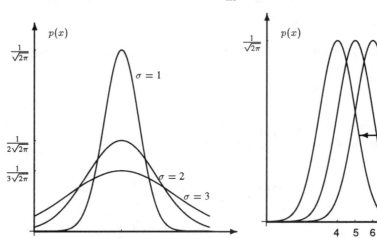

(b) Recall that the mean is the "balancing point." In other words, if the area under the curve was made of cardboard, we'd expect it to balance at the mean. All of the graphs are symmetric across the line $x = \mu$, so μ is the "balancing point" and hence the mean.

As the graphs also show, increasing σ flattens out the graph, in effect lessening the concentration of the data near the mean. Thus, the smaller the σ value, the more data is clustered around the mean.

6. (a) P is the cumulative distribution function, so the percentage of the population that made between \$20,000 and \$50,000 is

$$P(50) - P(20) = 99\% - 75\% = 24\%.$$

Therefore $\frac{6}{25}$ of the population made between \$20,000 and \$50,000.

(b) The median income is the income such that half the people made less than this amount. Looking at the chart, we see that $P(12.6) = 50\%$, so the median must be \$12,600.

(c) The cumulative distribution function looks something like this:

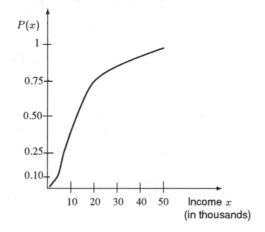

The density function is the derivative of the cumulative distribution. Qualitatively it looks like:

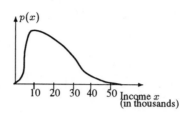

The density function has a maximum at about $8000. This means that more people have incomes around $8000 than around any other amount. On the density function, this is the highest point. On the cumulative distribution, this is the point of steepest slope (because $P' = p$), which is also the point of inflection.

7.   (a)   Since $\int_0^\infty p(x)\,dx = 1$, we have

$$1 = \int_0^\infty ae^{-0.122x}\,dx$$

$$= \frac{a}{-0.122}e^{-0.122x}\Big|_0^\infty = \frac{a}{0.122}.$$

So $a = 0.122$.

(b)

$$P(x) = \int_0^x p(t)\,dt$$

$$= \int_0^x 0.122e^{-0.122t}\,dt$$

$$= -e^{0.122t}\Big|_0^x = 1 - e^{-0.122x}.$$

(c)   Median is the x such that

$$P(x) = 1 - e^{-0.122x} = 0.5.$$

So $e^{-0.122x} = 0.5$. Thus,

$$x = -\frac{\ln 0.5}{0.122} \approx 5.68 \text{ seconds}$$

and

$$\text{Mean} = \int_0^\infty x(0.122)e^{-0.122x}\,dx = -\int_0^\infty x\left(-0.122e^{-0.122x}\right)\,dx.$$

We now use integration by parts. Let $u = -x$ and $v' = -0.122e^{-0.122x}$. Then $u' = -1$, and $v = e^{-0.122x}$. Therefore,

$$\text{Mean} = -xe^{-0.122x}\Big|_0^\infty + \int_0^\infty e^{-0.122x}\, dx = \frac{1}{0.122} \approx 8.20 \text{ seconds.}$$

(d)

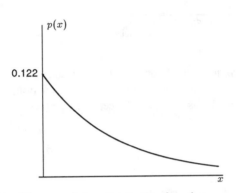
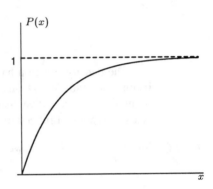

8. (a) The cumulative distribution function

$$P(t) = \int_0^t p(x)dx = \text{Area under graph of density function } p(x) \text{ for } 0 \leq x \leq t$$

$$= \text{Fraction of population who survive } t \text{ years or less after treatment}$$

$$= \text{Fraction of population who survive up to } t \text{ years after treatment.}$$

(b) The probability that a randomly selected person survives for at least t years is the probability that he lives t years or longer, so

$$S(t) = \int_t^\infty p(x)\, dx = \lim_{b \to \infty} \int_t^b Ce^{-Ct}\, dx$$

$$= \lim_{b \to \infty} -e^{-Ct}\Big|_t^b = \lim_{b \to \infty} -e^{-Cb} - (-e^{-Ct}) = e^{-Ct},$$

or equivalently,

$$S(t) = 1 - \int_0^t p(x)\, dx = 1 - \int_0^t Ce^{-Ct}\, dx = 1 + e^{-Ct}\Big|_0^t = 1 + (e^{-Ct} - 1) = e^{-Ct}$$

(c) The probability of surviving at least two years is

$$S(2) = e^{-C(2)} = 0.70$$

so

$$\ln e^{-C(2)} = \ln 0.70$$

$$-2C = \ln 0.7$$

$$C = -\frac{1}{2}\ln 0.7 \approx 0.178$$

9. (a)   We want to find a such that $\int_0^\infty p(v)\, dv = \lim_{r \to \infty} a \int_0^r v^2 e^{-mv^2/2kT}\, dv = 1$. Therefore,

$$\frac{1}{a} = \lim_{r \to \infty} \int_0^r v^2 e^{-mv^2/2kT}\, dv. \tag{8.1}$$

To evaluate the integral, use integration by parts with the substitutions $u = v$ and $w' = ve^{-mv^2/2kT}$:

$$\int_0^r \underbrace{v}_{u}\underbrace{ve^{-mv^2/2kT}}_{w'}\, dv = \underbrace{v}_{u}\underbrace{\frac{e^{-mv^2/2kT}}{-m/kT}}_{w}\bigg|_0^r - \int_0^r \underbrace{1}_{u'}\underbrace{\frac{e^{-mv^2/2kT}}{-m/kT}}_{w}\, dv$$

$$= -\frac{kTr}{m}e^{-mr^2/2kT} + \frac{kT}{m}\int_0^r e^{-mv^2/2kT}\, dv.$$

From the normal distribution we know that $\int_0^\infty \frac{1}{\sqrt{2\pi}}e^{-x^2/2}\, dx = \frac{1}{2}$, so

$$\int_0^\infty e^{-x^2/2}\, dx = \frac{\sqrt{2\pi}}{2}.$$

Therefore in the above integral, make the substitution $x = \sqrt{\frac{m}{kT}}v$, so that $dx = \sqrt{\frac{m}{kT}}\, dv$, or $dv = \sqrt{\frac{kT}{m}}\, dx$. Then

$$\frac{kT}{m}\int_0^r e^{-mv^2/2kT}\, dv = \left(\frac{kT}{m}\right)^{3/2}\int_0^{\sqrt{\frac{m}{kT}}r} e^{-x^2/2}\, dx.$$

Substituting this into Equation 8.1 we get

$$\frac{1}{a} = \lim_{r \to \infty}\left(-\frac{kTr}{m}e^{-mr^2/2kT} + \left(\frac{kT}{m}\right)^{3/2}\int_0^{\sqrt{\frac{m}{kT}}r} e^{-x^2/2}\, dx\right) = 0 + \left(\frac{kT}{m}\right)^{3/2}\cdot\frac{\sqrt{2\pi}}{2}.$$

Therefore, $a = \frac{2}{\sqrt{2\pi}}\left(\frac{m}{kT}\right)^{3/2}$. Substituting the values for k, T, and m gives $a \approx 3.4 \times 10^{-8}$ SI units.

(b)   To find the median, we wish to find the speed x such that

$$\int_0^x p(v)\, dv = \int_0^x av^2 e^{-\frac{mv^2}{2kT}}\, dv = \frac{1}{2},$$

where $a = \frac{2}{\sqrt{2\pi}}(\frac{m}{kT})^{3/2}$. Using a calculator, by trial and error we get $x \approx 441$ m/sec.
To find the mean, we find

$$\int_0^\infty vp(v)\,dv = \int_0^\infty av^3 e^{-\frac{mv^2}{2kT}}\,dv.$$

This integral can be done by substitution. Let $u = v^2$, so $du = 2v\,dv$. Then

$$\int_0^\infty av^3 e^{-\frac{mv^2}{2kT}}\,dv = \frac{a}{2}\int_{v=0}^{v=\infty} v^2 e^{-\frac{mv^2}{2kT}} 2v\,dv$$

$$= \frac{a}{2}\int_{u=0}^{u=\infty} ue^{-\frac{mu}{2kT}}\,du$$

$$= \lim_{r\to\infty} \frac{a}{2}\int_0^r ue^{-\frac{mu}{2kT}}\,du.$$

Now, using the integral table, we have

$$\int_0^\infty av^3 e^{-\frac{mv^2}{2kT}}\,dv = \lim_{r\to\infty} \frac{a}{2}\left[-\frac{2kT}{m}ue^{-\frac{mu}{2kT}} - \left(-\frac{2kT}{m}\right)^2 e^{-\frac{mu}{2kT}}\right]\Big|_0^r$$

$$= \frac{a}{2}\left(-\frac{2kT}{m}\right)^2$$

$$\approx 457.7 \text{ m/sec.}$$

The maximum for $p(v)$ will be at a point where $p'(v) = 0$.

$$p'(v) = a(2v)e^{-\frac{mv^2}{2kT}} + av^2\left(-\frac{2mv}{2kT}\right)e^{-\frac{mv^2}{2kT}}$$

$$= ae^{-\frac{mv^2}{2kT}}\left(2v - v^3\frac{m}{kT}\right).$$

Thus $p'(v) = 0$ at $v = 0$ and at $v = \sqrt{\frac{2kT}{m}} \approx 405$. It's obvious that $p(0) = 0$, and that $p \to 0$
as $v \to \infty$. So $v = 405$ gives us a maximum: $p(405) \approx 0.002$.

(c) The mean, as we found in part (b), is $\frac{a}{2}\frac{4k^2T^2}{m^2} = \frac{4}{\sqrt{2\pi}}\frac{k^{1/2}T^{1/2}}{m^{1/2}}$. It is clear, then, that as T
increases so does the mean. We found in part (b) that $p(v)$ reached its maximum at $v = \sqrt{\frac{2kT}{m}}$.
Thus

$$\text{the maximum value of } p(v) = \frac{2}{\sqrt{2\pi}}\left(\frac{m}{kT}\right)^{3/2}\frac{2kT}{m}e^{-1}$$

$$= \frac{4}{e\sqrt{2\pi}}\frac{m^{1/2}}{kT^{1/2}}.$$

Thus as T increases, the maximum value decreases.

10. (a) Let the $p(r)$ be the density function. Then $P(r) = \int_0^r p(x)\, dx$, and from the Fundamental Theorem of Calculus, $p(r) = \frac{d}{dr} P(r) = \frac{d}{dr}(1-(2r^2+2r+1)e^{-2r}) = -(4r+2)e^{-2r}+2(2r^2+2r+1)e^{-2r}$, or $p(r) = 4r^2 e^{-2r}$.

We have that $p'(r) = 8r(e^{-2r}) - 8r^2 e^{-2r} = e^{-2r} \cdot 8r(1-r)$, which is zero when $r = 0$ or $r = 1$, negative when $r > 1$, and positive when $r < 1$. Thus $p(1) = 4e^{-2} \approx 0.54$ is a relative maximum.

Here are sketches of $p(r)$ and the cumulative position $P(r)$.

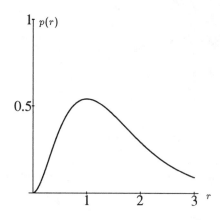 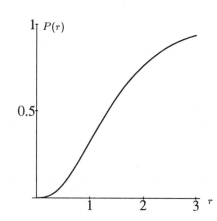

(b) The median distance is the distance r such that $P(r) = 1 - (2r^2 + 2r + 1)e^{-2r} = 0.5$, or equivalently, $(2r^2 + 2r + 1)e^{-2r} = 0.5$.

By experimentation with a calculator, we find that $r \approx 1.33$ Bohr radii is the median distance.

The mean distance is equal to the value of the integral $\int_0^\infty rp(r)\, dr = \lim_{x \to \infty} \int_0^x rp(r)\, dr$. We have that $\int_0^x rp(r)\, dr = \int_0^x 4r^3 e^{-2r}\, dr$. Using the integral table, we get

$$\int_0^x 4r^3 e^{-2r}\, dr = \left[\left(-\frac{1}{2}\right)4r^3 - \frac{1}{4}(12r^2) - \frac{1}{8}(24r) - \frac{1}{16}(24)\right]e^{-2x}\Big|_0^x$$

$$= \frac{3}{2} - \left[2x^3 + 3x^2 + 3x + \frac{3}{2}\right]e^{-2x}.$$

Taking the limit of this expression as $x \to \infty$, we see that all terms involving (powers of x or constants)$\cdot e^{-2x}$ have limit 0, and thus the mean distance is 1.5 Bohr radii.

The most likely distance is obtained by maximizing $p(r) = 4r^2 e^{-2r}$; as we have already seen this corresponds to $r = 1$ Bohr unit.

(c) Because it is the most likely distance of the electron from the nucleus.

SOLUTIONS TO REVIEW PROBLEMS FOR CHAPTER EIGHT

1. (a)

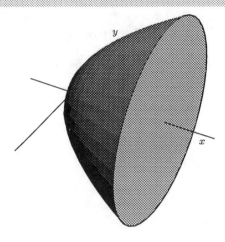

Figure 8.14: Rotated Region

(b) Divide [0,1] into N subintervals of width $\Delta x = \frac{1}{N}$. The volume of the ith disc is $\pi(\sqrt{x_i})^2 \Delta x = \pi x_i \Delta x$. So, $V \approx \sum_{i=1}^{N} \pi x_i \Delta x$.

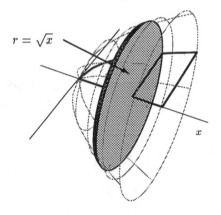

Figure 8.15: Cutaway View

(c)

$$\text{Volume} = \int_0^1 \pi x \, dx = \frac{\pi}{2} x^2 \Big|_0^1 = \frac{\pi}{2} \approx 1.57.$$

2.   (a)

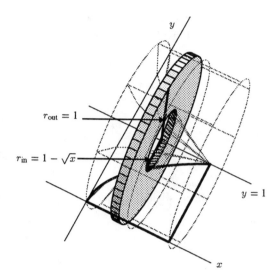

Slice the figure perpendicular to the x–axis. One gets washers of inner radius $1 - \sqrt{x}$ and outer radius 1. Therefore,

$$V = \int_0^1 \left(\pi 1^2 - \pi(1 - \sqrt{x})^2 \right) \, dx$$

$$= \pi \int_0^1 \left(1 - [1 - 2\sqrt{x} + x] \right) dx$$

$$= \pi \left[\frac{4}{3} x^{\frac{3}{2}} - \frac{1}{2} x^2 \right]_0^1 = \frac{5\pi}{6} \approx 2.62.$$

(b)

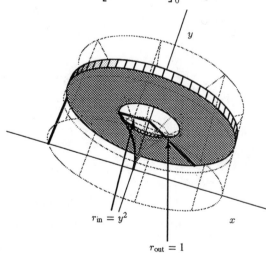

Note that $x = y^2$. We now integrate over y instead of x, slicing perpendicular to the y–axis. This gives us washers of inner radius x and outer radius 1. So

$$V = \int_{y=0}^{y=1} (\pi 1^2 - \pi x^2)\, dy$$

$$= \int_0^1 \pi(1 - y^4)\, dy$$

$$= \left(\pi y - \frac{\pi}{5} y^5\right)\Big|_0^1 = \pi - \frac{\pi}{5} = \frac{4\pi}{5} \approx 2.51.$$

3. (a) The line $y = ax$ must pass through (l, b). Hence $b = al$, so $a = b/l$.

   (b) Cut the cone into N slices, slicing perpendicular to the x–axis. Each piece is almost a cylinder. The radius of the ith cylinder is $r(x_i) = \dfrac{bx_i}{l}$, so the volume

   $$V \approx \sum_{i=1}^N \pi \left(\frac{bx_i}{l}\right)^2 \Delta x.$$

   Therefore, as $N \to \infty$, we get

   $$V = \int_0^l \pi b^2 l^{-2} x^2\, dx$$

   $$= \pi \frac{b^2}{l^2}\left[\frac{x^3}{3}\right]_0^l = \left(\pi \frac{b^2}{l^2}\right)\left(\frac{l^3}{3}\right) = \frac{1}{3}\pi b^2 l.$$

4. (a) Slice the mountain horizontally into N cylinders of height Δh. The sum of the volumes of the cylinders will be

   $$\sum_{i=1}^N \pi r^2 \Delta h = \sum_{i=1}^N \pi \left(\frac{3.5 \cdot 10^5}{\sqrt{h + 600}}\right)^2 \Delta h.$$

   (b)

   $$\text{Volume} = \int_{400}^{14400} \pi \left(\frac{3.5 \cdot 10^5}{\sqrt{h + 600}}\right)^2 dh$$

   $$= 1.23 \cdot 10^{11} \pi \int_{400}^{14400} \frac{1}{(h + 600)}\, dh$$

   $$= 1.23 \cdot 10^{11} \pi \ln(h + 600)\Big|_{400}^{14400}\, dh$$

   $$= 1.23 \cdot 10^{11} \pi \left[\ln 15000 - \ln 1000\right]$$

   $$= 1.23 \cdot 10^{11} \pi \ln(15000/1000)$$

   $$= 1.23 \cdot 10^{11} \pi \ln 15 \approx 1.05 \cdot 10^{12} \text{ cubic feet.}$$

5. (a) Slice the headlight into N disks of height Δx by cutting perpendicular to the x–axis. The radius of each disk is y; the height is Δx. The volume of each disk is $\pi y^2 \Delta x$. Therefore, the Riemann sum approximating the volume of the headlight is

$$\sum_{i=1}^{N} \pi y_i^2 \Delta x = \sum_{i=1}^{N} \pi \frac{9x_i}{4} \Delta x.$$

(b)

$$\pi \int_0^4 \frac{9x}{4} \, dx = \pi \frac{9}{8} x^2 \Big|_0^4 = 18\pi.$$

6.

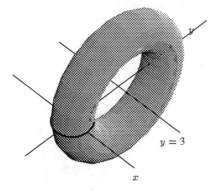

Figure 8.16: The Torus

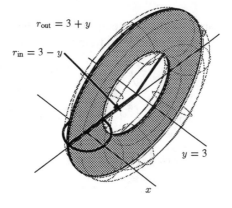

Figure 8.17: Slice of Torus

As shown in Figure 8.17, we slice the torus perpendicular to the line $y = 3$. We obtain washers with width dx, inner radius $r_{\text{in}} = 3 - y$, and outer radius $r_{\text{out}} = 3 + y$. Therefore, the area of the washer is $\pi r_{\text{out}}^2 - \pi r_{\text{in}}^2 = \pi[(3+y)^2 - (3-y)^2] = 12\pi y$. Since $y = \sqrt{1-x^2}$, the volume is gotten by summing up the volumes of the washers: we get

$$\int_{-1}^{1} 12\pi\sqrt{1-x^2}\,dx = 12\pi\int_{-1}^{1}\sqrt{1-x^2}\,dx.$$

But $\int_{-1}^{1}\sqrt{1-x^2}\,dx$ is the area of a semicircle of radius 1, which is $\frac{\pi}{2}$. So we get $12\pi\cdot\frac{\pi}{2} = 6\pi^2 \approx 59.22$. (Or, you could use

$$\int\sqrt{1-x^2}\,dx = \left[x\sqrt{1-x^2} + \arcsin(x)\right],$$

by Formula VI-31 and Formula VI-28.)

7.

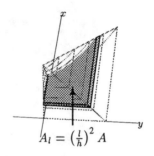

$$A_l = \left(\frac{l}{h}\right)^2 A$$

Slice the "pyramid" with planes perpendicular to the z-axis. The slices are horizontal and parallel to the xy-plane. If one is l units down from the top, the figure you get is l/h the size of the base in every direction, so its area is $\left(\dfrac{l}{h}\right)^2$ the area of the base. (This is the "scaled down" version.) So

$$\text{Volume} = \int_0^h \left(\frac{l}{h}\right)^2 A\,dl = A\int_0^h \frac{l^2}{h^2}\,dl = \frac{A}{h^2}\frac{l^3}{3}\bigg|_0^h = \frac{Ah}{3}.$$

8.   The arc length of $\sqrt{1-x^2}$ from $x=0$ to $x=1$ is one quarter of the perimeter of the unit circle. Hence the length is $\dfrac{2\pi}{4} = \dfrac{\pi}{2}$.

9.

$$L = \int_1^2 \sqrt{1+e^{2x}}\,dx \approx 4.79.$$

Note that $\sqrt{1+e^{2x}}$ does not have an obvious elementary antiderivative, so we use an approximation method to find an approximate value for L.

10.

$$L = \int_1^2 \sqrt{1 + \left(x^4 + \frac{1}{(16x^4)} - \frac{1}{2}\right)}\, dx$$

$$= \int_1^2 \sqrt{\left(x^2 + \frac{1}{(4x^2)}\right)^2}\, dx$$

$$= \int_1^2 \left(x^2 + \frac{1}{4}x^{-2}\right)\, dx = \left[\frac{x^3}{3} - \frac{1}{4x}\right]\Bigg|_1^2 = \frac{59}{24}.$$

11. (a) The function $f(x) = 0$ clearly passes through $(0,0)$ and has length x from $(0,0)$ to $(x,0)$.

(b) We want to find f so that

$$\int_0^x \sqrt{1 + [f'(t)]^2}\, dt = ax.$$

Taking the derivative of both sides with respect to x yields $1 + [f'(x)]^2 = a$, so $f'(x) = \sqrt{a^2 - 1}$. Integrating this yields $f(x) = \sqrt{a^2 - 1}\, x + C$, but $f(0) = 0$, so $C = 0$ and $f(x) = \sqrt{a^2 - 1}\, x$.

If $a < 1$, this tells us that no such f can be found. Geometrically, this is because the arc length of f from 0 to x must be at least x, since f has to move that far horizontally.

12. Since $f(x) = \sin x$, $f'(x) = \cos(x)$, so

$$\text{Arc Length} = \int_0^\pi \sqrt{1 + \cos^2 x}\, dx.$$

13. We'll find the arc length of the top half of the ellipse, and multiply that by 2. In the top half of the ellipse, the equation $(x^2/a^2) + (y^2/b^2) = 1$ implies

$$y = +b\sqrt{1 - \frac{x^2}{a^2}}.$$

Differentiating $(x^2/a^2) + (y^2/b^2) = 1$ implicitly with respect to x gives us

$$\frac{2x}{a^2} + \frac{2y}{b^2}\frac{dy}{dx} = 0,$$

so

$$\frac{dy}{dx} = \frac{\frac{-2x}{a^2}}{\frac{2y}{b^2}} = -\frac{b^2 x}{a^2 y}.$$

Substituting this into the arc length formula, we get

$$\text{Arc Length} = \int_{-a}^a \sqrt{1 + \left(-\frac{b^2 x}{a^2 y}\right)^2}\, dx$$

$$= \int_{-a}^{a} \sqrt{1 + \left(\frac{b^4 x^2}{a^4 (b^2)(1 - \frac{x^2}{a^2})} \right)} \, dx$$

$$= \int_{-a}^{a} \sqrt{1 + \left(\frac{b^2 x^2}{a^2 (a^2 - x^2)} \right)} \, dx.$$

Hence the arc length of the entire ellipse is

$$2 \int_{-a}^{a} \sqrt{1 + \left(\frac{b^2 x^2}{a^2 (a^2 - x^2)} \right)} \, dx.$$

14. The average horizontal width of A is the area of A divided by the vertical span of A. The area of A is $\int_{0}^{\pi} \sin x \, dx = -\cos x \big|_{0}^{\pi} = 2$. The vertical span is 1. Therefore, the average width of A is $2/1 = 2$.

15. (a)

$$\text{Future Value} = \int_{0}^{20} 100 e^{0.10(20-t)} dt$$

$$= 100 \int_{0}^{20} e^2 e^{-0.10t} dt$$

$$= \frac{100 e^2}{-0.10} e^{-0.10t} \Big|_{0}^{20}$$

$$= \frac{100 e^2}{0.10} (1 - e^{-0.10(20)}) \approx \$6389.06.$$

The present value of the income stream is

$$\int_{0}^{20} 100 e^{-0.10t} dt = 100 \left(\frac{1}{-0.10} \right) e^{-0.10t} \Big|_{0}^{20}$$

$$= 1000 \left(1 - e^{-2} \right) = \$864.66.$$

Note that this is also the present value of the sum $6389.06.

(b)   Let T be the number of years for the balance to reach $5000. Then

$$5000 = \int_{0}^{T} 100 e^{0.10(T-t)} dt$$

$$50 = e^{0.10T} \int_{0}^{T} e^{-0.10t} dt$$

$$= \frac{e^{0.10T}}{-0.10} e^{-0.10t} \Big|_{0}^{T}$$

$$= 10 e^{0.10T} (1 - e^{-0.10T}) = 10 e^{0.10} T - 10.$$

So, $60 = 10 e^{0.10T}$, and $T = 10 \ln 6 \approx 17.92$ years.

16. (a) For Δx and Δy very small, Δs is almost a straight line. Therefore, applying the Pythagorean Theorem to the triangle in the figure, we see that

$$v = \lim_{\Delta t \to 0} \frac{\Delta s}{\Delta t}$$
$$= \lim_{\Delta t \to 0} \frac{\sqrt{(\Delta x)^2 + (\Delta y)^2}}{\Delta t}$$
$$= \lim_{\Delta t \to 0} \sqrt{\left(\frac{\Delta x}{\Delta t}\right)^2 + \left(\frac{\Delta y}{\Delta t}\right)^2}$$
$$= \sqrt{\left(\frac{dx}{dt}\right)^2 + \left(\frac{dy}{dt}\right)^2}.$$

But we know that $\frac{dx}{dt} = 1$ and $\frac{dy}{dt} = 2t$ since $x = t$ and $y = t^2$. Therefore,

$$v = \frac{ds}{dt} = \sqrt{1^2 + (2t)^2} = \sqrt{4t^2 + 1}.$$

(b) Since $x = t$ and $y = t^2 = x^2$, Marie-Jolaine traces out the curve $f(x) = x^2$ in the xy-plane. So the distance traveled from the origin to the point (b, b^2) is the arc length of this curve from $x = 0$ to $x = b$, given by

$$s = \int_0^b \sqrt{1 + \left(\frac{df}{dx}\right)^2}\, dx = \int_0^b \sqrt{1 + 4x^2}\, dx.$$

Since $v = \frac{ds}{dt}$, we have, by the Fundamental Theorem of Calculus, $s(b) = \int_0^b v\, dt$ since $s(0) = 0$.

Hence, the distance traveled from time $t = 0$ to $t = b$ is

$$s = \int_0^b v\, dt = \int_0^b \sqrt{1 + 4t^2}\, dt.$$

Since $x = t$, the limits of integration are the same for both integrals of s, so the two results are equal.

17. (a) The area under the graph of the height density function $p(x)$ is concentrated in two humps centered at 0.5 m and 1.1 m. The plants can therefore be separated into two groups, those with heights in the range 0.3 m to 0.7 m, corresponding to the first hump, and those with heights in the range 0.9 m to 1.3 m, corresponding to the second hump. This grouping of the grasses according to height is probably close to the species grouping. Since the second hump contains more area than the first, there are more plants of the tall grass species in the meadow.

(b) As do all cumulative distribution functions, the cumulative distribution function $P(x)$ of grass heights rises from 0 to 1 as x increases. Most of this rise is achieved in two spurts, the first as x goes from 0.3 m to 0.7 m, and the second as x goes from 0.9 m to 1.3 m. The plants can therefore be separated into two groups, those with heights in the range 0.3 m to 0.7 m, corresponding to the first spurt, and those with heights in the range 0.9 m to 1.3 m, corresponding to the second spurt. This grouping of the grasses according to height is the same as the grouping we made in part (a), and is probably close to the species grouping.

(c) The fraction of grasses with height less than 0.7 m equals $P(0.7) = 0.25 = 25\%$. The remaining 75% are the tall grasses.

18. (a)

$$c \int_0^6 e^{-ct} dt = -e^{-ct}\Big|_0^6 = 1 - e^{-6c} = 0.1,$$

so

$$c = -\frac{1}{6}\ln 0.9 \approx 0.0176.$$

(b)

$$c \int_6^{12} e^{-ct} dt = -e^{-ct}\Big|_6^{12}$$

$$= e^{-6c} - e^{-12c} = 0.9 - 0.81 = 0.09,$$

so the probability is 9%.

19. (a) First, we find the critical points of $p(x)$:

$$\frac{d}{dx}p(x) = \frac{1}{\sigma\sqrt{2\pi}}\left[\frac{-2(x-\mu)}{2\sigma^2}\right]e^{-\frac{(x-\mu)^2}{2\sigma^2}}$$

$$= -\frac{(x-\mu)}{\sigma^3\sqrt{2\pi}}e^{-\frac{(x-\mu)^2}{2\sigma^2}}.$$

This implies $x = \mu$ is the only critical point of $p(x)$.

To confirm that $p(x)$ is maximized at $x = \mu$, we rely on the first derivative test. As $-\frac{1}{\sigma^3\sqrt{2\pi}}e^{-\frac{(x-\mu)^2}{2\sigma^2}}$ is always negative, the sign of $p'(x)$ is the opposite of the sign of $(x - \mu)$; thus $p'(x) > 0$ when $x < \mu$, and $p'(x) < 0$ when $x > \mu$.

(b) To find the inflection points, we need to find where $p''(x)$ changes sign; that will happen only when $p''(x) = 0$. As

$$\frac{d^2}{dx^2}p(x) = -\frac{1}{\sigma^3\sqrt{2\pi}}e^{-\frac{(x-\mu)^2}{2\sigma^2}}\left[-\frac{(x-\mu)^2}{\sigma^2} + 1\right],$$

$p''(x)$ changes sign when $\left[-\frac{(x-\mu)^2}{\sigma^2} + 1\right]$ does, since the sign of the other factor is always negative. This occurs when

$$-\frac{(x-\mu)^2}{\sigma^2} + 1 = 0,$$

$$-(x-\mu)^2 = -\sigma^2,$$

$$x - \mu = \pm\sigma.$$

Thus, $x = \mu + \sigma$ or $x = \mu - \sigma$. Since $p''(x) > 0$ for $x < \mu - \sigma$ and $x > \mu + \sigma$ and $p''(x) < 0$ for $\mu - \sigma \leq x \leq \mu + \sigma$, these are in fact points of inflection.

(c) μ represents the mean of the distribution, while σ is the standard deviation. In other words, σ gives a measure of the "spread" of the distribution, i.e. how tightly the observations are clustered about the mean. A small σ tells us that most of the data are close to the mean; a large σ tells us that the data is spread out.

20. We'll divide up time between 1971 and 1992 into intervals of length dt, and figure out how much of the strontium-90 produced during that time interval is still around.

First, strontium-90 decays exponentially, so if a quantity S_0 was produced t years ago, and S is the quantity around today, $S = S_0 e^{-kt}$. Since the half-life is 28 years, $\frac{1}{2} = e^{-k(28)}$, giving $k = \frac{-\ln(\frac{1}{2})}{28} \approx 0.025$.

Suppose we measure t in years from 1971, so that 1992 is $t = 21$.

Since strontium-90 is produced at a rate of 1 kg/year, during the interval dt we know that a quantity $1\,dt$ kg was produced. Since this was $(21 - t)$ years ago, the quantity remaining now is $1\,dt e^{-0.025(21-t)}$. Summing over all such intervals gives

$$\text{Strontium in 1992} \approx \int_0^{21} e^{-0.025(21-t)}\, dt$$

$$= \left.\frac{e^{-0.025(21-t)}}{0.025}\right|_0^{21} = 16.34 \text{ kg.}$$

[Note: This is exactly like a future value problem from economics, with a negative interest rate.]

21. Let x be the height from ground to the weight. It follows that $0 \leq x \leq 20$. At height x, to lift the weight Δx more, the work needed is $200\Delta x + 2(20 - x)\Delta x = (240 - 2x)\Delta x$. So the total work is

$$W = \int_0^{20} (240 - 2x)dx$$

$$= \left.(240x - x^2)\right|_0^{20}$$

$$= 240(20) - 20^2 = 4400 \quad \text{ft-lb.}$$

22. Let x be the distance from the bucket to the surface of the water. It follows that $0 \leq x \leq 40$. At x feet, the bucket weighs $(30 - \frac{1}{4}x)$, where the $\frac{1}{4}x$ term is due to the leak. When the bucket is x feet from the surface of the water, the work done by raising it Δx feet is $(30 - \frac{1}{4}x)\,\Delta x$. So the total work required to raise the bucket to the top is

$$W = \int_0^{40} (30 - \frac{1}{4}x)\,dx$$
$$= \left(30x - \frac{1}{8}x^2\right)\Big|_0^{40}$$
$$= 30(40) - \frac{1}{8}40^2 = 1000 \quad \text{ft-lb.}$$

23. Let y represent depth below the surface of the can. Slice the water in the can horizontally into cylinders of height Δy and radius 1. To find the weight of such a slice, we multiply its volume by its weight per cubic foot: we obtain

$$\text{Weight} = \pi 1^2 (\Delta y)(62.4) \approx 196.04\,\Delta y.$$

So the work required to lift a slice at depth y to the surface is $196.04y\,\Delta y$.

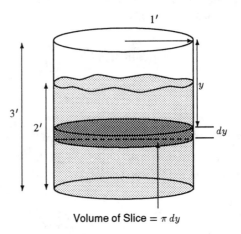

Volume of Slice $= \pi\,dy$

To find the total work required to drain the can, we integrate:

$$\text{Total Work} \approx \int_1^3 196.04y\,dy = 196.04\frac{y^2}{2}\Big|_1^3 \approx 784.14 \text{ ft-lb.}$$

24.

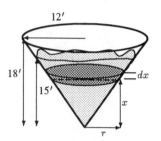

Let x be the depth of the water measured from the bottom of the tank. It follows that $0 \leq x \leq 15$. Let r be the radius of the section of the cone with height x. By similar triangles, $\frac{r}{x} = \frac{12}{18}$, so $r = \frac{2}{3}x$. Then the work required to pump a layer of water with thickness of Δx at depth x over the top of the tank is $62.4\pi \left(\frac{2}{3}x\right)^2 \Delta x(18 - x)$. So the total work done by pumping the water over the top of the tank is

$$
\begin{aligned}
W &= \int_0^{15} 62.4\pi \left(\frac{2}{3}x\right)^2 (18 - x)dx \\
&= \frac{4}{9} \, 62.4\pi \int_0^{15} x^2(18 - x)dx \\
&= \frac{4}{9} \, 62.4\pi \left(6x^3 - \frac{1}{4}x^4\right)\Big|_0^{15} \\
&= \frac{4}{9} \, 62.4\pi(7593.75) \approx 661{,}619.41 \text{ ft-lb.}
\end{aligned}
$$

25. Bottom: The pressure on the bottom of the can is $2 \cdot 62.4 = 124.8$ pounds per square foot. The area of the bottom is $\pi r^2 = \pi$. So the force on the bottom of the can is $197.2 \times \pi \approx 618.3$ pounds. (This is just the weight of all the water.)

Side: To find the total force on the side of the can, we unfold the side to form a rectangle whose length is the circumference of the base, 2π feet. (This unfolding is like peeling off a label.) Next, we divide the label into strips of height dy. The area of each strip is $2\pi \, dy$ square feet, and the pressure at depth y is $62.4y$ pounds per square foot.

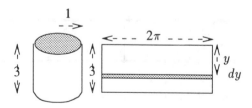

The force on each strip, therefore, is

$$(62.4y)(2\pi \, dy) \approx 392.07y \, dy \text{ pounds.}$$

So the force on the whole side is approximately

$$\int_0^2 392.07y \, dy = 392.07\frac{y^2}{2}\bigg|_0^2 = 794.14 \text{ pounds.}$$

26. (a) If you slice the apple perpendicular to the core, you expect that the cross section will be approximately a circle.

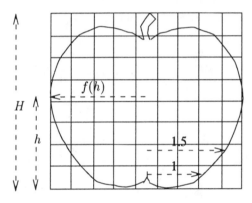

If $f(h)$ is the radius of the apple at height h above the bottom, and H is the height of the apple, then

$$\text{Volume} = \int_0^H \pi f(h)^2 \, dh.$$

Ignoring the stem, $H \approx 3.5$. Although we do not have a formula for $f(h)$, we can estimate it at various points. (Remember, we measure here from the bottom of the *apple*, which is not quite the bottom of the graph.)

TABLE 8.6

h	0	0.5	1	1.5	2	2.5	3	3.5
$f(h)$	1	1.5	2	2.1	2.3	2.2	1.8	1.2

Now let $g(h) = \pi f(h)^2$, the area of the cross-section at height h. From our approximations above, we get the following table.

TABLE 8.7

h	0	0.5	1	1.5	2	2.5	3	3.5
$g(h)$	3.14	7.07	12.57	13.85	16.62	13.85	10.18	4.52

We can now take left- and right-hand sum approximations. Note that $\Delta h = 0.5$ inches. Thus

$$\text{LEFT}(9) = (3.14 + 7.07 + 12.57 + 13.85 + 16.62 + 13.85 + 10.18)(0.5)$$
$$= 38.64.$$
$$\text{RIGHT}(9) = (7.07 + 12.57 + 13.85 + 16.62 + 13.85 + 10.18 + 4.52)(0.5)$$
$$= 39.33.$$

Thus the volume of the apple is ≈ 39 cu.in.

(b)   The apple weighs $0.03 \times 39 \approx 1.17$ pounds, so it costs about 94¢. (Expensive apple!)

27. (a)   The volume of water in the centrifuge is $\pi(1^2) \cdot 1 = \pi$ cubic meters. The centrifuge has total volume 2π cubic meters, so the volume of the air in the centrifuge is π cubic meters. Now suppose the equation of the parabola is $y = h + bx^2$. We know that the volume of air in the centrifuge is the volume of the top part (a cylinder) plus the volume of the middle part (shaped like a bowl).

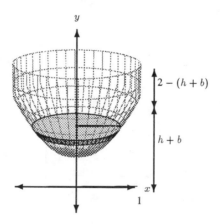

The Volume of Air

To find the volume of the cylinder of air, we find the maximum water depth. If $x = 1$, then $y = h + b$. Therefore the height of the water at the edge of the bowl, 1 meter away from the center, is $h + b$. The volume of the cylinder of air is therefore $[2 - (h + b)] \cdot \pi \cdot (1)^2 = [2 - h - b]\pi$.

To find the volume of the bowl of air, we note that the bowl is a volume of rotation with radius x at height y, where $y = h + bx^2$. Solving for x^2 gives $x^2 = (y - h)/b$. Hence, slicing horizontally as shown in the picture:

$$\text{Bowl Volume} = \int_h^{h+b} \pi x^2 \, dy$$

$$= \int_h^{h+b} \pi \frac{y - h}{b} \, dy$$

$$= \frac{\pi (y - h)^2}{2b} \Big|_h^{h+b} = \frac{b\pi}{2}.$$

So the volume of both pieces together is $[2 - h - b]\pi + b\pi/2 = (2 - h - b/2)\pi$. But we know the volume of air should be π, so $(2 - h - b/2)\pi = \pi$, hence $h + b/2 = 1$ and $b = 2 - 2h$. Therefore, the equation of the parabolic cross-section is $y = h + (2 - 2h)x^2$.

(b) The water spills out the top when $h + b = h + (2 - 2h) = 2$, or when $h = 0$. The bottom is exposed when $h = 0$. Therefore, the two events happen simultaneously.

28. Look at the disc-shaped slab of water at height y and of thickness dy. The rate at which water is flowing out when it is at depth y is $k\sqrt{y}$ (Torricelli's Law, with k constant). Then, if $x = g(y)$, we have

$$dt = \begin{pmatrix} \text{Time for water to} \\ \text{drop by this amount} \end{pmatrix} = \frac{\text{Volume}}{\text{Rate}} = \frac{\pi(g(y))^2 \, dy}{k\sqrt{y}}.$$

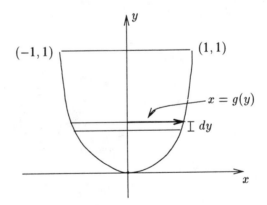

If the rate at which the depth of the water is dropping is constant, then $\frac{dy}{dt}$ is constant, so we want

$$\frac{\pi(g(y))^2}{k\sqrt{y}} = \text{constant},$$

or $\frac{(g(y))^2}{\sqrt{y}} = \text{constant}$, so $g(y) = c\sqrt[4]{y}$, for some constant c. Since $x = 1$ when $y = 1$, we have $c = 1$ and so $x = \sqrt[4]{y}$, or $y = x^4$.

29. Any small piece of mass ΔM on either of the two spheres has kinetic energy $\frac{1}{2}v^2\Delta M$. Since the angular velocity of the two spheres is the same, the actual velocity of the piece ΔM will depend on how far away it is from the axis of revolution. The further away a piece is from the axis, the faster it must be moving and the larger its velocity v. This is because if ΔM is at a distance r from the axis, in one revolution it must trace out a circular path of length $2\pi r$ about the axis. Since every piece in either sphere takes 1 minute to make 1 revolution, pieces farther from the axis must move faster, as they travel a greater distance.

Thus, since the thin spherical shell has more of its mass concentrated farther from the axis of rotation than does the solid sphere, the bulk of it is traveling faster than the bulk of the solid sphere. So, it has the higher kinetic energy.

30. Any small piece of mass ΔM on either of the two hoops has kinetic energy $\frac{1}{2}v^2\Delta M$. Since the angular velocity of the two hoops is the same, the actual velocity of the piece ΔM will depend on how far away it is from the axis of revolution. The further away a piece is from the axis, the faster it must be moving and the larger its velocity v. This is because if ΔM is at a distance r from the axis, in one revolution it must trace out a circular path of length $2\pi r$ about the axis. Since every piece in either hoop takes 1 minute to make 1 revolution, pieces farther from the axis must move faster, as they travel a greater distance.

The hoop rotating about the cylindrical axis has all of its mass at a distance R from the axis, whereas the other hoop has a good bit of its mass close (or on) the axis of rotation. So, since the bulk of the hoop rotating about the cylindrical axis is traveling faster than the bulk of the other hoop, it must have the higher kinetic energy.

31. (a) Let y represent height, and let x represent horizontal distance from the lowest point of the cable. Then the stretched cable is a parabola of the form $y = kx^2$ passing through the point $(1280/2, 143) = (640, 143)$. Therefore, $143 = k(640)^2$ so $k \approx 3.491 \times 10^{-4}$. To find the arc length of the parabola, we take twice the arc length of the part to the right of the lowest point. Since $dy/dx = 2kx$,

$$\text{Arc Length} = 2\int_0^{640}\sqrt{1+(2kx)^2}\,dx = 2\int_0^{640}\sqrt{1+4k^2x^2}\,dx.$$

The easiest way to find this integral is to substitute the value of k and find the integral's value numerically, giving
$$\text{Arc Length} \approx 1321.4 \text{ meters.}$$

Alternatively, we can make the substitution $w = 2kx$:

$$\text{Arc Length} = \frac{2}{2k}\int_0^{1280k}\sqrt{1+w^2}\,dw$$
$$= \frac{1}{k}\int_0^{1280k}\sqrt{1+w^2}\,dw$$
$$= \frac{1}{2k}\left(w\sqrt{1+w^2}\Big|_0^{1280k}\right) + \frac{1}{2k}\left(\int_0^{1280k}\frac{1}{\sqrt{1+w^2}}\,dw\right)$$

[Using the integral table, Formula VI-29]

$$= \frac{1}{2k}\left(1280k\sqrt{1+(1280k)^2}\right) + \frac{1}{2k}\left(\ln\left|x + \sqrt{1+x^2}\right|\Big|_0^{1280k}\right)$$

$$= \frac{1}{2k}\left(1280k\sqrt{1+(1280k)^2}\right) + \frac{1}{2k}\left(\ln\left|1280k + \sqrt{1+(1280k)^2}\right|\right)$$

$$\approx 1321.4 \text{ meters.}$$

(b)   Adding 0.05% to the length of the cable gives a cable length of $(1321.4)(1.0005) = 1322.1$. We now want to calculate the new shape of the parabola; that is, we want to find a new k so that the arc length is 1322.1. Since

$$\text{Arc Length} = 2\int_0^{640} \sqrt{1 + 4k^2x^2}\, dx$$

we can find k numerically by trial and error. Trying values close to our original value of k, we find $k \approx 3.52 \times 10^{-4}$. To find the sag for this new k, we find the height $y = kx^2$ for which the cable hangs from the towers. This is

$$y = k(640)^2 \approx 144.2.$$

Thus the cable sag is 144.2 meters, over a meter more than on a cold winter day. Notice, though, that although the length increases by 0.05%, the sag increases by more: $144.2/143 \approx 1.0084$, an increase of 0.84%.

32.   Let us make coordinate axes with the origin at the center of the box. The x and y axes will lie along the central axes of the cylinders, and the (height) axis will extend vertically to the top of the box. If one slices the cylinders horizontally, one gets a cross. The cross is what you get if you cut out four corner squares from a square of side length 2. If h is the height of the cross above (or below) the xy plane, the equation of a cylinder is $h^2 + y^2 = 1$ (or $h^2 + x^2 = 1$). Thus the "armpits" of the cross occur where $y^2 - 1 = -h^2 = x^2 - 1$ for some fixed height h—that is, out $\sqrt{1 - h^2}$ units from the center, or $1 - \sqrt{1 - h^2}$ units away from the edge. Each corner square has area $(1 - \sqrt{1 - h^2})^2 = 2 - h^2 - 2\sqrt{1 - h^2}$. The whole big square has area 4. Therefore, the area of the cross is

$$4 - 4(2 - h^2 - 2\sqrt{1 - h^2}) = -4 + 4h^2 + 8\sqrt{1 - h^2}.$$

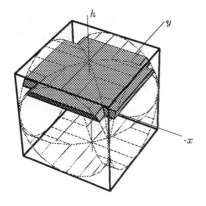

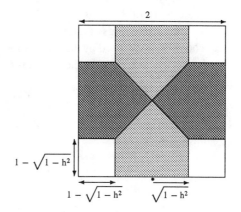

We integrate this from $h = -1$ to $h = 1$, and obtain the volume, V:

$$V = \int_{-1}^{1} -4 + 4h^2 + 8\sqrt{1 - h^2} \, dh$$

$$= \left[-4h + \frac{4h^3}{3} + 8 \cdot \frac{1}{2} \left(h\sqrt{1 - h^2} + \arcsin h \right) \right]\Bigg|_{-1}^{1}$$

$$= -8 + \frac{8}{3} + 4\pi = 4\pi - \frac{16}{3} \approx 7.23.$$

This is a reasonable answer, as the volume of the cube is 8, and the volume of one cylinder alone is $2\pi \approx 6.28$.

33.

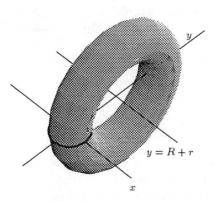

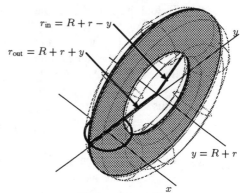

Figure 8.18: The Bagel

Figure 8.19: Slice of Bagel

Looking back on Problem 6, we see one way to approach the problem. We will get a bagel–also known as a torus–by rotating a circle of radius R centered at the origin around the line $y = r + R$. (See Fig 8.18 and Fig 8.19.) Notice that r is the inner radius of the torus, so $r = d/2$. Further, $r + 2R$ is the outer radius of the torus, so $r + 2R = D/2$, or $R = \frac{1}{4}(D - d)$. Now, to find the volume of the torus, we slice it into rings of thickness Δx, perpendicular to the x-axis, just as we did in Problem 6. The volume enclosed by the outer ring is $\pi(R + r + y)^2 \, \Delta x$, and the volume enclosed by the inner ring is $\pi(R + r - y)^2 \, \Delta x$, so the volume of a slice is

$$\pi(R + r + y)^2 \, \Delta x - \pi(R + r - y)^2 \, \Delta x = 4\pi(R + r)y\,\Delta x.$$

On the original circle, centered at the origin, $y = \sqrt{R^2 - x^2}$, so the total volume can be found by integrating:

$$V = \int_{-R}^{R} 4\pi(R + r)\sqrt{R^2 - x^2} \, dx$$

$$= 4\pi(R + r) \left[\frac{1}{2}x\sqrt{R^2 - x^2} + R^2 \arcsin \frac{x}{R} \right] \Big|_{-R}^{R}$$

$$= 2\pi(R + r)R^2 \left(\frac{\pi}{2} - \left(-\frac{\pi}{2} \right) \right) = 2\pi^2(R + r)R^2,$$

using Formula 30 of the integral table to find $\int \sqrt{R^2 - x^2} \, dx$. Substituting for R and r, we get

$$V = 2\pi^2 \left[\frac{1}{4}(D + d) \right] \left[\frac{1}{4}(D - d) \right]^2 = \frac{1}{32}\pi^2(D^2 - d^2)(D - d).$$

34. (a) The area under the graph of $p(x)$ from $x = a$ to $x = b$ should be 1.
Therefore $1 = \frac{1}{2}(\text{base}) \cdot (\text{height}) = \frac{1}{2}(b - a) \cdot p(c)$, and so $p(c) = \frac{2}{b-a}$.

(b) We have $a = 6$, $b = 10$, and $c = 9$. Using $p(c) = \frac{2}{b-a}$, we have $p(9) = \frac{2}{10-6} = 0.5$.

(c) To find the equation for the first line, we note that $(6, 0)$ and $(9, 0.5)$ are points on the line, so $m_1 = \Delta y/\Delta x = (0.5 - 0)/(9 - 6) = 1/6$. And if $y = m_1 x + b_1$, substituting in $x = 6$, $y = 0$, yields $0 = (1/6)6 + b_1$, so $b_1 = -1$.

To find the equation for the second line, we note that $(10, 0)$ and $(9, 0.5)$ are points on the line, so $m_2 = \Delta y/\Delta x = (0.5 - 0)/(9 - 10) = -1/2$. And if $y = m_2 x + b_2$, substituting in $x = 10$, $y = 0$, yields $0 = (-1/2)10 + b_2$, so $b_2 = 5$.
Thus

$$p(x) = \begin{cases} \frac{x}{6} - 1 & 6 \le x \le 9 \\ -\frac{x}{2} + 5 & 9 \le x \le 10. \end{cases}$$

(d) The probability that production cost is under \$8 is given by the area under $p(x)$ from $x = 6$ to $x = 8$. The area is $\frac{1}{2}(8 - 6) \cdot p(8) = p(8) = \frac{8}{6} - 1 = \frac{1}{3}$.

(e) The median cost is the value $x = m$ such that the area under $p(x)$ from $x = 6$ to $x = m$ is $\frac{1}{2}$. To find m, we solve $\frac{1}{2}(m - 6) \cdot p(m) = \frac{1}{2}$, or $(m - 6) \cdot p(m) = 1$. We know that $6 \le m \le 9$ since the area under $p(x)$ from $x = 6$ to $x = 9$ is greater than $\frac{1}{2}$. Therefore $p(m) = \frac{m}{6} - 1$ and so

$$(m - 6) \cdot \left(\frac{m}{6} - 1\right) = 1$$

$$\frac{m^2}{6} - 2m + 6 = 1$$

$$m^2 - 12m + 36 = 6$$

$$m^2 - 12m + 30 = 0$$

By the quadratic formula,

$$m = \frac{12 \pm \sqrt{144 - 120}}{2} = 6 \pm \sqrt{6}.$$

Since $6 \le m \le 9$, we must have $m = 6 + \sqrt{6}$.

(f)   The cumulative probability distribution function $P(x)$ gives the area under $p(x)$ from $x = a$ to x.

(i)   For $6 \le x \le 9$, the area is given by

$$\frac{1}{2}(x - 6) \cdot p(x) = \frac{1}{2}(x - 6) \cdot \left(\frac{x}{6} - 1\right) = \frac{1}{2}\left(\frac{x^2}{6} - 2x + 6\right)$$

$$= \frac{x^2}{12} - x + 3$$

(ii)   For $9 \le x \le 10$, the area is given by the area under $p(x)$ from $x = 6$ to $x = 10$, which is equal to 1, minus the area under $p(x)$ from x to $x = 10$, which is given by $\frac{1}{2} \cdot (10 - x) \cdot p(x)$. Since $9 \le x \le 10$, $p(x) = -\frac{x}{2} + 5$.
Therefore

$$P(x) = 1 - \frac{1}{2}(10 - x) \cdot \left(-\frac{x}{2} + 5\right) = -\frac{x^2}{4} + 5x - 24.$$

Therefore

$$P(x) = \begin{cases} \frac{x^2}{12} - x + 3 & 6 \le x \le 9 \\ -\frac{x^2}{4} + 5x - 24 & 9 \le x \le 10. \end{cases}$$

and its graph is given in Figure 8.20.

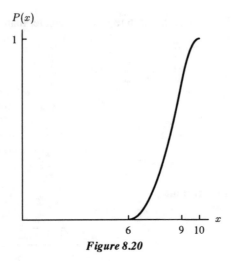

Figure 8.20

CHAPTER NINE

9.1 SOLUTIONS

1. (a) = (III), (b) = (IV), (c) = (I), (d) = (II).

2. If $P = P_0 e^t$, then

$$\frac{dP}{dt} = \frac{d}{dt}(P_0 e^t) = P_0 e^t = P.$$

3. If $y = \sin 2t$, then $\frac{dy}{dt} = 2\cos 2t$, and $\frac{d^2 y}{dt^2} = -4\sin 2t$.
   Thus $\frac{d^2 y}{dt^2} + 4y = -4\sin 2t + 4\sin 2t = 0.$

4. If $Q = Ce^{kt}$, then

$$\frac{dQ}{dt} = Cke^{kt} = k(Ce^{kt}) = kQ.$$

We are given that $\frac{dQ}{dt} = -0.03Q$, so we know that $kQ = -0.03Q$. Thus we either have $Q = 0$ (in which case $C = 0$ and k is anything) or $k = -0.03$. Notice that if $k = -0.03$, then C can be any number.

5. If $y = \cos \omega t$, then

$$\frac{dy}{dt} = -\omega \sin \omega t, \quad \frac{d^2 y}{dt^2} = -\omega^2 \cos \omega t.$$

Thus, if $\frac{d^2 y}{dt^2} + 9y = 0$, then

$$-\omega^2 \cos \omega t + 9\cos \omega t = 0$$
$$(9 - \omega^2)\cos \omega t = 0.$$

Thus $9 - \omega^2 = 0$, or $\omega^2 = 9$, so $\omega = \pm 3$.

6. (a) $P = \frac{1}{1+e^{-t}} = (1 + e^{-t})^{-1}$
   $\frac{dP}{dt} = -(1 + e^{-t})^{-2}(-e^{-t}) = \frac{e^{-t}}{(1+e^{-t})^2}.$
   Then $P(1 - P) = \frac{1}{1+e^{-t}}\left(1 - \frac{1}{1+e^{-t}}\right) = \left(\frac{1}{1+e^{-t}}\right)\left(\frac{e^{-t}}{1+e^{-t}}\right) = \frac{e^{-t}}{(1+e^{-t})^2} = \frac{dP}{dt}.$
   (b) As t tends to ∞, e^{-t} goes to 0. Thus $\lim\limits_{t \to \infty} \frac{1}{1+e^{-t}} = 1.$

7. At the end of 5 days, $\frac{dy}{dt} = 100 - 67.2 = 32.8\%$ per week. Thus during the next working day, which is the first day of the second week, the amount learned is about $32.8(\frac{1}{5}) = 6.6\%$.
   At the end of 6 working days,

$$y \approx 67.2\% + 6.6\% = 73.8\%.$$

Continuing in this manner gives the data in the table below.

TABLE 9.1

Time (days)	0	1	2	3	4	5	6	7
% learned (approximate)	0	20	36	48.8	59.0	67.2	73.8	79.0

8	9	10	11	12	13	14	15	16	17
83.2	86.6	89.3	91.4	93.1	94.5	95.6	96.5	97.2	97.7

18	19	20	21	22	23	24	25	26	27
98.2	98.6	98.8	99.1	99.3	99.4	99.5	99.6	99.7	99.8

28	29	30	31	32	33
99.8	99.8	99.9	99.9	99.9	99.9

8. (a) If $y = \frac{e^x + e^{-x}}{2}$, then $\frac{dy}{dx} = \frac{e^x - e^{-x}}{2}$, and $\frac{d^2y}{dx^2} = \frac{e^x + e^{-x}}{2}$.
If $k = 1$, then

$$k\sqrt{1 + \left(\frac{dy}{dx}\right)^2} = \sqrt{1 + \left(\frac{e^x - e^{-x}}{2}\right)^2} = \sqrt{1 + \frac{e^{2x}}{4} - \frac{1}{2} + \frac{e^{-2x}}{4}}$$

$$= \sqrt{\frac{e^{2x}}{4} + \frac{1}{2} + \frac{e^{-2x}}{4}} = \sqrt{\left(\frac{e^x + e^{-x}}{2}\right)^2}$$

$$= \left|\frac{e^x + e^{-x}}{2}\right| = \frac{e^x + e^{-x}}{2} \quad \text{since } e^x + e^{-x} > 0$$

$$= \frac{d^2y}{dx^2}.$$

(b) $y = \frac{e^{Ax} + e^{-Ax}}{2A}$, so

$$\frac{dy}{dx} = \frac{e^{Ax} - e^{-Ax}}{2} \quad \text{and} \quad \frac{d^2y}{dx^2} = A\left(\frac{e^{Ax} + e^{-Ax}}{2}\right).$$

Therefore we have

$$1 + \left(\frac{dy}{dx}\right)^2 = 1 + \left(\frac{e^{Ax} - e^{-Ax}}{2}\right)^2 = 1 + \frac{1}{4}\left(e^{2Ax} + e^{-2Ax} - 2\right)$$

$$= \frac{1}{4}\left(e^{2Ax} + e^{-2Ax} + 2\right) = \frac{1}{4}\left(e^{Ax} + e^{-Ax}\right)^2.$$

$$k\sqrt{1+\left(\frac{dy}{dx}\right)^2} = k\sqrt{\frac{1}{4}\left(e^{Ax}+e^{-Ax}\right)^2} = \frac{k}{2}\cdot\left|e^{Ax}+e^{-Ax}\right|$$

$$= k\frac{\left(e^{Ax}+e^{-Ax}\right)}{2}, \quad \text{since } e^{Ax}+e^{-Ax}>0.$$

Since we want $\frac{d^2y}{dx^2} = k\sqrt{1+\left(\frac{dy}{dx}\right)^2}$, we must have $A = k$.

9.

(I) $y = 2\sin x$,	$dy/dx = 2\cos x$,	$d^2y/dx^2 = -2\sin x$
(II) $y = \sin 2x$,	$dy/dx = 2\cos 2x$,	$d^2y/dx^2 = -4\sin 2x$
(III) $y = e^{2x}$,	$dy/dx = 2e^{2x}$,	$d^2y/dx^2 = 4e^{2x}$
(IV) $y = e^{-2x}$,	$dy/dx = -2e^{-2x}$,	$d^2y/dx^2 = 4e^{-2x}$

and so:

(a) (IV)
(b) (III)
(c) (III), (IV)
(d) (II)

10. For (I): $y = xe^x$, $y' = e^x + xe^x$, and $y'' = 2e^x + xe^x$.
     For (II): $y = xe^{-x}$, $y' = e^{-x} - xe^{-x}$, and $y'' = -2e^{-x} + xe^{-x}$.
     Thus (I) satisfies equation (d).
     (II) satisfies equation (c).

11.

(I) $y = e^x$,	$y' = e^x$,	$y'' = e^x$
(II) $y = x^3$,	$y' = 3x^2$,	$y'' = 6x$
(III) $y = e^{-x}$,	$y' = -e^{-x}$,	$y'' = e^{-x}$
(IV) $y = x^{-2}$,	$y' = -2x^{-3}$,	$y'' = 6x^{-4}$

and so:

(a) (I),(III) because $y'' = y$ in each case.
(b) (IV) because $x^2y'' + 2xy' - 2y = x^2(6x^{-4}) + 2x(-2x^{-3}) - 2x^{-2} = 6x^{-2} - 4x^{-2} - 2x^{-2} = 0.$
(c) (II),(IV) because $x^2y'' = 6y$ in each case.

12.

(I) $y = xe^{kx}$,	$dy/dx = (kx+1)e^{kx}$
(II) $y = x^p$,	$dy/dx = px^{p-1}$
(III) $y = e^{kx}$,	$dy/dx = ke^{kx}$
(IV) $y = mx$,	$dy/dx = m$

and so:

(a) (IV) because $y/x = mx/x = m = dy/dx$.
(b) (III) because $(y\ln y)/x = (e^{kx}\ln e^{kx})/x = (e^{kx}kx)/x = ke^{kx} = dy/dx$.
(c) (I) because $(y/x)(1+\ln(y/x)) = (xe^{kx}/x)(1+\ln(xe^{kx}/x)) = e^{kx}(1+kx) = dy/dx$.
(d) (II) because $(y\ln y)/(x\ln x) = (x^p\ln x^p)/(x\ln x) = (px^p\ln x)/(x\ln x) = px^{p-1} = dy/dx$.

9.2 SOLUTIONS

1. (a)

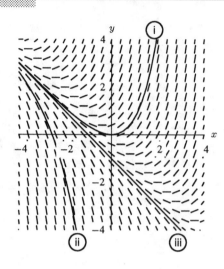

(b) The solution through $(-1, 0)$ appears to be linear with the equation $y = -x - 1$.
(c) If $y = -x - 1$, then $y' = -1$ and $x + y = x + (-x - 1) = -1$.

2. (a)

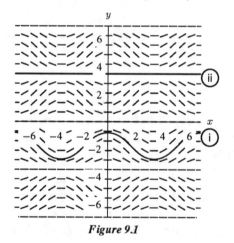

Figure 9.1

(b) The solution is $y = n\pi$.

   To check this, we note that if $y = n\pi$, then $(\sin x)(\sin y) = (\sin x)(\sin n\pi) = 0 = y'$. Thus $y = n\pi$ is a solution to $y' = (\sin x)(\sin y)$, and it passes through $(0, n\pi)$.

3. (a)

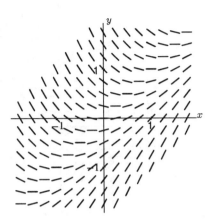

(b) From the graph, the solution through $(1, 0)$ appears linear with the equation $y = x - 1$.

In fact, if $y = x - 1$, then $x - y = x - (x - 1) = 1 = y'$, so $y = x - 1$ is the solution through $(1, 0)$.

4.

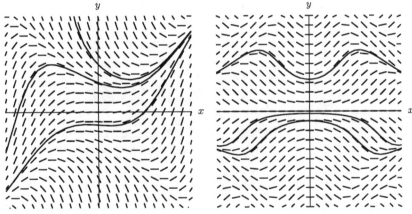

Figure 9.2

Other choices of solution curves are, of course, possible.

5. The first graph has the equation $y' = x^2 - y^2$. We can see this by looking along the line $y = x$. On the first slope field, it seems that $y' = 0$ along this line, as it should if $y' = x^2 - y^2$. This is not the case for the second graph.

At $(0, 1)$, $y' = -1$, and at $(1, 0)$, $y' = 1$, so you are looking for points on the axes where the line is sloped at $45°$.

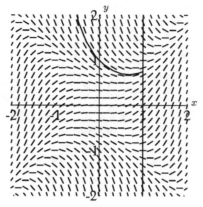

Figure 9.3

6. (a)
   (b)

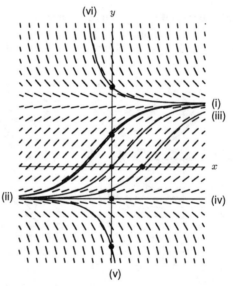

Figure 9.4

(c) The graph shows that a solution will be increasing if its y values fall in the range $-1 < y < 2$. This makes sense since $y' = 0.5(1 + y)(2 - y)$, so $y' > 0$ if $-1 < y < 2$. Notice that if the y value ever gets to 2, then $y' = 0$ and the function becomes constant, following the line $y = 2$. (The same is true if ever $y = -1$.)

From the graph, the solution is decreasing if $y > 2$ or $y < -1$. Again, this also follows from the equation, since in either case $y' < 0$.

The curve has a horizontal tangent if $y' = 0$, which only happens if $y = 2$ or $y = -1$. This also can be seen on the graph of the slope field.

7. When $a = 1$ and $b = 2$, the Gompertz equation is $y' = -y\ln(y/2) = y\ln(2/y) = y(\ln 2 - \ln y)$. This differential equation is similar to the differential equation $y' = y(2 - y)$ in certain ways. For example, in both equations y' is positive for $0 < y < 2$ and negative for $y > 2$. Also, for y values close to 2, $(\ln 2 - \ln y)$ and $y(2 - y)$ are both close to 0, so $y(\ln 2 - \ln y)$ and $(2 - y)$ are about equal. Thus around $y = 2$ the slope fields look almost the same. This happens again around $y = 0$, since around $y = 0$ both $y(2 - y)$ and $y(\ln 2 - \ln y)$ go to 0. (Note that $\lim\limits_{y \to 0^+} y \ln y = 0$.) For y values close to 1 the slope fields look similar since the local linearization of $\ln y$ near $y = 1$ is $y - 1$; hence, near $y = 1$, $y(\ln 2 - \ln y) \approx y(\ln 2 - (y - 1)) \approx y(1.69 - y) \approx y(2 - y)$. Finally, for $y > 2$, $\ln y$ grows much slower than y, so the slope field for $y' = y(\ln 2 - \ln y)$ is less steep, negatively, than for $y' = y(2 - y)$.

8. (a) II   (b) VI   (c) IV   (d) I   (e) III   (f) V

9. If the starting point has $y > 0$, then $y \to \infty$ as $x \to \infty$. If the starting point has $y = 0$, then y stays at 0 as $x \to \infty$. If the starting point has $y < 0$, then $y \to -\infty$ as $x \to \infty$.

10. As $x \to \infty$, y diverges.

11. As $x \to \infty$, $y \to \infty$, no matter what the starting point.

12. As $x \to \infty$, y seems to oscillate within a certain range. The range will depend on the starting point, but the *size* of the range appears independent of the starting point.

13. If $y = 4$ for the starting point, then $y = 4$ always, so $y = 4$ as $x \to \infty$. If $y \neq 4$ for the starting point, then $y \to 4$ as $x \to \infty$.

14. From the slope field, the function looks like a parabola of the form $y = x^2 + C$, where C depends on the starting point. In any case, $y \to \infty$ as $x \to \infty$.

15. The slope is 0 on the line $y = 0$, except for at $(0,0)$. The slope is undefined when $3y^2 = x$. The slope is positive when $y > 0$ and $3y^2 > x$, or when $y < 0$ and $3y^2 < x$. It is negative elsewhere, when $y < 0$ and $3y^2 > x$, or when $y > 0$ and $3y^2 < x$. From this information we can find regions, shown in the graph below, where the slope is positive, negative, 0, or undefined.

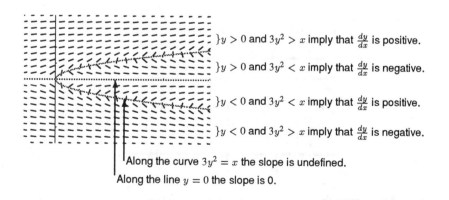

$\}y > 0$ and $3y^2 > x$ imply that $\frac{dy}{dx}$ is positive.

$\}y > 0$ and $3y^2 < x$ imply that $\frac{dy}{dx}$ is negative.

$\}y < 0$ and $3y^2 < x$ imply that $\frac{dy}{dx}$ is positive.

$\}y < 0$ and $3y^2 > x$ imply that $\frac{dy}{dx}$ is negative.

Along the curve $3y^2 = x$ the slope is undefined.
Along the line $y = 0$ the slope is 0.

The solution curves through the points $(7, 2)$, $(7, 1)$, and $(7, -3)$ are shown in the graph below.

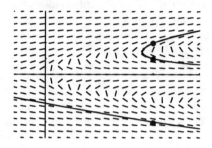

9.3 SOLUTIONS

1. (a) (i)

TABLE 9.2 *Euler's method for*
$y' = (\sin x)(\sin y)$, *starting at* $(0, 2)$

x	y	$\Delta y =(\text{slope})\Delta x$
0	2	$0 = (\sin 0)(\sin 2)(0.1)$
0.1	2	$0.009 = (\sin 0.1)(\sin 2)(0.1)$
0.2	2.009	$0.018 = (\sin 0.2)(\sin 2.009)(0.1)$
0.3	2.027	

(ii)

TABLE 9.3 *Euler's method for*
$y' = (\sin x)(\sin y)$, *starting at* $(0, \pi)$

x	y	$\Delta y =(\text{slope})\Delta x$
0	π	$0 = (\sin 0)(\sin \pi)(0.1)$
0.1	π	$0 = (\sin 0.1)(\sin \pi)(0.1)$
0.2	π	$0 = (\sin 0.2)(\sin \pi)(0.1)$
0.3	π	

(b) The slope field shows that the slope of the solution curve through $(0, \pi)$ is always 0. Thus the solution curve is the horizontal line with equation $y = \pi$.

2. (a)

TABLE 9.4 *Euler's method for*
$y' = x + y$ *with* $y(0) = 1$

x	y	$\Delta y =$(slope)Δx
0	1	$0.1 = (1)(0.1)$
0.1	1.1	$0.12 = (1.2)(0.1)$
0.2	1.22	$0.142 = (1.42)(0.1)$
0.3	1.362	$0.1662 = (1.662)(0.1)$
0.4	1.5282	

So $y(0.4) \approx 1.5282$.

(b)

TABLE 9.5 *Euler's method for*
$y' = x + y$ *with* $y(-1) = 0$

x	y	$\Delta y =$(slope)Δx
-1	0	$-0.1 = (-1)(0.1)$
-0.9	-0.1	$-0.1 = (-1)(0.1)$
-0.8	-0.2	$-0.1 = (-1)(0.1)$
-0.7	-0.3	
$\vdots$	$\vdots$	Notice that y
0	-1	decreases by 0.1
$\vdots$	$\vdots$	for every step
0.4	-1.4	

So $y(0.4) = -1.4$. (This answer is exact.)

3. (a)

TABLE 9.6

t	y	slope $= \frac{1}{t}$	$\Delta y = $(slope)$\Delta t = \frac{1}{t}(0.1)$
1	0	1	0.1
1.1	0.1	0.909	0.091
1.2	0.191	0.833	0.083
1.3	0.274	0.769	0.077
1.4	0.351	0.714	0.071
1.5	0.422	0.667	0.067
1.6	0.489	0.625	0.063
1.7	0.552	0.588	0.059
1.8	0.610	0.556	0.056
1.9	0.666	0.526	0.053
2	0.719		

(b)   Since $\frac{dy}{dt} = \frac{1}{t}$, then $y = \ln|t| + C$.
Starting at $(1,0)$ means $y = 0$ when $t = 1$, so $C = 0$ and $y = \ln|t|$.
After ten steps, $t = 2$, so $y = \ln 2 \approx 0.693$.

(c)   Approximate $y = 0.719$, Exact $y = 0.693$.
Thus the approximate answer is too big. This is because the solution curve is concave down, and so the tangent lines are above the curve. Figure 9.5 shows the slope field of $y' = 1/t$ with the solution curve $y = \ln t$ plotted on top of it.

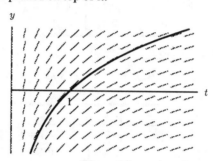

4.   (a)

Figure 9.5

TABLE 9.7

x	y	$\Delta y = (\text{slope})\Delta x$
0	0	0
0.2	0	0.0016
0.4	0.0016	0.0128
0.6	0.0144	0.0432
0.8	0.0576	0.1024
1	0.1600	

At $x = 1$, $y \approx 0.16$.

(b)

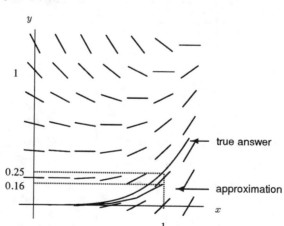

(c) Our answer to (a) appears to be an underestimate. This is as we would expect, since the curve is concave up.

5. (a) $\Delta x = 0.5$

TABLE 9.8 *Euler's method for* $y' = 2x$, *with* $y(0) = 1$

x	y	$\Delta y =$(slope)Δx
0	1	$0 = (2 \cdot 0)(0.5)$
0.5	1	$0.5 = (2 \cdot 0.5)(0.5)$
1	1.5	

(b) $\Delta x = 0.25$

TABLE 9.9 *Euler's method for* $y' = 2x$, *with* $y(0) = 1$

x	y	$\Delta y =$(slope)Δx
0	1	$0 = (2 \cdot 0)(0.25)$
0.25	1	$0.125 = (2 \cdot 0.25)(0.25)$
0.50	1.125	$0.25 = (2 \cdot 0.5)(0.25)$
0.75	1.375	$0.375 = (2 \cdot 0.75)(0.25)$
1	1.75	

(c) General Solution is $y = x^2 + C$, and $y(0) = 1$ gives $C = 1$. Thus, the solution is $y = x^2 + 1$.

(d) True value of y when $x = 1$ is $y = 1^2 + 1 = 2$.
When $\Delta x = 0.5$, error $= 0.5$.
When $\Delta x = 0.25$, error $= 0.25$.
Thus, decreasing Δx by a factor of 2 has decreased the error by a factor of 2, as expected.

6. (a)

TABLE 9.10

x	y	$\Delta y = $(slope)$\Delta x$
0	1.000	-0.200
0.2	0.800	-0.120
0.4	0.680	-0.060
0.6	0.620	-0.005
0.8	0.615	0.052
1	0.667	

(b)

TABLE 9.11

x	y	$\Delta y = $ (slope)Δx
0	1.000	−0.100
0.1	0.900	−0.080
0.2	0.820	−0.063
0.3	0.757	−0.048
0.4	0.709	−0.034
0.5	0.674	−0.020
0.6	0.654	−0.007
0.7	0.647	0.007
0.8	0.654	0.021
0.9	0.675	0.035
1	0.710	

7. By looking at the slope fields, or by computing the second derivative $\frac{d^2y}{dx^2} = 2x - 2y\frac{dy}{dx} = 2x - 2x^2y + 2y^3$, we see that the actual curve should be concave up, so Euler's method gives an underestimate.

8. Since the error is proportional to the reciprocal of the number of subintervals, the error using 10 intervals should be roughly half the error obtained using 5 intervals. Since both the estimates are underestimates, if we let A be the actual value we have:

$$\frac{1}{2}(A - 0.667) = A - 0.710$$
$$A - 0.667 = 2A - 1.420$$
$$A = 0.753$$

Therefore, 0.753 should be a better approximation.

9. (a) Using one step, $\frac{\Delta B}{\Delta t} = 0.05$, so $\Delta B = \left(\frac{\Delta B}{\Delta t}\right)\Delta t = 50$. Therefore we get an approximation of $B \approx 1050$ after one year.

(b) With two steps, $\Delta t = 0.5$ and we have

TABLE 9.12

t	B	$\Delta B = (0.05\,B)\Delta t$
0	1000	25
0.5	1025	25.63
1.0	1050.63	

(c) Keeping track to the nearest hundredth with $\Delta t = 0.25$, we have

TABLE 9.13

t	B	$\Delta B = (0.05\,B)\Delta t$
0	1000	12.5
0.25	1012.5	12.66
0.5	1025.16	12.81
0.75	1037.97	12.97
1	1050.94	

(d) In part (a), we get our approximation by making a single increment, ΔB, where ΔB is just $0.05\,B$. If we think in terms of interest, ΔB is just like getting one end of the year interest payment. Since ΔB is 0.05 times the balance B, it is like getting 5% interest at the end of the year.

(e) Part (b) is equivalent to computing the final amount in an account that begins with \$1000 and earns 5% interest compounded twice annually. Each step is like computing the interest after 6 months. When $t = 0.5$, for example, the interest is $\Delta B = (0.05B)\cdot\frac{1}{2}$, and we add this to \$1000 to get the new balance.

Similarly, part (c) is equivalent to the final amount in an account that has an initial balance of \$1000 and earns 5% interest compounded quarterly.

10. Assume that $x > 0$ and that we use n steps in Euler's method. Label the x-coordinates we use in the process $x_0, x_1, \ldots, x_n$, where $x_0 = 0$ and $x_n = x$. Then using Euler's method to find $y(x)$, we get

TABLE 9.14

	x	y	$\Delta y = (\text{slope})\Delta x$
P_0	$0 = x_0$	0	$f(x_0)\Delta x$
P_1	x_1	$f(x_0)\Delta x$	$f(x_1)\Delta x$
P_2	x_2	$f(x_0)\Delta x + f(x_1)\Delta x$	$f(x_2)\Delta x$
$\vdots$	$\vdots$	$\vdots$	$\vdots$
P_n	$x = x_n$	$\displaystyle\sum_{i=0}^{n-1} f(x_i)\Delta x$	

Thus the result from Euler's method is $\displaystyle\sum_{i=0}^{n-1} f(x_i)\Delta x$. We recognize this as the left-hand Riemann sum that approximates $\int_0^x f(t)\,dt$.

11.

x	y	Δy
7	2	0.02
7.05	2.02	0.019456
7.1	2.039456	0.0189606
7.15	2.0584166	0.01850682
7.2	2.07692342	

The approximation is within 0.001 of the actual answer.

9.4 SOLUTIONS

1. $\frac{dP}{dt} = 0.02P$ implies that $\frac{dP}{P} = 0.02\,dt$.

    $\int \frac{dP}{P} = \int 0.02\,dt$ implies that $\ln|P| = 0.02t + C$.

    $|P| = e^{0.02t+C}$ implies that $P = Ae^{0.02t}$, where $A = \pm e^{C}$.
    We are given $P(0) = 20$. Therefore, $P(0) = Ae^{(0.02)\cdot 0} = A = 20$. So the solution is $P = 20e^{0.02t}$.

2. $\frac{dQ}{dt} = \frac{Q}{5}$ implies that $\frac{dQ}{Q} = \frac{dt}{5}$.

    $\int \frac{dQ}{Q} = \int \frac{dt}{5}$ implies that $\ln|Q| = \frac{1}{5}t + C$.

    So $|Q| = e^{\frac{1}{5}t+C} = e^{\frac{1}{5}t}e^{C}$ implies that $Q = Ae^{\frac{1}{5}t}$, where $A = \pm e^{C}$. From the initial conditions
    we know that $Q(0) = 50$, so $Q(0) = Ae^{(\frac{1}{5})\cdot 0} = A = 50$. Thus $Q = 50e^{\frac{1}{5}t}$.

3. $\frac{dm}{dt} = 3m$. As in problems 1 and 2, we get

    $$m = Ae^{3t}.$$

    Since $m = 5$ when $t = 1$, we have $5 = Ae^{3}$, so $A = \frac{5}{e^{3}}$. Thus $m = \frac{5}{e^{3}}e^{3t} = 5e^{3t-3}$.

4. $\frac{dI}{dx} = 0.2I$ implies that $\frac{dI}{I} = 0.2\,dx$ implies that $\int \frac{dI}{I} = \int 0.2\,dx$ implies that $\ln|I| = 0.2x + C$.
    $I = Ae^{0.2x}$, where $A = e^{C}$. According to the given boundary condition, $I(-1) = 6$. Therefore,
    $I(-1) = Ae^{0.2(-1)} = Ae^{-0.2} = 6$ implies that $A = 6e^{0.2}$. Thus $I = 6e^{0.2}e^{0.2x} = 6e^{0.2(x+1)}$.

5. $\frac{dy}{dx} + \frac{y}{3} = 0$ implies $\frac{dy}{dx} = -\frac{y}{3}$ implies $\int \frac{dy}{y} = -\int \frac{1}{3}\,dx$.
    Integrating and moving terms, we have $y = Ae^{-\frac{1}{3}x}$. Since $y(0) = A = 10$, we have $y = 10e^{-\frac{1}{3}x}$.

6. $\frac{1}{z}\frac{dz}{dt} = 5$ implies $\frac{dz}{z} = 5\,dt$.
    Integrating and moving terms, we have $z = Ae^{5t}$. Using the fact that $z(1) = 5$, we have $z(1) = Ae^{5} = 5$, so $A = \frac{5}{e^{5}}$. Therefore, $z = \frac{5}{e^{5}}e^{5t} = 5e^{5t-5}$.

7. $\frac{dP}{dt} = P + 4$ implies that $\frac{dP}{P+4} = dt$.

    $\int \frac{dP}{P+4} = \int dt$ implies that $\ln|P + 4| = t + C$.

    $P + 4 = Ae^{t}$ implies that $P = Ae^{t} - 4$. $P = 100$ when $t = 0$, so $P(0) = Ae^{0} - 4 = 100$,
    and $A = 104$. Therefore $P = 104e^{t} - 4$.

8. $\frac{dy}{dx} = 2y - 4 = 2(y - 2)$.

    Factoring out a 2 makes the integration easier: $\frac{dy}{y-2} = 2\,dx$ implies that $\int \frac{dy}{y-2} = \int 2\,dx$ implies
    that $\ln|y - 2| = 2x + C$.

$|y - 2| = e^{2x+C}$ implies that $y - 2 = Ae^{2x}$ where $A = \pm e^C$. The curve passes through (2,5), which means $3 = Ae^4$, so $A = \frac{3}{e^4}$. Thus, $y = 2 + \frac{3}{e^4}e^{2x} = 2 + 3e^{2x-4}$.

9. Factoring out the 0.1 gives $\frac{dm}{dt} = 0.1m + 200 = 0.1(m + 2000)$.
    $\frac{dm}{m+2000} = 0.1\, dt$ implies that $\int \frac{dm}{m+2000} = \int 0.1\, dt$, so $\ln|m+2000| = 0.1t+C$. So $m = Ae^{0.1t} - 2000$. Using the initial condition, $m(0) = Ae^{(0.1)\cdot 0} - 2000 = 1000$, gives $A = 3000$. Thus $m = 3000e^{0.1t} - 2000$.

10. $\frac{dB}{dt} + 2B = 50$ implies $\frac{dB}{dt} = -2B + 50 = -2(B - 25)$ implies $\int \frac{dB}{B-25} = -\int 2\, dt$.

    After integrating and doing some algebra, we have $B - 25 = Ae^{-2t}$. Using the initial condition, we have $75 = Ae^{-2}$, so $A = 75e^2$. Thus $B = 25 + 75e^2e^{-2t} = 25 + 75e^{2-2t}$.

11. $\frac{dz}{dt} = te^z$ implies $e^{-z}dz = tdt$ implies $\int e^{-z}\, dz = \int t\, dt$ implies $-e^{-z} = \frac{t^2}{2} + C$.
    Since the solution passes through the origin, $z = 0$ when $t = 0$, we must have $-e^{-0} = \frac{0}{2} + C$, so $C = -1$. Thus $-e^{-z} = \frac{t^2}{2} - 1$, or $z = -\ln(1 - \frac{t^2}{2})$.

12. $dy/dx = 5y/x$ implies $\int dy/y = \int 5dx/x$. So $\ln|y| = 5\ln|x| + C = 5\ln x + C$ implies $|y| = e^{5\ln x}e^C$, and thus $y = Ax^5$ where $A = \pm e^C$. $y = 3$ when $x = 1$, so $A = 3$. Thus $y = 3x^5$.

13. $\frac{dy}{dt} = y^2(1+t)$ implies that $\int \frac{dy}{y^2} = \int(1+t)\, dt$ implies that $-\frac{1}{y} = t + \frac{t^2}{2} + C$ implies that $y = -\frac{1}{t+\frac{t^2}{2}+C}$.
    Since $y = 2$ when $t = 1$, then $2 = -\frac{1}{1+\frac{1}{2}+C}$. So $2C + 3 = -1$, and $C = -2$. Thus $y = -\frac{1}{\frac{t^2}{2}+t-2} = -\frac{2}{t^2+2t-4}$.

14. $\frac{dz}{dt} = z + zt^2 = z(1 + t^2)$ implies that $\int \frac{dz}{z} = \int(1 + t^2)dt$ implies that $\ln|z| = t + \frac{t^3}{3} + C$ implies that $z = Ae^{t+\frac{t^3}{3}}$.
    $z = 5$ when $t = 0$, so $A = 5$ and $z = 5e^{t+\frac{t^3}{3}}$.

15. $\frac{dw}{d\theta} = \theta w^2 \sin\theta^2$ implies $\int \frac{dw}{w^2} = \int \theta \sin\theta^2\, d\theta$ implies that $-\frac{1}{w} = -\frac{1}{2}\cos\theta^2 + C$. According to the initial conditions, $w(0) = 1$, so $-1 = -\frac{1}{2} + C$ and $C = -\frac{1}{2}$. Thus $-\frac{1}{w} = -\frac{1}{2}\cos\theta^2 - \frac{1}{2}$ implies that $\frac{1}{w} = \frac{\cos\theta^2+1}{2}$ implies that $w = \frac{2}{\cos\theta^2+1}$.

16. $x(x + 1)\frac{du}{dx} = u^2$ implies $\int \frac{du}{u^2} = \int \frac{dx}{x(x+1)} = \int(\frac{1}{x} - \frac{1}{1+x})dx$ implies $-\frac{1}{u} = \ln|x| - \ln|x + 1| + C$. $u(1) = 1$, so $-\frac{1}{1} = \ln|1| - \ln|1 + 1| + C$. So $C = \ln 2 - 1$. Solving for u yields $-\frac{1}{u} = \ln|x| - \ln|x + 1| + \ln 2 - 1 = \ln\frac{2|x|}{|x+1|} - 1$, so $u = \frac{-1}{\ln|\frac{2x}{x+1}|-1}$.

17. (a) Separating variables

$$\int \frac{dy}{100 - y} = \int dt$$
$$-\ln|100 - y| = t + C$$
$$|100 - y| = e^{-t-C}$$
$$100 - y = (\pm e^{-C})e^{-t} = Ae^{-t} \quad \text{where } A = \pm e^{-C}$$
$$y = 100 - Ae^{-t}.$$

(b)

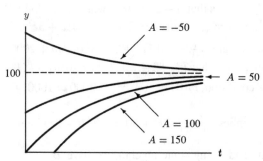

Figure 9.6

(c)   Substituting $y = 0$ when $t = 0$ gives

$$0 = 100 - Ae^{-0}$$

so $A = 100$. Thus solution is

$$y = 100 - 100e^{-t}.$$

18. $\frac{dR}{dt} = kR$ implies that $\frac{dR}{R} = k\,dt$ which implies that $\int \frac{dR}{R} = \int k\,dt$. Integrating gives $\ln|R| = kt + C$, so $|R| = e^{kt+C} = e^{kt}e^{C}$. $R = Ae^{kt}$, where $A = \pm e^{C}$.

19. $\frac{dQ}{dt} - \frac{Q}{k} = 0$ so $\frac{dQ}{dt} = \frac{Q}{k}$. This is now the exact same problem as Problem 20, except the constant factor on the right is $\frac{1}{k}$ instead of k. Thus the solution is $Q = Ae^{\frac{1}{k}t}$ for any constant A.

20. $\frac{dP}{dt} = P - a$, implying that $\frac{dP}{P-a} = dt$ so $\int \frac{dP}{P-a} = \int dt$. Integrating yields $\ln|P - a| = t + C$, so $|P - a| = e^{t+C} = e^{t}e^{C}$. $P = a + Ae^{t}$, where $A = \pm e^{C}$ or $A = 0$.

21. $\frac{dQ}{dt} = b - Q$ implies that $\frac{dQ}{b-Q} = dt$ which, in turn, implies $\int \frac{dQ}{b-Q} = \int dt$. Integrating yields $-\ln|b - Q| = t + C$, so $|b - Q| = e^{-(t+C)} = e^{-t}e^{-C}$. $Q = b - Ae^{-t}$, where $A = \pm e^{-C}$ or $A = 0$.

22. $\frac{dP}{dt} = k(P - a)$, so $\frac{dP}{P-a} = k\,dt$, so $\int \frac{dP}{P-a} = \int k\,dt$. Integrating yields $\ln|P - a| = kt + C$ so $P = a + Ae^{kt}$ where $A = \pm e^{C}$ or $A = 0$.

23. $\frac{dR}{dt} = aR + b$. If $a = 0$, then this is just $\frac{dR}{dt} = b$, where b is a constant. Thus in this case $R = bt + C$ is a solution for any constant C.
       If $a \neq 0$, then $\frac{dR}{dt} = a(R + \frac{b}{a})$.
       Now this is just the same as Problem 22, except here we have a in place of k and $-\frac{b}{a}$ in place of a, so the solutions are $R = -\frac{b}{a} + Ae^{at}$ where A can be any constant.

24. $\frac{dy}{dt} = y(2-y)$ which implies that $\frac{dy}{y(y-2)} = -dt$, implying that $\int \frac{dy}{(y-2)(y)} = -\int dt$, so $-\frac{1}{2}\int (\frac{1}{y} - \frac{1}{y-2})dy - \int dt$.
       Integrating yields $\frac{1}{2}(\ln|y - 2| - \ln|y|) = -t + C$, so $\ln \frac{|y-2|}{|y|} = -2t + 2C$.
       Exponentiating both sides yields $|1 - \frac{2}{y}| = e^{-2t+2C} \Rightarrow \frac{2}{y} = 1 - Ae^{-2t}$, where $A = \pm e^{2C}$. Hence $y = \frac{2}{1-Ae^{-2t}}$. But $y(0) = \frac{2}{1-A} = 1$, so $A = -1$, and $y = \frac{2}{1+e^{-2t}}$.

25. $t\frac{dx}{dt} = (1+2\ln t)\tan x$ implies that $\frac{dx}{\tan x} = \left(\frac{1+2\ln t}{t}\right) dt$ which implies that $\int \frac{\cos x}{\sin x} dx = \int \left(\frac{1}{t} + \frac{2\ln t}{t}\right) dt$. $\ln|\sin x| = \ln t + (\ln t)^2 + C$. (We can write $\ln t$, since $t > 0$.)
$|\sin x| = e^{\ln t + (\ln t)^2 + C} = t(e^{\ln t})^{\ln t} e^C = t(t^{\ln t})e^C$. So $\sin x = At^{(\ln t + 1)}$, where $A = \pm e^C$. Therefore $x = \arcsin(At^{\ln t + 1})$.

26. $\frac{dx}{dt} = \frac{x\ln x}{t}$, so $\int \frac{dx}{x\ln x} = \int \frac{dt}{t}$ and thus $\ln|\ln x| = \ln|t| + C$, so $|\ln x| = e^C e^{\ln|t|} = e^C |t|$. Therefore $\ln x = At$, where $A = \pm e^C$, so $x = e^{At}$.

27. $\frac{dy}{dt} = -y\ln\left(\frac{y}{2}\right)$ implies that $\frac{dy}{y\ln\left(\frac{y}{2}\right)} = -dt$ implies that $\int \frac{dy}{y\ln\left(\frac{y}{2}\right)} = \int(-dt)$.
Substituting $w = \ln\left(\frac{y}{2}\right)$, $dw = \frac{1}{y} dy$ gives:
$\int \frac{dw}{w} = \int(-dt)$ implies that $\ln|w| = \ln\left|\ln\left(\frac{y}{2}\right)\right| = -t + C$. Since $y(0) = 1$, we have $C = \ln\left|\ln\frac{1}{2}\right| = \ln|-\ln 2| = \ln(\ln 2)$. Thus $\ln\left|\ln\left(\frac{y}{2}\right)\right| = -t + \ln(\ln 2)$, or

$$\left|\ln\left(\frac{y}{2}\right)\right| = e^{-t+\ln(\ln 2)} = (\ln 2)e^{-t}$$

Again, since $y(0) = 1$, we see that $-\ln(y/2) = (\ln 2)e^{-t}$ and thus $y = 2(2^{-e^{-t}})$. (Note that $\ln(y/2) = (\ln 2)e^{-t}$ does not satisfy $y(0) = 1$.)

28. (a) See (b).
    (b)

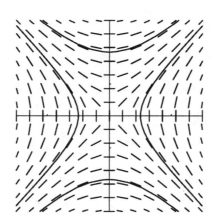

(c) $\frac{dy}{dx} = \frac{x}{y}$, so $\int y\, dy = \int x\, dx$ and thus $\frac{y^2}{2} = \frac{x^2}{2} + C$, or $y^2 - x^2 = 2C$. This is the equation of the hyperbolas in (b).

29. (a) See (b).

(b)

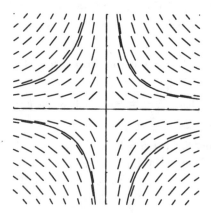

(c) $\frac{dy}{dx} = -\frac{y}{x}$, which implies that $\int \frac{dy}{y} = -\int \frac{dx}{x}$, so $\ln |y| = -\ln |x| + C$ implies that $|y| = e^{-\ln |x| + C} = (|x|)^{-1} e^{C}$.
$y = \frac{A}{x}$, where $A = \pm e^{C}$.

30. By looking at the slope fields, we see that any solution curve of $y' = \frac{x}{y}$ intersects any solution curve to $y' = -\frac{y}{x}$. Now if the two curves intersect at (x, y), then the two slopes at (x, y) are negative reciprocals of each other, because $-\frac{1}{x/y} = -\frac{y}{x}$. Hence, the two curves intersect at right angles.

9.5 SOLUTIONS

1. (a) If the world's population grows exponentially, satisfying $\frac{dP}{dt} = kP$, and if the arable land used is proportional to the population, then we'd expect A to satisfy $\frac{dA}{dt} = kA$. One is, of course, also assuming that the amount of arable land is large compared to the amount that is now being used.
    (b) We must solve $A = A_0 e^{kt} = (1 \times 10^9) e^{kt}$, where t is the number of years after 1950. Since $2 \times 10^9 = (1 \times 10^9) e^{k(30)}$, we have $e^{30k} = 2$, so $k = \frac{\ln 2}{30} \approx 0.023$. Thus, $A \approx (1 \times 10^9) e^{0.023t}$. We want to find t such that $3.2 \times 10^9 = A = (1 \times 10^9) e^{0.023t}$. Taking logarithms yields

    $$t = \frac{\ln(3.2)}{0.023} \approx 50.6 \text{ years.}$$

    Thus the arable land will have run out by the year 2001.

2. (a) Separating variables, we have $\frac{dH}{H-200} = -k \, dt$, so $\int \frac{dH}{H-200} = \int -k \, dt$, whence $\ln |H - 200| = -kt + C$, and $H - 200 = Ae^{-kt}$, where $A = \pm e^{C}$. The initial condition is that the yam is $20°C$ at the time $t = 0$. Thus $20 - 200 = A$, so $A = -180$. Thus $H = 200 - 180 e^{-kt}$.
    (b) Using part (a), we have $120 = 200 - 180 e^{-k(30)}$. Solving for k, we have $e^{-30k} = \frac{-80}{-180}$, giving

    $$k = \frac{\ln \frac{4}{9}}{-30} \approx 0.027.$$

Note that this k is correct if t is given in *minutes*. (If t is given in hours, $k = \frac{\ln \frac{4}{9}}{-\frac{1}{2}} \approx 1.62$.)

3. (a) = (I), (b) = (IV), (c) = (II) and (IV), (d) = (II) and (III).

4. (a) = (I), (b) = (IV), (c) = (II). Graph (III) could represent an egg taken out of a fridge at 4°C and put on the kitchen table (20°C).

5. (a) The rate of growth of the money in the account is proportional to the amount of money in the account. Thus

$$\frac{dM}{dt} = rM.$$

(b) Solving, we have $\frac{dM}{M} = r\,dt$.

$$\int \frac{dM}{M} = \int r\,dt$$
$$\ln|M| = rt + C$$
$$M = e^{rt+C} = Ae^{rt}$$

When $t = 0$ (in 1970), $M = 1000$, so $A = 1000$ and $M = 1000e^{rt}$.

(c)

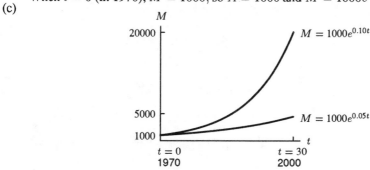

6. (a) $\frac{dB}{dt} = \frac{r}{100}B$. The constant of proportionality is $\frac{r}{100}$.

(b) Solving, we have

$$\frac{dB}{B} = \frac{r\,dt}{100}$$
$$\int \frac{dB}{B} = \int \frac{r}{100}\,dt$$
$$\ln|B| = \frac{r}{100}t + C$$
$$B = e^{\frac{r}{100}t+C} = Ae^{\frac{r}{100}t}.$$

A is the initial amount in the account, since A is the amount at time $t = 0$.

(c)

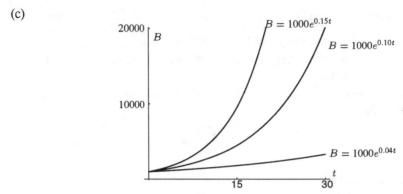

$B = 1000e^{0.15t}$

$B = 1000e^{0.10t}$

$B = 1000e^{0.04t}$

7. Since it takes 6 years to reduce the pollution to 10%, another 6 years would reduce the pollution to 10% of 10%, which is equivalent to 1% of the original. Therefore it takes 12 years for 99% of the pollution to be removed. (Note that the value of Q_0 does not affect this.) Thus the second time is double the first because the fraction remaining, 0.01, in the second instance is the square of the fraction remaining, 0.1, in the first instance.

8. Michigan:

$$\frac{dQ}{dt} = -\frac{r}{V}Q = -\frac{158}{4.9 \times 10^3}Q = -0.032Q$$

so

$$Q = Q_0 e^{-0.032t}$$

and

$$0.1Q_0 = Q_0 e^{-0.032t}$$

so

$$t = \frac{-\ln(0.1)}{0.032} \approx 71 \text{ years.}$$

Ontario:

$$\frac{dQ}{dt} = -\frac{r}{V}Q = \frac{-209}{1.6 \times 10^3}Q = -0.13Q$$

so

$$Q = Q_0 e^{-0.13t}$$

and

$$0.1Q_0 = Q_0 e^{-0.13t}$$

so

$$t = \frac{-\ln(0.1)}{0.13} \approx 18 \text{ years.}$$

Lake Michigan will take longer because it is larger (4900 km^3 compared to 1600 km^3) and water is flowing through it at a slower rate (158 km^3/year compared to 209 km^3/year).

9. Lake Superior will take the longest, because the lake is largest (V is largest) and water is moving through it most slowly (r is smallest). Lake Erie looks as though it will take the least time because V is smallest and r is close to the largest. For Erie, $k = r/V = 175/460 = 0.38$. The lake with the largest value of r is Ontario, where $k = r/V = 209/1600 = 0.13$. Since e^{-kt} decreases faster for larger k, Lake Erie will take the shortest time for any fixed fraction of the pollution to be removed.

For Lake Superior

$$\frac{dQ}{dt} = -\frac{r}{V}Q = -\frac{65.2}{12,200}Q = -0.0053Q$$

so

$$Q = Q_0 e^{-0.0053t}.$$

When 80% of the pollution has been removed, 20% remains so $Q = 0.2Q_0$. Substituting

$$0.2Q_0 = Q_0 e^{-0.0053t}$$

so

$$t = -\frac{\ln(0.2)}{0.0053} \approx 301 \text{ years.}$$

(Note: The 301 is obtained by using the exact value of $\frac{r}{V} = \frac{65.2}{12200}$, rather than 0.0053. Using 0.0053 gives 304 years.) For Lake Erie, as in the text

$$\frac{dQ}{dt} = -\frac{r}{V}Q = -\frac{175}{460}Q = -0.38Q$$

so

$$Q = Q_0 e^{-0.38t}.$$

When 80% of the pollution has been removed

$$0.2Q_0 = Q_0 e^{-0.38t}$$
$$t = -\frac{\ln(0.2)}{0.38} \approx 4 \text{ years.}$$

So the ratio is

$$\frac{\text{Time for Lake Superior}}{\text{Time for Lake Erie}} \approx \frac{301}{4} \approx 75.$$

In other words it will take about 75 times as long to clean Lake Superior as Lake Erie.

10. (a)

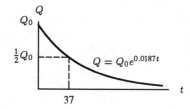

(b) $\dfrac{dQ}{dt} = -kQ$

(c) Since $Q = Q_0 e^{-kt}$ and $\frac{1}{2} = e^{-k(37)}$, we have

$$k = -\frac{\ln(1/2)}{37} = 0.0187.$$

Therefore $Q = Q_0 e^{-0.0187t}$. We know that when the drug level is 25% of the original level that $Q = 0.25Q_0$. Setting these equal, we get

$$0.25Q_0 = e^{-0.0187t}.$$

giving

$$t = -\frac{\ln(0.25)}{0.0187} \approx 74 \text{ hours} \approx 3 \text{ days}.$$

11. (a) Since the rate of change is proportional to the amount present, $\frac{dy}{dt} = ky$ for some constant k.

(b) Solving the differential equation, we have $y = Ae^{kt}$, where A is the initial amount. Since 100 grams become 54.9 grams in one hour, $54.9 = 100e^k$, so $k = \ln \frac{54.9}{100} \approx -0.6$.

Thus, after 10 hours, there remains $100e^{(-0.6)10} \approx 0.249$ grams.

12. (a) If P = pressure and h = height, $\frac{dP}{dh} = -3.7 \times 10^{-5}P$, so $P = P_0 e^{-3.7 \times 10^{-5}h}$. Now $P_0 = 29.92$, since pressure at sea level (when $h = 0$) is 29.92, so $P = 29.92e^{-3.7 \times 10^{-5}h}$. At the top of Mt. Whitney, the pressure is

$$P = 29.92e^{-3.7 \times 10^{-5}(14500)} \approx 17.50 \text{ inches of mercury}.$$

At the top of Mt. Everest, the pressure is

$$P = 29.92e^{-3.7 \times 10^{-5}(29000)} \approx 10.23 \text{ inches of mercury}.$$

(b) The pressure is 15 inches of mercury when

$$15 = 29.92e^{-3.7 \times 10^{-5}h}$$

Solving for h gives $h = \frac{-1}{3.7 \times 10^{-5}} \ln(\frac{15}{29.92}) \approx 18,661.5$ feet.

13. (a) If I is intensity and l is the distance traveled through the water, then for some $k > 0$,

$$\frac{dI}{dl} = -kI.$$

(The proportionality constant is negative because intensity decreases with distance) Thus $I = Ae^{-kl}$. Since $I = A$ when $l = 0$, A represents the initial intensity of the light.

(b) If 50% of the light is absorbed in 10 feet, then $0.50A = Ae^{-10k}$, so $e^{-10k} = \frac{1}{2}$, giving

$$k = \frac{-\ln \frac{1}{2}}{10} = \frac{\ln 2}{10}.$$

In 20 feet, the percentage of light left is

$$e^{-\frac{\ln 2}{10} \cdot 20} = e^{-2\ln 2} = (e^{\ln 2})^{-2} = 2^{-2} = \frac{1}{4},$$

so $\frac{3}{4}$ or 75% of the light has been absorbed. Similarly, after 25 feet,

$$e^{-\frac{\ln 2}{10} \cdot 25} = e^{-2.5\ln 2} = (e^{\ln 2})^{-\frac{5}{2}} = 2^{-\frac{5}{2}} \approx 0.177.$$

Approximately 17.7% of the light is left, so 82.3% of the light has been absorbed.

14. (a)

$$\frac{dT}{dt} = -k(T - A),$$

where $A = 10$ is the outside temperature.

(b) Integrating both sides yields

$$\int \frac{dT}{T - A} = -\int k\, dt.$$

Then $\ln |T - A| = -kt + C$, $T = A + Be^{-kt}$. So $T = A + (T_0 - A)e^{-kt}$, where $T_0 = 68$ is the initial temperature. Thus

$$T = 10 + 58e^{-kt}.$$

Let 1:00 pm be $t = 0$; at 10:00 pm ($t = 9$),

$$57 = 10 + (58)e^{-9k}$$
$$\frac{47}{58} = e^{-9k}$$
$$\ln \frac{47}{58} = -9k$$
$$k = -\frac{1}{9} \ln \frac{47}{58} \approx 0.0234.$$

At 7:00 the next morning ($t = 18$) we have

$$T \approx 10 + 58e^{18(-0.0234)}$$
$$= 10 + 58(0.66)$$
$$\approx 48°F$$

Your pipes won't freeze.

(c) We assumed that the temperature outside the house stayed constant at 10°F. This is probably incorrect because the temperature was most likely warmer during the day (between 1 pm and 10 pm) and colder after (between 10 pm and 7 am). Thus, when the temperature in the house dropped from 68°F to 57°F between 1 pm and 10 pm, the outside temperature was probably higher than 10°F, which changes our calculation of the value of the constant k. The house temperature will most certainly be lower than 48°F at 7 am, but not by much—not enough to freeze.

15.   We find the temperature of the orange juice as a function of time. Newton's Law of Heating says that the rate of change of the temperature is proportional to the temperature difference. If S is the temperature of the juice, this gives us the equation

$$\frac{dS}{dt} = -k(S - 65) \text{ for some constant } k.$$

Note that k is positive, since $S = 40$ initially and S increases towards the temperature of the room. Separating variables gives:

$\int \frac{dS}{S-65} = -\int k\, dt$
$\ln |S - 65| = -kt + C$
$S - 65 = Ae^{-kt}$, where $A = \pm e^C$.
So $S = 65 + Ae^{-kt}$.

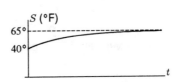

Since at $t = 0$, $S = 40$, we have $40 = 65 + A$, so $A = -25$. Thus $S = 65 - 25e^{-kt}$ for some positive constant k.

16.   (a) $\dfrac{dT}{dt} = -k(T - A)$, where $A = 68$ is the temperature of the room.

(b) $\displaystyle\int \frac{dT}{T - A} = -\int k\, dt,\ \ln |T - A| = -kt + C,\ T = A + Be^{-kt},\ \text{so } T = A + (T_0 - A)e^{-kt},$
where $T_0 = 90.3$ is the initial temperature. Thus

$$T = 68 + (90.3 - 68)e^{-kt}.$$

Letting 9 am be $t = 0$ (with initial temperature of $90.3°F$), then at 10 am, $t = 1$, so

$$89.0 = 68 + (90.3 - 68)e^{-k}$$
$$21 = 22.3e^{-k}$$
$$k = -\ln \frac{21}{22.3} \approx 0.06.$$

We want to know when T was equal to $98.6°F$, the temperature of a live body, so

$$98.6 = 68 + (90.3 - 68)e^{(-0.06)t}$$
$$\ln \frac{30.6}{22.3} = -0.06t$$
$$t = \left(-\frac{1}{0.06}\right) \ln \frac{30.6}{22.3}$$
$$t \approx -5.27.$$

The victim was killed approximately $5\frac{1}{4}$ hours prior to 9 am, at 3:45 am.

17.

$$\left(\begin{array}{c}\text{Rate at which quantity of}\\ \text{carbon-14 is increasing}\end{array}\right) = -k(\text{current quantity}).$$

If Q is the quantity of carbon-14 at time t (in years)

$$\text{Rate at which quantity is increasing} = \frac{dQ}{dt} = -kQ.$$

This differential equation has solution

$$Q = Q_0 e^{-kt}$$

where Q_0 is the initial quantity. Since at the end of one year 9999 parts are left out of 10,000, we know that

$$9999 = 10,000e^{-k(1)}.$$

Solving for k gives

$$k = \ln 0.9999 = 0.0001.$$

Thus $Q = Q_0 e^{-0.0001t}$. See Figure 9.7.

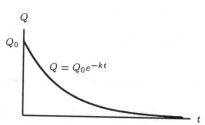

Figure 9.7: Exponential decay

18. (a) If $C' = -kC$, and then $C = C_0 e^{-kt}$. Since the half-life is 5730 years, $\frac{1}{2}C_0 = C_0 e^{-5730k}$. Solving for k, we have $-5730k = \ln \frac{1}{2}$ so $k = \frac{-\ln \frac{1}{2}}{5730} \approx 0.000121$.

   (b) From the given information, we have $0.91 = e^{-kt}$, where t is the age of the shroud. Solving for t, we have $t = \frac{-\ln 0.91}{k} \approx 779.4$ years.

19. The rate of disintegration is proportional to the quantity of carbon-14 present. Let Q be the quantity of carbon-14 present at time t, with $t = 0$ in 1977. Then

$$Q = Q_0 e^{-kt},$$

where Q_0 is the quantity of carbon-14 present in 1977 when $t = 0$. Then we know that

$$\frac{Q_0}{2} = Q_0 e^{-k(5730)}$$

so that

$$k = -\frac{\ln(1/2)}{5730} = 0.000121.$$

Thus

$$Q = Q_0 e^{-0.000121t}.$$

The quantity present at any time is proportional to the rate of disintegration at that time so

$$Q_0 = c8.2 \quad \text{and} \quad Q = c13.5$$

where c is a constant of proportionality. Thus substituting for Q and Q_0 in

$$Q = Q_0 e^{-0.000121t}$$

gives

$$c13.5 = c8.2e^{-0.000121t}$$

so

$$t = -\frac{\ln(13.5/8.2)}{0.000121} \approx -4120.$$

Thus Stonehenge was built about 4120 years before 1977, in about 2150 B.C.

20. (a) Since speed is the derivative of distance, Galileo's mistaken conjecture was $\frac{dD}{dt} = kD$.

(b) We know that if Galileo's conjecture were true, then $D(t) = D_0 e^{kt}$, where D_0 would be the initial distance fallen. But if we drop an object, it starts out not having traveled any distance, so $D_0 = 0$. This would lead to $D(t) = 0$ for all t.

9.6 SOLUTIONS

1. Let $D(t)$ be the quantity of dead leaves (in grams) per square centimeter. Then $\frac{dD}{dt} = 3 - 0.75D$, where t is in years. We factor out -0.75 and then separate variables.

$$\frac{dD}{dt} = -0.75(D - 4)$$
$$\int \frac{dD}{D - 4} = \int -0.75 \, dt$$
$$\ln|D - 4| = -0.75t + C$$
$$|D - 4| = e^{-0.75t + C} = e^{-0.75t} e^{C}$$
$$D = 4 + Ae^{-0.75t}, \text{ where } A = \pm e^{C}.$$

If initially the ground is clear, the solution looks like:

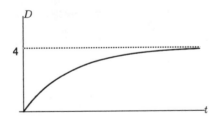

The equilibrium level is 4 grams per square centimeter, regardless of the initial condition.

2. (a) $\frac{dW}{dt} = \frac{1}{3500}(I - 20W)$

(b) $\frac{dW}{dt} = -\frac{2}{350}(W - \frac{I}{20}) \Rightarrow \int \frac{dW}{W - \frac{I}{20}} = -\int \frac{2}{350}\,dt \Rightarrow \ln|W - \frac{I}{20}| = -\frac{2}{350}t + C \Rightarrow W - \frac{I}{20} = Ae^{-\frac{2}{350}t} \Rightarrow W = \frac{I}{20} + Ae^{-\frac{2}{350}t}$

Let us call the person's initial weight W_0 at $t = 0$. Then $W_0 = \frac{I}{20} + Ae^0$, so $A = W_0 - \frac{I}{20}$. Thus

$$W = \frac{I}{20} + \left(W_0 - \frac{I}{20}\right)e^{-\frac{2}{350}t}.$$

(c)   Using (b), we have $W = 150 + 15e^{-\frac{2}{350}t}$. This means that $W \to 150$ as $t \to \infty$.

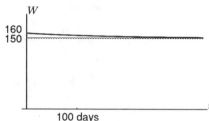

3. (a) $c'(t) = a(k - c(t))$ where $a > 0$ is a constant.

(b)

$$\int \frac{dc}{k - c} = \int a\,dt$$

$$-\ln|k - c| = at + C, \quad C \text{ is a constant of integration}$$

$$k - c = Ae^{-at}$$

If $c = c_0$ when $t = 0$, then $k - c_0 = A$, so

$$k - c = (k - c_0)e^{-at}$$
$$c = k + (c_0 - k)e^{-at}$$

(c)   If $c_0 = 0$, then $c = k - ke^{-at} = k(1 - e^{-at})$.

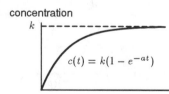

4. (a)   Since the interest rate oscillates from 7% to 9%, we will model it by an oscillation around 8% of the form

$$r = 0.08 + A \sin kt$$

where t is in years. The amplitude $A = 0.01$. Since the period is 6 years, we have $2\pi/k = 6$ so $k = \pi/3$.

(b)   The differential equation is

$$\frac{dB}{dt} = \left(0.08 + 0.01 \sin\left(\frac{\pi t}{3} \right) \right) B.$$

Separating variables,

$$\int \frac{dB}{B} = \int \left(0.08 + 0.01 \sin\left(\frac{\pi t}{3} \right) \right) dt$$

$$\ln B = 0.08t - \frac{0.01}{\pi/3} \cos\left(\frac{\pi t}{3} \right) + C$$

$$B = B_0 e^{0.08t - (0.03/\pi)\cos(\pi t/3)} \quad \text{where } B_0 = e^C.$$

5.   Let the depth of the water at time t be y. Then $\dfrac{dy}{dt} = -k\sqrt{y}$, where k is a positive constant. Separating variables,

$$\int \frac{dy}{\sqrt{y}} = -\int k \, dt,$$

so

$$2\sqrt{y} = -kt + C.$$

When $t = 0$, $y = 36$; $2\sqrt{36} = -k \cdot 0 + C$, so $C = 12$.
When $t = 1$, $y = 35$; $2\sqrt{35} = -k + 12$, so $k \approx 0.17$.
Thus, $2\sqrt{y} \approx -0.17t + 12$. We are looking for t such that $y = 0$; this happens when $t \approx \frac{12}{0.17} \approx 71$ hours, or about 3 days.

6.   (a)   Quantity of A present at time t equals $(a - x)$.
      Quantity of B present at time t equals $(b - x)$.
      So

$$\text{Rate of formation of } C = k(\text{Quantity of } A)(\text{Quantity of } B)$$

gives

$$\frac{dx}{dt} = k(a - x)(b - x)$$

(b)   Separating gives

$$\int \frac{dx}{(a - x)(b - x)} = \int k \, dt$$

Rewriting the denominator as $(a - x)(b - x) = (x - a)(x - b)$ enables us to use Formula 26 in the Table of Integrals provided $a \neq b$. For some constant K, this gives

$$\frac{1}{a - b} \left(\ln |x - a| - \ln |x - b| \right) = kt + K$$

Thus

$$\ln\left|\frac{x-a}{x-b}\right| = (a-b)kt + K(a-b)$$

$$\left|\frac{x-a}{x-b}\right| = e^{K(a-b)}e^{(a-b)kt}$$

$$\frac{x-a}{x-b} = Me^{(a-b)kt} \quad \text{where } M = \pm e^{K(a-b)}$$

Since $x = 0$ when $t = 0$, we have $M = \frac{a}{b}$. Thus

$$\frac{x-a}{x-b} = \frac{a}{b}e^{(a-b)kt}$$

Solving for x

$$bx - ba = ae^{(a-b)kt}(x-b)$$

$$x(b - ae^{(a-b)kt}) = ab - abe^{(a-b)kt}$$

$$x = \frac{ab(1 - e^{(a-b)kt})}{b - ae^{(a-b)kt}} = \frac{ab(e^{bkt} - e^{akt})}{be^{bkt} - ae^{akt}}$$

7. Quantity of A left at time t = Quantity of B left at time t equals $(a - x)$.
   Thus

   Rate of formation of $C = k$(Quantity of A)(Quantity of B)

gives

$$\frac{dx}{dt} = k(a - x)(a - x) = k(a - x)^2.$$

Separating gives

$$\int \frac{dx}{(x-a)^2} = \int k\, dt$$

Integrating gives, for some constant K,

$$-(x - a)^{-1} = kt + K.$$

When $t = 0$, $x = 0$ so $K = a^{-1}$. Solving for x:

$$-(x - a)^{-1} = kt + a^{-1}$$

$$x - a = -\frac{1}{kt + a^{-1}}$$

$$x = a - \frac{a}{akt + 1} = \frac{a^2 kt}{akt + 1}$$

8. (a) Use the fact that

$$\left(\begin{array}{c} \text{Rate at which} \\ \text{balance is increasing} \end{array} \right) = \left(\begin{array}{c} \text{Rate interest} \\ \text{is accrued} \end{array} \right) - \left(\begin{array}{c} \text{Rate payments} \\ \text{are made} \end{array} \right).$$

Thus $\frac{dB}{dt} = 0.05 B - 12000$.

(b) We solve the equation by separation of variables. First, however, we factor out a 0.05 on the right hand side of the equation to make the work easier.
$\frac{dB}{dt} = 0.05(B - 240000) \Rightarrow \frac{dB}{B-240000} = 0.05 \, dt \Rightarrow \int \frac{dB}{B-240000} = \int 0.05 \, dt$, so
$\ln|B - 240000| = 0.05t + C \Rightarrow |B - 240000| = e^{0.05t+C} = e^{0.05t}e^C$, so
$B - 240000 = Ae^{0.05t}$, where $A = \pm e^C$.
If the initial balance is B_0, then $B_0 - 240000 = Ae^0 = A$, thus $B - 240000 = (B_0 - 240000)e^{0.05t}$,
so $B = (B_0 - 240000)e^{0.05t} + 240000$.

(c) To find the initial balance such that the account has a 0 balance after 20 years, we solve $0 = (B_0 - 240000)e^{(0.05)20} + 240000 = (B_0 - 240000)e^1 + 240000$,

$$B_0 = 240000 - \frac{240000}{e} \approx \$151,708.93.$$

9. Using (rate balance increasing) = (rate interest added) − (rate payments made), when the interest rate is i, we have

$$\frac{dB}{dt} = iB - 100.$$

Solving this equation, we find:

$$\frac{dB}{dt} = i \left(B - \frac{100}{i} \right)$$

$$\int \frac{dB}{B - \frac{100}{i}} = \int i \, dt$$

$$\ln \left| B - \frac{100}{i} \right| = it + C$$

$$B - \frac{100}{i} = Ae^{it}, \text{ where } A = \pm e^C.$$

At time $t = 0$ we start with a balance of $\$1000$. Thus
$1000 - \frac{100}{i} = Ae^0$, so $A = 1000 - \frac{100}{i}$.
Thus $B = \frac{100}{i} + (1000 - \frac{100}{i})e^{it}$.
When $i = 0.05$, $B = 2000 - 1000e^{0.05t}$.
When $i = 0.1$, $B = 1000$.
When $i = 0.15$, $B = 666.67 + 333.33e^{0.15t}$.
We now look at the graph when $i = 0.05, i = 0.1$, and $i = 0.15$.

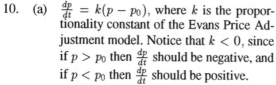

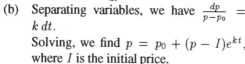

10. (a) $\frac{dp}{dt} = k(p - p_0)$, where k is the proportionality constant of the Evans Price Adjustment model. Notice that $k < 0$, since if $p > p_0$ then $\frac{dp}{dt}$ should be negative, and if $p < p_0$ then $\frac{dp}{dt}$ should be positive.

(c)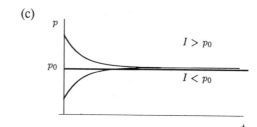

(b) Separating variables, we have $\frac{dp}{p - p_0} = k\,dt$.
Solving, we find $p = p_0 + (p - I)e^{kt}$, where I is the initial price.

(d) As $t \to \infty, p \to p_0$. We see this in the solution in (b), since as $t \to \infty, e^{kt} \to 0$. (Remember $k < 0$!) In other words, as $t \to \infty$, p approaches the equilibrium price p_0.

11. (a) $\frac{dy}{dt} = -k(y - a)$, where $k > 0$ and a are constants.

(b) $\int \frac{dy}{y - a} = \int -k\,dt$, so $\ln|y - a| = \ln(y - a) = -kt + C$. Thus, $y - a = Ae^{-kt}$ where $A = e^C$. Initially nothing has been forgotten, so $y(0) = 1$. Therefore, $1 - a = Ae^0 = A$, so $y - a = (1 - a)e^{-kt}$ or $y = (1 - a)e^{-kt} + a$.

(c) As $t \to \infty, e^{-kt} \to 0$, so $y \to a$.
Thus, a represents the fraction of material which is remembered in the long run. The constant k tells us about the rate at which material is forgotten.

12. (a) The quantity and the concentration both increase with time. As the concentration increases, the rate at which the drug is excreted also increases, and so the rate at which the drug builds up in the blood decreases; thus the graph of concentration against time is concave down. The concentration rises until the rate of excretion exactly balances the rate at which the drug is entering; at this concentration there is a horizontal asymptote. (See Figure 9.8.)

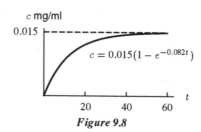

Figure 9.8

(b) Let's start by writing a differential equation for the quantity, $Q(t)$.

$$\begin{pmatrix} \text{Rate quantity} \\ \text{of drug changes} \end{pmatrix} = (\text{Rate in}) - (\text{Rate out})$$

$$\frac{dQ}{dt} = 43.2 - 0.082Q$$

where Q is measured in mg. We want an equation for concentration $c(t) = \frac{Q(t)}{v}$, where $c(t)$ is measured in mg/ml with $v = 35,000$ ml.

$$\frac{1}{v}\frac{dQ}{dt} = \frac{43.2}{v} - 0.082\frac{Q}{v},$$

giving

$$\frac{dc}{dt} = \frac{43.2}{35,000} - 0.082c.$$

(c) Factor out -0.082 and separate variables to solve.

$$\frac{dc}{dt} = -0.082(c - 0.015)$$

$$\int \frac{dc}{c - 0.015} = -0.082 \int dt$$

$$\ln|c - 0.015| = -0.082t + B$$

$$c - 0.015 = Ae^{-0.082t} \quad \text{where} \quad A = \pm e^B$$

Since $c = 0$ when $t = 0$, we have $A = -0.015$, so

$$c = 0.015 - 0.015e^{-0.082t} = 0.015(1 - e^{-0.082t}).$$

Thus $c \to 0.015$ mg/ml as $t \to \infty$.

13. (a)

$$\frac{dQ}{dt} = r - \alpha Q = -\alpha(Q - \frac{r}{\alpha})$$

$$\int \frac{dQ}{Q - r/\alpha} = = -\alpha \int dt$$

$$\ln\left|Q - \frac{r}{\alpha}\right| = -\alpha t + C$$

$$Q - \frac{r}{\alpha} = Ae^{-\alpha t}$$

When $t = 0$, $Q = 0$, so $A = -\frac{r}{\alpha}$ and

$$Q = \frac{r}{\alpha}(1 - e^{-\alpha t})$$

So,

$$Q_\infty = \lim_{t \to \infty} Q = \frac{r}{\alpha}.$$

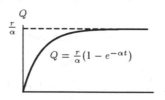

(b) Doubling r doubles Q_∞. Since $Q_\infty = r/\alpha$, the time to reach $\frac{1}{2}Q_\infty$ is obtained by solving

$$\frac{r}{2\alpha} = \frac{r}{\alpha}(1 - e^{-\alpha t})$$

$$\frac{1}{2} = 1 - e^{-\alpha t}$$

$$e^{-\alpha t} = \frac{1}{2}$$

$$t = -\frac{\ln(1/2)}{\alpha} = \frac{\ln 2}{\alpha}.$$

So altering r doesn't alter the time it takes to reach $\frac{1}{2}Q_\infty$.

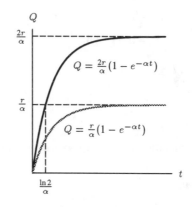

(c) Q_∞ is halved by doubling α, and so is the time, $t = \frac{\ln 2}{\alpha}$, to reach $\frac{1}{2}Q_\infty$.

14. (a) Concentration of carbon monoxide $= \dfrac{\text{Quantity in room}}{\text{Volume}}$.
     If $Q(t)$ represents the quantity of carbon monoxide in the room at time t, $c(t) = Q(t)/60$.

$$\begin{matrix}\text{Rate quantity of} \\ \text{carbon monoxide in room} \\ \text{changes}\end{matrix} = \text{rate in} - \text{rate out}$$

Now

$$\text{Rate in} = 5\%(0.002 \text{m}^3/\text{min}) = 0.05(0.002) = 0.0001 \text{m}^3/\text{min}.$$

Since smoky air is leaving at $0.002 \text{m}^3/\text{min}$, containing a concentration $c(t) = Q(t)/60$ of carbon monoxide

$$\text{Rate out} = 0.002 \frac{Q(t)}{60}$$

Thus

$$\frac{dQ}{dt} = 0.0001 - \frac{0.002}{60} Q$$

Since $c = Q/60$, we can substitute $Q = 60c$, giving

$$\frac{d(60c)}{dt} = 0.0001 - \frac{0.002}{60}(60c)$$

$$\frac{dc}{dt} = \frac{0.0001}{60} - \frac{0.002}{60}(c)$$

(b) Factoring the right side of the differential equation and separating gives

$$\frac{dc}{dt} = -\frac{0.0001}{3}(c - 0.05) \approx 3 \times 10^{-5}(c - 0.05)$$

$$\int \frac{dc}{c - 0.05} = -\int 3 \times 10^{-5} dt$$

$$\ln|c - 0.05| = -3 \times 10^{-5}t + K$$

$$c - 0.05 = Ae^{-3 \times 10^{-5}t} \quad \text{where} A = \pm e^K.$$

Since $c = 0$ when $t = 0$, we have $A = -0.05$, so

$$c = 0.05 - 0.05e^{-3 \times 10^{-5}t}$$

(c) As $t \to \infty$, $e^{-3 \times 10^{-5}t} \to 0$ so $c \to 0.05$.
Thus in the long run, the concentration of carbon monoxide tends to 5%, the concentration of the incoming air.

15. $c = 0.05 - 0.05e^{-3 \times 10^{-5}t}$
We want to solve for t when $c = 0.001$

$$0.001 = 0.05 - 0.05e^{-3 \times 10^{-5}t}$$

$$-0.049 = -0.05e^{-3 \times 10^{-5}t}$$

$$e^{-3 \times 10^{-5}t} = 0.98$$

$$t = \frac{-\ln(0.98)}{3 \times 10^{-5}} = 673 \text{ min} \approx 11 \text{ hours } 13 \text{ min}.$$

16. (a) Now

$$\frac{dS}{dt} = \text{(Rate at which salt enters the pool)} - \text{(Rate at which salt leaves the pool)},$$

and, for example,

$$\left(\begin{array}{c} \text{Rate at which salt} \\ \text{enters the pool} \end{array} \right) = \left(\begin{array}{c} \text{Concentration of} \\ \text{salt solution} \end{array} \right) \times \left(\begin{array}{c} \text{Flow rate of} \\ \text{salt solution} \end{array} \right)$$

$$\text{(grams/minute)} = \text{(grams/liter)} \times \text{(liters/minute)}$$

so

$$\text{Rate at which salt enters the pool} =$$
$$\text{(10 grams/liter)} \times \text{(60 liters/minute)} = \text{(600 grams/minute)}$$

The rate at which salt leaves the pool depends on the concentration of salt in the pool. At time t, the concentration is $\frac{S(t)}{2 \times 10^6 \text{ liters}}$, where $S(t)$ is measured in grams.
Thus

$$\text{Rate at which salt leaves the pool} =$$
$$\frac{S(t) \text{ grams}}{2 \times 10^6 \text{ liters}} \times \frac{60 \text{ liters}}{\text{minute}} = \frac{3S(t) \text{ grams}}{10^5 \text{ minutes}}.$$

Thus

$$\frac{dS}{dt} = 600 - \frac{3S}{100,000}.$$

(b) $\frac{dS}{dt} = -\frac{3}{100,000}(S - 20,000,000)$
$\int \frac{dS}{S - 20,000,000} = \int -\frac{3}{100,000} \, dt$
$\ln |S - 20,000,000| = -\frac{3}{100,000}t + C$
$S = 20,000,000 - Ae^{-\frac{3}{100,000}t}$
Since $S = 0$ at $t = 0$, $A = 20,000,000$. Thus $S(t) = 20,000,000 - 20,000,000e^{-\frac{3}{100,000}t}$.

(c) As $t \to \infty$, $e^{-\frac{3}{100,000}t} \to 0$, so $S(t) \to 20,000,000$ grams. The concentration approaches 10 grams/liter. Note that this makes sense; we'd expect the concentration of salt in the pool to become closer and closer to the concentration of salt being poured into the pool as $t \to \infty$.

17. (a) If $B = f(t)$ (where t is in years)

$$\frac{dB}{dt} = \text{(rate of money earned by interest)} + \text{(rate of money deposited)}$$
$$= 0.10B + 1000.$$

(b)

$$\frac{dB}{dt} = 0.1(B + 10000)$$

$$\int \frac{dB}{B + 10000} = \int 0.1 \, dt$$

$$\ln|B + 10000| = 0.1t + C$$

$$B = Ae^{0.1t} - 10000.$$

Since the initial balance is 0, then $B = 10000e^{0.1t} - 10000$.

(c) Suppose a deposit is made at time x. Then at time $t > x$, this deposit will have earned interest for $t - x$ years. We use this fact to set up the Riemann sum. Suppose we want to find the balance at time t. Divide it up into pieces of size Δx. The deposit made at time x is thus $\$1000 \cdot \Delta x$, and at time t it is worth $\$1000 \cdot \Delta x e^{0.1(t-x)}$. Thus our Riemann sum looks like $\sum 1000 e^{0.1(t-x)} \Delta x$, and the corresponding integral is $f(t) = \int_0^t 1000 e^{0.1(t-x)} \, dx$.

(d) $\int_0^t 1000 e^{0.1(t-x)} \, dx = 1000 \left[-10 e^{0.1(t-x)} \right] \Big|_0^t = 10000 e^{0.1t} - 10000$. This is the same answer as in part (b).

(e) If the initial deposit is B_0, then $B_0 = A - 10000$, so the solution is $B = (B_0 + 10000)e^{0.1t} - 10000$.

(f) The integral in part (d) actually stays the same. If the initial deposit is B_0, though, our integral doesn't take into account what happens to it. At time t, the initial deposit of B_0 is worth $B_0 e^{0.1t}$, so adding this in we would get

$$B = f(t) = B_0 e^{0.1t} + \int_0^t 1000 e^{0.1(t-x)} \, dx$$

$$= B_0 e^{0.1t} + 10000 e^{0.1t} - 10000$$

$$= (B_0 + 10000)e^{0.1t} - 10000.$$

This matches the answer of part (e).

18. (a) Newton's Law of Motion says that

$$\text{Force} = (\text{mass}) \times (\text{acceleration}).$$

Since acceleration, dv/dt, is measured upward and the force due to gravity acts downward,

$$-\frac{mgR^2}{(R+h)^2} = m\frac{dv}{dt}$$

so

$$\frac{dv}{dt} = -\frac{gR^2}{(R+h)^2}.$$

(b) Since $v = \frac{dh}{dt}$, the chain rule gives

$$\frac{dv}{dt} = \frac{dv}{dh} \cdot \frac{dh}{dt} = \frac{dv}{dh} \cdot v.$$

Substituting into the differential equation in part (a) gives

$$v\frac{dv}{dh} = -\frac{gR^2}{(R+h)^2}.$$

(c) Separating variables gives

$$\int v\, dv = -\int \frac{gR^2}{(R+h)^2}\, dh$$

$$\frac{v^2}{2} = \frac{gR^2}{(R+h)} + C$$

Since $v = v_0$ when $h = 0$,

$$\frac{v_0{}^2}{2} = \frac{gR^2}{(R+0)} + C \quad \text{gives} \quad C = \frac{v_0{}^2}{2} - gR,$$

so the solution is

$$\frac{v^2}{2} = \frac{gR^2}{(R+h)} + \frac{v_0{}^2}{2} - gR$$

$$v^2 = v_0{}^2 + \frac{2gR^2}{(R+h)} - 2gR$$

(d) The escape velocity v_0 ensures that $v^2 \geq 0$ for all $h \geq 0$. Since the positive quantity $\dfrac{2gR^2}{(R+h)} \to 0$ as $h \to \infty$, to ensure that $v^2 \geq 0$ for all h, we must have

$$v_0{}^2 \geq 2gR.$$

When $v_0{}^2 = 2gR$ so $v_0 = \sqrt{2gR}$, we say that v_0 is the escape velocity.

19. Since $R' > 0$ currently, R is increasing and R' is given by

$$R' = \sqrt{\frac{2GM_0}{R} - K},$$

where $C = -K$ and $K > 0$. Now R increases until $\frac{2GM_0}{R} = K$, giving $R_{max} = \frac{2GM_0}{K}$. At this value of R, we have $R' = 0$. Since R' has decreased to 0, and since $R'' < 0$ always, R' will go on decreasing. (The original second order differential equation shows that $R'' < 0$.) Thus R' becomes negative, and is now given by

$$R' = -\sqrt{\frac{2GM_0}{R} - K}.$$

Since R' is now negative, R decreases, thereby making R' more and more negative – so the universe collapses. (See Figure 9.9.)

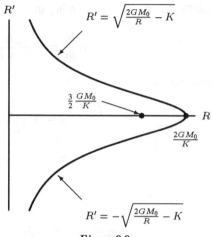

Figure 9.9

20. Separating variables gives

$$\frac{dR}{dt} = \frac{\sqrt{2GM_0}}{R^{1/2}}$$

$$\int R^{1/2}\, dR = \int \sqrt{2GM_0}\, dt$$

$$\frac{2}{3} R^{3/2} = \sqrt{2GM_0}\, t + A$$

Since $R = 0$ when $t = 0$, we have $A = 0$, so

$$R = \left(\frac{3\sqrt{2GM_0}}{2}\right)^{2/3} t^{2/3} = kt^{2/3} \quad \text{where } k = \left(\frac{3\sqrt{2GM_0}}{2}\right)^{2/3}, \text{ a constant.}$$

Therefore in the flat universe, $R = kt^{2/3}$ and $R' = \frac{2k}{3} t^{-1/3}$, meaning that the universe expands for all t, but the rate at which it expands goes to zero as $t \to \infty$.

21. (a) For a stable universe, we need $R' = 0$, so $R'' = 0$. However the differential equation for R'' shows that $R'' < 0$ for every R, so we never have $R'' = 0$. Thus R' and R must both be changing with time.

    (b) If the universe were expanding at a constant rate of $R'(t_0)$, then $R(t_0)/R'(t_0)$ would be the time it took for the radius to grow from 0 to $R(t_0)$ – a reasonable estimate for the age of the universe. Since in fact R' has been decreasing, in other words, the universe has actually been expanding faster than $R'(t_0)$, the Hubble constant is an overestimate (i.e. the universe is actually younger than the Hubble constant suggests.)

22. Since $f(r)$ is proportional to a power of r, we have $f(r) = kr^\alpha$. Since $p(r)$ is proportional to $f(r)$, we also have $p(r) = cr^\alpha$. Thus substituting

$$c\alpha r^{\alpha - 1} = \frac{-Gkr^\alpha}{r^2} \int_0^r 4\pi t^2 \cdot kt^\alpha\, dt$$

$$= -4\pi G k^2 r^{\alpha-2} \int_0^r t^{\alpha+2}\, dt$$

$$= -4\pi G k^2 r^{\alpha-2} \left[\frac{t^{\alpha+3}}{\alpha+3} \right]_0^r$$

$$= -\frac{4\pi G k^2}{\alpha+3} r^{\alpha-2} r^{\alpha+3} = -\frac{4\pi G k^2}{\alpha+3} r^{\alpha-2+\alpha+3}$$

$$= -\frac{4\pi G k^2}{\alpha+3} r^{2\alpha+1}$$

Since the powers of r on each side of the equation must be equal

$$\alpha - 1 = 2\alpha + 1$$

so

$$\alpha = -2$$

Thus $f(r) = kr^{-2}$.

23. (a)

$$p(x) = \text{the number of people with incomes} \geq x.$$

$$p(x + \Delta x) = \text{the number of people with incomes} \geq x + \Delta x.$$

So the number of people with incomes between x and $x + \Delta x$ is

$$p(x) - p(x + \Delta x) = -\Delta p.$$

Since all the people with incomes between x and $x + \Delta x$ have incomes of about x (if Δx is small), the total amount of money earned by people in this income bracket is approximately $x(-\Delta p) = -x\Delta p$.

(b) Pareto's law claims that the average income of all the people with incomes $\geq x$ is kx. Since there are $p(x)$ people with income $\geq x$, the total amount of money earned by people in this group is $kxp(x)$.

The total amount of money earned by people with incomes $\geq (x + \Delta x)$ is therefore $k(x + \Delta x)p(x + \Delta x)$. Then the total amount of money earned by people with incomes between x and $x + \Delta x$ is

$$kxp(x) - k(x + \Delta x)p(x + \Delta x).$$

Since $\Delta p = p(x + \Delta x) - p(x)$, we can substitute $p(x + \Delta x) = p(x) + \Delta p$. Thus the total amount of money earned by people with incomes between x and $x + \Delta x$ is

$$kxp(x) - k(x + \Delta x)(p(x) + \Delta p).$$

Multiplying out, we have

$$kxp(x) - kxp(x) - k(\Delta x)p(x) - kx\Delta p - k\Delta x\Delta p$$

Simplifying and dropping the second order term $\Delta x\Delta p$ gives the total amount of money earned by people with incomes between x and $x + \Delta x$ as

$$-kp\Delta x - kx\Delta p.$$

(c) Setting the answers to parts (a) and (b) equal gives

$$-x\Delta p = -kp\Delta x - kx\Delta p.$$

Dividing by Δx, and letting $\Delta x \to 0$ so that $\frac{\Delta p}{\Delta x} \to p'$,

$$x\frac{\Delta p}{\Delta x} = kp + kx\frac{\Delta p}{\Delta x}$$
$$xp' = kp + kxp'$$

so

$$(1-k)xp' = kp.$$

(d) We solve this equation by separating variables

$$\int \frac{dp}{p} = \int \frac{k}{(1-k)}\frac{dx}{x}$$

$$\ln p = \frac{k}{(1-k)}\ln x + C \quad \text{(no absolute values needed since } p, x > 0)$$

$$\ln p = \ln x^{k/(1-k)} + \ln A \quad \text{(writing } C = \ln A)$$

$$\ln p = \ln Ax^{k/(1-k)} \quad \text{(using } \ln(AB) = \ln A + \ln B)$$

$$p = Ax^{k/(1-k)}$$

(e) We take $A = 1$. For $k = 10$, $p = x^{-10/9} \approx x^{-1}$. For $k = 1.1$, $p = x^{-11}$. The functions are graphed in Figure 9.10. Notice that the larger the value of k, the less negative the value of $k/(1-k)$ (remember $k > 1$), and the slower $p(x) \to 0$ as $x \to \infty$).

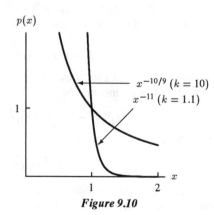

Figure 9.10

9.7 SOLUTIONS

1. A continuous growth rate of 0.2% means that

    $$\frac{1}{P}\frac{dP}{dt} = 0.2\% = 0.002.$$

    Separating variables and integrating gives

    $$\int \frac{dP}{P} = \int 0.002\, dt$$

    $$P = P_0 e^{0.002t} = (6.6 \times 10^6)e^{0.002t}.$$

2. (a)

    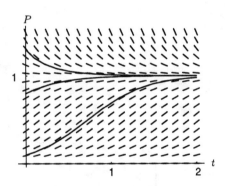

    Figure 9.11

    (b) The value $P = 1$ is a stable equilibrium. (See (d) below for a more detailed discussion.)

    (c) Looking at the solution curves, we see that P is increasing for $0 < P < 1$ and decreasing for $P > 1$. The values of $P = 0$, $P = 1$ are equilibria. In the long run, P tends to 1, unless you start with $P = 0$. The solution curves with initial populations of less than $P = \frac{1}{2}$ have inflection points at $P = \frac{1}{2}$. (This will be demonstrated algebraically in (d) below.) At the inflection point, the population is growing fastest.

    (d)

    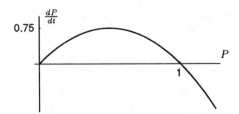

    Figure 9.12

Since $\frac{dP}{dt} = 3P - 3P^2 = 3P(1 - P)$, the graph of $\frac{dP}{dt}$ against P is a parabola, opening downwards with P intercepts at 0 and 1. The quantity $\frac{dP}{dt}$ is positive for $0 < P < 1$, negative for $P > 1$ (and $P < 0$). The quantity $\frac{dP}{dt}$ is 0 at $P = 0$ and $P = 1$, and maximum at $P = \frac{1}{2}$. The fact that $\frac{dP}{dt} = 0$ at $P = 0$ and $P = 1$ tells us that these are equilibria. Further, since $\frac{dP}{dt} > 0$ for $0 < P < 1$, we see that solution curves starting here will increase toward $P = 1$.

If the population starts at a value $P < \frac{1}{2}$, it increases at an increasing rate up to $P = \frac{1}{2}$. After this, P continues to increase, but at a decreasing rate. The fact that $\frac{dP}{dt}$ has a maximum at $P = \frac{1}{2}$ tells us that there is a point of inflection when $P = \frac{1}{2}$. Similarly, since $\frac{dP}{dt} < 0$ for $P > 1$, solution curves starting with $P > 1$ will decrease to $P = 1$. Thus, $P = 1$ is a stable equilibrium.

3. (a) $\frac{dp}{dt} = kp(B - p)$, where $k > 0$.

(b) To find when $\frac{dp}{dt}$ is largest, we notice that $\frac{dp}{dt} = kp(B - p)$ is a parabola opening downwards with the maximum at $p = \frac{B}{2}$, i.e. when $\frac{1}{2}$ the tin has turned to powder. This is the time when the tin is crumbling fastest.

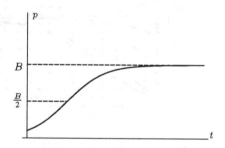

(c) If $p = 0$ initially, then $\frac{dp}{dt} = 0$, so we would expect p to remain 0 forever. However, since many organ pipes get tin pest, we must reconcile the model with reality. There are two possible ideas which solve this problem. First, we could assume that p is never 0. In other words, we assume that all tin pipes, no matter how new, must contain some small amount of tin pest. Assuming this means that all organ pipes must deteriorate due to tin pest eventually. Another explanation is that the powder forms at a slow rate even if there was none present to begin with. Since not all organ pipes suffer, it is possible that the conversion is catalyzed by some other impurities not present in all pipes.

4. Rewriting the equation as $\frac{1}{P}\frac{dP}{dt} = \frac{(100 - P)}{1000}$, we see that this is a logistic equation. Before looking at its solution, we explain why there must always be at least 100 individuals. Since the population begins at 200, $\frac{dP}{dt}$ is initially negative, so the population decreases. It continues to do so while $P > 100$. If the population ever reached 100, however, then $\frac{dP}{dt}$ would be 0. This means the population would stop changing – so if the population ever decreased to 100, that's where it would stay.

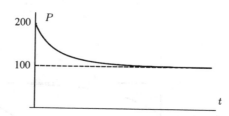

The solution, as given by the formula derived in the chapter, is

$$P = \frac{20000}{200 - 100e^{-t/10}}$$

5. (a) Let I be the number of informed people at time t, and I_0 the number who know initially. Then this model predicts that $\frac{dI}{dt} = k(M - I)$ for some positive constant k. Solving this, we find the solution is

$$I = M - (M - I_0)e^{-kt}.$$

We sketch the solution with $I_0 = 0$. Notice that $\frac{dI}{dt}$ is largest when I is smallest, so the information spreads fastest in the beginning, at $t = 0$. In addition, the graph shows that $I \to M$ as $t \to \infty$, meaning that everyone gets the information eventually.

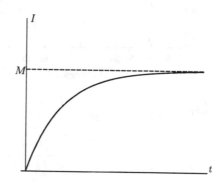

(b) In this case, the model suggests that $\frac{dI}{dt} = kI(M - I)$ for some positive constant k. This is a logistic model with carrying capacity M. We sketch the solutions for three different values of I_0.

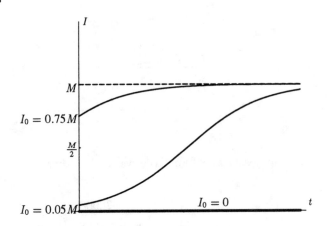

(i) If $I_0 = 0$. Then $I = 0$ for all t. In other words, if nobody knows something, it doesn't spread by word of mouth!

(ii) If $I_0 = 0.05M$, then $\frac{dI}{dt}$ is increasing up to $I = \frac{M}{2}$. Thus, the information is spreading fastest at $I = \frac{M}{2}$.

(iii) If $I_0 = 0.75M$, then $\frac{dI}{dt}$ is always decreasing for $I > \frac{M}{2}$, so $\frac{dI}{dt}$ is largest when $t = 0$.

6. (a) Figure 9.13 shows that the yeast population seems to stabilize at about 13, so we take this to be the limiting value, L.

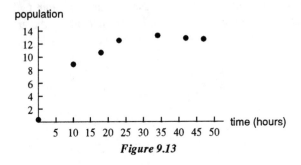

Figure 9.13

(b) Solving $\frac{dP}{dt} = kP(1 - \frac{P}{L})$ for k, we get:

$$k = \frac{dP/dt}{P \cdot (1 - \frac{P}{L})}$$

We now find $\frac{dP}{dt}$ from the first two data points.

$$\frac{dP}{dt} \approx \frac{\Delta P}{\Delta t} = \frac{P(10) - P(0)}{10 - 0} = \frac{8.87 - 0.37}{10} = 0.85$$

Putting in our values for dP/dt, L, and $P(10)$, we get:

$$k \approx \frac{dP/dt}{P(10) \cdot (1 - \frac{P(10)}{L})} = \frac{0.85}{(8.87)(1 - \frac{8.87}{13})} = 0.30$$

(c) For $k = 0.3$ and $L = 13$,

$$A = \frac{L - P_0}{P_0} = \frac{13 - 0.37}{0.37} = 34.1.$$

Putting this into the equation for P we get:

$$P = \frac{13}{1 + Ae^{-kt}} = \frac{13}{1 + 34.1e^{-0.3t}},$$

which is plotted below.

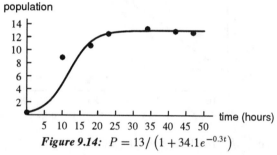

Figure 9.14: $P = 13/\left(1 + 34.1e^{-0.3t}\right)$

7. (a) The population seems to level off around 5.8, which leads us to believe that the population is growing logistically. If it were growing exponentially, we would expect the rate of increase to continue increasing with time.

(b) To find k, we solve the logistic equation, $\frac{dP}{dt} = kP(1 - \frac{P}{L})$, for k:

$$k = \frac{dP/dt}{P \cdot (1 - \frac{P}{L})}.$$

We now need to estimate dP/dt and L from the data. The population seems to level off at 5.8, so we take this as as the carrying capacity, L. We use the first two data points to find dP/dt:

$$\frac{dP}{dt} \approx \frac{\Delta P}{\Delta t} = \frac{P(13) - P(0)}{13 - 0} = \frac{1.7 - 1.00}{13} = 0.054$$

Putting in our values for dP/dt, L, and $P(13)$, we get:

$$k \approx \frac{dP/dt}{P(13) \cdot (1 - \frac{P(13)}{L})} = \frac{0.054}{(1.7)(1 - \frac{1.7}{5.8})} = 0.045$$

(c)   The solution curve for $\frac{dP}{dt} = kP\left(1 - \frac{P}{L}\right)$ with $k = 0.045$, and $L = 5.8$ has equation

$$P = \frac{5.8}{\left(1 + Ae^{-kt}\right)} \quad \text{where} \quad A = \frac{L - P_0}{P_0}.$$

Since $P_0 = 1$ then $A = \frac{5.8-1}{1} = 4.8$, we have

$$P = \frac{5.8}{1 + 4.8e^{-0.045t}}$$

The data and the curve are sketched in Figure 9.15.

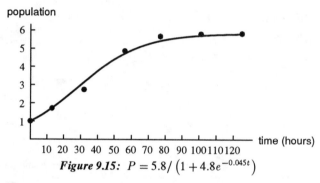

population

Figure 9.15: $P = 5.8/\left(1 + 4.8e^{-0.045t}\right)$

8.   (a)   To estimate $\frac{dP}{dt}$ for 1810, for example, we'll take

$$\frac{(\text{pop. at } 1820) - (\text{pop. at } 1800)}{20 \text{ years}} = \frac{(9.6 - 5.3) \text{ million}}{20 \text{ years}} = 0.215 \frac{\text{million}}{\text{yr}}.$$

Thus $\frac{1}{P}\frac{dP}{dt} = \frac{0.215}{7.2} \approx 0.03$. We do this for several other points.

TABLE 9.15

Year	P	$\frac{dP}{dt} \approx \frac{P(t+10)-P(t-10)}{20}$	$\frac{1}{P}\frac{dP}{dt}$
1800	5.3	$(7.2 - 3.9)/20 = 0.165$	0.0311
1830	12.9	$(17.1 - 9.6)/20 = 0.375$	0.0291
1860	31.4	$(38.6 - 23.1)/20 = 0.775$	0.0247
1890	62.9	$(76.0 - 50.2)/20 = 1.29$	0.0205
1920	105.7	$(122.8 - 92.0)/20 = 1.54$	0.0146
1950	150.7	$(179.0 - 131.7)/20 = 2.365$	0.0157
1980	226.5	$(248.7 - 205.0)/20 = 2.185$	0.0096

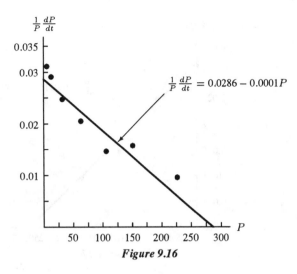

Figure 9.16

Plotting the data and fitting a line to it, we obtain

$$\frac{1}{P}\frac{dP}{dt} = 0.0286 - 0.0001P.$$

Thus $k \approx 0.0286$ and $a \approx 0.0001$.

(b) According to this model, $\frac{1}{P}\frac{dP}{dt} = 0.0001(286 - P)$. Thus, P will increase up to about 286 million, and then level off.

9. (a) Here we have, where $t =$ years since 1800:

TABLE 9.16

Year	t	$\frac{1}{P}\frac{dP}{dt}$
1800	0	0.0311
1830	30	0.0291
1860	60	0.0247
1890	90	0.0205
1920	120	0.0146
1950	150	0.0157
1980	180	0.0096

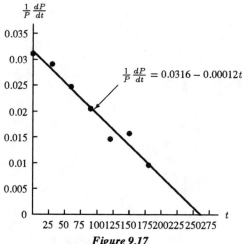

Figure 9.17

Graphing the data and fitting a line, we get $\frac{1}{P}\frac{dP}{dt} = 0.0316 - 0.00012t$ as our guess. So we have $a = 0.0316$ and $b = 0.00012$.

(b) $\frac{dP}{dt}$ will be positive and P will increase until $0.0316 = 0.00012t$, i.e. until $t \approx 260$ or about the year 2060.

(c) $\frac{dP}{P} = (0.0316 - 0.00012t)\,dt$.

$\int \frac{dP}{P} = \int (0.0316 - 0.00012t)\,dt$.

$P = Ae^{0.0316t - 0.00006t^2}$.

Using the fact that $P = 5.3$ when $t = 0$, we get $P = 5.3e^{0.0316t - 0.00006t^2}$.

10. (a) By the chain rule
$$\frac{dP}{dt} = \frac{d}{dt}\left(\frac{1}{u}\right) = \frac{d}{du}\left(\frac{1}{u}\right) \cdot \frac{du}{dt} = -\frac{1}{u^2}\frac{du}{dt}$$

(b) Substituting for $P = 1/u$ in the equation
$$\frac{dP}{dt} = kP\left(1 - \frac{P}{L}\right)$$

gives
$$-\frac{1}{u^2}\frac{du}{dt} = k\frac{1}{u}\left(1 - \frac{1}{Lu}\right).$$

Simplifying leads to
$$\frac{du}{dt} = -k\left(u - \frac{1}{L}\right)$$

and separating variables gives
$$\int \frac{du}{u - 1/L} = -\int k\,dt$$

$$\ln\left|u - \frac{1}{L}\right| = -kt + C$$

$$u - \frac{1}{L} = Ae^{-kt} \quad \text{where } A = \pm e^{C}$$

$$u = \frac{1}{L} + Ae^{-kt}$$

(c) Since $u = 1/P$, we have

$$\frac{1}{P} = \frac{1}{L} + Ae^{-kt} = \frac{1 + LAe^{-kt}}{L}$$

so

$$P = \frac{L}{1 + LAe^{-kt}} \quad \text{where } A \text{ is an arbitrary constant.}$$

11. (a)

TABLE 9.17

Year	P	$\frac{dP}{dt} \approx \frac{P(t+10)-P(t-10)}{20}$	$\frac{1}{P}\frac{dP}{dt}$
1790	3.9		
1800	5.3	$(7.2 - 3.9)/20 = 0.165$	0.0311
1810	7.2	$(9.6 - 5.3)/20 = 0.215$	0.0299
1820	9.6	$(12.9 - 7.2)/20 = 0.285$	0.0297
1830	12.9	$(17.1 - 9.6)/20 = 0.375$	0.0291
1840	17.1	$(23.2 - 12.9)/20 = 0.515$	0.0301
1850	23.2	$(31.4 - 17.1)/20 = 0.715$	0.0308
1860	31.4		

The method used in the text to calculate $k \approx 3.47\%$ is simply to average the values obtained for $\frac{1}{P}\frac{dP}{dt}$. Using this method on the values in Table 9.17 gives $k = 3.01\%$.

(b) To get $k \approx 2.98\%$, we assume k is the continuous growth constant satisfying $P = P_0 e^{kt}$. The data shows that, on average the population increased by 30.1% every ten years, meaning that if P_0 is the inital population and P is the population 10 years later:

$$\frac{P}{P_0} = 1.301 = e^{k(10)}.$$

Thus $k = \ln(1.301)/10 = 0.0263$.

12. Using a one-sided estimate for $f'(2)$, we get:

$$f'(2) \approx \frac{f(2 + h) - f(2)}{h} = \frac{(2 + h)^3 - (2)^3}{h}$$

$$= \frac{2^3 + 12h + 6h^2 + h^3 - 2^3}{h}$$

$$= 12 + 6h + h^2$$

If $h = 0.1$, we have $f'(2) \approx 12.61$.

If $h = 0.01$, we have $f'(2) \approx 12.0601$.

If $h = 0.001$, we have $f'(2) \approx 12.006001$.

As h decreases by a factor of ten, our approximation improves by one digit of accuracy.

Using a two-sided estimate for $f'(2)$, we get:

$$
\begin{aligned}
f'(2) &\approx \frac{f(2+h) - f(2-h)}{2h} = \frac{(2+h)^3 - (2-h)^3}{2h} \\
&= \frac{(2^3 + 12h + 6h^2 + h^3) - (2^3 - 12h + 6h^2 - h^3)}{2h} \\
&= \frac{24h + 2h^3}{2h} = 12 + h^2
\end{aligned}
$$

If $h = 0.1$, we have $f'(2) \approx 12.01$.

If $h = 0.01$, we have $f'(2) \approx 12.0001$.

If $h = 0.001$, we have $f'(2) \approx 12.000001$.

As h decreases by a factor of ten, our approximation improves by two digits of accuracy. The two-sided estimate is accurate to twice as many digits as the one-sided estimate.

13. If $f(x) = x^2$ then

$$
\begin{aligned}
\frac{f(x+h) - f(x-h)}{2h} &= \frac{(x+h)^2 - (x-h)^2}{2h} \\
&= \frac{(x^2 + 2xh + h^2) - (x^2 - 2xh + h^2)}{2h} \\
&= \frac{4xh}{2h} = 2x = f'(x) \quad \text{for all } x.
\end{aligned}
$$

14. The US population in 1860 was 31.4 million. If between 1860 and 1870 the population had increased at the same rate as previous decades, 34.7%, the population in 1870 would have been (31.4 million)(1.347) = 42.3 million. In actuality the US population in 1870 was only 38.6 million. This is a shortfall of 3.7 million people.

History records that about 618,000 soldiers died (total, both sides) during the Civil War (according to Collier's Encyclopedia, 1968). This accounts for only $\frac{1}{6}$ (roughly) of the shortfall. The rest of the shortfall can be attributed to civilian deaths and a decrease in the birth rate caused by absent males and an unwillingness to have babies under harsh economic conditions and political uncertainty.

15.

TABLE 9.18

Year	P	$\frac{dP}{dt} \approx \frac{P(t+10)-P(t-10)}{20}$
1790	3.9	
1800	5.3	$(7.2-3.9)/20 = 0.165$
1810	7.2	$(9.6-5.3)/20 = 0.215$
1820	9.6	$(12.9-7.2)/20 = 0.285$
1830	12.9	$(17.1-9.6)/20 = 0.375$
1840	17.1	$(23.2-12.9)/20 = 0.515$
1850	23.2	$(31.4-17.1)/20 = 0.715$
1860	31.4	$(38.6-23.2)/20 = 0.770$
1870	38.6	$(50.2-31.4)/20 = 0.940$
1880	50.2	$(62.9-38.6)/20 = 1.215$
1890	62.9	$(76.0-50.2)/20 = 1.290$
1900	76.0	$(92.0-62.9)/20 = 1.455$
1910	92.0	$(105.7-76.0)/20 = 1.485$
1920	105.7	$(122.8-92.0)/20 = 1.540$
1930	122.8	$(131.7-105.7)/20 = 1.300$
1940	131.7	$(150.7-122.8)/20 = 1.395$
1950	150.7	

According to these calculations, the largest value of dP/dt occurs in 1920 when the rate of change is $\frac{dP}{dt} = 1.540$ million people/year. The population in 1920 was 105.7 million. If we assume that the limiting value, L, is twice the population when it is changing most quickly, then $L = 2 \times 105.7 = 211.4$ million. This is greater than the estimate of 187 million computed in the text and closer to the actual 1990 population of 248.7 million.

16. (a)   (b)

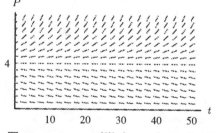

(c)   There are two equilibrium values, $P = 0$, and $P = 4$. The first, representing extinction, is stable. The equilibrium value $P = 4$ is unstable because the populations increase if greater than 4, and decrease if less than 4. Notice that the equilibrium values can be obtained by setting $dP/dt = 0$:

$$\frac{dP}{dt} = 0.02P^2 - 0.08P = 0.02P(P-4) = 0$$

so

$$P = 0 \text{ or } P = 4.$$

17. (a)

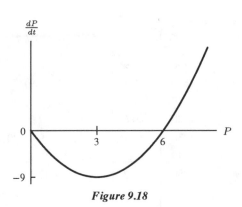

Figure 9.18

(b) Figure 9.18 shows that for $0 < P < 6$, the sign of dP/dt is negative. This means that P is decreasing over the interval $0 < P < 6$. As P decreases from $P(0) = 5$, the value of dP/dt gets more and more negative until $P = 3$. Thus the graph of P against t is concave down while P is decreasing from 5 to 3. As P decreases below 3, the slope of dP/dt increases toward 0, so the graph of P against t is concave up and asymptotic to the t-axis. At $P = 3$, there is an inflection point. See Figure 9.19.

(c) Figure 9.18 shows that for $P > 6$, the slope of dP/dt is positive and increases with P. Thus the graph of P against t is increasing and concave up. See Figure 9.19.

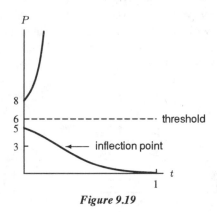

Figure 9.19

(d) For initial populations greater than the threshold value $P = 6$, the population increases without bound. Populations with initial value less than $P = 6$ decrease asymptotically towards 0, i.e. become extinct. Thus the initial population $P = 6$ is the dividing line, or threshold, between populations which grow without bound and those which die out.

18. (a)

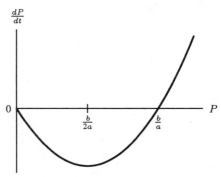

Figure 9.20

(b)

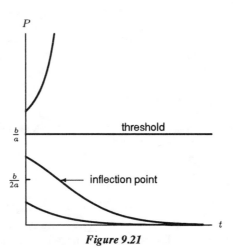

Figure 9.21

Figure 9.20 shows that dP/dt is negative for $P < \frac{b}{a}$, making P a decreasing function when $P(0) < \frac{b}{a}$. When $P > \frac{b}{a}$, the sign of dP/dt is positive, so P is an increasing function. Thus solution curves starting above $\frac{b}{a}$ are increasing, and those starting below $\frac{b}{a}$ are decreasing. See Figure 9.21.

For $P > \frac{b}{a}$, the slope, $\frac{dP}{dt}$, increases with P, so the graph of P against t is concave up. For $0 < P < \frac{b}{a}$, the value of P decreases with time. As P decreases, the slope $\frac{dP}{dt}$ decreases for $\frac{b}{2a} < P < \frac{b}{a}$, and increases towards 0 for $0 < P < \frac{b}{2a}$. Thus solution curves starting just below the threshold value of $\frac{b}{a}$ are concave down for $\frac{b}{2a} < P < \frac{b}{a}$ and concave up and asymptotic to the t-axis for $0 < P < \frac{b}{2a}$. See Figure 9.21.

(c) $P = \frac{b}{a}$ is called the threshold population because for populations greater than $\frac{b}{a}$, the population will increase without bound. For populations less than $\frac{b}{a}$, the population will go to zero, i.e. to extinction.

19. (a) When there is no fishing the rate of population change is given by $\frac{dP}{dt} = 2P - 0.01P^2$. If fishermen remove fish at a rate of 75 fish/year, then this results in a decrease in the growth rate, $\frac{dP}{dt}$, by 75 fish/year. This is reflected in the differential equation above by including the -75.

(b)

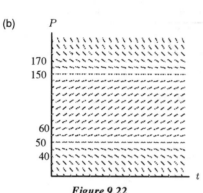

Figure 9.22

(c)

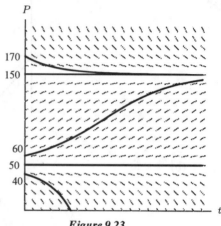

Figure 9.23

(d) The two equilibrium populations are $P = 50, 150$. The stable equilibrium is $P = 150$, while $P = 50$ is unstable.

Notice that setting $dP/dt = 0$ gives the two equilibria

$$\frac{dP}{dt} = 2P - 0.01P^2 - 75 = -0.01(P^2 - 200P + 7500) = -0.01(P - 50)(P - 150)$$

so $P = 50$ or $P = 150$.

20. (a) The equation $dP/dt = 2P - 0.01P^2$ represents logistic growth. The -75 term in $dP/dt = 2P - 0.01P^2 - 75$ represents an extra decrease at a continuous rate of 75 fish per unit time, perhaps due to fishing. The fact that it is negative means that it has the effect of decreasing the population. Its units are the same as dP/dt, which is fish/year.

(b)

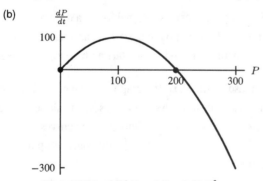

Figure 9.24: $dP/dt = 2P - 0.01P^2$

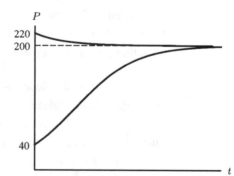

Figure 9.25: Solutions to $dP/dt = 2P - 0.01P^2$. Equilibrium values are $P = 0$ (unstable) and $P = 200$ (stable)

(c)

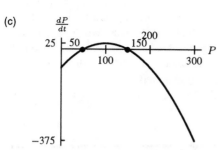

(d)

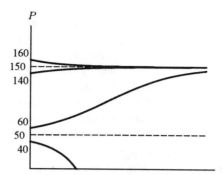

Figure 9.26: $dP/dt = 2P - 0.01P^2 - 75$

Figure 9.27: Solutions to $dP/dt = 2P - 0.01P^2 - 75$

(e) The two equilibrium populations for $dP/dt = 2P - 0.01P^2 - 75$ are $P = 50, 150$. The stable equilibrium is $P = 150$ while $P = 50$ is unstable.

Notice that the equilibria can be obtained by setting $dP/dt = 0$:

$$\frac{dP}{dt} = 2P - 0.01P^2 - 75 = -0.01(P^2 - 200P + 7500) = -0.01(P - 50)(P - 150)$$

so $P = 50$ or $P = 150$.

21. (a)

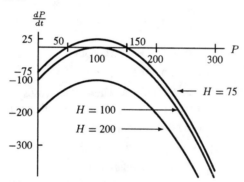

Figure 9.28

(b) For $H = 75$, the equilibrium populations (where $dP/dt = 0$) are $P = 50$ and $P = 150$. If the population is between 50 and 150, dP/dt is positive. This means that when the initial population is between 50 and 150, the population will increase until it reaches 150, when $dP/dt = 0$ and the population no longer increases or decreases. If the initial population is greater than 150, then dP/dt is negative, and the population decreases until it reaches 150. Thus 150 is a stable equilibrium. However, 50 is unstable.

For $H = 100$, the equilibrium population (where $dP/dt = 0$) is $P = 100$. For all other populations, dP/dt is negative and so the population decreases. If the initial population is greater than 100, it will decrease to the equilibrium value, $P = 100$. However, for populations less than 100, the population decreases until the species dies out.

For $H = 200$, there are no equilibrium points where $dP/dt = 0$, and dP/dt is always negative. Thus, no matter what the initial population, the population always dies out eventually.

(c) If the population is not to die out, looking at the three cases above, there must be an equilibrium value where $dP/dt = 0$, i.e. where the graph of dP/dt crosses the P axis. This happens if $H \leq 100$. Thus provided fishing is not more than 100 fish/year, there are initial values of the population for which the population will not be depleted.

(d) Fishing should be kept below the level of 100 per year.

9.8 SOLUTIONS

1. Since

$$\frac{dS}{dt} = -aSI,$$

$$\frac{dI}{dt} = aSI - bI,$$

$$\frac{dR}{dt} = bI$$

we have

$$\frac{dS}{dt} + \frac{dI}{dt} + \frac{dR}{dt} = -aSI + aSI - bI + bI = 0.$$

Thus $\frac{d}{dt}(S + I + R) = 0$, so $S + I + R = \text{constant}$.

2. Here x and y both increase at about the same rate.

3. Initially $x = 0$, so we start with only y. Then y decreases while x increases. Then x continues to increase while y starts to increase as well. Finally y continues to increase while x decreases.

4. x decreases quickly to zero while y increases slowly.

5. The closed trajectory represents populations which oscillate repeatedly.

6. This is an example of a predator-prey relationship. Normally, we would expect the worm population, in the absence predators, to increase without bound. As the number of worms w increases, so would the rate of increase $\frac{dw}{dt}$; in other words, the relation $\frac{dw}{dt} = w$ might be a reasonable model for the worm population in the absence of predators.

However, since there are predators (robins), $\frac{dw}{dt}$ won't be that big. We must lessen $\frac{dw}{dt}$. It makes sense that the more interaction there is between robins and worms, the more slowly the worms are able to increase their numbers. Hence we lessen $\frac{dw}{dt}$ by the amount wr to get the relation $\frac{dw}{dt} = w - wr$. The term $-wr$ reflects the fact that more interactions between the species means slower reproduction for the worms.

Similarly, we would expect the robin population to decrease in the absence of worms. We'd expect the population decrease at a rate related to the current population, making $\frac{dr}{dt} = -r$ a reasonable model for the robin population in absence of worms. The negative term reflects the fact that the greater the population of robins, the more quickly they are dying off. The wr term in $\frac{dr}{dt} = -r + rw$ reflects the fact that the more interactions between robins and worms, the greater the tendency for the robins will increase in population.

7. If there are no worms, then $w = 0$, and $\frac{dr}{dt} = -r$ giving $r = r_0 e^{-t}$, where r_0 is the initial robin population. If there are no robins, then $r = 0$, and $\frac{dw}{dt} = w$ giving $w = w_0 e^t$, where w_0 is the initial worm population.

8. There is symmetry across the line $r = w$. Indeed, since $\frac{dr}{dw} = \frac{r(w-1)}{w(1-r)}$, if we switch w and r we get $\frac{dw}{dr} = \frac{w(r-1)}{r(1-w)}$, so $\frac{dr}{dw} = \frac{r(1-w)}{w(r-1)}$. Since switching w and r changes nothing, the slope field must be symmetric across the line $r = w$. The slope field shows that the solution curves are either spirals or closed curves. Since there is symmetry about the line $r = w$, the solutions must in fact be closed curves.

9. If $w = 2$ and $r = 2$, then $\frac{dw}{dt} = -2$ and $\frac{dr}{dt} = 2$, so the number of worms decreases and the number of robins increases. In the long run, however, the populations will oscillate; they will even go back to $w = 2$ and $r = 2$.

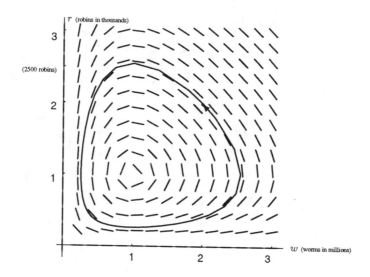

10. Sketching the trajectory through the point $(2, 2)$ on the slope field given shows that the maximum robin population is about 2500, and the minimum robin population is about 500. When the robin population is at its maximum, the worm population is about 1,000,000.

11.

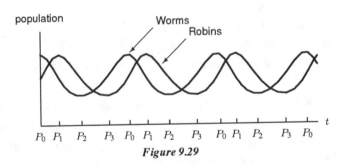

Figure 9.29

12.   It will work somewhat; the maximum number the robins reach will increase. However, the minimum number the robins reach will decrease as well. (See graph of slope field.) In the long term, the robin-worm populations will again fall into a cycle.

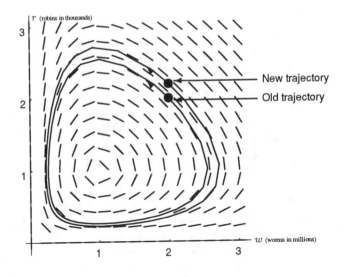

Note that if too many robins are added the minimum number may get so small the model may fail since a small number of robins are more susceptible to disaster.

13.   (a)   Thinking of y as a function of x and x as a function of t, then by the chain rule: $\dfrac{dy}{dt} = \dfrac{dy}{dx}\dfrac{dx}{dt}$, so:

$$\frac{dy}{dx} = \frac{dy/dt}{dx/dt} = \frac{-0.01x}{-0.05y} = \frac{x}{5y}$$

y (thousand Japanese troops)

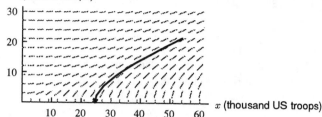

Figure 9.30: Slope field and trajectory describing Battle of Iwo Jima.
(parts (a) and (b))

(b) Figure 9.30 shows the slope field for this differential equation and the trajectory starting at $x_0 = 54$, $y_0 = 21.5$. The trajectory goes to the x-axis, where $y = 0$, meaning that the Japanese troops were all killed or wounded before the US troops were, and thus predicts the US victory (which did occur). Since the trajectory meets the x-axis at $x \approx 25$, the differential equation predicts that about 25,000 US troops would survive the battle.

(c) The fact that the US got reinforcements, while the Japanese did not, does not alter the predicted outcome (a US victory). The US reinforcements have the effect of changing the trajectory, altering the number of troops surviving the battle. See the graph in Figure 9.31.

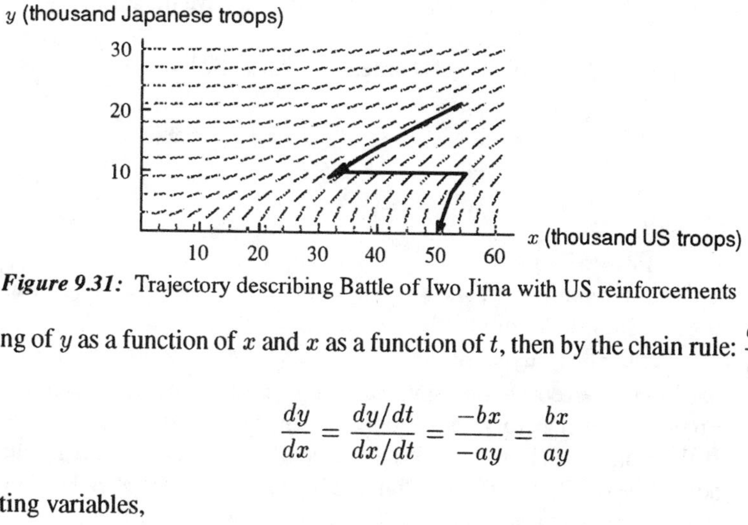

y (thousand Japanese troops)

Figure 9.31: Trajectory describing Battle of Iwo Jima with US reinforcements

14. (a) Thinking of y as a function of x and x as a function of t, then by the chain rule: $\dfrac{dy}{dt} = \dfrac{dy}{dx}\dfrac{dx}{dt}$, so:

$$\frac{dy}{dx} = \frac{dy/dt}{dx/dt} = \frac{-bx}{-ay} = \frac{bx}{ay}$$

(b) Separating variables,

$$\int ay\,dy = \int bx\,dx$$

$$a\frac{y^2}{2} = b\frac{x^2}{2} + k$$

$$ay^2 - bx^2 = C \quad \text{where } C = 2k$$

15. (a) Lanchester's square law for the battle of Iwo Jima is

$$0.05y^2 - 0.01x^2 = C.$$

If we measure x and y in thousands, $x_0 = 54$ and $y_0 = 21.5$, so $0.05(21.5)^2 - 0.01(54)^2 = C$ giving $C = -6.0475$. Thus the equation of the trajectory is

$$0.05y^2 - 0.01x^2 = -6.0475$$

giving

$$x^2 - 5y^2 = 604.75.$$

(b) Assuming that the battle did not end until all the Japanese were dead or wounded, that is, $y = 0$, then the number of US soldiers remaining is given by $x^2 - 5(0)^2 = 604.75$. This gives $x = 24.59$, or about 25,000 troops. This is approximately what happened.

16. (a) $\dfrac{dy}{dx} = \dfrac{-ax}{-ay} = \dfrac{x}{y}$ so $\displaystyle\int y\,dy = \int x\,dx$ giving $y^2 - x^2 = C$. When $t = 0$, $y = 46$, $x = 40$, so $C = 46^2 - 40^2 = 516$. Therefore, the solution is $y^2 - x^2 = 516$.

(b) The battle is over when $x = 0$. The number of French/Spanish ships remaining is the y-intercept, thus, $y^2 - 0^2 = 516$ giving $y \approx 22.7$ French/Spanish ships remaining.

(c) For both sub-battles, the solution trajectory will have the form $y^2 - x^2 = C$. Each sub-battle will have a different value of C.

For the 32 versus 23 sub-battle, $C = 23^2 - 32^2 = -495$, so the trajectory is:

$$y^2 - x^2 = -495$$

or

$$x^2 - y^2 = 495.$$

This has no y-intercept, but an x-intercept of $x = \sqrt{495} \approx 22.2$, meaning that the model predicts the British won the sub-battle with about 22.2 ships remaining.

For the 8 versus 23 sub-battle, $C = 23^2 - 8^2 = 465$ so the trajectory is $y^2 - x^2 = 465$. This has no x-intercept, but a y-intercept of $y = \sqrt{465} \approx 21.6$, meaning that the model predicts a French/Spanish victory with about 21.6 ships remaining.

(d) If the remaining ships from these two sub-battles then fight each other, the British have a slight advantage (22.2 versus 21.6). Thus the British could be expected to win the overall battle, although they started with a weaker fleet. This is in fact what happened.

The trajectory for this last battle has $C = 495 - 460 = 30$, so the equation is

$$x^2 - y^2 = 30.$$

This has an x-intercept of $x = \sqrt{30} \approx 5.5$, so the model predicts a British victory with about $5\frac{1}{2}$ ships remaining.

(French/Spanish)

Figure 9.32

17. (a) If B were not present, then we'd have $A' = 2A$, so company A's net worth would grow exponentially. Similarly, if A were not present, B would grow exponentially. The two companies restrain each other's growth, probably by competing for the market.

(b) To find equilibrium points, find the solutions of the pair of equations

$$A' = 2A - AB = 0$$
$$B' = B - AB = 0$$

The first equation has solutions $A = 0$ or $B = 2$. The second has solutions $B = 0$ or $A = 1$. Thus the equilibrium points are (0,0) and (1,2).

(c) In the long run, one of the companies will go out of business. Two of the trajectories in the figure below go towards the A axis; they represent A surviving and B going out of business. The trajectories going towards the B axis represent A going out of business. Notice both the equilibrium points are unstable.

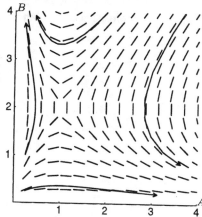

18. If alone, the x population grows exponentially, since if $y = 0$ we have $\frac{dx}{dt} = 0.01x$. If alone, the y population decreases to 0 exponentially, since if $x = 0$ we have $\frac{dy}{dt} = -0.2y$.

This is a predator-prey relationship: interaction between populations x and y decreases the x population and increases the y population.

19. If alone, the x and y populations each grow exponentially, because the equations become $\dfrac{dx}{dt} = 0.01x$ and $\dfrac{dy}{dt} = 0.2y$. For each population, the presence of the other decreases their growth rate. The two populations are therefore competitors—they may be eating each other's food, for instance.

20. The x population is unaffected by the y population—it grows exponentially no matter what the y population is, even if $y = 0$. If alone, the y population decreases to zero exponentially, because its equation becomes $\dfrac{dy}{dt} = -0.1y$. Here, interaction between the two populations helps the y population but doesn't effect the x population. This is not a predator-prey relationship; instead, this is a one-way relationship, where the y population is helped by the existence of x's.

21. (a) Equilibrium points are where $\frac{dx}{dt} = 0$ and $\frac{dy}{dt} = 0$.
    $15x - 3xy = 0$ gives $3x(5 - y) = 0$, so $x = 0$ or $y = 5$
    $-14y + 7xy = 0$ gives $7y(-2 + x) = 0$, so $x = 2$ or $y = 0$.
    The solutions are thus (0,0) and (2,5).
    (b) At $x = 2$, $y = 0$ we have $\frac{dy}{dt} = 0$ but $\frac{dx}{dt} = 15(2) - 3(2)(0) = 30 \neq 0$. Thus $x = 2$, $y = 0$ is not an equilibrium point.

22. (a) Equilibrium points are where $\frac{dx}{dt} = 0$ and $\frac{dy}{dt} = 0$.
    $x - 0.001x^2 - 0.005xy = x(1 - 0.001x - 0.005y) = 0$
    $0.02y - 3\frac{y}{x} = y(0.02 - \frac{3}{x}) = 0$.
    The first equation gives $x = 0$ or $1 = 0.001x + 0.005y$. But since x is a denominator in the second equation we can't have $x = 0$, so we must have $1 = 0.001x + 0.005y$. From the second equation, $y = 0$, giving $x = 1000$, or $0.02 - \frac{3}{x} = 0$, giving $x = 150$ and $y = 170$ (from the first equation). Thus, the solutions are $(1000, 0)$ and $(150, 170)$.
    (b) $x = 0$, $y = 0$ is not an equilibrium point because $\frac{dy}{dt}$ is undefined for $x = 0$, $y = 0$.

23. (a) Symbiosis, because both populations decrease while alone but are helped by the presence of the other.
    (b)

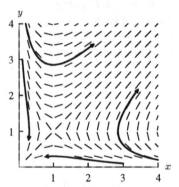

Both populations tend to infinity or both tend to zero.

24. (a) Competition, because both populations grow logistically when alone, but are harmed by the presence of the other.

(b)

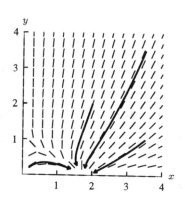

In the long run, $x \to 2$, $y \to 0$. In other words, y becomes extinct.

25. (a) Predator-prey, because x decreases while alone, but is helped by y, whereas y increases logistically when alone, and is harmed by x. Thus x is predator, y is prey.

(b)

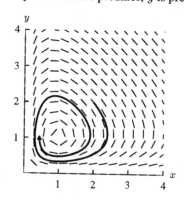

Provided neither initial population is zero, both populations tend to about 1. If x is initially zero, but y is not, then $y \to \infty$. If y is initially zero, but x is not, then $x \to 0$.

9.9 SOLUTIONS

1. (a) $dS/dt = 0$ where $S = 0$ or $I = 0$ (both axes).
   $dI/dt = 0.0026I(S - 192)$, so $dI/dt = 0$ where $I = 0$ or $S = 192$.
   Thus every point on the S axis is an equilibrium point (corresponding to no one being sick).

   (b) In region I, where $S > 192$, $\dfrac{dS}{dt} < 0$ and $\dfrac{dI}{dt} > 0$.

   In region II, where $S < 192$, $\dfrac{dS}{dt} < 0$ and $\dfrac{dI}{dt} < 0$. See Figure 9.33.

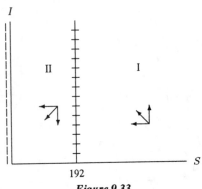

Figure 9.33

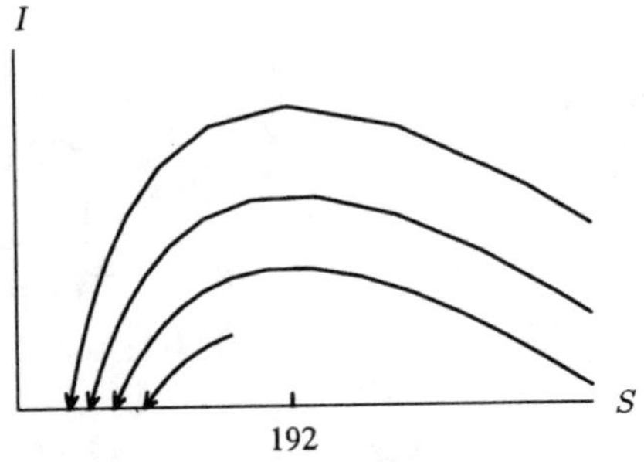

Figure 9.34

(c) If the trajectory starts with $S_0 > 192$, then I increases to a maximum when $S = 192$. If $S_0 < 192$, then I always decreases. See Figure 9.33. Regardless of the initial conditions, the trajectory always goes to a point on the S-axis (where $I = 0$). The S-intercept represents the number of students who never get the disease. See Figure 9.34.

2. The nullclines are where $\frac{dw}{dt} = 0$ or $\frac{dr}{dt} = 0$.
   $\frac{dw}{dt} = 0$ when $w - wr = 0$, so $w(1 - r) = 0$ giving $w = 0$ or $r = 1$.
   $\frac{dr}{dt} = 0$ when $-r + rw = 0$, so $r(w - 1) = 0$ giving $r = 0$ or $w = 1$.

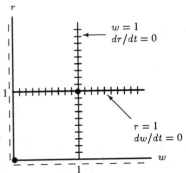

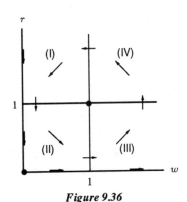

Figure 9.35: Nullclines and equilibrium points (dots)

Figure 9.36

The equilibrium points are where the nullclines intersect: $(0, 0)$ and $(1, 1)$. The nullclines split the first quadrant into four sectors. See Figure 9.35. We can get a feel for how the populations interact by seeing the direction of the trajectories in each sector. See Figure 9.36.

If the populations reach an equilibrium point, they will stay there. If the worm population dies out, the robin population will also die out, too. However, if the robin population dies out, the worm population will continue to grow.

Otherwise, it seems that the populations cycle around the equilibrium $(1, 1)$. The trajectory moves from sector to sector:

trajectories in sector (I) move to sector (II); trajectories in sector (II) move to sector (III); trajectories in sector (III) move to sector (IV); trajectories in sector (IV) move back to sector (I).

The robins keep the worm population down by feeding on them, but the robins need the worms (as food) to sustain the population. These conflicting needs keep the populations moving in a cycle around the equilibrium.

3. We first find the nullclines. Again, we assume x, $y \geq 0$.

    Vertical nullclines occur where $dx/dt = 0$, which happens when $\frac{dx}{dt} = x(2 - x - y) = 0$, i.e. when $x = 0$ or $x + y = 2$.

    Horizontal nullclines occur where $dy/dt = 0$, which happens when $\frac{dy}{dt} = y(1 - x - y) = 0$, i.e. when $y = 0$ or $x + y = 1$.

    These nullclines are shown in Figure 9.37.

    Equilibrium points (also shown in Figure 9.37) occur where both dy/dt and dx/dt are 0, i.e. at the intersections of vertical and horizontal nullclines. There are three such points for these equations: $(0, 0)$, $(0, 1)$, and $(2, 0)$.

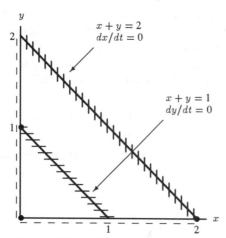

Figure 9.37: Nullclines and equilibrium points (dots)

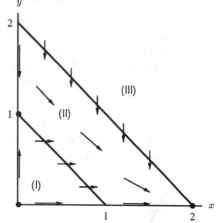

Figure 9.38: General directions of trajectories and equilibrium points (dots)

Looking at sectors in Figure 9.38, we see that no matter in what sector the initial point lies, the trajectory will head toward the equilibrium point $(2, 0)$.

4. We first find the nullclines. Again, we assume x, $y \geq 0$.

    $\frac{dx}{dt} = x(1 - x - \frac{y}{3}) = 0$ when $x = 0$ or $x + y/3 = 1$.

    $\frac{dy}{dt} = y(1 - y - \frac{x}{2}) = 0$ when $y = 0$ or $y + x/2 = 1$.

    These nullclines are shown in Figure 9.39. There are four equilibrium points for these equations. Three of them are the points, $(0, 0)$, $(0, 1)$, and $(1, 0)$. The fourth is the intersection of the two lines $x + y/3 = 1$ and $y + x/2 = 1$. This point is $(\frac{4}{5}, \frac{3}{5})$.

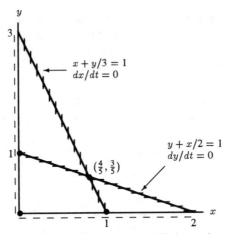

Figure 9.39: Nullclines and equilibrium points (dots)

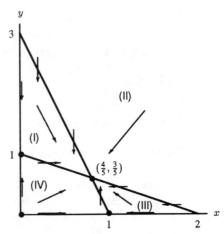

Figure 9.40: General directions of trajectories and equilibrium points (dots)

Looking at sectors in Figure 9.40, we see that no matter in what sector the initial point lies, the trajectory will head toward the equilibrium point $(\frac{4}{5}, \frac{3}{5})$. Only if the initial point lies on the x- or y-axis, will the trajectory head towards the equilibrium points at $(1, 0)$, $(0, 1)$, or $(0, 0)$. In fact, the trajectory will go to $(0, 0)$ only if it starts there, in which case $x(t) = y(t) = 0$ for all t. From direction of the trajectories in Figure 9.40, it appears that if the initial point is in sectors (I) or (III), then it will remain in that sector as it heads towards the equilibrium.

5. We assume that x, $y \geq 0$ and then find the nullclines. $\frac{dx}{dt} = x(1 - \frac{x}{2} - y) = 0$ when $x = 0$ or $y + \frac{x}{2} = 1$. $\frac{dy}{dt} = y(1 - \frac{y}{3} - x) = 0$ when $y = 0$ or $x + \frac{y}{3} = 1$.
    We find the equilibrium points. They are $(2, 0)$, $(0, 3)$, $(0, 0)$, and $(\frac{4}{5}, \frac{3}{5})$. The nullclines and equilibrium points are shown in Figure 9.41.

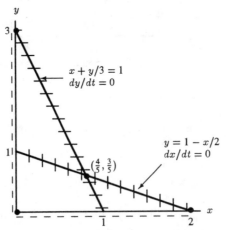

Figure 9.41: Nullclines and equilibrium points (dots)

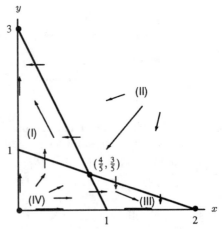

Figure 9.42: General directions of trajectories and equilibrium points (dots)

Figure 9.42 shows that if the initial point is in sector (I), the trajectory heads towards the equilibrium point $(0, 3)$. Similarly, if the trajectory begins in sector (III), then it heads towards the equilibrium $(2, 0)$ over time. If the trajectory begins in sector (II) or (IV), it can go to any of the three equilibrium points $(2, 0)$, $(0, 3)$, or $\left(\frac{4}{5}, \frac{3}{5}\right)$.

6. (a) We simplify the equations by factoring:

$$\frac{dP_2}{dt} = 0.09 P_2 \left(1 - \frac{P_2}{15}\right) - 0.45 P_2 P_3 = 0.001 P_2 (90 - 6 P_2 - 450 P_3)$$

$$\frac{dP_3}{dt} = 0.06 P_3 \left(1 - \frac{P_3}{10}\right) - 0.001 P_2 P_3 = 0.001 P_3 (60 - P_2 - 6 P_3)$$

From these equations we see that $dP_2/dt = 0$ (i.e. trajectory is vertical) along the lines $P_2 = 0$ and $90 - 6P_2 - 450P_3 = 0$. The trajectory is horizontal when $dP_3/dt = 0$, which occurs along the lines $P_3 = 0$ and $60 - P_2 - 6P_3 = 0$. These nullclines are shown in Figure 9.43. The equilibrium points occur where both $dP_2/dt = dP_3/dt = 0$. These points are at $P_2 = P_3 = 0$, and $P_2 = 15$, $P_3 = 0$ (extinction of P_3), and $P_2 = 0$, $P_3 = 10$ (extinction of P_2), each marked with a dot in Figure 9.43.

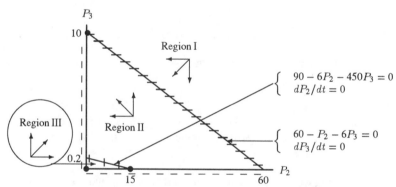

Figure 9.43: Nullclines and equilibrium points (dots)
(not to scale)

(b) We'll investigate the behavior of the trajectories in each region by calculating the signs of dP_2/dt and dP_3/dt:

In region I, where P_2 and P_3 are both large, try $P_2 = 60$, $P_3 = 10$, giving

$$\frac{dP_2}{dt} = 0.001 P_2 (90 - 6 P_2 - 450 P_3)$$

$$= 0.001 (60) \left(90 - 6(60) - 450(10)\right) = 0.001 (+)(-) < 0$$

$$\frac{dP_3}{dt} = 0.001 P_3 (60 - P_2 - 6 P_3)$$

$$= 0.001 (10) \left(60 - 60 - 6(10)\right) = 0.001 (+)(-) < 0$$

In region II, try $P_2 = 20$, $P_3 = 1$, giving

$$\frac{dP_2}{dt} < 0, \quad \frac{dP_3}{dt} > 0.$$

In region III, try $P_2 = P_3 = 0.1$, giving

$$\frac{dP_2}{dt} > 0, \quad \frac{dP_3}{dt} > 0.$$

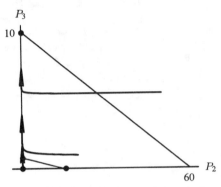

Figure 9.44: Trajectories showing exclusion of P_2

(c) The trajectories in Figure 9.44 show that if $P_3 \neq 0$ initially, the system tends towards the equilibrium $P_2 = 0$, $P_3 = 10$, meaning the extinction of P_2. At the same time, $P_3 \to 10$, its carrying capacity.

7. (a) By factoring, we can rewrite the expressions for $\dfrac{dP_1}{dt}$ and $\dfrac{dP_3}{dt}$ as:

$$\frac{dP_1}{dt} = 0.001\,P_1(50 - 2.5P_1 - 500P_3)$$
$$\frac{dP_3}{dt} = 0.001\,P_3(60 - 10P_1 - 6P_3)$$

We find the nullclines by setting $dP_1/dt = 0$ and $dP_3/dt = 0$. From the above equations, we see that $dP_1/dt = 0$ along the lines $P_1 = 0$ and $50 - 2.5P_1 - 500P_3 = 0$ and that $dP_3/dt = 0$ along the lines $P_3 = 0$ and $60 - 10P_1 - 6P_3 = 0$. The nullclines are sketched in Figure 9.45. The equilibrium points are where $dP_1/dt = dP_3/dt = 0$. There are four such points: at $P_1 = P_3 = 0$, and $P_1 = 20$, $P_3 = 0$, and $P_1 = 0$, $P_3 = 10$, and $P_1 \approx 6$, $P_3 \approx 0.07$. The equilibrium at $P_1 \approx 6$, $P_3 \approx 0.07$ is unstable, because if the populations are near, but not at, these values, the populations generally tend away from these equilibrium values.

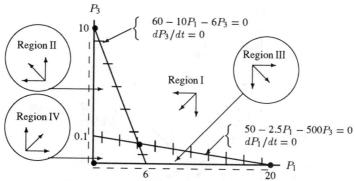

Figure 9.45: Nullclines and equilibrium points (dots)
(not to scale)

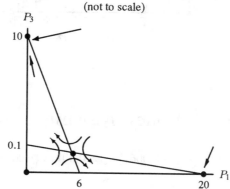

Figure 9.46: In the long run, trajectories tend
towards one of the equilibrium points (not to scale)

(b) The equilibriums at $P_1 = 20$, $P_3 = 0$ (corresponding to extinction of P_3) and $P_1 = 0$, $P_3 = 10$ (corresponding to the extinction of P_1) are both stable. This is because trajectories near equilibrium points tend towards them. Thus, in the long run, the populations will tend towards the values at one of these two equilibrium points, meaning that one of the two populations will die out. However, which one of the two points the trajectory tends towards, and which population becomes extinct, depend upon the initial populations of the two parasites.

8. (a)
$$\frac{dP_1}{dt} = 0.1P_1\left(1 - \frac{P_1}{16}\right) - 0.013P_1P_2 = 0.001P_1\left(100 - \frac{100}{16}P_1 - 13P_2\right)$$
$$\frac{dP_2}{dt} = 0.2P_2\left(1 - \frac{P_2}{20}\right) - 0.05P_1P_2 = 0.01P_2(20 - 5P_1 - P_2)$$

The arrows show the general direction of the trajectories in the region.

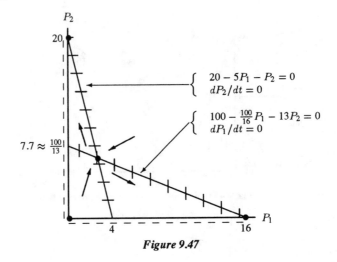

$$
\begin{cases} 20 - 5P_1 - P_2 = 0 \\ dP_2/dt = 0 \end{cases}
$$

$$
\begin{cases} 100 - \frac{100}{16}P_1 - 13P_2 = 0 \\ dP_1/dt = 0 \end{cases}
$$

Figure 9.47

(b)

$$
\frac{dP_1}{dt} = 0.5P_1\left(1 - \frac{P_1}{4}\right) - 0.025P_1P_2 = 0.025P_1(20 - 5P_1 - P_2)
$$

$$
\frac{dP_2}{dt} = 0.1P_2\left(1 - \frac{P_2}{8}\right) - 0.006P_1P_2 = 0.001P_2\left(100 - 6P_1 - \frac{100}{8}P_2\right)
$$

The arrows show the general direction of the trajectories in the region.

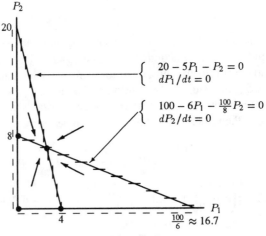

$$
\begin{cases} 20 - 5P_1 - P_2 = 0 \\ dP_1/dt = 0 \end{cases}
$$

$$
\begin{cases} 100 - 6P_1 - \frac{100}{8}P_2 = 0 \\ dP_2/dt = 0 \end{cases}
$$

Figure 9.48

(c) $$\frac{dP_1}{dt} = 0.06P_1\left(1 - \frac{P_1}{16}\right) - 0.008P_1P_2 = 0.001P_1\left(60 - \frac{15}{4}P_1 - 8P_2\right)$$
$$\frac{dP_2}{dt} = 0.12P_2\left(1 - \frac{P_2}{12}\right) - 0.007P_1P_2 = 0.001P_2(120 - 7P_1 - 10P_2)$$

The arrows show the general direction of the trajectories in the region.

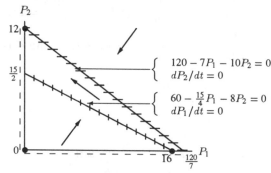

Figure 9.49

The first set of equations is the appropriate set, because some trajectories in Figure 9.47 tend towards a point on the P_1 axis (corresponding to exclusion of P_2), and some go to a point on the P_2 axis (corresponding to exclusion of P_1). In the second case, trajectories which start off the axes all go to the equilibrium point where both $P_1 \neq 0$ and $P_2 \neq 0$. In the third case, if $P_2 \neq 0$ initially, P_1 always becomes extinct because trajectories tend to the equilibrium point $P_1 = 0$, $P_2 = 12$.

9. (a)   The nullclines are $P = 0$ or $P_1 + 3P_2 = 13$ (where $dP_1/dt = 0$) and $P = 0$ or $P_2 + 0.4P_1 = 6$ (where $dP_2/dt = 0$).

    (b)   The phase plane in Figure 9.50 shows that P_2 will eventually exclude P_1 regardless of where the experiment starts so long as there were some P_2 originally. Consequently the data points would have followed a trajectory that starts at the origin, crosses the first nullcline and goes left and upwards between the two nullclines to the point $P_1 = 0$, $P_2 = 6$.

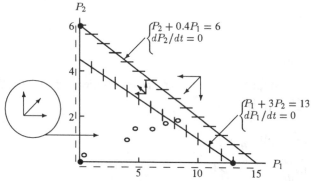

Figure 9.50: Nullclines and equilibrium points (dots)
for Gauses's yeast data (hollow dots)

10. (a)

$$\frac{dx}{dt} = 0 \text{ when } x = \frac{10.5}{0.45} = 23.3$$

$$\frac{dy}{dt} = 0 \text{ when } 8.2x - 0.8y - 142 = 0$$

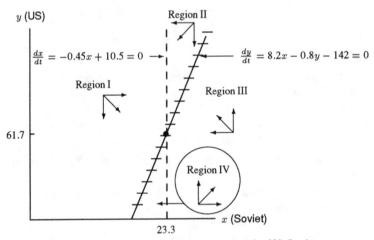

Figure 9.51: Nullclines and equilibrium point (dot) for US-Soviet arms race

There is an equilibrium point where the trajectories cross at $x = 23.3$, $y = 61.7$.

In region I, $\dfrac{dx}{dt} > 0$, $\dfrac{dy}{dt} < 0$.

In region II, $\dfrac{dx}{dt} < 0$, $\dfrac{dy}{dt} < 0$.

In region III, $\dfrac{dx}{dt} < 0$, $\dfrac{dy}{dt} > 0$.

In region IV, $\dfrac{dx}{dt} > 0$, $\dfrac{dy}{dt} > 0$.

(b)

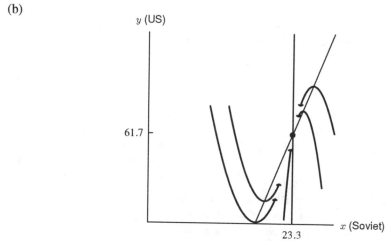

Figure 9.52: Trajectories for US-Soviet arms race.

(c) All the trajectories tend towards the equilibrium point $x = 23.3$, $y = 61.7$. Thus the model predicts that in the long run the arms race will level off with the Soviet Union spending 23.3 billion dollars a year on arms and the US 61.7 billion dollars.

(d) As the model predicts, yearly arms expenditure did tend towards 23 billion for the Soviet Union and 62 billion for the US.

9.10 SOLUTIONS

1. If $y = 2\cos t + 3\sin t$, then $y' = -2\sin t + 3\cos t$ and $y'' = -2\cos t - 3\sin t$. Thus, $y'' + y = 0$.

2. If $y = A\cos t + B\sin t$, then $y' = -A\sin t + B\cos t$ and $y'' = -A\cos t - B\sin t$. Thus, $y'' + y = 0$.

3. $y = A\cos\alpha t$
    $y' = -\alpha A\sin\alpha t$
    $y'' = -\alpha^2 A\cos\alpha t$
    If $y'' + 5y = 0$, then $-\alpha^2 A\cos\alpha t + 5A\cos\alpha t = 0$, so $A(5 - \alpha^2)\cos\alpha t = 0$. This is true for all t if $A = 0$, or if $\alpha = \pm\sqrt{5}$.
    We also have the initial condition: $y'(1) = -\alpha A\sin\alpha = 3$. Notice that this equation will not work if $A = 0$. If $\alpha = \sqrt{5}$, then
    $A = -\frac{3}{\sqrt{5}\sin\sqrt{5}} \approx -1.705$.
    Similarly, if $\alpha = -\sqrt{5}$, we find that $A \approx -1.705$. Thus, the possible values are $A = -\frac{3}{\sqrt{5}\sin\sqrt{5}} \approx -1.705$ and $\alpha = \pm\sqrt{5}$.

4. Since the general solution to $y'' + 16y = 0$ is

$$y = A\cos 4t + B\sin 4t,$$

we must have $\omega = 4$. The condition $y(0) = 2$ tells us that

$$y(0) = A\cos(4 \cdot 0) + B\sin(4 \cdot 0) = A \cdot 1 + B \cdot 0 = A = 2.$$

Thus we know

$$y(t) = 2\cos 4t + B\sin 4t.$$

Since $y(\pi/8) = 3$, we have

$$y(\frac{\pi}{8}) = 2\cos(4 \cdot \frac{\pi}{8}) + B\sin(4 \cdot \frac{\pi}{8}) = 2 \cdot 0 + B \cdot 1 = B = 3.$$

Therefore $\omega = 4$, $A = 2$, and $B = 3$.

5. At $t = 0$, we find that $y = 2$, which is clearly the highest point since $-1 \leq \cos 3t \leq 1$. Thus, at $t = 0$ the mass is at its highest point. Since $y' = -6\sin 3t$, we see $y' = 0$ when $t = 0$. Thus, at $t = 0$ the object is at rest, although it will move down after $t = 0$.

6. At $t = 0$, we find that $y = 0$. Since $-1 \leq \sin 3t \leq 1$, y ranges from -0.5 to 0.5, so at $t = 0$ it is starting in the middle. Since $y' = -1.5\cos 3t$, we see $y' = -1.5$ when $t = 0$, so the mass is moving downward.

7. At $t = 0$, we find that $y = -1$, which is clearly the lowest point on the path. Since $y' = 3\sin 3t$, we see that $y' = 0$ when $t = 0$. Thus, at $t = 0$ the object is at rest, although it will move up after $t = 0$.

8. (a) We recall that the chapter stated that the general solution to the equation
    $\frac{d^2 s}{dt^2} + \omega^2 s = 0$ is $s(t) = C_1\cos\omega t + C_2\sin\omega t$. Using this, we find that the general solution of $y'' = -4y$ is $y(t) = C_1\cos 2t + C_2\sin 2t$.
    (b) Notice that $y'(t) = -2C_1\sin 2t + 2C_2\cos 2t$.

    (i)

    $$y(0) = 5 = C_1\cos 0 + C_2\sin 0 = C_1, \text{ so } C_1 = 5.$$
    $$y'(0) = 0 = -2C_1\sin 0 + 2C_2\cos 0 = C_2, \text{ so } C_2 = 0.$$

    Thus, $y(t) = 5\cos 2t$ is the solution.

    (ii)

    $$y(0) = 0 = C_1\cos 0 + C_2\sin 0 = C_1, \text{ so } C_1 = 0.$$
    $$y'(0) = 10 = -2C_1\sin 0 + 2C_2\cos 0 = C_2, \text{ so } C_2 = 5.$$

    Thus, $y(t) = 5\sin 2t$ is the solution.

    (iii) As in part i), $y(0) = 5$. So, $C_1 = 5$.
    $y'(0) = 5$. So, $C_2 = \frac{5}{2}$.
    Thus, $y(t) = 5\cos 2t + \frac{5}{2}\sin 2t$ is the solution.

(c)

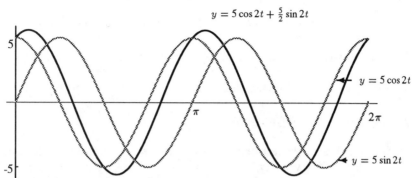

$$y = 5\cos 2t + \tfrac{5}{2}\sin 2t$$

$$y = 5\cos 2t$$

$$y = 5\sin 2t$$

Notice that the third function (like the other two) is just a single oscillation.

9. First, we note that the solutions of:
    (a) $x'' + x = 0$ are $x = A\cos t + B\sin t$;
    (b) $x'' + 4x = 0$ are $x = A\cos 2t + B\sin 2t$;
    (c) $x'' + 16x = 0$ are $x = A\cos 4t + B\sin 4t$.
    This follows from what we know about the general solution to $x'' + \omega^2 x = 0$.
    The period of the solutions to (a) is 2π, the period of the solutions to (b) is π, and the period of the solutions of (c) is $\frac{\pi}{2}$.
    Since the t-scales are the same on all of the graphs, we see that graphs (I) and (IV) have the same period, which is twice the period of graph (III). Graph (II) has twice the period of graphs (I) and (IV). Since each graph represents a solution, we have the following:

    - equation (a) goes with graph (II)
      equation (b) goes with graphs (I) and (IV)
      equation (c) goes with graph (III)

    - The graph of (I) passes through $(0,0)$, so $0 = A\cos 0 + B\sin 0 = A$. Thus, the equation is $x = B\sin 2t$. Since the amplitude is 2, we see that $x = 2\sin 2t$ is the equation of the graph. Similarly, the equation for (IV) is $x = -3\sin 2t$.
      The graph of (II) also passes through $(0,0)$, so, similarly, the equation must be $x = B\sin t$. In this case, we see that $B = -1$, so $x = -\sin t$.
      Finally, the graph of (III) passes through $(0,1)$, and 1 is the maximum value. Thus, $1 = A\cos 0 + B\sin 0$, so $A = 1$. Since it reaches a local maximum at $(0,1)$, $x'(0) = 0 = -4A\sin 0 + 4B\cos 0$, so $B = 0$. Thus, the solution is $x = \cos 4t$.

10. All the differential equations have solutions of the form $s(t) = C_1\sin \omega t + C_2\cos \omega t$. Since for all of them, $s'(0) = 0$, we have $s'(0) = 0 = C_1\omega\cos 0 - C_2\omega\sin 0 = 0$, giving $C_1\omega = 0$. Thus, either $C_1 = 0$ or $\omega = 0$. If $\omega = 0$, then $s(t)$ is a constant function, and since the equations represent oscillating springs, we don't want $s(t)$ to be a constant function. Thus, $C_1 = 0$, so all four equations have solutions of the form $s(t) = C\cos \omega t$.
    i) $s'' + 4s = 0$, so $\omega = \sqrt{4} = 2$. $s(0) = C\cos 0 = C = 5$. Thus, $s(t) = 5\cos 2t$.
    ii) $s'' + \frac{1}{4}s = 0$, so $\omega = \sqrt{\frac{1}{4}} = \frac{1}{2}$. $s(0) = C\cos 0 = C = 10$. Thus, $s(t) = 10\cos \frac{1}{2}t$.

iii) $s'' + 6s = 0$, so $\omega = \sqrt{6}$. $s(0) = C = 4$, Thus, $s(t) = 4\cos\sqrt{6}t$.

iv) $s'' + \frac{1}{6}s = 0$, so $\omega = \sqrt{\frac{1}{6}}$. $s(0) = C = 20$. Thus, $s(t) = 20\cos\sqrt{\frac{1}{6}}t$.

(a) Spring iii) has the shortest period, $\frac{2\pi}{\sqrt{6}}$. (Other periods are $\pi, 4\pi, 2\pi\sqrt{6}$)

(b) Spring iv) has the largest amplitude, 20.

(c) Spring iv) has the longest period, $2\pi\sqrt{6}$.

(d) Spring i) has the largest maximum velocity. We can see this by looking at $v(t) = s'(t) = -C\omega\sin\omega t$. The velocity is just a sine function, so we look for the derivative with the biggest amplitude, which will have the greatest value. The velocity function for Spring i) has amplitude 10, the largest of the four springs. (The other velocity amplitudes are $10 \cdot \frac{1}{2} = 5, 4\sqrt{6} \approx 9.8$, $\frac{20}{\sqrt{6}} \approx 8.2$)

11. (a) We are given $\frac{d^2x}{dt^2} = -\frac{g}{l}x$, so $x = C_1\cos\sqrt{\frac{g}{l}}t + C_2\sin\sqrt{\frac{g}{l}}t$. We use the initial conditions to find C_1 and C_2.

$$x(0) = C_1\cos 0 + C_2\sin 0 = C_1 = 0$$

$$x'(0) = -C_1\sqrt{\frac{g}{l}}\sin 0 + C_2\sqrt{\frac{g}{l}}\cos 0 = C_2\sqrt{\frac{g}{l}} = v_0$$

Thus, $C_1 = 0$ and $C_2 = v_0\sqrt{\frac{l}{g}}$, so $x = v_0\sqrt{\frac{l}{g}}\sin\sqrt{\frac{g}{l}}t$.

(b) Again, $x = C_1\cos\sqrt{\frac{g}{l}}t + C_2\sin\sqrt{\frac{g}{l}}t$, but this time, $x(0) = x_0$, and $x'(0) = 0$.
Thus, as before, $x(0) = C_1 = x_0$, and $x'(0) = C_2\sqrt{\frac{g}{l}} = 0$. In this case, $C_1 = x_0$ and $C_2 = 0$.
Thus, $x = x_0\cos\sqrt{\frac{g}{l}}t$.

12. (a) If x_0 is increased, the amplitude of the function x is increased, but the period remains the same. In other words, the pendulum will start higher, but the time to swing back and forth will stay the same.

(b) If l is increased, the period of the function x is increased. (Remember, the period of $x_0\cos\sqrt{\frac{g}{l}}t$ is $\frac{2\pi}{\sqrt{g/l}} = 2\pi\sqrt{l/g}$.) In other words, it will take longer for the pendulum to swing back and forth.

13. The amplitude is $\sqrt{3^2 + 7^2} = \sqrt{58}$.

14. The amplitude is $A = \sqrt{7^2 + 24^2} = \sqrt{625} = 25$.
The phase shift, φ, is given by $\tan\varphi = \frac{24}{7}$, so $\varphi = \arctan\frac{24}{7} \approx 1.287$ or $\varphi \approx -1.855$.
Since $C_1 = 24 > 0$, we want $\varphi = 1.287$, so the solution is $25\sin(\omega t + 1.287)$.

15. (a) Let $x = \omega t$ and $y = \varphi$. Then

$$A\sin(\omega t + \varphi) = A(\sin\omega t\cos\varphi + \cos\omega t\sin\varphi)$$
$$= (A\sin\varphi)\cos\omega t + (A\cos\varphi)\sin\omega t.$$

(b)   If we want $A \sin(\omega t + \varphi) = C_1 \cos \omega t + C_2 \sin \omega t$ to be true for all t, then by looking at the answer to (a), we must have $C_1 = A \sin \varphi$ and $C_2 = A \cos \varphi$. Thus,

$$\frac{C_1}{C_2} = \frac{A \sin \varphi}{A \cos \varphi} = \tan \varphi,$$

and

$$\sqrt{C_1^2 + C_2^2} = \sqrt{A^2 \sin^2 \varphi + A^2 \cos^2 \varphi} = A\sqrt{\sin^2 \varphi + \cos^2 \varphi} = A,$$

so our formulas are justified.

16.   (a) $36\dfrac{d^2 Q}{dt^2} + \dfrac{Q}{9} = 0$ so $\dfrac{d^2 Q}{dt^2} = -\dfrac{Q}{324}.$
Thus,

$$Q = C_1 \cos \frac{1}{18} t + C_2 \sin \frac{1}{18} t.$$
$$Q(0) = 0 = C_1 \cos 0 + C_2 \sin 0 = C_1,$$
$$\text{so} \quad C_1 = 0.$$

So, $Q = C_2 \sin \dfrac{1}{18} t$, and

$$Q' = I = \frac{1}{18} C_2 \cos \frac{1}{18} t.$$
$$Q'(0) = I(0) = 2 = \frac{1}{18} C_2 \cos \left(\frac{1}{18} \cdot 0 \right) = \frac{1}{18} C_2,$$
$$\text{so} \quad C_2 = 36.$$

Therefore, $Q = 36 \sin \dfrac{1}{18} t.$

(b)   As in part (a), $Q = C_1 \cos \dfrac{1}{18} t + C_2 \sin \dfrac{1}{18} t.$
According to the initial conditions:

$$Q(0) = 6 = C_1 \cos 0 + C_2 \sin 0 = C_1,$$
$$\text{so} \quad C_1 = 6.$$

So $Q = 6 \cos \dfrac{1}{18} t + C_2 \sin \dfrac{1}{18} t.$
Thus,

$$Q' = I = -\frac{1}{3} \sin \frac{1}{18} t + \frac{1}{18} C_2 \cos \frac{1}{18} t.$$
$$Q'(0) = I(0) = 0 = -\frac{1}{3} \sin \left(\frac{1}{18} \cdot 0 \right) + \frac{1}{18} C_2 \cos \left(\frac{1}{18} \cdot 0 \right) = \frac{1}{18} C_2,$$
$$\text{so} \quad C_2 = 0.$$

Therefore, $Q = 6 \cos \dfrac{1}{18} t.$

17.   The equation we have for the charge tells us that:

$$\frac{d^2Q}{dt^2} = -\frac{Q}{LC},$$

where L and C are positive.

If we let $\omega = \sqrt{\frac{1}{LC}}$, we know the solution is of the form:

$$Q = C_1 \cos \omega t + C_2 \sin \omega t.$$

Since $Q(0) = 0$, we find that $C_1 = 0$, so $Q = C_2 \sin \omega t$.

Since $Q'(0) = 4$, and $Q' = \omega C_2 \cos \omega t$, we have $C_2 = \dfrac{4}{\omega}$, so $Q = \dfrac{4}{\omega} \sin \omega t$.

But we want the maximum charge, meaning the amplitude of Q, to be $2\sqrt{2}$ coulombs. Thus, we have $\dfrac{4}{\omega} = 2\sqrt{2}$, which gives us $\omega = \sqrt{2}$.

So we now have: $\sqrt{2} = \frac{1}{\sqrt{LC}} = \frac{1}{\sqrt{10C}}$. Thus, $C = \frac{1}{20}$ farads.

18.   We know that the general formula for Q will be of the form:

$$Q = C_1 \cos \omega t + C_2 \sin \omega t.$$

and

$$I = Q' = -C_1 \sin \omega t + C_2 \cos \omega t$$

Thus, as $t \to \infty$, neither one approaches a limit. Instead, they vary sinusoidally, with the same frequency but out of phase. We can think of the charge on the capacitor as being analogous to the displacement of a mass on a spring, oscillating from positive to negative. The current is then like the velocity of the mass, also oscillating from positive to negative. When the charge is maximal or minimal, the current is zero (just like when the spring is at the top or bottom of its motion), and when the current is maximal, the charge is zero (just like when the spring is at the middle of its motion).

9.11   SOLUTIONS

1.   (a)   The data in Table 9.17 on page 570 shows that each peak is 0.53 times the height of the previous one (since $0.5039/0.9445 \approx 0.53$ and $0.2668/0.5039 \approx 0.53$, etc.). Assuming that the peaks are a distance π apart, this means that every time t is increased by π, the value of the exponential function should decrease by a factor of 0.53. Writing $a^t = (0.53)^{t/\pi}$ achieves this.

(b)   We can write $(0.53)^{t/\pi} = e^{kt}$ for some value of k. Solving for k:

$$\left((0.53)^{1/\pi} \right)^t = (e^k)^t$$

so

$$e^k = (0.53)^{1/\pi}.$$

Taking logs:

$$k = \frac{1}{\pi}\ln(0.53) = -0.20$$

Thus

$$(0.53)^{1/\pi} = e^{-0.20}$$

and

$$(0.53)^{t/\pi} = \left((0.53)^{1/\pi}\right)^t = (e^{-0.20})^t = e^{-0.20t}.$$

2. (a) $\dfrac{d^2y}{dt^2} = -\dfrac{dx}{dt} = -y$ so $\dfrac{d^2y}{dt^2} + y = 0.$

   (b) General solution is $y = C_1\cos t + C_2\sin t.$

   Since $x = -\dfrac{dy}{dt}$, we have $x = C_1\sin t - C_2\cos t.$

3. (a) $\dfrac{d^2u}{dt^2} = -4\dfrac{ds}{dt} = -4u$ so $\dfrac{d^2u}{dt^2} + 4u = 0.$

   (b) General solution is

$$u = C_1\cos 2t + C_2\sin 2t$$

$$s = -\frac{1}{4}\frac{du}{dt} = \frac{C_1}{2}\sin 2t - \frac{C_2}{2}\cos 2t.$$

4. (a) $\dfrac{dy}{dx} = \dfrac{dy/dt}{dx/dt} = -\dfrac{x}{y}$

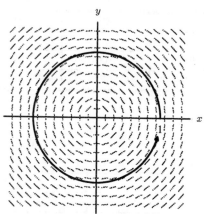

Figure 9.53: Slope field for $\dfrac{dy}{dx} = -\dfrac{x}{y}$

   (b) Differentiating the second equation with respect to t and substituting for x:

$$\frac{d^2y}{dt^2} = \frac{dx}{dt} = -y \quad \text{so} \quad \frac{d^2y}{dt^2} + y = 0.$$

Thus $y = C_1 \cos t + C_2 \sin t$. Since $y(0) = 0$, we must have $C_1 = 0$ so $y = C_2 \sin t$. Now $x = \dfrac{dy}{dx} = C_2 \cos t$. Since $x(0) = 1$, we must have $C_2 = 1$, so

$$x = \cos t \quad \text{and} \quad y = \sin t.$$

5.

s	v	$ds = v\Delta t$	$dv = -s\Delta t$
0	1	0.5	0
0.5	1	0.5	−0.25
1	0.75	0.375	−0.5

6.

s	v	$ds = v\Delta t$	$dv = -s\Delta t$
0	1	0.5	0
0.5	1	0.5	−0.25
1	0.75	0.375	−0.5
1.375	0.25	0.125	−0.687
1.5	−0.437	−0.219	0.75
1.281	−1.187	−0.594	−0.641
0.687	−1.828	−0.914	−0.344
−0.227	−2.172	−1.086	0.113
−1.313	−2.059	−1.029	0.656

7. Solution depends on software. Here are formulas for an Excel spreadsheet:

TABLE 9.19

	A	B	C	D	E	F
1	i	t_i	y_i	v_i	$\frac{dy}{dt}$	$\frac{dv}{dt}$
2	1	0.00	2.00	0.00	=D2	= −2*(D2−C2)
3	=A2	=B2+0.1	=C2+E2*0.1	=D2+F2*0.1	=D3	= −2*(D3−C3)

8. (a) $\dfrac{dy}{dt} = v, \quad \dfrac{dv}{dt} = y$

   (b)

TABLE 9.20

t	y	v	y'	v'
0	1	1	1	1
0.25	1.25	1.25	1.25	1.25
0.5	1.563	1.563	1.563	1.563
0.75	1.953	1.953	1.953	1.953
1	2.441	2.441		

So $y(1) \approx 2.441$.

(c)   If $y = e^t$, $y' = e^t$ and $y'' = e^t$, so y satisfies the equation $y'' = y$. The true value of the solution is therefore $y(1) = e^1 \approx 2.718$. The difference is a little less than 0.3. To get more accuracy, take Δt smaller.

9.

$i = t$	S	I	dS/dt	dI/dt
0	762	1	−1.98	1.48
1	760.02	2.48	−4.90	3.66
2	755.12	6.14	−12.06	8.99
3	743.05	15.13	−29.24	21.67
4	713.82	36.80	−68.30	49.90
5	645.51	86.71	−145.52	102.17

10.   The numbers show that I is severely underestimated; I should come close to passing S at around $t = 5$. The fact that I is underestimated occurs because Euler's Method linearizes the differential equations for I and S; since the graph of I against t starts off nearly flat, and is concave up, the approximation will tend to keep below the true solution curve (because tangent lines to a concave up curve lie below the curve).

11.

i	t	r	w	dw/dt	dr/dt
0	0.0	2	2	−2	2
1	0.1	2.2	1.8	−2.16	1.76
2	0.2	2.38	1.58	−2.18	1.39
3	0.3	2.51	1.37	−2.07	0.92

12.   The step size is much too big: it fails to capture the cyclic nature of the solutions. Moreover, it gives $w(1) = w(0) + dw/dt = 2 - 2 = 0$, that is, the worm population becomes zero.

9.12 SOLUTIONS

1.   The characteristic equation is $r^2 + 4r + 3 = 0$, so $r = -1$ or -3.
     Therefore $y(t) = C_1 e^{-t} + C_2 e^{-3t}$.

2.   The characteristic equation is $r^2 + 4r + 4 = 0$, so $r = -2$.
     Therefore $y(t) = (C_1 t + C_2)e^{-2t}$.

3.   The characteristic equation is $r^2 + 4r + 5 = 0$, so $r = -2 \pm i$.
     Therefore $y(t) = C_1 e^{-2t} \cos t + C_2 e^{-2t} \sin t$.

4.   The characteristic equation is $r^2 - 7 = 0$, so $r = \pm\sqrt{7}$.
     Therefore $s(t) = C_1 e^{\sqrt{7}t} + C_2 e^{-\sqrt{7}t}$.

5.   The characteristic equation is $r^2 + 7 = 0$, so $r = \pm\sqrt{7}i$.
     Therefore $s(t) = C_1 \cos \sqrt{7}t + C_2 \sin \sqrt{7}t$.

6.   The characteristic equation is $4r^2 + 8r + 3 = 0$, so $r = -1/2$ or $-3/2$.
     Therefore $z(t) = C_1 e^{-t/2} + C_2 e^{-3t/2}$.

7. The characteristic equation is $r^2 + 4r + 8 = 0$, so $r = -2 \pm 2i$.
   Therefore $x(t) = C_1 e^{-2t} \cos 2t + C_2 e^{-2t} \sin 2t$.

8. The characteristic equation is $r^2 + r + 1 = 0$, so $r = -\frac{1}{2} \pm \frac{\sqrt{3}}{2} i$.
   Therefore $p(t) = C_1 e^{-t/2} \cos \frac{\sqrt{3}}{2} t + C_2 e^{-t/2} \sin \frac{\sqrt{3}}{2} t$.

9. The characteristic equation is $r^2 + 6r + 5 = 0$, so $r = -1$ or -5.
   Therefore $y(t) = C_1 e^{-t} + C_2 e^{-5t}$.
   $y'(t) = -C_1 e^{-t} - 5C_2 e^{-5t}$
   $y'(0) = 0 = -C_1 - 5C_2$
   $y(0) = 1 = C_1 + C_2$
   　　　Therefore $C_2 = -1/4$, $C_1 = 5/4$ and $y(t) = \frac{5}{4} e^{-t} - \frac{1}{4} e^{-5t}$.

10. The characteristic equation is $r^2 + 6r + 5 = 0$, so $r = -1$ or -5.
    Therefore $y(t) = C_1 e^{-t} + C_2 e^{-5t}$.
    $y'(t) = -C_1 e^{-t} - 5C_2 e^{-5t}$
    $y'(0) = 5 = -C_1 - 5C_2$
    $y(0) = 5 = C_1 + C_2$
    　　　Therefore $C_2 = -5/2$, $C_1 = 15/2$ and $y(t) = \frac{15}{2} e^{-t} - \frac{5}{2} e^{-5t}$.

11. The characteristic equation is $r^2 + 6r + 10 = 0$, so $r = -3 \pm i$.
    Therefore $y(t) = C_1 e^{-3t} \cos t + C_2 e^{-3t} \sin t$.
    $y'(t) = C_1 [e^{-3t}(-\sin t) + (-3e^{-3t}) \cos t] + C_2 [e^{-3t} \cos t + (-3e^{-3t}) \sin t]$
    $y'(0) = 2 = -3C_1 + C_2$
    $y(0) = 0 = C_1$
    　　　Therefore $C_1 = 0, C_2 = 2$ and $y(t) = 2e^{-3t} \sin t$.

12. The characteristic equation is $r^2 + 6r + 10 = 0$, so $r = -3 \pm i$.
    Therefore $y(t) = C_1 e^{-3t} \cos t + C_2 e^{-3t} \sin t$.
    $y'(t) = C_1 [e^{-3t}(-\sin t) + (-3e^{-3t}) \cos t] + C_2 [e^{-3t} \cos t + (-3e^{-3t}) \sin t]$
    $y'(0) = 0 = -3C_1 + C_2$
    $y(0) = 0 = C_1$
    　　　Therefore $C_1 = C_2 = 0$ and $y(t) = 0$.

13. The characteristic equation is $r^2 + 2r + 2 = 0$, so $r = -1 \pm i$.
    Therefore $p(t) = C_1 e^{-t} \cos t + C_2 e^{-t} \sin t$.
    $p(0) = 0 = C_1$ so $p(t) = C_2 e^{-t} \sin t$
    $p(\pi/2) = 20 = C_2 e^{-\pi/2} \sin \frac{\pi}{2}$ so $C_2 = 20 e^{\pi/2}$
    　　　Therefore $p(t) = 20 e^{\frac{\pi}{2}} e^{-t} \sin t = 20 e^{\frac{\pi}{2} - t} \sin t$.

14. The characteristic equation is $r^2 + 4r + 5 = 0$, so $r = -2 \pm i$.
    Therefore $p(t) = C_1 e^{-2t} \cos t + C_2 e^{-2t} \sin t$.
    $p(0) = 1 = C_1$ so $p(t) = e^{-2t} \cos t + C_2 e^{-2t} \sin t$
    $p(\pi/2) = 5 = C_2 e^{-\pi}$ so $C_2 = 5 e^{\pi}$.
    　　　Therefore $p(t) = e^{-2t} \cos t + 5 e^{\pi} e^{-2t} \sin t = e^{-2t} \cos t + 5 e^{\pi - 2t} \sin t$.

15. (a) $x'' + 4x = 0$ represents an undamped oscillator, and so goes with (IV).

(b) $x''-4x=0$ has characteristic equation $r^2-4=0$ and so $r=\pm2$. The solution is $C_1e^{-2t}+C_2e^{2t}$. This represents non-oscillating motion, so it goes with (II).

(c) $x''-0.2x'+1.01x=0$ has characteristic equation $r^2-0.2+1.01=0$ so $b^2-4ac=0.04-4.04=-4$, and $r=0.1\pm i$. So the solution is

$$C_1e^{(0.1+i)t}+C_2e^{(0.1-i)t}=e^{0.1t}(A\sin t+B\cos t).$$

The negative coefficient in the x' term represents an amplifying force. This is reflected in the solution by $e^{0.1t}$, which increases as t increases, so this goes with (I).

(d) $x''+0.2x'+1.01x$ has characteristic equation $r^2+0.2r+1.01=0$ so $b^2-4ac=-4$. This represents a damped oscillator. We have $r=-0.1\pm i$ and so the solution is $x=e^{-0.1t}(A\sin t+B\cos t)$, which goes with (III).

16. Recall that $F_{\text{drag}}=-c\frac{ds}{dt}$, so to find the largest coefficient of damping we look at the coefficient of s'. Thus spring (iii) has the largest coefficient of damping.

17. The restoring force is given by $F_{\text{spring}}=-ks$, so we look for the smallest coefficient of s. Spring (iv) exerts the smallest restoring force.

18. The frictional force is $F_{\text{drag}}=-c\frac{ds}{dt}$. Thus spring (iv) has the smallest frictional force.

19. All of these differential equations have solutions of the form $C_1e^{\alpha t}\cos\beta t+C_2e^{\alpha t}\sin\beta t$. The spring with the longest period has the smallest β. Since $i\beta$ is the complex part of the roots of the characteristic equation, $\beta=\frac{1}{2}(\sqrt{4c-b^2})$. Thus spring (iii) has the longest period.

20. The stiffest spring exerts the greatest restoring force for a small displacement. Recall that by Hooke's Law $F_{\text{spring}}=-ks$, so we look for the differential equation with the greatest coefficient of s. This is spring (ii).

21. Recall that $s''+bs'+c=0$ is overdamped if the discriminant $b^2-4c>0$, critically damped if $b^2-4c=0$, and underdamped if $b^2-4c<0$. Since $b^2-4c=16-4c$, the circuit is overdamped if $c<4$, critically damped if $c=4$, and underdamped if $c>4$.

22. Recall that $s''+bs'+cs=0$ is overdamped if the discriminant $b^2-4c>0$, critically damped if $b^2-4c=0$, and underdamped if $b^2-4c<0$. Since $b^2-4c=8-4c$, the solution is overdamped if $c<2$, critically damped if $c=2$, and underdamped if $c>2$.

23. Recall that $s''+bs'+cs=0$ is overdamped if the discriminant $b^2-4c>0$, critically damped if $b^2-4c=0$, and underdamped if $b^2-4c<0$. Since $b^2-4c=36-4c$, the solution is overdamped if $c<9$, critically damped if $c=9$, and underdamped if $c>9$.

24. $0=\frac{d^2}{dt^2}(e^{2t})-5\frac{d}{dt}(e^{2t})+ke^{2t}=4e^{2t}-10e^{2t}+ke^{2t}=e^{2t}(k-6)$. Since $e^{2t}\neq0$, we must have $k-6=0$. Therefore $k=6$.

   The characteristic equation is $r^2-5r+6=0$, so $r=2$ or 3. Therefore $y(t)=C_1e^{2t}+C_2e^{3t}$.

25. The characteristic equation is $r^2+r-2=0$, so $r=1$ or -2. Therefore $z(t)=C_1e^t+C_2e^{-2t}$. Since $e^t\to\infty$ as $t\to\infty$, we must have $C_1=0$. Therefore $z(t)=C_2e^{-2t}$. Furthermore, $z(0)=3=C_2$, so $z(t)=3e^{-2t}$.

26. In the underdamped case, $b^2 - 4c < 0$ so $4c - b^2 > 0$. Since the roots of the characteristic equation are

$$\alpha \pm i\beta = \frac{-b \pm \sqrt{b^2 - 4c}}{2} = \frac{-b \pm i\sqrt{4c - b^2}}{2}$$

we have $\alpha = -b/2$ and $\beta = (\sqrt{4c - b^2})/2$ or $\beta = -(\sqrt{4c - b^2})/2$. Since the general solution is

$$y = C_1 e^{\alpha t} \cos \beta t + C_2 e^{\alpha t} \sin \beta t$$

and since α is negative, $y \to 0$ as $t \to \infty$.

27. (a) If $r_1 = \frac{-b - \sqrt{b^2 - 4c}}{2}$ then $r_1 < 0$ since both b and $\sqrt{b^2 - 4c}$ are positive.

    If $r_2 = \frac{-b + \sqrt{b^2 - 4c}}{2}$, then $r_2 < 0$ because

    $$b = \sqrt{b^2} > \sqrt{b^2 - 4c}.$$

    (b) The general solution to the differential equation is of the form

    $$y = C_1 e^{r_1 t} + C_2 e^{r_2 t}$$

    and since r_1 and r_2 are both negative, y must go to 0 as $t \to \infty$.

28. In the overdamped case, we have a solution of the form

    $$s = C_1 e^{r_1 t} + C_2 e^{r_2 t}$$

    where r_1 and r_2 are real. We find a t such that $s = 0$, hence $C_1 e^{r_1 t} = -C_2 e^{r_2 t}$.
    If $C_2 = 0$, then $C_1 = 0$, hence $s = 0$ for all t. But this doesn't match with Figure 9.79, so $C_2 \neq 0$.
    We divide by $C_2 e^{r_1 t}$, and get:

    $$-\frac{C_1}{C_2} = e^{(r_2 - r_1)t}, \quad \text{where} - \frac{C_1}{C_2} > 0,$$

    so the exponential is always positive. Therefore

    $$(r_2 - r_1)t = \ln(-\frac{C_1}{C_2})$$

    and

    $$t = \frac{\ln(-\frac{C_1}{C_2})}{(r_2 - r_1)}.$$

    So the mass passes through the equilibrium point only once, when $t = \frac{\ln(-\frac{C_1}{C_2})}{(r_2 - r_1)}$.

29. (a) $\dfrac{d^2 y}{dt^2} = -\dfrac{dx}{dt} = y$ so $\dfrac{d^2 y}{dt^2} - y = 0.$

    (b) Characteristic equation $r^2 - 1 = 0$, so $r = \pm 1$.
    The general solution for y is $y = C_1 e^t + C_2 e^{-t}$, so $x = C_2 e^{-t} - C_1 e^t$.

30. The differential equation is $Q'' + 2Q' + \frac{1}{4}Q = 0$, so the characteristic equation is $r^2 + 2r + \frac{1}{4} = 0$.
This has roots $\dfrac{-2 \pm \sqrt{3}}{2} = -1 \pm \dfrac{\sqrt{3}}{2}$. Thus, the general solution is

$$Q(t) = C_1 e^{(-1+\frac{\sqrt{3}}{2})t} + C_2 e^{(-1-\frac{\sqrt{3}}{2})t},$$

$$Q'(t) = C_1 \left(-1 + \frac{\sqrt{3}}{2}\right) e^{(-1+\frac{\sqrt{3}}{2})t} + C_2 \left(-1 - \frac{\sqrt{3}}{2}\right) e^{(-1-\frac{\sqrt{3}}{2})t}.$$

We have

(a)

$$Q(0) = C_1 + C_2 = 0$$

$$\text{and} \qquad Q'(0) = \left(-1 + \frac{\sqrt{3}}{2}\right) C_1 + \left(-1 - \frac{\sqrt{3}}{2}\right) C_2 = 2.$$

Using the formula for $Q(t)$, we have $C_1 = -C_2$. Using the formula for $Q'(t)$, we have:

$$2 = \left(-1 + \frac{\sqrt{3}}{2}\right)(-C_2) + \left(-1 - \frac{\sqrt{3}}{2}\right) C_2 = -\sqrt{3}C_2$$

$$\text{so,} \qquad C_2 = -\frac{2}{\sqrt{3}}.$$

Thus, $C_1 = \dfrac{2}{\sqrt{3}}$, and $Q(t) = \dfrac{2}{\sqrt{3}} \left(e^{(-1+\frac{\sqrt{3}}{2})t} - e^{(-1-\frac{\sqrt{3}}{2})t}\right).$

(b) We have

$$Q(0) = C_1 + C_2 = 2$$

$$\text{and} \qquad Q'(0) = \left(-1 + \frac{\sqrt{3}}{2}\right) C_1 + \left(-1 - \frac{\sqrt{3}}{2}\right) C_2 = 0.$$

Using the first equation, we have $C_1 = 2 - C_2$. Thus,

$$\left(-1 + \frac{\sqrt{3}}{2}\right)(2 - C_2) + \left(-1 - \frac{\sqrt{3}}{2}\right) C_2 = 0$$

$$-\sqrt{3}C_2 = 2 - \sqrt{3}$$

$$C_2 = -\frac{2 - \sqrt{3}}{\sqrt{3}}$$

$$\text{and} \qquad C_1 = 2 - C_2 = \frac{2 + \sqrt{3}}{\sqrt{3}}.$$

Thus, $Q(t) = \frac{1}{\sqrt{3}}\left((2+\sqrt{3})e^{(-1+\frac{\sqrt{3}}{2})t} - (2-\sqrt{3})e^{(-1-\frac{\sqrt{3}}{2})t}\right)$.

31. In this case, the differential equation describing the charge is $Q'' + Q' + \frac{1}{4}Q = 0$, so the characteristic equation is $r^2 + r + \frac{1}{4} = 0$. This equation has one root, $r = -\frac{1}{2}$, so the equation for charge is

$$Q(t) = (C_1 + C_2 t)e^{-\frac{1}{2}t},$$

$$Q'(t) = -\frac{1}{2}(C_1 + C_2 t)e^{-\frac{1}{2}t} + C_2 e^{-\frac{1}{2}t}$$

$$= \left(C_2 - \frac{C_1}{2} - \frac{C_2 t}{2}\right)e^{-\frac{1}{2}t}.$$

(a) We have

$$Q(0) = C_1 = 0,$$

$$Q'(0) = C_2 - \frac{C_1}{2} = 2.$$

Thus, $C_1 = 0, C_2 = 2$, and

$$Q(t) = 2te^{-\frac{1}{2}t}.$$

(b) We have

$$Q(0) = C_1 = 2,$$

$$Q'(0) = C_2 - \frac{C_1}{2} = 0.$$

Thus, $C_1 = 2, C_2 = 1$, and

$$Q(t) = (2+t)e^{-\frac{1}{2}t}.$$

(c) The resistance was decreased by exactly the amount to switch the circuit from the overdamped case to the critically damped case. Comparing the solutions of parts (a) and (b) in Problems 30, we find that in the critically damped case the net charge goes to 0 much faster as $t \to \infty$.

32. In this case, the differential equation describing charge is $8Q'' + 2Q' + \frac{1}{4}Q = 0$, so the characteristic equation is $8r^2 + 2r + \frac{1}{4} = 0$. This quadratic equation has solutions

$$r = \frac{-2 \pm \sqrt{4 - 4 \cdot 8 \cdot \frac{1}{4}}}{16} = -\frac{1}{8} \pm \frac{1}{8}i.$$

Thus, the equation for charge is

$$Q(t) = e^{-\frac{1}{8}t}\left(A \sin\frac{t}{8} + B \cos\frac{t}{8}\right).$$

$$Q'(t) = -\frac{1}{8}e^{-\frac{1}{8}t}\left(A \sin\frac{t}{8} + B \cos\frac{t}{8}\right) + e^{-\frac{1}{8}t}\left(\frac{1}{8}A \cos\frac{t}{8} - \frac{1}{8}B \sin\frac{t}{8}\right)$$

$$= \frac{1}{8}e^{-\frac{1}{8}t}\left((A - B)\cos\frac{t}{8} + (-A - B)\sin\frac{t}{8}\right).$$

(a) We have

$$Q(0) = B = 0,$$

$$Q'(0) = \frac{1}{8}(A - B) = 2.$$

Thus, $B = 0$, $A = 16$, and

$$Q(t) = 16e^{-\frac{1}{8}t} \sin \frac{t}{8}.$$

(b) We have

$$Q(0) = B = 2,$$

$$Q'(0) = \frac{1}{8}(A - B) = 0.$$

Thus, $B = 2$, $A = 2$, and

$$Q(t) = 2e^{-\frac{1}{8}t} \left(\sin \frac{t}{8} + \cos \frac{t}{8} \right).$$

(c) By increasing the inductance, we have gone from the overdamped case to the underdamped case. We find that while the charge still tends to 0 as $t \to \infty$, the charge in the underdamped case oscillates between positive and negative values. In the over-damped case of Problem 30, the charge starts nonnegative and remains positive.

33. The differential equation for the charge on the capacitor, given a resistance R, a capacitance C, and and inductance L, is

$$LQ'' + RQ' + \frac{Q}{C} = 0.$$

The corresponding characteristic equation is $Lr^2 + Rr + \frac{1}{C} = 0$. This equation has roots

$$r = -\frac{R}{2L} \pm \frac{\sqrt{R^2 - \frac{4L}{C}}}{2L}.$$

(a) If $R^2 - \frac{4L}{C} < 0$, the solution is

$$Q(t) = e^{-\frac{R}{2L}t}(A \sin \omega t + B \cos \omega t) \text{ for some } A \text{ and } B,$$

where $\omega = \dfrac{\sqrt{R^2 - \frac{4L}{C}}}{2L}$. As $t \to \infty$, $Q(t)$ clearly goes to 0.

(b) If $R^2 - \frac{4L}{C} = 0$, the solution is

$$Q(t) = e^{-\frac{R}{t}}(A + Bt) \text{ for some } A \text{ and } B.$$

Again, as $t \to \infty$, the charge goes to 0.

(c) If $R^2 - \dfrac{4L}{C} > 0$, the solution is

$$Q(t) = Ae^{r_1 t} + Be^{r_2 t} \text{ for some } A \text{ and } B,$$

where

$$r_1 = -\frac{R}{2L} + \frac{\sqrt{R^2 - \frac{4L}{C}}}{2L}, \quad \text{and} \quad r_2 = -\frac{R}{2L} - \frac{\sqrt{R^2 - \frac{4L}{C}}}{2L}.$$

Notice that r_2 is clearly negative. r_1 is also negative since

$$\frac{\sqrt{R^2 - \frac{4L}{C}}}{2L} < \frac{\sqrt{R^2}}{2L} \quad (L \text{ and } C \text{ are positive})$$

$$= \frac{R}{2L}.$$

Since r_1 and r_2 are negative, again $Q(t) \to 0$, as $t \to \infty$.

Thus, for any circuit with a resistor, a capacitor and an inductor, $Q(t) \to 0$ as $t \to \infty$. Compare this with Problem 18 in Section 9.10, where we showed that in a circuit with just a capacitor and inductor, the charge varied along a sine curve.

SOLUTIONS TO REVIEW PROBLEMS FOR CHAPTER NINE

1. $\frac{dP}{dt} = 0.03P + 400$ so $\int \frac{dP}{P + \frac{40000}{3}} = \int 0.03 \, dt$.

   $\ln |P + \frac{40000}{3}| = 0.03t + C$ giving $P = Ae^{0.03t} - \frac{40000}{3}$. Since $P(0) = 0, A = \frac{40000}{3}$, therefore $P = \frac{40000}{3}(e^{0.03t} - 1)$.

2. Using the solution of the logistic equation given on page 535 in Section 9.7, and using $y(0) = 1$, we get $y = \frac{10}{1 + 9e^{-10t}}$.

3. $\frac{df}{dx} = \sqrt{x f(x)}$ gives $\int \frac{df}{\sqrt{f(x)}} = \int \sqrt{x} \, dx$, so $2\sqrt{f(x)} = \frac{2}{3}x^{\frac{3}{2}} + C$. Since $f(1) = 1$, we have $2 = \frac{2}{3} + C$ so $C = \frac{4}{3}$. Thus, $2\sqrt{f(x)} = \frac{2}{3}x^{\frac{3}{2}} + \frac{4}{3}$, so $f(x) = (\frac{1}{3}x^{\frac{3}{2}} + \frac{2}{3})^2$.
   (Note: this is only defined for $x \geq 0$.)

4. $\frac{dy}{dx} = \frac{y(3-x)}{x(\frac{1}{2}y - 4)}$ gives $\int \frac{(\frac{1}{2}y - 4)}{y} \, dy = \int \frac{(3-x)}{x} \, dx$ so $\int (\frac{1}{2} - \frac{4}{y}) \, dy = \int (\frac{3}{x} - 1) \, dx$. Thus $\frac{1}{2}y - 4\ln|y| = 3\ln|x| - x + C$. Since $y(1) = 5$, we have $\frac{5}{2} - 4\ln 5 = \ln|1| - 1 + C$ so $C = \frac{7}{2} - 4\ln 5$. Thus,

$$\frac{1}{2}y - 4\ln|y| = 3\ln|x| - x + \frac{7}{2} - 4\ln 5.$$

We cannot solve for y in terms of x, so we leave the equation in this form.

5. $\frac{dy}{dx} = e^{x-y}$ giving $\int e^y \, dy = \int e^x \, dx$ so $e^y = e^x + C$. Since $y(0) = 1$, we have $e^1 = e^0 + C$ so $C = e - 1$. Thus, $e^y = e^x + e - 1$, so $y = \ln(e^x + e - 1)$.
   [Note: $e^x + e - 1 > 0$ always.]

6. $\frac{dk}{dt} = (1 + \ln t)k$ gives $\int \frac{dk}{k} = \int (1 + \ln t) dt$ so $\ln |k| = t \ln t + C$. $k(1) = 1$, so $0 = 0 + C$, or $C = 0$.
   Thus, $\ln |k| = t \ln t$ and $|k| = e^{t \ln t} = t^t$, giving $k = \pm t^t$.
   But recall $k(1) = 1$, so $k = t^t$ is the solution.

7. $2 \sin x - y^2 \frac{dy}{dx} = 0$ giving $2 \sin x = y^2 \frac{dy}{dx}$. $\int 2 \sin x \, dx = \int y^2 \, dy$ so $-2 \cos x = \frac{y^3}{3} + C$. Since $y(0) = 3$ we have $-2 = 9 + C$, so $C = -11$. Thus, $-2 \cos x = \frac{y^3}{3} - 11$ giving $y = \sqrt[3]{33 - 6 \cos x}$.

8. $1 + y^2 - \frac{dy}{dx} = 0$ gives $\frac{dy}{dx} = y^2 + 1$, so $\int \frac{dy}{1+y^2} = \int \, dx$ and $\arctan y = x + C$. Since $y(0) = 0$ we have $C = 0$, giving $y = \tan x$.

9. $\frac{dy}{dx} + xy^2 = 0$ means $\frac{dy}{dx} = -xy^2$, so $\int \frac{dy}{y^2} = \int -x \, dx$ giving $-\frac{1}{y} = -\frac{x^2}{2} + C$. Since $y(1) = 1$ we have $-1 = -\frac{1}{2} + C$ so $C = -\frac{1}{2}$. Thus, $-\frac{1}{y} = -\frac{x^2}{2} - \frac{1}{2}$ giving $y = \frac{2}{x^2+1}$.

10. $\frac{dy}{dx} = \frac{y(100-x)}{x(20-y)}$ gives $\int \left(\frac{20-y}{y}\right) dy = \int \left(\frac{100-x}{x}\right) dx$. Thus, $20 \ln |y| - y = 100 \ln |x| - x + C$. The curve passes through $(1, 20)$, so $20 \ln 20 - 20 = -1 + C$ giving $C = 20 \ln 20 - 19$. Therefore, $20 \ln |y| - y = 100 \ln |x| - x + 20 \ln 20 - 19$. We cannot solve for y in terms of x, so we leave the equation in this form.

11. $e^{-\cos \theta} \frac{dz}{d\theta} = \sqrt{1 - z^2} \sin \theta$ implies $\int \frac{dz}{\sqrt{1-z^2}} = \int e^{\cos \theta} \sin \theta \, d\theta$ implies $\arcsin z = -e^{\cos \theta} + C$. According to the initial conditions: $z(0) = \frac{1}{2}$, so $\arcsin \frac{1}{2} = -e^{\cos 0} + C$, therefore $\frac{\pi}{6} = -e + C$, and $C = \frac{\pi}{6} + e$. Thus $z = \sin(-e^{\cos \theta} + \frac{\pi}{6} + e)$.

12. $\frac{dy}{dt} = 2^y \sin^3 t$ implies $\int 2^{-y} \, dy = \int \sin^3 t \, dt$. Using Integral Table Formula 17, we have

$$-\frac{1}{\ln 2} 2^{-y} = -\frac{1}{3} \sin^2 t \cos t - \frac{2}{3} \cos t + C.$$

According to the initial conditions: $y(0) = 0$ so $-\frac{1}{\ln 2} = -\frac{2}{3} + C$, and $C = \frac{2}{3} - \frac{1}{\ln 2}$. Thus,

$$-\frac{1}{\ln 2} 2^{-y} = -\frac{1}{3} \sin^2 t \cos t - \frac{2}{3} \cos t + \frac{2}{3} - \frac{1}{\ln 2}.$$

Solving for y gives:

$$2^{-y} = \frac{\ln 2}{3} \sin^2 t \cos t + \frac{2 \ln 2}{3} \cos t - \frac{2 \ln 2}{3} + 1.$$

Taking natural logs, (Notice the right side is always > 0.)

$$y \ln 2 = -\ln \left(\frac{\ln 2}{3} \sin^2 t \cos t + \frac{2 \ln 2}{3} \cos t - \frac{2 \ln 2}{3} + 1\right),$$

so

$$y = \frac{-\ln \left(\frac{\ln 2}{3} \sin^2 t \cos t + \frac{2 \ln 2}{3} \cos t - \frac{2 \ln 2}{3} + 1\right)}{\ln 2}$$

13. $(1+t^2)y\frac{dy}{dt} = 1 - y$ implies that $\int \frac{y\,dy}{1-y} = \int \frac{dt}{1+t^2}$ implies that $\int \left(-1 + \frac{1}{1-y}\right) dy = \int \frac{dt}{1+t^2}$. Therefore $-y - \ln|1-y| = \arctan t + C$. $y(1) = 0$, so $0 = \arctan 1 + C$, and $C = -\frac{\pi}{4}$, so $-y - \ln|1-y| = \arctan t - \frac{\pi}{4}$. We cannot solve for y in terms of t.

14. $\frac{dy}{dx} = e^{x+y} = e^x e^y$ implies $\int e^{-y}\,dy = \int e^x\,dx$ implies $-e^{-y} = e^x + C$. Since $y = 0$ when $x = 1$, we have $-1 = e + C$, giving $C = -1 - e$. Therefore $-e^{-y} = e^x - 1 - e$ and $y = -\ln(1 + e - e^x)$.

15. $\frac{dy}{dx} = \frac{0.2y(18+0.1x)}{x(100+0.5y)}$ giving $\int \frac{(100+0.5y)}{0.2y}\,dy = \int \frac{18+0.1x}{x}\,dx$, so

$$\int \left(\frac{500}{y} + \frac{5}{2}\right) dy = \int \left(\frac{18}{x} + \frac{1}{10}\right) dx.$$

Therefore, $500\ln|y| + \frac{5}{2}y = 18\ln|x| + \frac{1}{10}x + C$. Since the curve passes through $(10,10)$, $500\ln 10 + 25 = 18\ln 10 + 1 + C$, so $C = 482\ln 10 + 24$. Thus, the solution is

$$500\ln|y| + \frac{5}{2}y = 18\ln|x| + \frac{1}{10}x + 482\ln 10 + 24.$$

We cannot solve for y in terms of x, so we leave the answer in this form.

16. Separation of variables yields $\int \frac{dy}{y\ln y} = \int \frac{dt}{t^2}$, so $\ln|\ln y| = -\frac{1}{t} + C$.
Exponentiating both sides gives:

$$|\ln y| = e^{(-\frac{1}{t}+C)} = e^{-\frac{1}{t}}e^C.$$

So, $\ln y = Ae^{-\frac{1}{t}}$, where $A = \pm e^C$. Exponentiating once more gives $y = e^{Ae^{(-\frac{1}{t})}}$.

17. $(y\sqrt{x^3+1})\frac{dy}{dx} + x^2y^2 + x^2 = 0$ is equivalent to $(y\sqrt{x^3+1})\frac{dy}{dx} = -x^2y^2 - x^2 = -x^2(y^2+1)$. Separating variables yields $\frac{y\,dy}{y^2+1} = -\frac{x^2}{\sqrt{x^3+1}}\,dx$. Integrating, we obtain $\int \frac{y\,dy}{y^2+1} = -\int \frac{x^2}{\sqrt{x^3+1}}\,dx$. This implies $\frac{1}{2}\ln|y^2+1| = -\frac{2}{3}\sqrt{x^3+1} + C$, whence $y^2 + 1 = Ae^{-\frac{4}{3}\sqrt{x^3+1}}$ where $A = \pm e^{2C}$. So $y = \pm\sqrt{Ae^{-\frac{4}{3}\sqrt{x^3+1}} - 1}$.
Note that A cannot be 0; in fact A must be greater than 1.

18. $\frac{dQ}{dt} = -t^2Q^2 - Q^2 + 4t^2 + 4 = -Q^2(t^2+1) + 4(t^2+1) = (t^2+1)(4-Q^2)$. Separating variables yields $\frac{dQ}{4-Q^2} = (t^2+1)\,dt$, so

$$-\int \frac{dQ}{(Q-2)(Q+2)} = -\frac{1}{4}\int \left(\frac{1}{Q-2} - \frac{1}{Q+2}\right)dQ = \int (t^2+1)\,dt.$$

Integrating, we obtain $-\frac{1}{4}(\ln|Q-2| - \ln|Q+2|) = \frac{t^3}{3} + t + C$, so $\ln\left|\frac{Q-2}{Q+2}\right| = -\frac{4t^3}{3} - 4t - 4C$. Exponentiating yields $\left|\frac{Q-2}{Q+2}\right| = e^{-\frac{4t^3}{3}-4t}e^{-4C}$. $\frac{Q-2}{Q+2} = Ae^{-\frac{4t^3}{3}-4t}$ where $A = \pm e^{4C}$. Solving for Q, $Q = \frac{4}{1-Ae^{-\frac{4t^3}{3}-4t}} - 2$. Notice that A could be any constant, including 0. In fact, we also lost the solution $Q = -2$ when we divided both sides by $4 - Q^2$. (The solution $Q = 2$ corresponds to $A = 0$, but $Q = -2$, another valid solution, is lost by our division.)

19. $\frac{x}{y}\frac{dx}{dy} = e^{\left(\frac{x}{a}\right)^2}\ln y \Rightarrow xe^{-\frac{x^2}{a^2}}\,dx = y\ln y\,dy \Rightarrow \int xe^{-\frac{x^2}{a^2}}\,dx = \int y\ln y\,dy.$ So $-\frac{a^2}{2}e^{-\frac{x^2}{a^2}} = \frac{y^2}{2}\ln y -$ $\frac{y^2}{4}+C.$ We could solve for x, but it would be much messier than this convenient form for the solution.

20. By separating variables, we see that solutions are of the form $y = \alpha + Ae^{-t}$

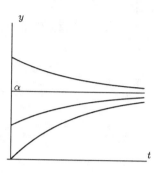

21. Using separation of variables and the integral tables, you can show that solutions are of the form $t = \frac{1}{4}(\ln|w-7| - \ln|w-3|) + C$, or $w = \frac{4}{1-Ae^{4t}} + 3$. The equilibrium values, where $\frac{dw}{dt} = 0$, are $w = 3$ and $w = 7$. Graphs of the solutions can also be sketched directly from the graph of $\frac{dw}{dt}$ against w.

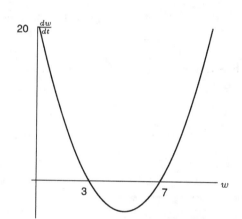

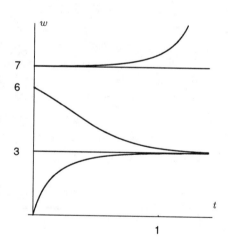

22. (a) $\Delta x = \frac{1}{5} = 0.2.$
At $x = 0$:
$y_0 = 1, y' = 4$; so $\Delta y = 4(0.2) = 0.8.$ Thus, $y_1 = 1 + 0.8 = 1.8.$
At $x = 0.2$:

$y_1 = 1.8, y' = 3.2$; so $\Delta y = 3.2(0.2) = 0.64$. Thus, $y_2 = 1.8 + 0.64 = 2.44$.
At $x = 0.4$:
$y_2 = 2.44, y' = 2.56$; so $\Delta y = 2.56(0.2) = 0.512$. Thus, $y_3 = 2.44 + 0.512 = 2.952$.
At $x = 0.6$:
$y_3 = 2.952, y' = 2.048$; so $\Delta y = 2.048(0.2) = 0.4096$. Thus, $y_4 = 3.3616$.
At $x = 0.8$:
$y_4 = 3.3616, y' = 1.6384$; so $\Delta y = 1.6384(0.2) = 0.32768$. Thus, $y_5 = 3.68928$. So $y(1) \approx$
3.689.

(b)

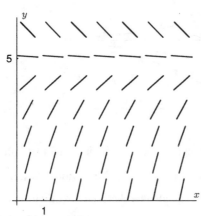

Since solution curves are concave down
for $0 \leq y \leq 5$, and $y(0) = 1 < 5$, the
estimate from Euler's method will be an
overestimate.

(c) Solving by separation:
$$\int \frac{dy}{5-y} = \int dx, \quad \text{so} \; -\ln|5-y| = x + C.$$
Then $5 - y = Ae^{-x}$ where $A = \pm e^{-C}$. Since $y(0) = 1$, we have $5 - 1 = Ae^0$, so $A = 4$.
Therefore, $y = 5 - 4e^{-x}$, and $y(1) = 5 - 4e^{-1} \approx 3.528$.
(Note: as predicted, the estimate in (a) is too large.)

(d) Doubling the value of n will probably halve the error and, therefore, give a value half way between
3.528 and 3.689, which is approximately 3.61.

23. (a) 1 step: $\Delta y = \frac{1}{(\cos x)(\cos y)}\Delta x = \frac{1}{(\cos 0)(\cos 0)}\frac{1}{2} = \frac{1}{2}$.
Thus, using 1 step, we get $(\frac{1}{2}, \frac{1}{2})$ as our approximation.

(b) 2 steps: $\Delta x = \frac{1}{4}$.

TABLE 9.21

x	y	$\Delta y = \frac{1}{(\cos x)(\cos y)}\Delta x$
0	0	0.25
0.25	0.25	0.266
0.5	0.516	

Thus, using 2 steps, we get (0.5, 0.516) as our approximation.

(c)   4 steps: $\Delta x = \frac{1}{8}$

TABLE 9.22

x	y	$\Delta y = \frac{1}{(\cos x)(\cos y)}\Delta x$
0	0	0.125
0.125	0.125	0.127
0.25	0.252	0.133
0.375	0.385	0.145
0.5	0.530	

Thus, using 4 steps, we get (0.5,0.530) as our approximation.

(d) $\frac{dy}{dx} = \frac{1}{(\cos x)(\cos y)}$, so $\int \cos y \, dy = \int \frac{dx}{\cos x}$, whence $\sin y = \frac{1}{2} \ln \left| \frac{(\sin x)+1}{(\sin x)-1} \right| + C$.

Our curve passes through (0,0), so, $0 = 0 + C$, and $C = 0$. Therefore

$$y = \arcsin \left(\frac{1}{2} \ln \left| \frac{(\sin x) + 1}{(\sin x) - 1} \right| \right).$$

When $x = \frac{1}{2}$, $y \approx 0.549$. Our answers in (a)-(c) are all underestimates. In each case, the error is about $\frac{1}{n+1}$, where n is the number of steps. We expect the error to be approximately proportional to $\frac{1}{n}$, so this seems reasonable.

24.   The characteristic equation of $y'' + 6y' + 8y = 0$ is

$$r^2 + 6r + 8 = 0.$$

We have that

$$b^2 - 4c = 6^2 - 4(8) = 4 > 0.$$

This indicates overdamped motion. Since the roots of the characteristic equation are $r_1 = -2$ and $r_2 = -4$, the general solution is

$$y(t) = C_1 e^{-2t} + C_2 e^{-4t}.$$

25.   The characteristic equation of $9z'' + z = 0$ is

$$9r^2 + 1 = 0$$

If we write this in the form $r^2 + br + c = 0$, we have that $r^2 + 1/9 = 0$ and

$$b^2 - 4c = 0 - (4)(1/9) = -4/9 < 0$$

This indicates underdamped motion and since the roots of the characteristic equation are $r = \pm \frac{1}{3}i$, the general equation is

$$y(t) = C_1 \cos \left(\frac{1}{3}t \right) + C_2 \sin \left(\frac{1}{3}t \right)$$

26. The characteristic equation of $9z'' - z = 0$ is

$$9r^2 - 1 = 0.$$

If this is written in the form $r^2 + br + c = 0$, we have that $r^2 - 1/9 = 0$ and

$$b^2 - 4c = 0 - (4)(-1/9) = 4/9 > 0$$

This indicates overdamped motion and since the roots of the characteristic equation are $r = \pm 1/3$, the general solution is

$$y(t) = C_1 e^{\frac{1}{3}t} + C_2 e^{-\frac{1}{3}t}.$$

27. The characteristic equation of $x'' + 2x' + 10x = 0$ is

$$r^2 + 2r + 10 = 0$$

We have that

$$b^2 - 4c = 2^2 - 4(10) = -36 < 0$$

This indicates underdamped motion and since the roots of the characteristic equation are $r = -1 \pm 3i$, the general solution is

$$y(t) = C_1 e^{-t} \cos 3t + C_2 e^{-t} \sin 3t$$

28. Recall that $s'' + bs' + cs = 0$ is overdamped if the discriminant $b^2 - 4c > 0$, critically damped if $b^2 - 4c = 0$, and underdamped if $b^2 - 4c < 0$. Since $b^2 - 4c = b^2 - 20$, the solution is overdamped if $b > 2\sqrt{5}$ or $b < -2\sqrt{5}$, critically damped if $b = \pm 2\sqrt{5}$, and underdamped if $-2\sqrt{5} < b < 2\sqrt{5}$.

29. Recall that $s'' + bs' + cs = 0$ is overdamped if the discriminant $b^2 - 4c > 0$, critically damped if $b^2 - 4c = 0$, and underdamped if $b^2 - 4c < 0$. This has discriminant $b^2 - 4c = b^2 + 64$. Since $b^2 + 64$ is always positive, the solution is always overdamped.

30. Recall that $s'' + bs' + cs = 0$ is overdamped if the discriminant $b^2 - 4c > 0$, critically damped if $b^2 - 4c = 0$, and underdamped if $b^2 - 4c < 0$. This has discriminant $b^2 - 4c = b^2 + 4$. For this to have a critically damped solution, we would need $b^2 + 4 = 0$. For real b, this is impossible. Notice that this equation also cannot have an underdamped solution, for real b. Any solution must be overdamped.

31. (a) Since the amount leaving the blood is proportional to the quantity in the blood,

$$\frac{dQ}{dt} = -kQ \quad \text{for some positive constant } k.$$

Thus $Q = Q_0 e^{-kt}$, where Q_0 is the initial quantity in the bloodstream. Only 20% is left in the blood after 3 hours. Thus $0.20 = e^{-3k}$, so $k = \frac{\ln 0.20}{-3} \approx 0.5365$. Therefore $Q = Q_0 e^{-0.5365t}$.

(b) Since 20% is left after 3 hours, after 6 hours only 20% of that 20% will be left. Thus after 6 hours only 4% will be left, so if the patient is given 100 mg, only 4 mg will be left 6 hours later.

32. (a) k is positive because if $T > A$, then the body will lose heat so that its temperature falls to A. Thus, $\frac{dT}{dt}$ should be negative, so k should be positive. Similarly, if $T < A$ then $\frac{dT}{dt}$ should be positive, so k again should be positive.

(b) The units for $\frac{dT}{dt}$ is $\frac{\text{degrees}}{\text{time}}$. Since the units for $T - A$ are degrees, the units for k are $(\text{time})^{-1}$ or $\frac{1}{\text{time}}$. Thus, if we change from days to hours, k would look different – for example, $\frac{1}{1\,\text{day}} = \frac{1}{24\,\text{hours}}$.

(c) Everything else being equal, coffee will cool faster in a thin china cup than in styrofoam. Thus, for a given temperature difference, $\frac{dT}{dt}$ should be larger in magnitude for china, and therefore k should be larger.

(d) We have $\frac{dT}{dt} = -0.14(T - 70)$, and $T = 170$ when $t = 0$

$\frac{dT}{T-70} = -0.14dt$. Solving this, we have $T = 70 + Ae^{-0.14t}$

The initial condition gives us that $170 = 70 + A$, so $A = 100$. Therefore the solution to the differential equation is $T = 70 + 100e^{-0.14t}$.

To find the amount of time we must wait for the coffee to cool to 120 degrees or less, we put $T = 120$ into the solution and solve for t.

$$120 = 70 + 100e^{-0.14t} \text{ so } t \approx 5 \text{ minutes.}$$

To find how soon we must drink the coffee before it cools to less than 90 degrees, we put $T = 90$ into the solution and solve for t.

$$90 = 70 + 100e^{-0.14t} \text{ so } t \approx 11.5 \text{ minutes.}$$

Therefore our fussiness requires that we not drink our coffee until it has cooled for 5 minutes and then we must finish it before it has cooled for more than 11 minutes. Of course as we drink it, it will cool faster as we increase the surface area to volume ratio!

33. (a) For this situation,

$$\left(\begin{array}{c} \text{Rate money added} \\ \text{to account} \end{array} \right) = \left(\begin{array}{c} \text{Rate money added} \\ \text{via interest} \end{array} \right) + \left(\begin{array}{c} \text{Rate money} \\ \text{deposited} \end{array} \right)$$

Translating this into an equation yields

$$\frac{dB}{dt} = 0.1B + 1200$$

(b) Solving this equation via separation of variables gives

$$\frac{dB}{dt} = 0.1B + 1200$$
$$= (0.1)(B + 12000)$$

So

$$\int \frac{dB}{B + 12000} = \int 0.1 \, dt$$

and

$$\ln|B + 12000| = 0.1t + C$$

solving for B,

$$|B + 12000| = e^{(0.1)t+C} = e^C e^{(0.1)t}$$

or

$$B = Ae^{0.1t} - 12000, \text{ (where } A = e^c)$$

We may find A using the initial condition $B_0 = f(0) = 0$

$$A - 12000 = 0 \quad \text{or} \quad A = 12000$$

So the solution is

$$B = f(t) = 12000(e^{0.1t} - 1)$$

(c)   After 5 years, the balance is

$$B = f(5) = 12000(e^{(0.1)(5)} - 1)$$
$$= 7784.66$$

34.   (a)   The balance in the account at the beginning of the month is given by the following sum

$$\left(\begin{array}{c} \text{balance in} \\ \text{account} \end{array} \right) = \left(\begin{array}{c} \text{previous month's} \\ \text{balance} \end{array} \right) + \left(\begin{array}{c} \text{interest on} \\ \text{previous month's balance} \end{array} \right) + \left(\begin{array}{c} \text{monthly deposit} \\ \text{of } \$100 \end{array} \right)$$

Denote month i's balance by B_i. Assuming the interest is compounded continuously, we have

$$\left(\begin{array}{c} \text{previous month's} \\ \text{balance} \end{array} \right) + \left(\begin{array}{c} \text{interest on previous} \\ \text{month's balance} \end{array} \right) = B_{i-1}e^{0.1/12}.$$

Since the interest rate is $10\% = 0.1$ per year, interest is $\frac{0.1}{12}$ per month. So at month i, the balance is

$$B_i = B_{i-1}e^{\frac{0.1}{12}} + 100$$

Explicitly, we have for the five years (60 months) the equations:

$$B_0 = 0$$
$$B_1 = B_0 e^{\frac{0.1}{12}} + 100$$
$$B_2 = B_1 e^{\frac{0.1}{12}} + 100$$
$$B_3 = B_2 e^{\frac{0.1}{12}} + 100$$
$$\vdots \quad \vdots$$
$$B_{60} = B_{59} e^{\frac{0.1}{12}} + 100$$

In other words,

$$B_1 = 100$$

$$B_2 = 100e^{\frac{0.1}{12}} + 100$$

$$B_3 = (100e^{\frac{0.1}{12}} + 100)e^{\frac{0.1}{12}} + 100$$

$$= 100e^{\frac{(0.1)2}{12}} + 100e^{\frac{0.1}{12}} + 100$$

$$B_4 = 100e^{\frac{(0.1)3}{12}} + 100e^{\frac{(0.1)2}{12}} + 100e^{\frac{(0.1)}{12}} + 100$$

$$\vdots \quad \vdots$$

$$B_{60} = 100e^{\frac{(0.1)59}{12}} + 100e^{\frac{(0.1)58}{12}} + \cdots + 100e^{\frac{(0.1)1}{12}} + 100$$

$$B_{60} = \sum_{k=0}^{59} 100e^{\frac{(0.1)k}{12}}$$

(b) The sum $B_{60} = \sum_{k=0}^{59} 100e^{\frac{(0.1)k}{12}}$ can be written as $B_{60} = \sum_{k=0}^{59} 1200e^{\frac{(0.1)k}{12}} \left(\frac{1}{12}\right)$ which is the left

Riemann sum for $\int_0^5 1200e^{0.1t} dt$, with $\Delta t = \dfrac{1}{12}$ and $N = 60$. Evaluating the sum on a calculator gives $B_{60} = 7752.26$.

(c) The situation described by this problem is almost the same as that in Problem 33, except that here the money is being deposited once a month rather than continuously; however the nominal yearly rates are the same. Thus we would expect the balance after 5 years to be approximately the same in each case. This means that the answer to part (b) of this problem should be approximately the same as the answer to part (c) to Problem 33. Since the deposits in this problem start at the end of the first month, as opposed to right away, we would expect the balance after 5 years to be slightly smaller than in Problem 33, as is the case.

Alternatively, we can use the Fundamental Theorem of Calculus to show that the integral can be computed exactly

$$\int_0^5 1200e^{0.1t} dt = 12000(e^{(0.1)5} - 1) = 7784.66$$

Thus $\int_0^5 1200e^{0.1t} dt$ represents the exact solution to Problem 33. Since $1200e^{0.1t}$ is an increasing function, the left hand sum we calculated in part (b) of this problem underestimates the integral. Thus the answer to part (b) of this problem should be less than the answer to part (c) of Problem 33.

35. (a) The model prescribes the growth in the bird population to be of the form

$$\frac{dP}{dt} = kP(10{,}000 - P)$$

where k is a constant. To determine k, we use the information that at $t = 0$, $P = 10$ and $\frac{dP}{dt} = 100$. Substituting into the differential equation gives:

$$100 = k(10)(10{,}000 - 10)$$

or
$$k = \frac{1}{999}$$

Thus the differential equation is,
$$\frac{dP}{dt} = \frac{P}{999}(10{,}000 - P)$$

(b) We may obtain the population at which maximum growth rate occurs by differentiating the expression for growth rate with respect to P and equating the result to zero:
$$\frac{d}{dP}\left(\frac{P}{999}(10{,}000 - P)\right) = \frac{1}{999}(10{,}000 - 2P) = 0$$
$$P = 5{,}000$$

(Note, we know that this is a maximum, since differentiating again with respect to P gives $\frac{-2}{999}$, implying that $P = 5{,}000$ maximizes $\frac{dP}{dt}$.) Substituting $P = 5{,}000$ into $\frac{dP}{dt}$, gives the maximum growth rate
$$\frac{dP}{dt} = \frac{5000}{999}(10000 - 5000) = 25{,}025$$

(c)

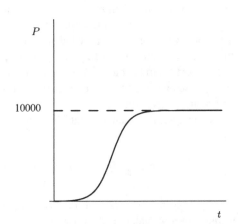

(d) This model is identical to the logistic growth model, and so the population is a function of time is given by
$$P = \frac{LP_0}{P_0 + (L - P_0)e^{-lkt}}$$

In this case, $L = 10{,}000$, $P_0 = 10$
$$P = \frac{100{,}000}{10 + (9990)e^{-\frac{10{,}000}{999}t}}$$

36. (a) The insects grow exponentially with no birds around (the equation becomes $\frac{dx}{dt} = 3x$); the birds die out exponentially with no insects to feed on ($\frac{dy}{dt} = -10y$). The interaction increases the birds' growth rate (the $+0.001xy$ term is positive), but decreases the insects' (the $-0.02xy$ term is negative). This is as you would expect: having the insects around helps the birds; having birds around hurts the insects.

(b) $(3 - 0.02y)x = 0$
$-(10 - 0.001x)y = 0$
Solutions are $(0, 0)$ and $(10,000, 150)$

(c) $\frac{dy}{dx} = \frac{y(-10+0.001x)}{x(3-0.02y)}$.
Solving $\int \frac{-10+0.001x}{x} dx = \int \frac{3-0.02y}{y} dy$ yields $3 \ln y - 0.02y = -10 \ln x + 0.001x + C$.
Using the initial point $A = (10,000, 160)$, we have

$$3 \ln 160 - 0.02(160) = -10 \ln 10{,}000 + 0.001(10{,}000) + C.$$

Thus $C \approx 94.13$ and $3 \ln y - 0.02y = -10 \ln x + 0.001x + 94.1$

(d) One can verify that the equation is satisfied by points B, C, D, as given, by plugging them in on a calculator.

(e)

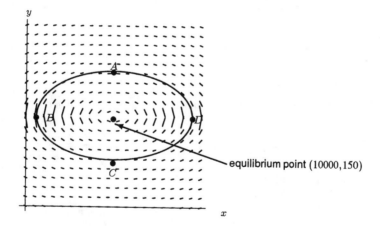

(f) Consider point A. $\frac{dy}{dt} = 0$, and $\frac{dx}{dt} = 3(10,000) - 0.02(10,000)(160) = -2000 < 0$ so x is decreasing at point A. Hence rotation is counterclockwise in the phase plane, and the order of traversal is $A \longrightarrow B \longrightarrow C \longrightarrow D$.

(g)

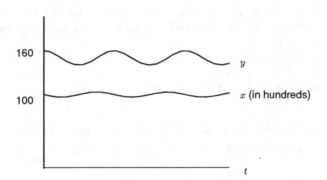

(h)   At points A and C, $\frac{dy}{dx} = 0$, and at B and D, $\frac{dx}{dy} = 0$, so as you may have already guessed, these points are extrema: y is maximized at A, minimized at C; x is maximized at D, minimized at B.

37. (a)   Since the guerrillas are hard to find, the rate at which they are put out of action is proportional to the number of chance encounters between a guerrilla and a conventional soldier, which is in turn proportional to the number of guerrillas and to the number of conventional soldiers. Thus the rate at which guerrillas are put out action is proportional to the product of the strengths of the two armies.

(b)
$$\frac{dx}{dt} = -xy$$
$$\frac{dy}{dt} = -x$$

(c)   Thinking of y as a function of x and x a function of of t, then by the chain rule: $\frac{dy}{dt} = \frac{dy}{dx}\frac{dx}{dt}$ so:

$$\frac{dy}{dx} = \frac{dy/dt}{dx/dt} = \frac{-x}{-xy} = \frac{1}{y}$$

Separating variables:

$$\int y \, dy = \int dx$$
$$\frac{y^2}{2} = x + C$$

The value of C is determined by the initial strengths of the two armies.

(d)   The sign of C determines which side wins the battle. Looking at the general solution $\frac{y^2}{2} = x + C$, we see that if $C > 0$ the y-intercept is at $\sqrt{2C}$, so y wins the battle by virtue of the fact that it still has troops when $x = 0$. If $C < 0$ then the curve intersects the axes at $x = -C$, so x wins the battle because it has troops when $y = 0$. If $C = 0$, then the solution goes to the point $(0, 0)$, which represents the case of mutual annihilation.

(e)   We assume that an army wins if the opposing force goes to 0 first. Figure 9.54 shows that the conventional force wins if $C > 0$ and the guerrillas win if $C < 0$. Neither side wins if $C = 0$ (all soldiers on both sides are killed in this case).

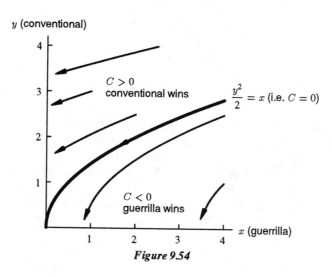

Figure 9.54

38. (a)   Taking the constants of proportionality to be a and b, with $a > 0$ and $b > 0$, the equations are

$$\frac{dx}{dt} = -axy$$
$$\frac{dy}{dt} = -bxy$$

(b) $\dfrac{dy}{dx} = \dfrac{dy/dt}{dx/dt} = \dfrac{-bxy}{-axy} = \dfrac{b}{a}$. Solving the differential equation gives $y = \dfrac{b}{a}x + C$, where C depends on the initial sizes of the two armies.

(c)   The sign of C determines which side wins the battle. Looking at the general solution $y = \dfrac{b}{a}x + C$, we see that if $C > 0$ the y-intercept is at C, so y wins the battle by virtue of the fact that it still has troops when $x = 0$. If $C < 0$ then the curve intersects the axes at $x = -\frac{a}{b}C$, so x wins the battle because it has troops when $y = 0$. If $C = 0$, then the solution goes to the point $(0, 0)$, which represents the case of mutual annihilation.

(d)   We assume that an army wins if the opposing force goes to 0 first.

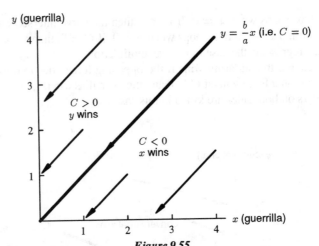

Figure 9.55

39. (a) In the equation for dx/dt, the term involving x, namely $-0.2x$, is negative meaning that as x increases, dx/dt decreases. This corresponds to the statement that the more a country spends on armaments, the less it wants to increase spending.

On the other hand, since $+0.15y$ is positive, as y increases, dx/dt increases, corresponding to the fact that the more a country's opponent arms, the more the country will arm itself.

The constant term, 20, is positive means that if both countries are unarmed initially, (so $x = y = 0$), then dx/dt is positive and so the country will start to arm. In other words, disarmament is not an equilibrium situation in this model.

(b) The nullclines are shown in Figure 9.56. When $dx/dt = 0$, the trajectories are vertical (on the line $-0.2x+0.15y+20 = 0$); when $dy/dt = 0$ the trajectories are horizontal (on $0.1x-0.2y+40 = 0$). There is only one equilibrium point, $x = y = 400$.

(c) In region I, try $x = 400$, $y = 0$, giving

$$\frac{dx}{dt} = -0.2(400) + 0.15(0) + 20 < 0$$

$$\frac{dy}{dt} = 0.1(400) - 0.2(0) + 4 - 0 > 0$$

In region II, try $x = 500$, $y = 500$, giving

$$\frac{dx}{dt} = -0.2(500) + 0.15(500) + 20 < 0$$

$$\frac{dy}{dt} = 0.1(500) - 0.2(500) + 40 < 0$$

In region III, try $x = 0$, $y = 400$, giving

$$\frac{dx}{dt} = -0.2(0) + 0.15(400) + 20 > 0$$

$$\frac{dy}{dt} = 0.1(0) - 0.2(400) + 40 < 0$$

In region IV, try $x = 0$, $y = 0$, giving

$$\frac{dx}{dt} = -0.2(0) + 0.15(0) + 20 > 0$$

$$\frac{dy}{dt} = 0.1(0) - 0.2(0) + 40 > 0$$

See Figure 9.56.

(d) The one equilibrium point is stable.

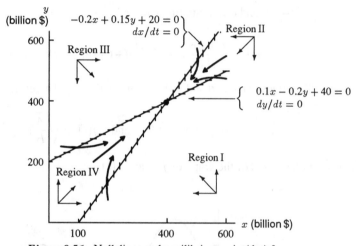

Figure 9.56: Nullclines and equilibrium point(dot) for arms race

(e) If both sides disarm, then both sides spend $0. Thus initially $x = y = 0$, and $dx/dt = 20$ and $dy/dt = 40$. Since both dx/dt and dy/dt are positive, both sides start arming. Figure 9.56 shows that they will both arm until each is spending about $400 billion.

(f) If the country spending y billion is unarmed, then $y = 0$ and the corresponding point on the phase plane is on the x-axis. Any trajectory starting on the x-axis tends towards the equilibrium point $x = y = 400$. Similarly, a trajectory starting on the y-axis represents the other country being unarmed; such a trajectory also tends to the same equilibrium point.

Thus, if either side disarms unilaterally, that is, if we start out with one of the countries spending nothing, then over time, they will still both end up spending roughly $400 billion.

(g) This model predicts that, in the long run, both countries will spend near to $400 billion, no matter where they start.

40. (a) When Juliet loves Romeo (i.e. $j > 0$), Romeo's love for her decreases (i.e. $\frac{dr}{dt} < 0$). When Juliet hates Romeo ($j < 0$), Romeo's love for her grows ($\frac{dr}{dt} > 0$). So j and $\frac{dr}{dt}$ have opposite signs, corresponding to the fact that $-B < 0$. When Romeo loves Juliet ($r > 0$), Juliet's love for him grows ($\frac{dj}{dt} > 0$). When Romeo hates Juliet ($r < 0$), Juliet's love for him decreases ($\frac{dj}{dt} < 0$). Thus r and $\frac{dj}{dt}$ have the same sign, corresponding to the fact that $A > 0$.

(b)   Since $\frac{dr}{dt} = -Bj$, we have

$$\frac{d^2r}{dt^2} = \frac{d}{dt}(-Bj) = -B\frac{dj}{dt} = -ABr.$$

Rewriting the above equation as $r'' + ABr = 0$, we see that the characteristic equation is $R^2 + AB = 0$. Therefore $R = \pm\sqrt{AB}i$ and the general solution is

$$r(t) = C_1 \cos \sqrt{AB}t + C_2 \sin \sqrt{AB}t.$$

(c)   Using $\frac{dr}{dt} = -Bj$, and differentiating r to find j, we obtain

$$j(t) = -\frac{1}{B}\frac{dr}{dt} = -\frac{\sqrt{AB}}{B}(-C_1 \sin \sqrt{AB}t + C_2 \cos \sqrt{AB}t).$$

Now, $j(0) = 0$ gives $C_2 = 0$ and $r(0) = 1$ gives $C_1 = 1$. Therefore, the particular solutions are

$$r(t) = \cos \sqrt{AB}t \quad \text{and} \quad j(t) = \sqrt{\frac{A}{B}} \sin \sqrt{AB}t$$

(d)   Consider one period of the graph of $j(t)$ and $r(t)$:

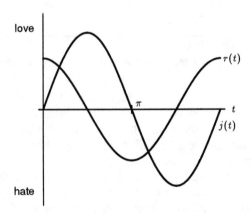

From the graph, we see that they both love each other only a quarter of the time.

CHAPTER TEN

1. Let $f(x) = \cos x$. Then $f(0) = \cos(0) = 1$, and

$$
\begin{array}{ll}
f'(x) = -\sin x & f'(0) = 0 \\
f''(x) = -\cos x & f''(0) = -1 \\
f'''(x) = \sin x & f'''(0) = 0 \\
f^{(4)}(x) = \cos x & f^{(4)}(0) = 1 \\
f^{(5)}(x) = -\sin x & f^{(5)}(0) = 0 \\
f^{(6)}(x) = -\cos x & f^{(6)}(0) = -1.
\end{array}
$$

Thus,

$$
P_2(x) = 1 - \frac{x^2}{2!};
$$

$$
P_4(x) = 1 - \frac{x^2}{2!} + \frac{x^4}{4!};
$$

$$
P_6(x) = 1 - \frac{x^2}{2!} + \frac{x^4}{4!} - \frac{x^6}{6!}.
$$

2. Let $f(x) = \sqrt{1+x} = (1+x)^{1/2}$. Then $f(0) = 1$, and

$$
\begin{array}{ll}
f'(x) = \frac{1}{2}(1+x)^{-1/2} & f'(0) = \frac{1}{2} \\
f''(x) = -\frac{1}{4}(1+x)^{-3/2} & f''(0) = -\frac{1}{4} \\
f'''(x) = \frac{3}{8}(1+x)^{-5/2} & f'''(0) = \frac{3}{8} \\
f^{(4)}(x) = -\frac{15}{16}(1+x)^{-7/2} & f^{(4)}(0) = -\frac{15}{16}
\end{array}
$$

Thus,

$$
P_2(x) = 1 + \frac{1}{2}x - \frac{1}{8}x^2;
$$

$$
P_3(x) = 1 + \frac{1}{2}x - \frac{1}{8}x^2 + \frac{1}{16}x^3;
$$

$$
P_4(x) = 1 + \frac{1}{2}x - \frac{1}{8}x^2 + \frac{1}{16}x^3 - \frac{5}{128}x^4.
$$

3. Let $f(x) = \dfrac{1}{1-x} = (1-x)^{-1}$. Then $f(0) = 1$.

$$
\begin{aligned}
f'(x) &= 1!(1-x)^{-2} & f'(0) &= 1! \\
f''(x) &= 2!(1-x)^{-3} & f''(0) &= 2! \\
f'''(x) &= 3!(1-x)^{-4} & f'''(0) &= 3! \\
f^{(4)}(x) &= 4!(1-x)^{-5} & f^{(4)}(0) &= 4! \\
f^{(5)}(x) &= 5!(1-x)^{-6} & f^{(5)}(0) &= 5! \\
f^{(6)}(x) &= 6!(1-x)^{-7} & f^{(6)}(0) &= 6! \\
f^{(7)}(x) &= 7!(1-x)^{-8} & f^{(7)}(0) &= 7!
\end{aligned}
$$

$$
\begin{aligned}
P_3(x) &= 1 + x + x^2 + x^3; \\
P_5(x) &= 1 + x + x^2 + x^3 + x^4 + x^5; \\
P_7(x) &= 1 + x + x^2 + x^3 + x^4 + x^5 + x^6 + x^7.
\end{aligned}
$$

4. Let $\dfrac{1}{1+x} = (1+x)^{-1}$. Then $f(0) = 1$.

$$
\begin{aligned}
f'(x) &= -1!(1+x)^{-2} & f'(0) &= -1 \\
f''(x) &= 2!(1+x)^{-3} & f''(0) &= 2! \\
f'''(x) &= -3!(1+x)^{-4} & f'''(0) &= -3! \\
f^{(4)}(x) &= 4!(1+x)^{-5} & f^{(4)}(0) &= 4! \\
f^{(5)}(x) &= -5!(1+x)^{-6} & f^{(5)}(0) &= -5! \\
f^{(6)}(x) &= 6!(1+x)^{-7} & f^{(6)}(0) &= 6! \\
f^{(7)}(x) &= -7!(1+x)^{-8} & f^{(7)}(0) &= -7! \\
f^{(8)}(x) &= 8!(1+x)^{-9} & f^{(8)}(0) &= 8!
\end{aligned}
$$

$$
\begin{aligned}
P_4(x) &= 1 - x + x^2 - x^3 + x^4; \\
P_6(x) &= 1 - x + x^2 - x^3 + x^4 - x^5 + x^6; \\
P_8(x) &= 1 - x + x^2 - x^3 + x^4 - x^5 + x^6 - x^7 + x^8.
\end{aligned}
$$

5. Let $f(x) = \tan x$. So $f(0) = \tan 0 = 0$, and

$$
\begin{aligned}
f'(x) &= 1/\cos^2 x & f'(0) &= 1, \\
f''(x) &= 2\sin x/\cos^3 x & f''(0) &= 0, \\
f'''(x) &= (2/\cos^2 x) + (6\sin^2 x/\cos^4 x) & f'''(0) &= 2, \\
f^{(4)}(x) &= (16\sin x/\cos^3 x) + (24\sin^3 x/\cos^5 x) & f^{(4)}(0) &= 0.
\end{aligned}
$$

Thus,

$$
P_3(x) = P_4(x) = x + \frac{x^3}{3}.
$$

6. Let $f(x) = \arctan x$. Then $f(0) = \arctan 0 = 0$, and

$$
\begin{aligned}
f'(x) &= 1/(1+x^2) = (1+x^2)^{-1} & f'(0) &= 1, \\
f''(x) &= (-1)(1+x^2)^{-2}2x & f''(0) &= 0, \\
f'''(x) &= 2!(1+x^2)^{-3}2^2x^2 + (-1)(1+x^2)^{-2}2 & f'''(0) &= -2, \\
f^{(4)}(x) &= -3!(1+x^2)^{-4}2^3x^3 + 2!(1+x^2)^{-3}2^3x & \\
&\quad + 2!(1+x^2)^{-3}2^2x & f^{(4)}(0) &= 0.
\end{aligned}
$$

Therefore,

$$
P_3(x) = P_4(x) = x - \frac{1}{3}x^3.
$$

7. Let $f(x) = \ln(1+x)$. Then $f(0) = \ln 1 = 0$, and

$$
\begin{aligned}
f'(x) &= (1+x)^{-1} & f'(0) &= 1, \\
f''(x) &= (-1)(1+x)^{-2} & f''(0) &= -1, \\
f'''(x) &= 2(1+x)^{-3} & f'''(0) &= 2, \\
f^{(4)}(x) &= -3!(1+x)^{-4} & f^{(4)}(0) &= -3!, \\
f^{(5)}(x) &= 4!(1+x)^{-5} & f^{(5)}(0) &= 4!, \\
f^{(6)}(x) &= -5!(1+x)^{-6} & f^{(6)}(0) &= -5!, \\
f^{(7)}(x) &= 6!(1+x)^{-7} & f^{(7)}(0) &= 6!, \\
f^{(8)}(x) &= -7!(1+x)^{-8} & f^{(8)}(0) &= -7!, \\
f^{(9)}(x) &= 8!(1+x)^{-9} & f^{(9)}(0) &= 8!
\end{aligned}
$$

So,

$$
P_5(x) = x - \frac{x^2}{2} + \frac{x^3}{3} - \frac{x^4}{4} + \frac{x^5}{5},
$$

$$
P_7(x) = x - \frac{x^2}{2} + \frac{x^3}{3} - \frac{x^4}{4} + \frac{x^5}{5} - \frac{x^6}{6} + \frac{x^7}{7},
$$

$$
P_9(x) = x - \frac{x^2}{2} + \frac{x^3}{3} - \frac{x^4}{4} + \frac{x^5}{5} - \frac{x^6}{6} + \frac{x^7}{7} - \frac{x^8}{8} + \frac{x^9}{9}.
$$

8. Let $f(x) = \sqrt[3]{1-x} = (1-x)^{1/3}$. Then $f(0) = 1$, and

$$
\begin{aligned}
f'(x) &= -\tfrac{1}{3}(1-x)^{-2/3} & f'(0) &= -\tfrac{1}{3}, \\
f''(x) &= -\tfrac{2}{3^2}(1-x)^{-5/3} & f''(0) &= -\tfrac{2}{3^2}, \\
f'''(x) &= -\tfrac{10}{3^3}(1-x)^{-8/3} & f'''(0) &= -\tfrac{10}{3^3}, \\
f^{(4)}(x) &= -\tfrac{80}{3^4}(1-x)^{-11/3} & f^{(4)}(0) &= -\tfrac{80}{3^4}.
\end{aligned}
$$

Then,

$$
P_2(x) = 1 - \frac{1}{3}x - \frac{1}{2!}\frac{2}{3^2}x^2 = 1 - \frac{1}{3}x - \frac{1}{9}x^2,
$$

$$P_3(x) = P_2(x) - \frac{1}{3!}\left(\frac{10}{3^3}\right)x^3 = 1 - \frac{1}{3}x - \frac{1}{9}x^2 - \frac{5}{81}x^3,$$

$$P_4(x) = P_3(x) - \frac{1}{4!}\frac{80}{3^4}x^4 = 1 - \frac{1}{3}x - \frac{1}{9}x^2 - \frac{5}{81}x^3 - \frac{10}{243}x^4.$$

9. Let $f(x) = \dfrac{1}{\sqrt{1+x}} = (1+x)^{-1/2}$. Then $f(0) = 1$

$$\begin{array}{ll}
f'(x) = -\frac{1}{2}(1+x)^{-3/2} & f'(0) = -\frac{1}{2}, \\
f''(x) = \frac{3}{2^2}(1+x)^{-5/2} & f''(0) = \frac{3}{2^2}, \\
f'''(x) = -\frac{3\cdot5}{2^3}(1+x)^{-7/2} & f'''(0) = -\frac{3\cdot5}{2^3}, \\
f^{(4)}(x) = \frac{3\cdot5\cdot7}{2^4}(1+x)^{-9/2} & f^{(4)}(0) = \frac{3\cdot5\cdot7}{2^4}.
\end{array}$$

Then,

$$P_2(x) = 1 - \frac{1}{2}x + \frac{1}{2!}\frac{3}{2^2}x^2 = 1 - \frac{1}{2}x + \frac{3}{8}x^2,$$

$$P_3(x) = P_2(x) - \frac{1}{3!}\frac{3\cdot5}{2^3}x^3 = 1 - \frac{1}{2}x + \frac{3}{8}x^2 - \frac{5}{16}x^3,$$

$$P_4(x) = P_3(x) + \frac{1}{4!}\frac{3\cdot5\cdot7}{2^4}x^4 = 1 - \frac{1}{2}x + \frac{3}{8}x^2 - \frac{5}{16}x^3 + \frac{35}{128}x^4.$$

10. Let $f(x) = (1+x)^p$.

   (a) Suppose that $p = 0$. Then $f(x) = 1$ and $f^{(k)}(x) = 0$ for any $k \geq 1$. Thus $P_2(x) = P_3(x) = P_4(x) = 1$.

   (b) If $p = 1$ then $f(x) = 1 + x$, so

   $$\begin{aligned}
   f(0) &= 1, \\
   f'(x) &= 1, \\
   f^{(k)}(x) &= 0 \qquad k \geq 2.
   \end{aligned}$$

   Thus $P_2(x) = P_3(x) = P_4(x) = 1 + x$.

   (c) In general:

   $$\begin{aligned}
   f(x) &= (1+x)^p \\
   f'(x) &= p(1+x)^{p-1} \\
   f''(x) &= p(p-1)(1+x)^{p-2} \\
   f'''(x) &= p(p-1)(p-2)(1+x)^{p-3} \\
   f^{(4)}(x) &= p(p-1)(p-2)(p-3)(1+x)^{p-4}
   \end{aligned}$$

   $$f(0) = 1$$

$$f'(0) = p$$
$$f''(0) = p(p-1)$$
$$f'''(0) = p(p-1)(p-2)$$
$$f^{(4)}(0) = p(p-1)(p-2)(p-3)$$

$$P_2(x) = 1 + px + \frac{p(p-1)}{2}x^2,$$

$$P_3(x) = 1 + px + \frac{p(p-1)}{2}x^2 + \frac{p(p-1)(p-2)}{6}x^3,$$

$$P_4(x) = 1 + px + \frac{p(p-1)}{2}x^2 + \frac{p(p-1)(p-2)}{6}x^3$$
$$+ \frac{p(p-1)(p-2)(p-3)}{24}x^4.$$

11.   For Problem 2, substitute $p = \frac{1}{2}$ in the result of Problem 10:

$$(1+x)^{\frac{1}{2}} = 1 + \frac{1}{2}x + \frac{\frac{1}{2}(\frac{1}{2}-1)}{2}x^2 + \frac{\frac{1}{2}(\frac{1}{2}-1)(\frac{1}{2}-2)}{6}x^3$$
$$+ \frac{\frac{1}{2}(\frac{1}{2}-1)(\frac{1}{2}-2)(\frac{1}{2}-3)}{24}x^4$$
$$= 1 + \frac{1}{2}x - \frac{1}{8}x^2 + \frac{1}{16}x^3 - \frac{5}{128}x^4,$$

as before.

For Problem 3, substitute $p = -1$ and replace x by $-x$ in Problem 10, giving $(1-x)^{-1} = \frac{1}{1-x}$.

For Problem 4, substitute $p = -1$ in Problem 10, giving $(1+x)^{-1} = \frac{1}{1+x}$.

For Problem 8, let $p = 1/3$ and replace x by $-x$ in Problem 10, giving:

$$(1-x)^{1/3} = \sqrt[3]{1-x}.$$

For Problem 9, let $p = -1/2$ in Problem 10, giving $\frac{1}{\sqrt{1+x}} = (1+x)^{-\frac{1}{2}}$

12.   Let $f(x) = e^x$. Since $f^{(k)}(x) = e^x = f(x)$ for all $k \geq 1$, the Taylor polynomial of degree 4 for $f(x) = e^x$ about $x = 1$ is

$$P_4(x) = e^1 + e^1(x-1) + \frac{e^1}{2!}(x-1)^2 + \frac{e^1}{3!}(x-1)^3 + \frac{e^1}{4!}(x-1)^4$$
$$= e\left[1 + (x-1) + \frac{1}{2}(x-1)^2 + \frac{1}{6}(x-1)^3 + \frac{1}{24}(x-1)^4\right].$$

13. Let $f(x) = \cos x$. $f(\frac{\pi}{2}) = 0$.

$$
\begin{array}{ll}
f'(x) = -\sin x & f'(\frac{\pi}{2}) = -1, \\
f''(x) = -\cos x & f''(\frac{\pi}{2}) = 0, \\
f'''(x) = \sin x & f'''(\frac{\pi}{2}) = 1, \\
f^{(4)}(x) = \cos x & f^{(4)}(\frac{\pi}{2}) = 0.
\end{array}
$$

So,

$$
\begin{aligned}
P_4(x) &= 0 - \left(x - \frac{\pi}{2}\right) + 0 + \frac{1}{3!}\left(x - \frac{\pi}{2}\right)^3 \\
&= -\left(x - \frac{\pi}{2}\right) + \frac{1}{3!}\left(x - \frac{\pi}{2}\right)^3.
\end{aligned}
$$

14. Let $f(x) = \sin x$. $f(\frac{\pi}{2}) = 1$.

$$
\begin{array}{ll}
f'(x) = \cos x & f'(\frac{\pi}{2}) = 0, \\
f''(x) = -\sin x & f''(\frac{\pi}{2}) = -1, \\
f'''(x) = -\cos x & f'''(\frac{\pi}{2}) = 0, \\
f^{(4)}(x) = \sin x & f^{(4)}(\frac{\pi}{2}) = 1.
\end{array}
$$

So,

$$
\begin{aligned}
P_4(x) &= 1 + 0 - \frac{1}{2!}\left(x - \frac{\pi}{2}\right)^2 + 0 + \frac{1}{4!}\left(x - \frac{\pi}{2}\right)^4 \\
&= 1 - \frac{1}{2!}\left(x - \frac{\pi}{2}\right)^2 + \frac{1}{4!}\left(x - \frac{\pi}{2}\right)^4.
\end{aligned}
$$

15. Let $f(x) = \cos x$. Then $\cos \frac{\pi}{4} = \sin \frac{\pi}{4} = \frac{\sqrt{2}}{2}$.
    Then $f'(x) = -\sin x$, $f''(x) = -\cos x$, and $f'''(x) = \sin x$, so the Taylor polynomial for $\cos x$ of degree three about $x = \pi/4$ is

$$
\begin{aligned}
P_3(x) &= \cos\frac{\pi}{4} + \left(-\sin\frac{\pi}{4}\right)\left(x - \frac{\pi}{4}\right) + \frac{-\cos\frac{\pi}{4}}{2!}\left(x - \frac{\pi}{4}\right)^2 + \frac{\sin\frac{\pi}{4}}{3!}\left(x - \frac{\pi}{4}\right)^3 \\
&= \frac{\sqrt{2}}{2}\left(1 - \left(x - \frac{\pi}{4}\right) - \frac{1}{2}\left(x - \frac{\pi}{4}\right)^2 + \frac{1}{6}\left(x - \frac{\pi}{4}\right)^3\right).
\end{aligned}
$$

16. Let $f(x) = \sin x$.
    Then $f'(x) = \cos x$, $f''(x) = -\sin x$, and $f'''(x) = -\cos x$, so the Taylor polynomial for $\sin x$ of degree three about $x = -\pi/4$ is

$$
P_3(x) = \sin\left(-\frac{\pi}{4}\right) + \cos\left(-\frac{\pi}{4}\right)\left(x + \frac{\pi}{4}\right)
$$

$$+\frac{-\sin\left(-\frac{\pi}{4}\right)}{2!}\left(x+\frac{\pi}{4}\right)^2+\frac{-\cos\left(-\frac{\pi}{4}\right)}{3!}\left(x+\frac{\pi}{4}\right)^3$$

$$=\frac{\sqrt{2}}{2}\left(-1+\left(x+\frac{\pi}{4}\right)+\frac{1}{2}\left(x+\frac{\pi}{4}\right)^2-\frac{1}{6}\left(x+\frac{\pi}{4}\right)^3\right).$$

17. Let $f(x)=\sqrt{1-x}=(1-x)^{1/2}$. Then $f'(x)=-\frac{1}{2}(1-x)^{-1/2}$, $f''(x)=-\frac{1}{4}(1-x)^{-3/2}$, $f'''(x)=-\frac{3}{8}(1-x)^{-5/2}$. So $f(0)=1$, $f'(0)=-\frac{1}{2}$, $f''(0)=-\frac{1}{4}$, $f'''(0)=-\frac{3}{8}$, and

$$P_3(x)=1-\frac{1}{2}x-\frac{1}{4}\frac{1}{2!}x^2-\frac{3}{8}\frac{1}{3!}x^3$$

$$=1-\frac{x}{2}-\frac{x^2}{8}-\frac{x^3}{16}.$$

18. Let $f(x)=\sqrt{1+x}=(1+x)^{1/2}$.

Then $f'(x)=\frac{1}{2}(1+x)^{-1/2}$, $f''(x)=-\frac{1}{4}(1+x)^{-3/2}$, and $f'''(x)=\frac{3}{8}(1+x)^{-5/2}$. The Taylor polynomial of degree three about $x=1$ is thus

$$P_3(x)=(1+1)^{1/2}+\frac{1}{2}(1+1)^{-1/2}(x-1)+\frac{-\frac{1}{4}(1+1)^{-3/2}}{2!}(x-1)^2$$

$$+\frac{\frac{3}{8}(1+1)^{-5/2}}{3!}(x-1)^3$$

$$=\sqrt{2}\left(1+\frac{x-1}{4}-\frac{(x-1)^2}{32}+\frac{(x-1)^3}{128}\right).$$

19. Let $f(x)=\frac{1}{1+x}=(1+x)^{-1}$. Then $f'(x)=-(1+x)^{-2}$, $f''(x)=2(1+x)^{-3}$, $f'''(x)=-6(1+x)^{-4}$, $f^{(4)}(x)=24(1+x)^{-5}$. So $f(2)=\frac{1}{3}$, $f'(2)=-\frac{1}{3^2}$, $f''(2)=\frac{2}{3^3}$, $f'''(2)=-\frac{6}{3^4}$, and $f^{(4)}(2)=\frac{24}{3^5}$. Therefore,

$$P_4(x)=\frac{1}{3}-\frac{1}{3^2}(x-2)+\frac{2}{3^3}\frac{1}{2!}(x-2)^2-\frac{6}{3^4}\frac{1}{3!}(x-2)^3+\frac{24}{3^5}\frac{1}{4!}(x-2)^4$$

$$=\frac{1}{3}\left(1-\frac{x-2}{3}+\frac{(x-2)^2}{3^2}-\frac{(x-2)^3}{3^3}+\frac{(x-2)^4}{3^4}\right).$$

20. Let $f(x)=\frac{1}{1-x}=(1-x)^{-1}$. Then $f'(x)=(1-x)^{-2}$, $f''(x)=2(1-x)^{-3}$, $f'''(x)=6(1-x)^{-4}$, and $f^{(4)}(x)=24(1-x)^{-5}$. The Taylor polynomial of degree 4 about $a=2$ is thus

$$P_4(x)=(1-2)^{-1}+(1-2)^{-2}(x-2)+\frac{2(1-2)^{-3}}{2!}(x-2)^2$$

$$+ \frac{6(1-2)^{-4}}{3!}(x-2)^3 + \frac{24(1-2)^{-5}}{4!}(x-4)^4$$
$$= -1 + (x-2) - (x-2)^2 + (x-2)^3 - (x-2)^4.$$

21. This is the same as Example 8, Page 597 except we need two more terms:

$$f^{(5)}(x) = 24x^{-5} \qquad f^{(5)}(1) = 24,$$
$$f^{(6)}(x) = -120x^{-6} \quad f^{(6)}(1) = -120.$$

So,

$$P_6(x) = P_4(x) + \frac{24}{5!}(x-1)^5 + \frac{-120}{6!}(x-1)^6$$
$$= (x-1) - \frac{(x-1)^2}{2} + \frac{(x-1)^3}{3} - \frac{(x-1)^4}{4} + \frac{(x-1)^5}{5} - \frac{(x-1)^6}{6}.$$

22. Let $f(x) = \ln x$. Then $f'(x) = x^{-1}$, $f''(x) = -x^{-2}$, $f'''(x) = 2x^{-3}$, and $f^{(4)}(x) = -3 \cdot 2x^{-4}$.
    So,

$$P_4(x) = \ln 2 + 2^{-1}(x-2) + \frac{-2^{-2}}{2!}(x-2)^2$$
$$+ \frac{2 \cdot 2^{-3}}{3!}(x-2)^3 + \frac{-3 \cdot 2 \cdot 2^{-4}}{4!}(x-2)^4$$
$$= \ln 2 + \frac{x-2}{2} - \frac{(x-2)^2}{8} + \frac{(x-2)^3}{24} - \frac{(x-2)^4}{64}.$$

23. Since $P_2(x)$ is the second degree Taylor polynomial for $f(x)$ about $x = 0$, $P_2(0) = f(0)$, which says $a = f(0)$; Since

$$\frac{d}{dx}P_2(x)\bigg|_{x=0} = f'(0),$$

$b = f'(0)$; and since

$$\frac{d^2}{dx^2}P_2(x)\bigg|_{x=0} = f''(0),$$

$2c = f''(0)$. As we can see now, a is the y-intercept of $f(x)$, b is the slope of the tangent line to $f(x)$ at $x = 0$ and c tells us the concavity of $f(x)$ near $x = 0$. So $c < 0$ since f is concave down; $b > 0$ since f is increasing; $a > 0$ since $f(0) > 0$.

24. As we can see from Problem 23, a is the y-intercept of $f(x)$, b is the slope of the tangent line to $f(x)$ at $x = 0$ and c tells us the concavity of $f(x)$ near $x = 0$.
    So $a < 0$, $b < 0$ and $c > 0$.

25. As we can see from Problem 23, a is the y-intercept of $f(x)$, b is the slope of the tangent line to $f(x)$ at $x = 0$ and c tells us the concavity of $f(x)$ near $x = 0$.
So $a < 0$, $b > 0$ and $c > 0$.

26. As we can see from Problem 23, a is the y-intercept of $f(x)$, b is the slope of the tangent line to $f(x)$ at $x = 0$ and c tells us the concavity of $f(x)$ near $x = 0$.
So $a > 0$, $b < 0$ and $c < 0$.

27.
$$\lim_{x\to 0} \frac{\sin x}{x} = \lim_{x\to 0} \frac{x - \frac{x^3}{3!}}{x} = \lim_{x\to 0}\left(1 - \frac{x^2}{3!}\right) = 1.$$

28.
$$\lim_{x\to 0} \frac{1 - \cos x}{x^2} = \lim_{x\to 0} \frac{1 - (1 - \frac{x^2}{2!} + \frac{x^4}{4!})}{x^2} = \lim_{x\to 0}\left(\frac{1}{2} - \frac{x^2}{4!}\right) = \frac{1}{2}.$$

29. For $f(h) = e^h$, $P_4(h) = 1 + h + \frac{h^2}{2} + \frac{h^3}{3!} + \frac{h^4}{4!}$. So

(a)
$$\lim_{h\to 0} \frac{e^h - 1 - h}{h^2} = \lim_{h\to 0} \frac{e^h - 1 - h}{h^2}$$
$$= \lim_{h\to 0} \frac{\frac{h^2}{2} + \frac{h^3}{3!} + \frac{h^4}{4!}}{h^2} = \lim_{h\to 0}\left(\frac{1}{2} + \frac{h}{3!} + \frac{h^2}{4!}\right)$$
$$= \frac{1}{2}.$$

(b)
$$\lim_{h\to 0} \frac{e^h - 1 - h - \frac{h^2}{2}}{h^3} = \lim_{h\to 0} \frac{P_4(h) - 1 - h - \frac{h^2}{2}}{h^3}$$
$$= \lim_{h\to 0} \frac{\frac{h^3}{3!} + \frac{h^4}{4!}}{h^3} = \lim_{h\to 0}\left(\frac{1}{3!} + \frac{h}{4!}\right)$$
$$= \frac{1}{3!} = \frac{1}{6}.$$

Using Taylor polynomials of higher degree would not have changed the results since the terms with higher powers of h all go to zero as $h \to 0$.

30. Changing $\sin\theta$ into θ makes sense if the two values are almost the same. If we measure θ in radians, this will be true for values of θ close to zero. (Recall the first degree Taylor polynomial: $\sin\theta \approx \theta$.) In other words, the switch is justified when the pendulum does not swing very far from the vertical.

31.

$$
\begin{array}{ll}
f(x) = 4x^2 - 7x + 2 & f(0) = 2 \\
f'(x) = 8x - 7 & f'(0) = -7 \\
f''(x) = 8 & f''(0) = 8,
\end{array}
$$

so $P_2(x) = 2 + (-7)x + \frac{8}{2}x^2 = 4x^2 - 7x + 2$. We notice that $f(x) = P_2(x)$ in this case.

32. $f'(x) = 3x^2 + 14x - 5$, $f''(x) = 6x + 14$, $f'''(x) = 6$. Thus, about $a = 0$,

$$
\begin{aligned}
P_3(x) &= 1 + \frac{-5}{1!}x + \frac{14}{2!}x^2 + \frac{6}{3!}x^3 \\
&= 1 - 5x + 7x^2 + x^3 \\
&= f(x).
\end{aligned}
$$

33.   (a)   We'll make the following conjecture:

"If $f(x)$ is a polynomial of degree n, i.e.

$$
f(x) = a_0 + a_1 x + a_2 x^2 + \cdots + a_{n-1}x^{n-1} + a_n x^n,
$$

then $P_n(x)$, the nth degree Taylor polynomial for $f(x)$ about $x = 0$, is $f(x)$ itself."

(b)   All we need to do is to calculate $P_n(x)$, the nth degree Taylor polynomial for f about $x = 0$ and see if it is the same as $f(x)$.

$$
\begin{aligned}
C_0 &= f(0) = a_0; \\
C_1 &= f'(0) = (a_1 + 2a_2 x + \cdots + na_n x^{n-1})\big|_{x=0} \\
&= a_1; \\
C_2 &= f''(0) = (2a_2 + 3 \cdot 2a_3 x + \cdots + n(n-1)a_n x^{n-2})\big|_{x=0} \\
&= 2! a_2.
\end{aligned}
$$

If we continue doing this, we'll see in general

$$
C_k = f^{(k)}(0) = k! a_k, \qquad k = 1, 2, 3, \cdots, n.
$$

So, $a_k = \dfrac{C_k}{k!}$, $k = 1, 2, 3, \cdots, n$. Therefore,

$$
\begin{aligned}
P_n(x) &= C_0 + \frac{C_1}{1!}x + \frac{C_2}{2!}x^2 + \cdots + \frac{C_n}{n!}x^n \\
&= a_0 + a_1 x + a_2 x^2 + \cdots + a_n x^n \\
&= f(x).
\end{aligned}
$$

34. (a) $f(x) = e^{x^2}$.

$f'(x) = 2xe^{x^2}$, $f''(x) = 2(1 + 2x^2)e^{x^2}$, $f'''(x) = 4(3x + 2x^3)e^{x^2}$,

$f^{(4)}(x) = 4(3 + 6x^2)e^{x^2} + 4(3x + 2x^3)2xe^{x^2}$.

The Taylor polynomial about $x = 0$ is

$$P_4(x) = 1 + \frac{0}{1!}x + \frac{2}{2!}x^2 + \frac{0}{3!}x^3 + \frac{12}{4!}x^4$$
$$= 1 + x^2 + \frac{1}{2}x^4.$$

(b) $f(x) = e^x$. The Taylor polynomial of degree 2 is

$$Q_2(x) = 1 + \frac{x}{1!} + \frac{x^2}{2!} = 1 + x + \frac{1}{2}x^2.$$

If we substitute x^2 for x in the Taylor polynomial for e^x of degree 2, we will get $P_4(x)$, the Taylor polynomial for e^{x^2} of degree 4:

$$Q_2(x^2) = 1 + x^2 + \frac{1}{2}(x^2)^2$$
$$= 1 + x^2 + \frac{1}{2}x^4$$
$$= P_4(x).$$

(c) Let $Q_{10}(x) = 1 + \frac{x}{1!} + \frac{x^2}{2!} + \cdots + \frac{x^{10}}{10!}$ be the Taylor polynomial of degree 10 for e^x about $x = 0$. Then

$$P_{20}(x) = Q_{10}(x^2)$$
$$= 1 + \frac{x^2}{1!} + \frac{(x^2)^2}{2!} + \cdots + \frac{(x^2)^{10}}{10!}$$
$$= 1 + \frac{x^2}{1!} + \frac{x^4}{2!} + \cdots + \frac{x^{20}}{10!}.$$

(d) Let $e^x \approx Q_5(x) = 1 + \frac{x}{1!} + \cdots + \frac{x^5}{5!}$. Then

$$e^{-2x} \approx Q_5(-2x)$$
$$= 1 + \frac{-2x}{1!} + \frac{(-2x)^2}{2!} + \frac{(-2x)^3}{3!} + \frac{(-2x)^4}{4!} + \frac{(-2x)^5}{5!}$$
$$= 1 - 2x + 2x^2 - \frac{4}{3}x^3 + \frac{2}{3}x^4 - \frac{4}{15}x^5.$$

35.   Let $f(x)$ be a function that has derivatives up to order n at $x = a$. Let

$$P_n(x) = C_0 + C_1(x - a) + \cdots + C_n(x - a)^n$$

be the polynomial of degree n that approximates $f(x)$ about $x = a$. We require that $P_n(x)$ and all of its first n derivatives agree with those of the function $f(x)$ at $x = a$, i.e. we want

$$f(a) = P_n(a),$$
$$f'(a) = P_n'(a),$$
$$f''(a) = P_n''(a),$$
$$\vdots$$
$$f^{(n)}(a) = P_n^{(n)}(a).$$

When we substitute $x = a$ in $P_n(x)$, all the terms except the first drop out, so

$$f(a) = C_0.$$

Now differentiate $P_n(x)$:

$$P_n'(x) = C_1 + 2C_2(x - a) + 3C_3(x - a)^2 + \cdots + nC_n(x - a)^{n-1}.$$

Substituting $x = a$ again, which yields

$$f'(a) = P_n'(a) = C_1.$$

Differentiate $P_n'(x)$:

$$P_n''(x) = 2C_2 + 3 \cdot 2C_3(x - a) + \cdots + n(n - 1)C_n(x - a)^{n-2}$$

and substitute $x = a$ again:

$$f''(a) = P_n''(a) = 2C_2.$$

Differentiating and substituting again gives

$$f'''(a) = P_n'''(a) = 3 \cdot 2C_3.$$

Similarly,

$$f^{(k)}(a) = P_n{}^{(k)}(a) = k!C_k.$$

So, $C_0 = f(a)$, $C_1 = f'(a)$, $C_2 = \frac{f''(a)}{2!}$, $C_3 = \frac{f'''(a)}{3!}$, and so on.
   If we adopt the convention that $f^{(0)}(a) = f(a)$ and $0! = 1$, then

$$C_k = \frac{f^{(k)}(a)}{k!}, \quad k = 0, 1, 2, \cdots, n.$$

Therefore,

$$f(x) \approx P_n(x) = C_0 + C_1(x - a) + C_2(x - a)^2 \cdots + C_n(x - a)^n$$

$$= f(a) + f'(a)(x - a) + \frac{f''(a)}{2!}(x - a)^2 + \cdots + \frac{f^{(n)}(a)}{n!}(x - a)^n.$$

10.2 SOLUTIONS

1. Yes.

2. No, because it contains negative powers of x.

3. No, each term is a power of a different quantity.

4. Yes. It's a Taylor polynomial or a series with all coefficients beyond the 7th being zero.

5. Yes.

6.
$$\begin{array}{ll}
f(x) = \frac{1}{1-x} = (1 - x)^{-1} & f(0) = 1 \\
f'(x) = -(1 - x)^{-2}(-1) = (1 - x)^{-2} & f'(0) = 1 \\
f''(x) = -2(1 - x)^{-3}(-1) = 2(1 - x)^{-3} & f''(0) = 2 \\
f'''(x) = -6(1 - x)^{-4}(-1) = 6(1 - x)^{-4} & f'''(0) = 6
\end{array}$$

$$f(x) = \frac{1}{1 - x} = 1 + 1 \cdot x + \frac{2x^2}{2!} + \frac{6x^3}{3!} + \cdots$$

$$= 1 + x + x^2 + x^3 + \cdots$$

7.
$$\begin{array}{ll}
f(x) = \sqrt{1 + x} = (1 + x)^{\frac{1}{2}} & f(0) = 1 \\
f'(x) = \frac{1}{2}(1 + x)^{-\frac{1}{2}} & f'(0) = \frac{1}{2} \\
f''(x) = -\frac{1}{4}(1 + x)^{-\frac{3}{2}} & f''(0) = -\frac{1}{4} \\
f'''(x) = \frac{3}{8}(1 + x)^{-\frac{5}{2}} & f'''(0) = \frac{3}{8}
\end{array}$$

$$f(x) = \sqrt{1 + x} = 1 + \frac{1}{2}x + \frac{(-\frac{1}{4})x^2}{2!} + \frac{(\frac{3}{8})x^3}{3!} + \cdots$$

$$= 1 + \frac{x}{2} - \frac{x^2}{8} + \frac{x^3}{16} + \cdots$$

8.
$$f(z) = \arctan z$$

$$f'(z) = \frac{1}{1 + z^2} = (1 + z^2)^{-1}$$

$$f''(z) = -(1 + z^2)^{-2}(2z)$$

$$f'''(z) = -2(1 + z^2)^{-2} + 2z \left(2(1 + z^2)^{-3}\right) 2z$$
$$= -2(1 + z^2)^{-2} + 8z^2(1 + z^2)^{-3}$$
$$f^{(4)}(z) = 4(1 + z^2)^{-3}(2z) + 16z(1 + z^2)^{-3} + 8z^2(-3)(1 + z^2)^{-4}(2z)$$

$$f(0) = 0$$
$$f'(0) = 1$$
$$f''(0) = 0$$
$$f'''(0) = -2$$
$$f^4(0) = 0$$

$$f(z) = \arctan z = 0 + 1 \cdot z + \frac{0 \cdot z^2}{2!} + \frac{(-2)z^3}{3!} + \frac{0 \cdot z^4}{4!} + \cdots$$
$$= z - \frac{2z^3}{3!} + \cdots$$

9.

$$\begin{array}{ll} f(t) = \ln(1 - t) & f(0) = 0 \\ f'(t) = -\frac{1}{1-t} = -(1 - t)^{-1} & f'(0) = -1 \\ f''(t) = (1 - t)^{-2}(-1) = -(1 - t)^{-2} & f''(0) = -1 \\ f'''(t) = 2(1 - t)^{-3}(-1) = -2(1 - t)^{-3} & f'''(0) = -2 \end{array}$$

$$f(t) = \ln(1 - t) = -t - \frac{t^2}{2!} - \frac{2t^3}{3!} - \cdots$$

10.

$$\begin{array}{ll} f(x) = \frac{1}{\sqrt{1+x}} = (1 + x)^{-\frac{1}{2}} & f(0) = 1 \\ f'(x) = -\frac{1}{2}(1 + x)^{-\frac{3}{2}} & f'(0) = -\frac{1}{2} \\ f''(x) = \frac{3}{4}(1 + x)^{-\frac{5}{2}} & f''(0) = \frac{3}{4} \\ f'''(x) = -\frac{15}{8}(1 + x)^{-\frac{7}{2}} & f'''(0) = -\frac{15}{8} \end{array}$$

$$f(x) = \frac{1}{\sqrt{1 + x}} = 1 + \left(-\frac{1}{2}\right)x + \frac{(\frac{3}{4})x^2}{2!} + \frac{(-\frac{15}{8})x^3}{3!} + \cdots$$
$$= 1 - \frac{x}{2} + \frac{3x^2}{8} - \frac{5x^3}{16} + \cdots$$

11.

$$f(y) = \sqrt[3]{1-y} = (1-y)^{\frac{1}{3}} \qquad f(0) = 1$$
$$f'(y) = \frac{1}{3}(1-y)^{-\frac{2}{3}}(-1) = -\frac{1}{3}(1-y)^{-\frac{2}{3}} \qquad f'(0) = -\frac{1}{3}$$
$$f''(y) = \frac{2}{9}(1-y)^{-\frac{5}{3}}(-1) = -\frac{2}{9}(1-y)^{-\frac{5}{3}} \qquad f''(0) = \frac{2}{9}$$
$$f'''(y) = \frac{10}{27}(1-y)^{-\frac{8}{3}}(-1) = -\frac{10}{27}(1-y)^{-\frac{8}{3}} \qquad f'''(0) = -\frac{10}{27}$$

$$f(y) = \sqrt[3]{1-y} = 1 + \left(-\frac{1}{3}\right)y + \frac{(-\frac{2}{9})y^2}{2!} + \frac{(-\frac{10}{27})y^3}{3!} + \cdots$$

$$= 1 - \frac{y}{3} - \frac{y^2}{9} - \frac{5y^3}{81} - \cdots$$

12.

$$f(x) = \frac{1}{x} \qquad f(1) = 1$$
$$f'(x) = -\frac{1}{x^2} \qquad f'(1) = -1$$
$$f''(x) = \frac{2}{x^3} \qquad f''(1) = 2$$
$$f'''(x) = -\frac{6}{x^4} \qquad f'''(1) = -6$$

$$\frac{1}{x} = 1 - (x-1) + \frac{2(x-1)^2}{2!} - \frac{6(x-1)^3}{3!} + \cdots$$

$$= 1 - (x-1) + (x-1)^2 - (x-1)^3 + \cdots.$$

13. Using the derivatives from Problem 12, we have

$$f(-1) = -1, \quad f'(-1) = -1, \quad f''(-1) = -2, \quad f'''(-1) = -6.$$

Hence,

$$\frac{1}{x} = -1 - (x+1) - \frac{2(x+1)^2}{2!} - \frac{6(x+1)^3}{3!} - \cdots$$

$$= -1 - (x+1) - (x+1)^2 - (x+1)^3 - \cdots$$

14. Again using the derivatives found in Problem 12, we have

$$f(2) = \frac{1}{2}, \qquad f'(2) = -\frac{1}{4}, \qquad f''(2) = \frac{1}{4}, \qquad f'''(2) = -\frac{3}{8}.$$

$$\frac{1}{x} = \frac{1}{2} - \frac{x-2}{4} + \frac{(x-2)^2}{4 \cdot 2!} - \frac{3(x-2)^3}{8 \cdot 3!} + \cdots$$

$$= \frac{1}{2} - \frac{(x-2)}{4} + \frac{(x-2)^2}{8} - \frac{(x-2)^3}{16} + \cdots$$

15.

$$f(x) = \sin x \qquad f(\tfrac{\pi}{4}) = \tfrac{\sqrt{2}}{2}$$
$$f'(x) = \cos x \qquad f'(\tfrac{\pi}{4}) = \tfrac{\sqrt{2}}{2}$$
$$f''(x) = -\sin x \qquad f''(\tfrac{\pi}{4}) = -\tfrac{\sqrt{2}}{2}$$
$$f'''(x) = -\cos x \qquad f'''(\tfrac{\pi}{4}) = -\tfrac{\sqrt{2}}{2}$$

$$\sin x = \frac{\sqrt{2}}{2} + \frac{\sqrt{2}}{2}\left(x - \frac{\pi}{4}\right) - \frac{\sqrt{2}}{2}\frac{(x - \frac{\pi}{4})^2}{2!} - \frac{\sqrt{2}}{2}\frac{(x - \frac{\pi}{4})^3}{3!} - \cdots$$
$$= \frac{\sqrt{2}}{2} + \frac{\sqrt{2}}{2}\left(x - \frac{\pi}{4}\right) - \frac{\sqrt{2}}{4}\left(x - \frac{\pi}{4}\right)^2 - \frac{\sqrt{2}}{12}\left(x - \frac{\pi}{4}\right)^3 - \cdots$$

16.

$$f(\theta) = \cos\theta \qquad f(\tfrac{\pi}{4}) = \tfrac{\sqrt{2}}{2}$$
$$f'(\theta) = -\sin\theta \qquad f'(\tfrac{\pi}{4}) = -\tfrac{\sqrt{2}}{2}$$
$$f''(\theta) = -\cos\theta \qquad f''(\tfrac{\pi}{4}) = -\tfrac{\sqrt{2}}{2}$$
$$f'''(\theta) = \sin\theta \qquad f'''(\tfrac{\pi}{4}) = \tfrac{\sqrt{2}}{2}$$

$$\cos\theta = \frac{\sqrt{2}}{2} - \frac{\sqrt{2}}{2}\left(\theta - \frac{\pi}{4}\right) - \frac{\sqrt{2}}{2}\frac{(\theta - \frac{\pi}{4})^2}{2!} + \frac{\sqrt{2}}{2}\frac{(\theta - \frac{\pi}{4})^3}{3!} - \cdots$$
$$= \frac{\sqrt{2}}{2} - \frac{\sqrt{2}}{2}\left(\theta - \frac{\pi}{4}\right) - \frac{\sqrt{2}}{4}\left(\theta - \frac{\pi}{4}\right)^2 + \frac{\sqrt{2}}{12}\left(\theta - \frac{\pi}{4}\right)^3 - \cdots$$

17.

$$f(\theta) = \sin\theta \qquad f(-\tfrac{\pi}{4}) = -\tfrac{\sqrt{2}}{2}$$
$$f'(\theta) = \cos\theta \qquad f'(-\tfrac{\pi}{4}) = \tfrac{\sqrt{2}}{2}$$
$$f''(\theta) = -\sin\theta \qquad f''(-\tfrac{\pi}{4}) = \tfrac{\sqrt{2}}{2}$$
$$f'''(\theta) = -\cos\theta \qquad f'''(-\tfrac{\pi}{4}) = -\tfrac{\sqrt{2}}{2}$$

$$\sin\theta = -\frac{\sqrt{2}}{2} + \frac{\sqrt{2}}{2}\left(\theta + \frac{\pi}{4}\right) + \frac{\sqrt{2}}{2}\frac{(\theta + \frac{\pi}{4})^2}{2!} - \frac{\sqrt{2}}{2}\frac{(\theta + \frac{\pi}{4})^3}{3!} + \cdots$$
$$= -\frac{\sqrt{2}}{2} + \frac{\sqrt{2}}{2}\left(\theta + \frac{\pi}{4}\right) + \frac{\sqrt{2}}{4}\left(\theta + \frac{\pi}{4}\right)^2 - \frac{\sqrt{2}}{12}\left(\theta + \frac{\pi}{4}\right)^3 + \cdots$$

18.

$$f(x) = \tan x \qquad\qquad f(\tfrac{\pi}{4}) = 1$$
$$f'(x) = \frac{1}{\cos^2 x} \qquad\qquad f'(\tfrac{\pi}{4}) = 2$$
$$f''(x) = \frac{-2(-\sin x)}{\cos^3 x} = \frac{2\sin x}{\cos^3 x} \qquad f''(\tfrac{\pi}{4}) = 4$$
$$f'''(x) = \frac{-6\sin x(-\sin x)}{\cos^4 x} + \frac{2}{\cos^2 x} \qquad f'''(\tfrac{\pi}{4}) = 16$$

$$\tan x = 1 + 2\left(x - \frac{\pi}{4}\right) + 4\frac{\left(x - \frac{\pi}{4}\right)^2}{2!} + 16\frac{\left(x - \frac{\pi}{4}\right)^3}{3!} + \cdots$$

$$= 1 + 2\left(x - \frac{\pi}{4}\right) + 2\left(x - \frac{\pi}{4}\right)^2 + \frac{8}{3}\left(x - \frac{\pi}{4}\right)^3 + \cdots$$

19.

$$\lim_{\theta \to 0} \frac{\theta - \sin \theta}{\theta^3} = \lim_{\theta \to 0} \frac{\theta - \left(\theta - \frac{\theta^3}{3!} + \frac{\theta^5}{5!} - \cdots\right)}{\theta^3}$$

$$= \lim_{\theta \to 0} \frac{\frac{\theta^3}{3!} - \frac{\theta^5}{5!} + \cdots}{\theta^3} = \lim_{\theta \to 0} \left(\frac{1}{3!} - \frac{\theta^2}{5!} + \cdots\right)$$

$$= \frac{1}{6}.$$

20. The derivatives for $\tan \alpha$ are given in Problem 18. Then $f(0) = 0$, $f'(0) = 1$, $f''(0) = 0$, and $f'''(0) = 2$. So $\tan \alpha \approx \alpha + \frac{\alpha^3}{3} + \cdots$

$$\lim_{\alpha \to 0} \frac{\tan \alpha}{\alpha} = \lim_{\alpha \to 0} \frac{\alpha + \frac{\alpha^3}{3} + \cdots}{\alpha}$$

$$= \lim_{\alpha \to 0} \left(1 + \frac{\alpha^2}{3} + \cdots\right)$$

$$= 1.$$

21. Using the Binomial series with $p = 1/2$, we have

$$\sqrt{1 + x} = (1 + x)^{1/2} = 1 + \frac{x}{2} - \frac{x^2}{8} + \cdots.$$

Hence

$$\lim_{x \to 0} \frac{\sqrt{1 + x} - 1}{x} = \lim_{x \to 0} \frac{\left(1 + \frac{x}{2} - \frac{x^2}{8} + \cdots\right) - 1}{x}$$

$$= \lim_{x \to 0} \left(\frac{1}{2} - \frac{x}{8} + \cdots\right)$$

$$= \frac{1}{2}.$$

22.   Using the same expansion as in Problem 21, we have

$$\lim_{h \to 0} \frac{h}{\sqrt{1 + h} - 1} = \lim_{h \to 0} \frac{h}{\left(1 + \frac{h}{2} - \frac{h^2}{8} + \cdots\right) - 1}$$

$$= \lim_{h \to 0} \frac{1}{\frac{1}{2} - \frac{h}{8} + \cdots}$$

$$= 2.$$

23.   We need to expand $\sin x$ at $x = \pi$.

$$\sin x\big|_{x=\pi} = 0$$

$$\frac{d \sin x}{dx}\bigg|_{x=\pi} = \cos x\big|_{x=\pi} = -1$$

$$\frac{d^2 \sin x}{dx^2}\bigg|_{x=\pi} = -\sin x\big|_{x=\pi} = 0$$

$$\frac{d^3 \sin x}{dx^3}\bigg|_{x=\pi} = -\cos x\big|_{x=\pi} = 1.$$

So, $\sin x = -(x - \pi) + \dfrac{1}{3!}(x - \pi)^3 - \cdots$. Thus,

$$\lim_{x \to \pi} \frac{\sin x}{x - \pi} = \lim_{x \to \pi} \frac{-(x - \pi) + \frac{1}{3!}(x - \pi)^3 - \cdots}{x - \pi}$$

$$= \lim_{x \to \pi} \left(-1 + \frac{1}{3!}(x - \pi)^2 - \cdots\right)$$

$$= -1.$$

24.   Expand $\cos \theta$ at $\theta = \pi/2$ first.

$$\cos \theta\big|_{\theta = \frac{\pi}{2}} = 0$$

$$\frac{d \cos \theta}{d\theta}\bigg|_{\theta = \frac{\pi}{2}} = -\sin \theta\big|_{\theta = \frac{\pi}{2}} = -1$$

$$\frac{d^2 \cos \theta}{d\theta^2}\bigg|_{\theta = \frac{\pi}{2}} = -\cos \theta\big|_{\theta = \frac{\pi}{2}} = 0$$

$$\frac{d^3 \cos \theta}{d\theta^3}\bigg|_{\theta = \frac{\pi}{2}} = \sin \theta\big|_{\theta = \frac{\pi}{2}} = 1.$$

So, $\cos\theta = -\left(\theta - \frac{\pi}{2}\right) + \frac{1}{3!}\left(\theta - \frac{\pi}{2}\right)^3 - \cdots$ Thus,

$$\lim_{\theta \to \frac{\pi}{2}} \frac{\cos\theta}{\theta - \frac{\pi}{2}} = \lim_{\theta \to \frac{\pi}{2}} \frac{-\left(\theta - \frac{\pi}{2}\right) + \frac{1}{3!}\left(\theta - \frac{\pi}{2}\right)^3 - \cdots}{\theta - \frac{\pi}{2}}$$

$$= \lim_{\theta \to \frac{\pi}{2}} \left(-1 + \frac{1}{3!}\left(\theta - \frac{\pi}{2}\right)^2 - \cdots\right)$$

$$= -1.$$

25. (a)

$$f(x) = \ln(1 + 2x) \qquad f(0) = 0$$
$$f'(x) = \frac{2}{1+2x} \qquad f'(0) = 2$$
$$f''(x) = -\frac{4}{(1+2x)^2} \qquad f''(0) = -4$$
$$f'''(x) = \frac{16}{(1+2x)^3} \qquad f'''(0) = 16$$

$$\ln(1 + 2x) = 2x - 2x^2 + \frac{8}{3}x^3 + \cdots$$

(b) To get the expression for $\ln(1 + 2x)$ from the series for $\ln(1 + x)$, substitute $2x$ for x in the series

$$\ln(1 + x) = x - \frac{x^2}{2} + \frac{x^3}{3} - \frac{x^4}{4} + \cdots$$

to get

$$\ln(1 + 2x) = 2x - \frac{(2x)^2}{2} + \frac{(2x)^3}{3} - \frac{(2x)^4}{4} + \cdots$$

$$= 2x - 2x^2 + \frac{8x^3}{3} - 4x^4 + \cdots$$

(c) Since the interval of convergence for $\ln(1 + x)$ is $-1 < x < 1$, substituting $2x$ for x suggests the interval of convergence of $\ln(1 + 2x)$ is $-1 < 2x < 1$ or $-\frac{1}{2} < x < \frac{1}{2}$

26. (a)
$$f(x) = \sin x^2$$
$$f'(x) = (\cos x^2)2x$$
$$f''(x) = (-\sin x^2)4x^2 + (\cos x^2)2$$
$$f'''(x) = (-\cos x^2)8x^3 + (-\sin x^2)8x + (-\sin x^2)4x$$
$$= (-\cos x^2)8x^3 + (-\sin x^2)12x$$
$$f^{(4)}(x) = (\sin x^2)16x^4 + (-\cos x^2)24x^2 + (-\cos x^2)24x^2 + (-\sin x^2)12$$
$$= (\sin x^2)16x^4 + (-\cos x^2)48x^2 + (-\sin x^2)12$$
$$f^{(5)}(x) = (\cos x^2)32x^5 + (\sin x^2)64x^3 + (\sin x^2)96x^3$$
$$+(-\cos x^2)96x + (-\cos x^2)24x$$
$$= (\cos x^2)32x^5 + (\sin x^2)160x^3 + (-\cos x^2)120x$$
$$f^{(6)}(x) = (-\sin x^2)64x^6 + (\cos x^2)160x^4 + (\cos x^2)320x^4 + (\sin x^2)480x^2$$
$$+(\sin x^2)240x^2 + (-\cos x^2)120$$
$$= (-\sin x^2)64x^6 + (\cos x^2)480x^4 + (\sin x^2)720x^2 + (-\cos x^2)120$$

So,

$$
\begin{array}{ll}
f(0) = 0 & f^{(4)}(0) = \quad 0 \\
f'(0) = 0 & f^{(5)}(0) = \quad 0 \\
f''(0) = 2 & f^{(6)}(0) = -120 \\
f'''(0) = 0 &
\end{array}
$$

Thus

$$f(x) = \sin x^2 = \frac{2}{2!}x^2 - \frac{120}{6!}x^6 + \cdots$$
$$= x^2 - \frac{1}{3!}x^6 + \cdots$$

As we can see, the amount of calculation in order to find the higher derivatives of $\sin x^2$ increases very rapidly. In fact, the next non-zero term in the Taylor expansion of $\sin x^2$ is the 10th derivative term, which really requires a lot of work to get.

(b)

$$\sin x = x - \frac{1}{3!}x^3 + \frac{1}{5!}x^5 - \cdots$$

The first couple of coefficients of the above expansion are the same as those in the previous part. If we substitute x^2 for x in the Taylor expansion of $\sin x$ we should get the Taylor expansion of $\sin x^2$.

$$\sin x^2 = x^2 - \frac{1}{3!}(x^2)^3 + \frac{1}{5!}(x^2)^5 - \cdots$$
$$= x^2 - \frac{1}{3!}x^6 + \frac{1}{5!}x^{10} - \cdots$$

27.

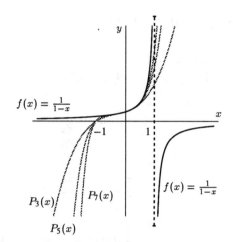

The graph suggests that the Taylor polynomials converge to $f(x) = \dfrac{1}{1-x}$ on the interval $(-1, 1)$.

28. By looking at the graph we can see that the Taylor polynomials are reasonable approximations for the function $f(x) = \sqrt{1+x}$ between $x = -0.25$ and $x = 0.25$. Thus a good guess is that the interval of convergence is $-0.25 < x < 0.25$.

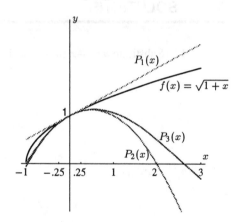

29. By looking at the graph we can see that the Taylor polynomials are reasonable approximations for the function $f(x) = \dfrac{1}{\sqrt{1+x}}$ between $x = -0.25$ and $x = 0.25$. Thus a good guess is that the interval of convergence is $-0.25 < x < 0.25$.

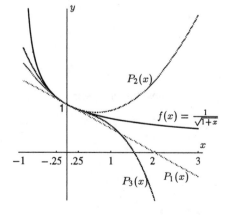

30. $C_1 = f'(0)/1!$, so $f'(0) = 1!C_1 = 1 \cdot 1 = 1$.
Similarly, $f''(0) = 2!C_2 = 2! \cdot \frac{1}{2} = 1$;
$f'''(0) = 3!C_3 = 3! \cdot \frac{1}{3} = 2! = 2$;
$f^{(10)}(0) = 10!C_{10} = 10! \cdot \frac{1}{10} = \frac{10!}{10} = 9! = 362880$.

31. Note that

$$0 = C_1 = \frac{d}{dx}(x^2 e^{x^2})\Big|_{x=0},$$

and since

$$\frac{1}{2} = C_6 = \frac{\frac{d^6}{dx^6}(x^2 e^{x^2})\Big|_{x=0}}{6!},$$

we have

$$\frac{d^6}{dx^6}(x^2 e^{x^2})\Big|_{x=0} = \frac{6!}{2} = 360.$$

10.3 SOLUTIONS

1. Substitute $y = -x$ into $e^y = 1 + y + \frac{y^2}{2!} + \frac{y^3}{3!} + \cdots$. We get

$$e^{-x} = 1 + (-x) + \frac{(-x)^2}{2!} + \frac{(-x)^3}{3!} + \cdots$$

$$= 1 - x + \frac{x^2}{2!} - \frac{x^3}{3!} + \cdots$$

2. We'll use

$$\sqrt{1+y} = (1+y)^{\frac{1}{2}} = 1 + \left(\frac{1}{2}\right)y + \left(\frac{1}{2}\right)\left(\frac{-1}{2}\right)\frac{y^2}{2!}$$

$$+ \left(\frac{1}{2}\right)\left(\frac{-1}{2}\right)\left(\frac{-3}{2}\right)\frac{y^3}{3!} + \cdots$$

$$= 1 + \frac{y}{2} - \frac{y^2}{8} + \frac{y^3}{16} - \cdots$$

Substitute $y = -2x$.

$$\sqrt{1-2x} = 1 + \frac{(-2x)}{2} - \frac{(-2x)^2}{8} + \frac{(-2x)^3}{16} - \cdots$$

$$= 1 - x - \frac{x^2}{2} - \frac{x^3}{2} - \cdots$$

3. Substitute $x = \theta^2$ into series for $\cos x$:

$$\cos(\theta^2) = 1 - \frac{(\theta^2)^2}{2!} + \frac{(\theta^2)^4}{4!} - \frac{(\theta^2)^6}{6!} + \cdots$$
$$= 1 - \frac{\theta^4}{2!} + \frac{\theta^8}{4!} - \frac{\theta^{12}}{6!} + \cdots$$

4. Substituting $x = -2y$ into $\ln(1+x) = x - \frac{x^2}{2} + \frac{x^3}{3} - \frac{x^4}{4} + \cdots$ gives

$$\ln(1 - 2y) = (-2y) - \frac{(-2y)^2}{2} + \frac{(-2y)^3}{3} - \frac{(-2y)^4}{4} + \cdots$$
$$= -2y - 2y^2 - \frac{8}{3}y^3 - 4y^4 - \cdots$$

5.

$$\frac{t}{1+t} = t(1+t)^{-1} = t\left(1 + (-1)t + \frac{(-1)(-2)}{2!}t^2 + \frac{(-1)(-2)(-3)}{3!}t^3 + \cdots\right)$$
$$= t - t^2 + t^3 - t^4 + \cdots$$

6. Substituting $x = -z^2$ into $\frac{1}{\sqrt{1+x}} = (1+x)^{-\frac{1}{2}} = 1 - \frac{1}{2}x + \frac{3}{8}x^2 - \frac{5}{16}x^3 + \cdots$ gives

$$\frac{1}{\sqrt{1-z^2}} = 1 - \frac{(-z^2)}{2} + \frac{3(-z^2)^2}{8} - \frac{5(-z^2)^3}{16} + \cdots$$
$$= 1 + \frac{1}{2}z^2 + \frac{3}{8}z^4 + \frac{5}{16}z^6 + \cdots$$

7. Since $\frac{d}{dx}(\arcsin x) = \frac{1}{\sqrt{1-x^2}} = 1 + \frac{1}{2}x^2 + \frac{3}{8}x^4 + \frac{5}{16}x^6 + \cdots$, integrating gives

$$\arcsin x = c + x + \frac{1}{6}x^3 + \frac{3}{40}x^5 + \frac{5}{112}x^7 + \cdots$$

Since $\arcsin 0 = 0$, $c = 0$.

8.

$$\frac{z}{e^{z^2}} = ze^{-z^2} = z\left(1 + (-z^2) + \frac{(-z^2)^2}{2!} + \frac{(-z^2)^3}{3!} + \cdots\right)$$
$$= z - z^3 + \frac{z^5}{2!} - \frac{z^7}{3!} + \cdots$$

9.

$$\phi^3 \cos(\phi^2) = \phi^3 \left(1 - \frac{(\phi^2)^2}{2!} + \frac{(\phi^2)^4}{4!} - \frac{(\phi^2)^6}{6!} + \cdots\right)$$

$$= \phi^3 - \frac{\phi^7}{2!} + \frac{\phi^{11}}{4!} - \frac{\phi^{15}}{6!} + \cdots$$

10. Substituting the series for $\sin\theta = \theta - \frac{\theta^3}{3!} + \frac{\theta^5}{5!} - \cdots$ into

$$\sqrt{1+y} = 1 + \frac{1}{2}y - \frac{1}{8}y^2 + \frac{1}{16}y^3 - \cdots$$

gives

$$\sqrt{1 + \sin\theta} = 1 + \left(\theta - \frac{\theta^3}{3!} + \frac{\theta^5}{5!} - \cdots\right) - \frac{1}{8}\left(\theta - \frac{\theta^3}{3!} + \frac{\theta^5}{5!} - \cdots\right)^2$$

$$+ \frac{1}{16}\left(\theta - \frac{\theta^3}{3!} + \frac{\theta^5}{5!} - \cdots\right)^3 - \cdots$$

$$= 1 + \theta - \frac{\theta^2}{8} + \left(\frac{\theta^3}{16} - \frac{\theta^3}{3!}\right) + \cdots$$

$$= 1 + \theta - \frac{1}{8}\theta^2 - \frac{5}{48}\theta^3 + \cdots$$

11.

$$e^t \cos t = \left(1 + t + \frac{t^2}{2!} + \frac{t^3}{3!} + \frac{t^4}{4!} + \cdots\right)\left(1 - \frac{t^2}{2!} + \frac{t^4}{4!} - \frac{t^6}{6!} + \cdots\right)$$

Multiplying out and collecting terms gives

$$e^t \cos t = 1 + t + \left(\frac{t^2}{2!} - \frac{t^2}{2!}\right) + \left(\frac{t^3}{3!} - \frac{t^3}{2!}\right) + \left(\frac{t^4}{4!} + \frac{t^4}{4!} - \frac{t^4}{(2!)^2}\right) + \cdots$$

$$= 1 + t - \frac{t^3}{3} - \frac{t^4}{6} + \cdots$$

12.

$$\sqrt{(1+t)}\sin t = \left(1 + \frac{t}{2} - \frac{t^2}{8} + \frac{t^3}{16} - \cdots\right)\left(t - \frac{t^3}{3!} + \frac{t^5}{5!} - \cdots\right)$$

Multiplying and collecting terms yields

$$\sqrt{(1+t)}\sin t = t + \frac{t^2}{2} - \left(\frac{t^3}{3!} + \frac{t^3}{8}\right) + \left(\frac{t^4}{16} - \frac{t^4}{12}\right) + \cdots$$

$$= t + \frac{1}{2}t^2 - \frac{7}{24}t^3 - \frac{1}{48}t^4 + \cdots$$

13.

$$\frac{1}{2+x} = \frac{1}{2(1+\frac{x}{2})} = \frac{1}{2}\left(1+\frac{x}{2}\right)^{-1}$$

$$= \frac{1}{2}\left(1 - \frac{x}{2} + \left(\frac{x}{2}\right)^2 - \left(\frac{x}{2}\right)^3 + \cdots\right)$$

14.

$$\frac{a}{\sqrt{a^2+x^2}} = \frac{a}{a(1+\frac{x^2}{a^2})^{\frac{1}{2}}} = \left(1+\frac{x^2}{a^2}\right)^{-\frac{1}{2}}$$

$$= 1 + \left(-\frac{1}{2}\right)\frac{x^2}{a^2} + \frac{1}{2!}\left(-\frac{1}{2}\right)\left(-\frac{3}{2}\right)\left(\frac{x^2}{a^2}\right)^2$$

$$+ \frac{1}{3!}\left(-\frac{1}{2}\right)\left(-\frac{3}{2}\right)\left(-\frac{5}{2}\right)\left(\frac{x^2}{a^2}\right)^3 + \cdots$$

$$= 1 - \frac{1}{2}\left(\frac{x}{a}\right)^2 + \frac{3}{8}\left(\frac{x}{a}\right)^4 - \frac{5}{16}\left(\frac{x}{a}\right)^6 + \cdots$$

15. From the series for $\ln(1+y)$,

$$\ln(1+y) = y - \frac{y^2}{2} + \frac{y^3}{3} - \frac{y^4}{4} + \cdots,$$

we get

$$\ln(1+y^2) = y^2 - \frac{y^4}{2} + \frac{y^6}{3} - \frac{y^8}{4} + \cdots$$

The Taylor series for $\sin y$ is

$$\sin y = y - \frac{y^3}{3!} + \frac{y^5}{5!} - \frac{y^7}{7!} + \cdots$$

So

$$\sin y^2 = y^2 - \frac{y^6}{3!} + \frac{y^{10}}{5!} - \frac{y^{14}}{7!} + \cdots$$

The Taylor series for $\cos y$ is

$$\cos y = 1 - \frac{y^2}{2!} + \frac{y^4}{4!} - \frac{y^6}{6!} + \cdots$$

So

$$1 - \cos y = \frac{y^2}{2!} - \frac{y^4}{4!} + \frac{y^6}{6!} + \cdots$$

Near $y = 0$, we can drop terms beyond the fourth degree in each expression:

$$\ln(1 + y^2) \approx y^2 - \frac{y^4}{2}$$

$$\sin y^2 \approx y^2$$

$$1 - \cos y \approx \frac{y^2}{2!} - \frac{y^4}{4!}$$

(Note: These functions are all even, so what holds for negative y will hold for positive y.) Clearly $1 - \cos y$ is smallest, because the y^2 term has a factor of $\frac{1}{2}$. Thus, for small y,

$$\frac{y^2}{2!} - \frac{y^4}{4!} < y^2 - \frac{y^4}{2} < y^2$$

so

$$1 - \cos y < \ln(1 + y^2) < \sin(y^2).$$

16. The Taylor expansion about $\theta = 0$ for $\sin \theta$ is

$$\theta - \frac{\theta^3}{3!} + \frac{\theta^5}{5!} - \frac{\theta^7}{7!} + \cdots.$$

So

$$1 + \sin \theta = 1 + \theta - \frac{\theta^3}{3!} + \frac{\theta^5}{5!} - \frac{\theta^7}{7!} + \cdots.$$

The Taylor expansion about $\theta = 0$ for $\cos \theta$ is

$$\cos \theta = 1 - \frac{\theta^2}{2!} + \frac{\theta^4}{4!} - \frac{\theta^6}{6!} + \cdots.$$

The Taylor expansion for $\dfrac{1}{1 + \theta}$ about $\theta = 0$ is

$$\frac{1}{1 + \theta} = 1 - \theta + \theta^2 - \theta^3 + \theta^4 - \cdots.$$

So, substituting $-\theta^2$ for θ:

$$\frac{1}{1 - \theta^2} = 1 - (-\theta^2) + (-\theta^2)^2 - (-\theta^2)^3 + (-\theta^2)^4 + \cdots$$

$$= 1 + \theta^2 + \theta^4 + \theta^6 + \theta^8 + \cdots.$$

For small θ, we can neglect the terms above quadratic in these expansions, giving:

$$1 + \sin \theta \approx 1 + \theta$$

$$\cos \theta \approx 1 - \frac{\theta^2}{2}$$

$$\frac{1}{1 - \theta^2} \approx 1 + \theta^2.$$

For all $\theta \neq 0$, we have

$$1 - \frac{\theta^2}{2} < 1 + \theta^2.$$

Also, since $\theta^2 < \theta$ for $0 < \theta < 1$, we have

$$1 - \frac{\theta^2}{2} < 1 + \theta^2 < 1 + \theta.$$

So, for small positive θ, we have

$$\cos\theta < \frac{1}{1 - \theta^2} < 1 + \sin\theta.$$

17. The Taylor series about 0 for $y = \dfrac{1}{1 - x^2}$ is

$$y = 1 + x^2 + x^4 + x^6 + \cdots.$$

The series for $y = (1 + x)^{\frac{1}{4}}$ is, using the binomial expansion,

$$y = 1 + \frac{1}{4}x + \frac{1}{4}\left(-\frac{3}{4}\right)\frac{x^2}{2!} + \frac{1}{4}\left(-\frac{3}{4}\right)\left(-\frac{7}{4}\right)\frac{x^3}{3!} + \cdots.$$

The series for $y = \sqrt{1 + \dfrac{x}{2}} = (1 + \dfrac{x}{2})^{\frac{1}{2}}$ is, again using the binomial expansion,

$$y = 1 + \frac{1}{2}\cdot\frac{x}{2} + \frac{1}{2}\left(-\frac{1}{2}\right)\cdot\frac{x^2}{8} + \frac{1}{2}\left(-\frac{1}{2}\right)\left(-\frac{3}{2}\right)\cdot\frac{x^3}{48} + \cdots.$$

Similarly for $y = \dfrac{1}{\sqrt{1 - x}} = (1 - x)^{-\frac{1}{2}}$,

$$y = 1 + \left(-\frac{1}{2}\right)(-x) + \left(-\frac{1}{2}\right)\left(-\frac{3}{2}\right)\cdot\frac{x^2}{2!} + \left(-\frac{1}{2}\right)\left(-\frac{3}{2}\right)\left(-\frac{5}{2}\right)\cdot\frac{-x^3}{3!} + \cdots.$$

Near 0, let's truncate these series after their x^2 terms:

$$\frac{1}{1 - x^2} \approx 1 + x^2,$$

$$(1 + x)^{\frac{1}{4}} \approx 1 + \frac{1}{4}x - \frac{3}{32}x^2,$$

$$\sqrt{1 + \frac{x}{2}} \approx 1 + \frac{1}{4}x - \frac{1}{32}x^2,$$

$$\frac{1}{\sqrt{1 - x}} \approx 1 + \frac{1}{2}x + \frac{3}{8}x^2.$$

Thus $\frac{1}{1-x^2}$ looks like a parabola opening upward near the origin, with y-axis as the axis of symmetry, so (a) = I.

Now $\frac{1}{\sqrt{1-x}}$ has the largest positive slope ($\frac{1}{2}$), and is concave up (because the coefficient of x^2 is positive). So (d) = II.

The last two both have positive slope ($\frac{1}{4}$) and are concave down. Since $(1+x)^{\frac{1}{4}}$ has the smallest second derivative (i.e. the most negative coefficient of x^2), (b) = IV and therefore (c) = III.

18.

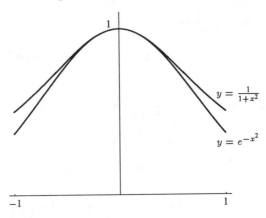

(a)

$$e^{-x^2} = 1 - x^2 + \frac{x^4}{2!} - \frac{x^6}{3!} + \cdots$$

$$\frac{1}{1+x^2} = 1 - x^2 + x^4 - x^6 + \cdots$$

Notice that the first two terms are the same in both series.

(b) $\frac{1}{1+x^2}$ is greater.

(c) Even, because the only terms involved are of even degree.

(d) The coefficients for e^{-x^2} become extremely small for higher powers of x, and we can "counteract" the effect of these powers for large values of x. The series for $\frac{1}{1+x^2}$ has no such coefficients.

19. (a) From a calculator, $4\tan^{-1}(1/5) - \tan^{-1}(1/239) = 0.7853981634$, which agrees with $\pi/4$ to ten decimal places. Notice that you cannot verify that Machin's formula is *exactly* true numerically (because any calculator has only a finite number of digits.) Showing that the formula is exactly true requires a theoretical argument.

(b) The Taylor polynomial of degree 5 approximating $\arctan x$ is

$$\arctan x \approx x - \frac{x^3}{3} + \frac{x^5}{5}.$$

Thus,

$$\pi = 4 \left(4 \arctan \left(\frac{1}{5} \right) - \arctan \left(\frac{1}{239} \right) \right)$$

$$= 4 \left(4 \left(\frac{1}{5} - \frac{1}{3} \left(\frac{1}{5} \right)^3 + \frac{1}{5} \left(\frac{1}{5} \right)^5 \right) - \left(\frac{1}{239} - \frac{1}{3} \left(\frac{1}{239} \right)^3 + \frac{1}{5} \left(\frac{1}{239} \right)^5 \right) \right)$$

$$\approx 3.141621029.$$

(c) Because the values of x, namely $x = 1/5$ and $x = 1/239$, are much smaller than 1, the terms in the series get smaller much faster.

20. (a) If $\phi = 0$,

$$\text{left side} = b(1 + 1 + 1) = 3b \approx 0$$

so the equation is almost satisfied and we expect a solution near $\phi = 0$.

(b) We have

$$\sin \phi = \phi - \frac{\phi^3}{3!} + \frac{\phi^5}{5!} - \cdots$$

$$\cos \phi = 1 - \frac{\phi^2}{2!} + \frac{\phi^4}{4!} - \cdots$$

So

$$\cos^2 \phi = \left(1 - \frac{\phi^2}{2!} + \frac{\phi^4}{4!} - \cdots \right) \left(1 - \frac{\phi^2}{2!} + \frac{\phi^4}{4!} - \cdots \right).$$

Neglecting terms of order ϕ^2 and higher, we get

$$\sin \phi \approx \phi$$
$$\cos \phi \approx 1$$
$$\cos^2 \phi \approx 1.$$

So $\phi + b(1 + 1 + 1) = 0$, whence $\phi = -3b$.

21.

$$E = kQ \left(\frac{1}{(R-1)^2} - \frac{1}{(R+1)^2} \right)$$

$$= \frac{kQ}{R^2} \left(\frac{1}{(1 - \frac{1}{R})^2} - \frac{1}{(1 + \frac{1}{R})^2} \right)$$

Since $|\frac{1}{R}| < 1$, we can expand the two terms using the binomial expansion:

$$\frac{1}{(1 - \frac{1}{R})^2} = \left(1 - \frac{1}{R}\right)^{-2}$$

$$= 1 - 2\left(-\frac{1}{R}\right) + (-2)(-3)\frac{(-\frac{1}{R})^2}{2!} + (-2)(-3)(-4)\frac{(-\frac{1}{R})^3}{3!} + \cdots$$

$$\frac{1}{(1 + \frac{1}{R})^2} = \left(1 + \frac{1}{R}\right)^{-2}$$

$$= 1 - 2\left(\frac{1}{R}\right) + (-2)(-3)\frac{(\frac{1}{R})^2}{2!} + (-2)(-3)(-4)\frac{(\frac{1}{R})^3}{3!} + \cdots$$

Substituting, we get:

$$E = \frac{kQ}{R^2}\left[1 + \frac{2}{R} + \frac{3}{R^2} + \frac{4}{R^3} + \cdots - \left(1 - \frac{2}{R} + \frac{3}{R^2} - \frac{4}{R^3} + \cdots\right)\right]$$

$$\approx \frac{kQ}{R^2}\left(\frac{4}{R} + \frac{8}{R^3}\right)$$

using only the first two non-zero terms.

22. (a) $\mu = \frac{mM}{m+M}$.

If $M >> m$, then the denominator $m + M \approx M$, so $\mu \approx \frac{mM}{M} = m$.

(b)

$$\mu = m\left(\frac{M}{m + M}\right) = m\left(\frac{\frac{1}{M}M}{\frac{m}{M} + \frac{M}{M}}\right) = m\left(\frac{1}{1 + \frac{m}{M}}\right)$$

We can use the binomial expansion since $\frac{m}{M} < 1$.

$$\mu = m\left[1 - \frac{m}{M} + \left(\frac{m}{M}\right)^2 - \left(\frac{m}{M}\right)^3 + \cdots\right]$$

(c) If $m \approx \frac{1}{1836}M$, then $\frac{m}{M} \approx \frac{1}{1836} \approx 0.000545$.

So a first order approximation to μ would give $\mu = m(1 - 0.000545)$. The percentage difference from $\mu = m$ is -0.0545%.

23. This time we are interested in how a function behaves at large values in its domain. Therefore, we don't want to expand $V = 2\pi\sigma(\sqrt{R^2 + a^2} - R)$ about $R = 0$. We want to find a variable which becomes small as R gets large. Since $R > a$

$$V = R2\pi\sigma\left(\sqrt{1 + \frac{a^2}{R^2}} - 1\right).$$

We can now expand a series in terms of $\left(\frac{a}{R}\right)^2$. This may seem strange, but suspend your disbelief. The Taylor series for $\sqrt{1 + \frac{a^2}{R^2}}$ is

$$1 + \frac{1}{2}\frac{a^2}{R^2} + \frac{(1/2)(-1/2)}{2}\left(\frac{a^2}{R^2}\right)^2 + \cdots$$

So $V = R2\pi\sigma\left(1 + \frac{1}{2}\frac{a^2}{R^2} - \frac{1}{8}\left(\frac{a^2}{R^2}\right)^2 + \cdots - 1\right)$. For large R, we can drop the $-\frac{1}{8}\frac{a^4}{R^4}$ term and terms of higher order, so

$$V \approx \frac{\pi\sigma a^2}{R}.$$

Notice that what we really did by expanding around $\left(\frac{a}{R}\right)^2 = 0$ was expanding around $R = \infty$. We then get a series that converges for large R.

24. (a)

$$\left(\omega_0 L - \frac{1}{\omega_0 C}\right)^2 = 0$$

$$\omega_0 L - \frac{1}{\omega_0 C} = 0$$

$$\omega_0 L = \frac{1}{\omega_0 C}$$

$$\omega_0^2 = \frac{1}{LC}$$

$$\omega_0 = \sqrt{\frac{1}{LC}}.$$

(Note: We discarded the negative root, because we need positive frequencies.)

(b) Set $\omega = \omega_0 + \Delta\omega$ and get

$$\left((\omega_0 + \Delta\omega)L - \frac{1}{(\omega_0 + \Delta\omega)C}\right)^2.$$

We need to find a Taylor expansion for the term $\frac{1}{C(\omega_0 + \Delta\omega)}$.

So

$$\frac{1}{C(\omega_0 + \Delta\omega)} = \frac{1}{C\omega_0}\left(1 + \frac{\Delta\omega}{\omega_0}\right)^{-1}$$

$$= \frac{1}{C\omega_0}\left(1 - \frac{\Delta\omega}{\omega_0} + \cdots\right)$$

So our expression becomes:

$$\omega_0 L + L\Delta\omega - \frac{1}{C\omega_0}\left(1 - \frac{\Delta\omega}{\omega_0} + \cdots\right)$$

$$= \sqrt{\frac{L}{C} + L\Delta\omega} - \sqrt{\frac{L}{C} + L\Delta\omega} - \cdots$$

$$= 2L\Delta\omega - \cdots$$

So $(\omega L - \frac{1}{\omega C})^2 \approx 4L^2(\Delta\omega)^2$.

Notice that if $\Delta\omega = 0$ in the above expression, we get 0, which is what we expected, since in this case $\omega = \omega_0$.

25. (a) At $r = a$, the force between the atoms is 0.
    (b) There will be an attractive force, pulling them back together.
    (c) There will be a repulsive force, pushing the atoms apart.
    (d) $F = F(a) + F'(a)(r - a) + F''(a)\frac{(r-a)^2}{2!} + \cdots$
    (e) $F(a) = 0$, so discarding all but the first non-zero terms, we get $F = F'(a)(r - a)$. $F'(a)$ is a negative number, so for r slightly greater than a, the force is negative (attractive). For r slightly less than a, the force is positive (repulsive).

26. (a) If h is much smaller than R, we can say that $(R + h) \approx R$, giving the approximation

$$F = \frac{mgR^2}{(R + h)^2} \approx \frac{mgR^2}{R^2} = mg.$$

    (b)

$$F = \frac{mgR^2}{(R + h)^2} = \frac{mg}{(1 + h/R)^2} = mg(1 + h/R)^{-2}$$

$$= mg\left(1 + \frac{(-2)}{1!}\left(\frac{h}{R}\right) + \frac{(-2)(-3)}{2!}\left(\frac{h}{R}\right)^2 + \frac{(-2)(-3)(-4)}{3!}\left(\frac{h}{R}\right)^3 + \cdots\right)$$

$$= mg\left(1 - \frac{2h}{R} + \frac{3h^2}{R^2} - \frac{4h^3}{R^3} + \cdots\right)$$

    (c) The first order correction comes from term $-2h/R$. The approximation for F is then given by

$$F \approx mg\left(1 - \frac{2h}{R}\right).$$

If the first order correction alters the estimate for F by 10%, we have

$$\frac{2h}{R} = 0.10 \quad \text{so} \quad h = 0.05R \approx 0.05(6400) = 320 \text{ km}.$$

The approximation $F \approx mg$ is good to within 10% — that is, up to about 300 km.

27. Since $C_0 = y(0)$, the initial condition $y(0) = 1$ gives $C_0 = 1$, so

$$y(x) = 1 + C_1 x + C_2 x^2 + C_3 x^3 + C_4 x^4 + C_5 x^5 + \cdots.$$

Taking the derivative of the series for y term by term, we get

$$\frac{dy}{dx} = C_1 + 2C_2 x + 3C_3 x^2 + 4C_4 x^3 + 5C_5 x^4 + 6C_6 x^5 + 7C_7 x^6 + \cdots.$$

Moreover, we know that

$$\frac{1}{1-x} = 1 + x + x^2 + x^3 + x^4 + x^5 + \cdots$$

is a Binomial series. Therefore, we must have

$$C_1 + 2C_2 x + 3C_3 x^2 + 4C_4 x^3 + 5C_5 x^4 + \cdots = 1 + x + x^2 + x^3 + x^4 + x^5 + \cdots.$$

Equate coefficients of corresponding powers of x:

Constant terms	$C_1 = 1$		
Coefficients of x	$2C_2 = 1$,	so	$C_2 = 1/2$
Coefficients of x^2	$3C_3 = 1$,	so	$C_3 = 1/3$
Coefficients of x^3	$4C_4 = 1$,	so	$C_4 = 1/4$.

We have found the approximation

$$y(x) \approx 1 + x + \frac{x^2}{2} + \frac{x^3}{3} + \frac{x^4}{4} \quad \text{for } x \text{ near } 0.$$

This is the Taylor series for $1 - \ln(1-x)$, since

$$1 - \ln(1-x) = 1 - \left((-x) - \frac{(-x)^2}{2} + \frac{(-x)^3}{3} - \frac{(-x)^4}{4} + \cdots \right)$$

$$= 1 + x + \frac{x^2}{2} + \frac{x^3}{3} + \frac{x^4}{4} + \cdots.$$

28. Since $C_0 = f(0)$, the initial condition $f(0) = 1$ gives $C_0 = 1$ and $C_1 = f'(0) = 0$, so

$$f(x) = 1 + 0x + C_2 x^2 + C_3 x^3 + C_4 x^4 + C_5 x^5 + \cdots.$$

Taking the derivative of the series for f term by term twice, we get

$$\frac{df}{dx} = 0 + 2C_2 x + 3C_3 x^2 + 4C_4 x^3 + 5C_5 x^4 + \cdots.$$

$$\frac{d^2 f}{dx^2} = 2 \cdot 1 C_2 + 3 \cdot 2 C_3 x + 4 \cdot 3 C_4 x^2 + 5 \cdot 4 C_5 x^3 + \cdots.$$

Since the differential equation tells us that $\dfrac{d^2 f}{dx^2} = -f$, we must have

$$2 \cdot 1 C_2 + 3 \cdot 2 C_3 x + 4 \cdot 3 C_4 x^2 + 5 \cdot 4 C_5 x^3 + \cdots = -1 - 0x - C_2 x^2 - C_3 x^3 - C_4 x^4 - \cdots.$$

Equate coefficients of corresponding powers of x:

Constant terms	$2C_2 = -1$ so $C_2 = -1/2$
Coefficients of x	$6C_3 = -0 = 0$, so $C_3 = 0$
Coefficients of x^2	$12C_4 = -C_2 = 1/2$, so $C_4 = 1/24$
Coefficients of x^3	$20C_5 = -C_3 = 0$ so $C_5 = 0$.

We have found the approximation

$$f(x) \approx 1 - \frac{x^2}{2} + \frac{x^4}{24} \quad \text{for } x \text{ near } 0.$$

In this case, we can see that the coefficients can be written as

$$C_2 = -\frac{1}{2} = -\frac{1}{2!}, \quad C_4 = \frac{1}{24} = \frac{1}{4!},$$

so we recognize the series as the Taylor series for $\cos x$ about $x = 0$.

29. Since $C_0 = f(0)$, the initial conditions $f(0) = 0$, $f'(0) = 1$ give $C_0 = 0$, $C_1 = 1$, so

$$f(\theta) = \theta + C_2\theta^2 + C_3\theta^3 + C_4\theta^4 + C_5\theta^5 + \cdots.$$

Taking the derivative of the series for f term by term twice, we get

$$\frac{df}{d\theta} = 1 + 2C_2\theta + 3C_3\theta^2 + 4C_4\theta^3 + 5C_5\theta^4 + \cdots.$$

$$\frac{d^2 f}{d\theta^2} = 2 \cdot 1C_2 + 3 \cdot 2C_3\theta + 4 \cdot 3C_4\theta^2 + 5 \cdot 4C_5\theta^3 + \cdots.$$

Since the differential equation tells us that $\dfrac{d^2 f}{d\theta^2} = -f$, we must have

$$2 \cdot 1C_2 + 3 \cdot 2C_3\theta + 4 \cdot 3C_4\theta^2 + 5 \cdot 4C_5\theta^3 + \cdots = -\theta - C_2\theta^2 - C_3\theta^3 - C_4\theta^4 \cdots.$$

Equate coefficients of corresponding powers of θ:

Constant terms	$2C_2 = 0$ so $C_2 = 0$
Coefficients of θ	$6C_3 = -C_1 = -1$, so $C_3 = -1/6$
Coefficients of θ^2	$12C_4 = -C_2 = 0$, so $C_4 = 0$
Coefficients of θ^3	$20C_5 = -C_3 = 1/6$ so $C_5 = 1/120$.

We have found the approximation

$$f(\theta) \approx \theta - \frac{\theta^3}{6} + \frac{\theta^5}{120} \quad \text{for } \theta \text{ near } 0.$$

In this case, we can see that the coefficients can be written as

$$C_3 = -\frac{1}{6} = -\frac{1}{3!}, \quad C_5 = \frac{1}{120} = \frac{1}{5!},$$

so we recognize the series as the Taylor series for $\sin \theta$ about $\theta = 0$.

30. The initial conditions $y(0) = 1$, $y'(0) = -1$ give $C_0 = 1$, $C_1 = -1$, so

$$y(x) = 1 - x + C_2 x^2 + C_3 x^3 + C_4 x^4 + C_5 x^5 + \cdots.$$

Taking the derivative of the series for y term by term twice, we get

$$\frac{dy}{dx} = -1 + 2C_2 x + 3C_3 x^2 + 4C_4 x^3 + 5C_5 x^4 + \cdots.$$

$$\frac{d^2 y}{dx^2} = 2 \cdot 1 C_2 + 3 \cdot 2 C_3 x + 4 \cdot 3 C_4 x^2 + 5 \cdot 4 C_5 x^3 + \cdots.$$

Since the differential equation tells us that $\dfrac{d^2 y}{dx^2} = xy$, we must have

$$2 \cdot 1 C_2 + 3 \cdot 2 C_3 x + 4 \cdot 3 C_4 x^2 + 5 \cdot 4 C_5 x^3 + \cdots = x - x^2 + C_2 x^3 - C_3 x^4 + C_4 x^5 + \cdots.$$

Equate coefficients of corresponding powers of x:

Constant terms	$2C_2 = 0$ so $C_2 = 0$
Coefficients of x	$6C_3 = 1$, so $C_3 = 1/6$
Coefficients of x^2	$12C_4 = -1$, so $C_4 = -1/12$
Coefficients of x^3	$20C_5 = C_2 = 0$ so $C_5 = 0$.

We have found the approximation

$$y(x) \approx 1 - x + \frac{x^3}{6} - \frac{x^4}{12} \quad \text{for } x \text{ near } 0.$$

31. The initial condition $y(0) = 2$ gives $C_0 = 2$, so

$$y(t) = 2 + C_1 t + C_2 t^2 + C_3 t^3 + C_4 t^4 + C_5 t^5 + \cdots.$$

The equation above translates into

$$C_1 + 2C_2 t + 3C_3 t^2 + 4C_4 t^3 + 5C_5 t^4 + \cdots = 1 - (2t + C_1 t^2 + C_2 t^3 + C_3 t^4 + C_4 t^4 + \cdots)$$

Equate coefficients of corresponding powers of t:

Constant terms	$C_1 = 1$
Coefficients of t	$2C_2 = -2$, so $C_2 = -1$
Coefficients of t^2	$3C_3 = -C_1 = -1$, so $C_3 = -1/3$
Coefficients of t^3	$4C_4 = -C_2 = 1$ so $C_4 = 1/4$.

We have found the approximation

$$y(t) \approx 2 + t - t^2 - \frac{t^3}{3} + \frac{t^4}{4} \quad \text{for } t \text{ near } 0.$$

10.4 SOLUTIONS

1. Yes, $a = 2$, ratio $= 1/2$.

2. Yes, $a = 1$, ratio $= -1/2$.

3. No. Ratio between successive terms is not constant: $\dfrac{1/3}{1/2} = 0.66\cdots$, while $\dfrac{1/4}{1/3} = 0.75$

4. Yes, $a = 5$, ratio $= -2$.

5. Yes, $a = 1$, ratio $= -x$.

6. No. Ratio between successive terms is not constant: $\dfrac{2x^2}{x} = 2x$, while $\dfrac{3x^3}{2x^2} = \dfrac{3}{2}x$.

7. Yes, $a = y^2$, ratio $= y$.

8. Yes, $a = 1$, ratio $= -y^2$.

9. Yes, $a = 1$, ratio $= 2z$.

10. No. Ratio between successive terms is not constant: $\dfrac{6z^2}{3z} = 2z$, while $\dfrac{9z^3}{6z^2} = \dfrac{3}{2}z$.

11. Sum $= \dfrac{1}{1-(-x)} = \dfrac{1}{1+x}, |x| < 1.$

12. Sum $= \dfrac{y^2}{1-y}, |y| < 1.$

13. Sum $= \dfrac{1}{1-(-y^2)} = \dfrac{1}{1+y^2}, |y| < 1.$

14. Sum $= \dfrac{1}{1-2z}, |z| < 1/2.$

15. $3 + \dfrac{3}{2} + \dfrac{3}{4} + \dfrac{3}{8} \cdots + \dfrac{3}{2^{10}} = 3\left(1 + \dfrac{1}{2} + \cdots + \dfrac{1}{2^{10}}\right) = \dfrac{3\left(1 - \frac{1}{2^{11}}\right)}{1 - \frac{1}{2}} = \dfrac{3\left(2^{11} - 1\right)}{2^{10}}$

16. $-2 + 1 - \dfrac{1}{2} + \dfrac{1}{4} - \dfrac{1}{8} + \dfrac{1}{16} - \cdots = \displaystyle\sum_{n=0}^{\infty} (-2)\left(-\dfrac{1}{2}\right)^n$, a geometric series.

    Let $a = -2$ and $x = -\frac{1}{2}$ then
    $$\sum_{n=0}^{\infty} (-2)\left(-\dfrac{1}{2}\right)^n = \dfrac{a}{1-x} = \dfrac{-2}{1-\left(-\frac{1}{2}\right)} = -\dfrac{4}{3}$$

17.
$$\sum_{n=4}^{\infty} \left(\dfrac{1}{3}\right)^n = \left(\dfrac{1}{3}\right)^4 + \left(\dfrac{1}{3}\right)^5 + \cdots = \left(\dfrac{1}{3}\right)^4 \left(1 + \dfrac{1}{3} + \left(\dfrac{1}{3}\right)^2 + \cdots\right) = \dfrac{\left(\frac{1}{3}\right)^4}{1 - \frac{1}{3}} = \dfrac{1}{54}$$

18. $\displaystyle\sum_{n=0}^{\infty} \dfrac{3^n + 5}{4^n} = \sum_{n=0}^{\infty} \left(\dfrac{3}{4}\right)^n + \sum_{n=0}^{\infty} \dfrac{5}{4^n}$, a sum of two geometric series.

$$\sum_{n=0}^{\infty} \left(\frac{3}{4}\right)^n = \frac{1}{1-\frac{3}{4}} = 4$$

$$\sum_{n=0}^{\infty} \frac{5}{4^n} = \frac{5}{1-\frac{1}{4}} = \frac{20}{3}$$

so $$\sum_{n=0}^{\infty} \frac{3^n + 5}{4^n} = 4 + \frac{20}{3} = \frac{32}{3}$$

19. (a) $0.232323\ldots = 0.23 + 0.23(0.01) + 0.23(0.01)^2 + \ldots$ which is a geometric series with $a = 0.23$ and $x = 0.01$.

   (b) The sum is $\dfrac{0.23}{1-0.01} = \dfrac{0.23}{0.99} = \dfrac{23}{99}$.

20. (a) The amount of atenolol in the blood is given by $Q(t) = Q_0 e^{-kt}$, where $Q_0 = Q(0)$ and k is a constant. Since the half-life is 6.3 hours,

$$\frac{1}{2} = e^{-6.3k}, \quad k = -\frac{1}{6.3} \ln \frac{1}{2} \approx 0.1.$$

After 24 hours

$$Q = Q_0 e^{-k(24)} \approx Q_0 e^{-0.1(24)} \approx Q_0(0.1).$$

Thus, the percentage of the atenolol that remains after 24 hours $\approx 10\%$.

   (b)

$$Q_0 = 50$$
$$Q_1 = 50 + 50(0.1)$$
$$Q_2 = 50 + 50(0.1) + 50(0.1)^2$$
$$Q_3 = 50 + 50(0.1) + 50(0.1)^2 + 50(0.1)^3$$
$$\cdots$$
$$Q_n = 50 + 50(0.1) + 50(0.1)^2 + \cdots + 50(0.1)^n$$
$$= \frac{50(1 - (0.1)^{n+1})}{1 - 0.1}$$

   (c)

$$P_1 = 50(0.1)$$
$$P_2 = 50(0.1) + 50(0.1)^2$$
$$P_3 = 50(0.1) + 50(0.1)^2 + 50(0.1)^3$$
$$P_4 = 50(0.1) + 50(0.1)^2 + 50(0.1)^3 + 50(0.1)^4$$
$$\cdots$$
$$P_n = 50(0.1) + 50(0.1)^2 + 50(0.1)^3 + \cdots + 50(0.1)^n$$
$$= 50(0.1) \left(1 + (0.1) + (0.1)^2 + \cdots + (0.1)^{n-1}\right)$$
$$= \frac{0.1(50)(1 - (0.1)^n)}{1 - 0.1}$$

21. (a)
$$P_1 = 0$$
$$P_2 = 250(0.04)$$
$$P_3 = 250(0.04) + 250(0.04)^2$$
$$P_4 = 250(0.04) + 250(0.04)^2 + 250(0.04)^3$$
$$\cdots$$
$$P_n = 250(0.04) + 250(0.04)^2 + 250(0.04)^3 + \cdots + 250(0.04)^{n-1}$$

(b)
$$P_n = 250(0.04)\left(1 + (0.04) + (0.04)^2 + (0.04)^3 + \cdots + (0.04)^{n-2}\right)$$
$$= 250\frac{0.04(1 - (0.04)^{n-1})}{1 - 0.04}$$

(c)
$$P = \lim_{n \to \infty} P_n$$
$$= \lim_{n \to \infty} 250\frac{0.04(1 - (0.04)^{n-1})}{1 - 0.04}$$
$$= \frac{(250)(0.04)}{0.96}$$
$$= 0.04Q$$
$$\approx 10.42$$

Thus, $\lim_{n \to \infty} P_n = 10.42$ and $\lim_{n \to \infty} Q_n = 260.42$. We'd expect these limits to differ because one is right before taking a tablet, one is right after. We'd expect the difference between them to be 250 mg, the amount of ampicillin in one tablet.

22.

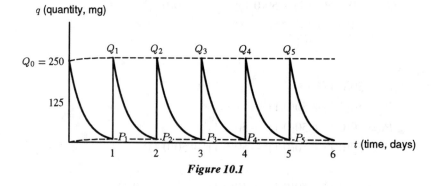

Figure 10.1

23. (a) Let h_n be the height of the nth bounce after the ball hits the floor for the nth time. Then from Figure 10.2,

$$h_0 = \text{height before first bounce} = 10 \text{ feet},$$

$$h_1 = \text{height after first bounce} = 10 \left(\frac{3}{4}\right) \text{ feet,}$$

$$h_2 = \text{height after second bounce} = 10 \left(\frac{3}{4}\right)^2 \text{ feet}$$

Generalizing gives

$$h_n = 10 \left(\frac{3}{4}\right)^n.$$

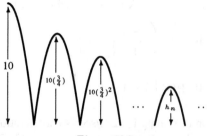

Figure 10.2

(b) When the ball hits the floor for the first time, the total distance it has traveled is just $D_1 = 10$ feet. (Notice that this is the same as $h_0 = 10$.) Then the ball bounces back to a height of $h_1 = 10 \left(\frac{3}{4}\right)$, comes down and hits the floor for the second time. The total distance it has traveled is

$$D_2 = h_0 + 2h_1 = 10 + 2 \cdot 10 \left(\frac{3}{4}\right) = 25 \text{ feet.}$$

Then the ball bounces back to a height of $h_2 = 10 \left(\frac{3}{4}\right)^2$, comes down and hits the floor for the third time. It has traveled

$$D_3 = h_0 + 2h_1 + 2h_2 = 10 + 2 \cdot 10 \left(\frac{3}{4}\right) + 2 \cdot 10 \left(\frac{3}{4}\right)^2 = 25 + 2 \cdot 10 \left(\frac{3}{4}\right)^2 = 36.25 \text{ feet.}$$

Similarly,

$$D_4 = h_0 + 2h_1 + 2h_2 + 2h_3$$
$$= 10 + 2 \cdot 10 \left(\frac{3}{4}\right) + 2 \cdot 10 \left(\frac{3}{4}\right)^2 + 2 \cdot 10 \left(\frac{3}{4}\right)^3$$
$$= 36.25 + 2 \cdot 10 \left(\frac{3}{4}\right)^3$$
$$\approx 44.69 \text{ feet.}$$

(c) When the ball hits the floor for the nth time, its last bounce was of height h_{n-1}. Thus, by the method used in part (b), we get

$$D_n = h_0 + 2h_1 + 2h_2 + 2h_3 + \cdots + 2h_{n-1}$$

$$= 10 + 2 \cdot 10 \left(\frac{3}{4}\right) + 2 \cdot 10 \left(\frac{3}{4}\right)^2 + 2 \cdot 10 \left(\frac{3}{4}\right)^3 + \cdots + 2 \cdot 10 \left(\frac{3}{4}\right)^{n-1}$$

$$\underbrace{\phantom{= 10 + 2 \cdot 10 \left(\frac{3}{4}\right) + 2 \cdot 10 \left(\frac{3}{4}\right)^2 + 2 \cdot 10 \left(\frac{3}{4}\right)^3 + \cdots + 2 \cdot 10 \left(\frac{3}{4}\right)^{n-1}}}_{\text{finite geometric series}}$$

$$= 10 + 2 \cdot 10 \cdot \left(\frac{3}{4}\right) \left(1 + \left(\frac{3}{4}\right) + \left(\frac{3}{4}\right)^2 + \cdots + \left(\frac{3}{4}\right)^{n-2}\right)$$

$$= 10 + 15 \left(\frac{1 - \left(\frac{3}{4}\right)^{n-1}}{1 - \left(\frac{3}{4}\right)}\right)$$

$$= 10 + 60 \left(1 - \left(\frac{3}{4}\right)^{n-1}\right).$$

24. (a) The acceleration of gravity is 32 ft/sec^2 so acceleration $= 32$ and velocity $v = 32t + C$. Since the ball is dropped, its initial velocity is 0 so $v = 32t$. Thus the position is $s = 16t^2 + C$. Calling the initial position $s = 0$, we have $s = 16t^2$. The distance traveled is h so $h = 16t^2$. Solving for t we get $t = \frac{1}{4}\sqrt{h}$.

(b) The first drop from 10 feet takes $\frac{1}{4}\sqrt{10}$ seconds. The first full bounce (to $10 \cdot \left(\frac{3}{4}\right)$ feet) takes $\frac{1}{4}\sqrt{10 \cdot \left(\frac{3}{4}\right)}$ seconds to rise, therefore the same time to come down. Thus, the full bounce, up and down, takes $2\left(\frac{1}{4}\right)\sqrt{10 \cdot \left(\frac{3}{4}\right)}$ seconds. The next full bounce takes $2\left(\frac{1}{4}\right)\sqrt{10 \cdot \left(\frac{3}{4}\right)^2} = 2\left(\frac{1}{4}\right)\sqrt{10}\left(\sqrt{\frac{3}{4}}\right)^2$ seconds. The nth bounce takes $2\left(\frac{1}{4}\right)\sqrt{10}\left(\sqrt{\frac{3}{4}}\right)^n$ seconds. Therefore the

Total amount of time

$$= \frac{1}{4}\sqrt{10} + \underbrace{\frac{2}{4}\sqrt{10}\sqrt{\frac{3}{4}} + \frac{2}{4}\sqrt{10}\left(\sqrt{\frac{3}{4}}\right)^2 + \frac{2}{4}\sqrt{10}\left(\sqrt{\frac{3}{4}}\right)^3}_{\text{Geometric series with } a = \frac{2}{4}\sqrt{10}\sqrt{\frac{3}{4}} = \frac{1}{2}\sqrt{10}\sqrt{\frac{3}{4}} \text{ and } x = \sqrt{\frac{3}{4}}} + \cdots$$

$$= \frac{1}{4}\sqrt{10} + \frac{1}{2}\sqrt{10}\sqrt{\frac{3}{4}}\left(\frac{1}{1 - \sqrt{3/4}}\right) \text{ seconds.}$$

25. As in the text,

Present value of first payment, in millions of dollars $= 3$

Since the second payment is made a year in the future, so with continuous compounding,

Present value of second payment, in millions of dollars $= 3e^{-0.07}$

Since the next payment is two years in the future,

$$\text{Present value of third payment, in millions of dollars} = 3e^{-0.07(2)}$$

Similarly,

$$\text{Present value of tenth payment, in millions of dollars} = 3e^{-0.07(9)}$$

Thus, in millions of dollars,

$$\text{Total present value} = 3 + 3e^{-0.07} + 3e^{-0.07(2)} + 3e^{-0.07(3)} + \cdots + 3e^{-0.07(9)}$$

Since $e^{-0.07(n)} = \left(e^{-0.07}\right)^n$ for any n, we can write

$$\text{Total present value} = 3 + 3e^{-0.07} + 3\left(e^{-0.07}\right)^2 + 3\left(e^{-0.07}\right)^3 + 3\left(e^{-0.07}\right)^9 .$$

This is a finite geometric series with $x = e^{-0.07}$ and sum

$$\text{Total present value of contract, in millions of dollars} = \frac{3\left(1 - (e^{-0.07})^{10}\right)}{1 - e^{-0.07}} \approx 22.3$$

26. An interest rate of 5% per year, compounded twice a year, means 2.5% interest every six months. In other words, the balance in a bank account is multiplied by a factor of 1.025 every six months.

$$\text{Present value of first payment, in millions of dollars} = 1.5$$

Since the second payment is made six months in the future

$$\text{Present value of second payment, in millions of dollars} = \frac{1.5}{(1 + .025)^1} = \frac{1.5}{1.025}$$

The third payment is made two six month periods, or one year in the future, so

$$\text{Present value of third payment, in millions of dollars} = \frac{1.5}{(1.025)^2}$$

Similarly, the last payment is made 19 six month periods, or nine and a half years in the future, so

$$\text{Present value of twentieth payment, in millions of dollars} = \frac{1.5}{(1.025)^{19}}$$

Thus, in millions of dollars,

$$\text{Total present value} = 1.5 + \frac{1.5}{(1.025)^1} + \frac{1.5}{(1.025)^2} + \cdots + \frac{1.5}{(1.025)^{19}}$$

This is a finite geometric series with $x = \frac{1}{1.025}$ and sum

$$\text{Total present value of contract in millions of dollars} = \frac{1.5\left(1 - \left(\frac{1}{1.025}\right)^{20}\right)}{1 - \frac{1}{1.025}}$$

Evaluating this expression shows that the total present value of the contract is about \$24.0 million.

The present value of ten \$3 million payments, one per year, if the interest rate is 5% per year, compounded annually, is shown to be \$24.3 million, on page 622. Thus the initial investment that the New York Knicks need to make in order to achieve the same dollar result (\$30 million) is lower for twice yearly compounding than for annual compounding at the same nominal rate. The Knicks gain, but Ewing loses, for he only gets half his annual pay at the first of every year. He must wait 6 months to get the second half.

27. (a) On the night of December 31, 1999,

First deposit will have grown to $2(1.04)^7$ million dollars
Second deposit will have grown to $2(1.04)^6$ million dollars
$\cdots$
Most recent deposit (Jan.1, 1999) will have grown to $2(1.04)$ million dollars

Thus

$$\begin{aligned}
\text{Total amount} &= 2(1.04)^7 + 2(1.04)^6 + \cdots + 2(1.04) \\
&= 2(1.04)\underbrace{(1 + 1.04 + \cdots + (1.04)^6)}_{\text{finite geometric series}} \\
&= 2(1.04)\left(\frac{1 - (1.04)^7}{1 - 1.04}\right) \\
&= 16.43 \text{ million dollars}
\end{aligned}$$

(b) Notice that if 10 payments are made, there are 9 years between the first and the last. On the day of the last payment:

First deposit will have grown to $2(1.04)^9$ million dollars
Second deposit will have grown to $2(1.04)^8$ million dollars
$\cdots$
Last deposit will be 2 million dollars

Therefore

$$\begin{aligned}
\text{Total amount} &= 2(1.04)^9 + 2(1.04)^8 + \cdots + 2 \\
&= 2\underbrace{(1 + 1.04 + (1.04)^2 + \cdots (1.04)^9)}_{\text{finite geometric series}} \\
&= 2\left(\frac{1 - (1.04)^{10}}{1 - 1.04}\right) \\
&= 24.01 \text{ million dollars}
\end{aligned}$$

(c)   In part (b) we found the future value of the contract 9 years in the future. Thus

$$\text{Present Value} = \frac{24.01}{(1.04)^9} = 16.87 \text{ million dollars}$$

Alternatively, we can calculate the present value of each of the payments separately:

$$\text{Present Value} = 2 + \frac{2}{1.04} + \frac{2}{(1.04)^2} + \cdots + \frac{2}{(1.04)^9}$$

$$= 2 \left(\frac{1 - (1/1.04)^{10}}{1 - 1/1.04} \right) = 16.87 \text{ million dollars}$$

Notice that the present value of the contract ($16.87 million) is considerably less than the face value of the contract, $20 million.

28.

$$\text{Total present value, in dollars} = 1000 + 1000e^{-0.04} + 1000e^{-0.04(2)} + 1000e^{-0.04(3)} + \cdots$$

$$= 1000 + 1000(e^{-0.04}) + 1000(e^{-0.04})^2 + 1000(e^{-0.04})^3 + \cdots$$

This is an infinite geometric series with $a = 1000$ and $x = e^{(-0.04)}$, and sum

$$\text{Total present value, in dollars} = \frac{1000}{1 - e^{-0.04}} = 25{,}503.$$

29.   A person should expect to pay the present value of the bond on the day it is bought.

$$\text{Present value of first payment} = \frac{10}{1.04}$$

$$\text{Present value of second payment} = \frac{10}{(1.04)^2} \text{ and so on.}$$

Therefore,

$$\text{Total present value} = \frac{10}{1.04} + \frac{10}{(1.04)^2} + \frac{10}{(1.04)^3} + \cdots$$

This is a geometric series with $a = \dfrac{10}{1.04}$ and $x = \dfrac{1}{1.04}$, so

$$\text{Total present value} = \frac{\frac{10}{1.04}}{1 - \frac{1}{1.04}} = \pounds 250.$$

30.

$$\text{Present value of first coupon} = \frac{50}{1.06}$$

$$\text{Present value of second coupon} = \frac{50}{(1.06)^2}, \text{ etc.}$$

$$\text{Total present value} = \underbrace{\frac{50}{1.06} + \frac{50}{(1.06)^2} + \cdots + \frac{50}{(1.06)^{10}}}_{\text{coupons}} + \underbrace{\frac{1000}{(1.06)^{10}}}_{\text{principal}}$$

$$= \frac{50}{1.06}\left(1 + \frac{1}{1.06} + \cdots + \frac{1}{(1.06)^9}\right) + \frac{1000}{(1.06)^{10}}$$

$$= \frac{50}{1.06}\left(\frac{1 - \left(\frac{1}{1.06}\right)^{10}}{1 - \frac{1}{1.06}}\right) + \frac{1000}{(1.06)^{10}}$$

$$= 368.004 + 558.395$$

$$= \$926.40$$

31.

$$\text{Present value of first coupon} = \frac{50}{1.04}$$

$$\text{Present value of second coupon} = \frac{50}{(1.04)^2}, \text{etc.}$$

$$\text{Total present value} = \underbrace{\frac{50}{1.04} + \frac{50}{(1.04)^2} + \cdots + \frac{50}{(1.04)^{10}}}_{\text{coupons}} + \underbrace{\frac{1000}{(1.04)^{10}}}_{\text{principal}}$$

$$= \frac{50}{1.04}\left(1 + \frac{1}{1.04} + \cdots + \frac{1}{(1.04)^9}\right) + \frac{1000}{(1.04)^{10}}$$

$$= \frac{50}{1.04}\left(\frac{1 - \left(\frac{1}{1.04}\right)^{10}}{1 - \frac{1}{1.04}}\right) + \frac{1000}{(1.04)^{10}}$$

$$= 405.545 + 675.564$$

$$= \$1081.11.$$

32. (a)

$$\text{Present value of first coupon} = \frac{50}{1.05}$$

$$\text{Present value of second coupon} = \frac{50}{(1.05)^2}, \text{etc.}$$

$$\text{Total present value} = \underbrace{\frac{50}{1.05} + \frac{50}{(1.05)^2} + \cdots + \frac{50}{(1.05)^{10}}}_{\text{coupons}} + \underbrace{\frac{1000}{(1.05)^{10}}}_{\text{principal}}$$

$$= \frac{50}{1.05}\left(1 + \frac{1}{1.05} + \cdots + \frac{1}{(1.05)^9}\right) + \frac{1000}{(1.05)^{10}}$$

$$= \frac{50}{1.05}\left(\frac{1 - \left(\frac{1}{1.05}\right)^{10}}{1 - \frac{1}{1.05}}\right) + \frac{1000}{(1.05)^{10}}$$

$$= 386.087 + 613.913$$

$$= \$1000.$$

(b) When interest rate is 5%, the present value equals the principal.

(c) When the interest rate is more than 5%, the present value is smaller, than it is when interest is 5% and must therefore be less than the principal. Since the bond will sell for around its present value, it will sell for less than the principal; hence the description *trading at discount.*

(d) When the interest rate is less than 5%, the present value is more than the principal. Hence the bound will be selling for more than the principal, and is described as *trading at a premium.*

33. (a)

$$\text{Total amount of money deposited} = 100 + 92 + 84.64 + \cdots$$

$$= 100 + 100(0.92) + 100(0.92)^2 + \cdots$$

$$= \frac{100}{1 - 0.92} = 1250 \quad \text{dollars}$$

(b) Credit multiplier $= 1250/100 = 12.50$

The 12.50 is the factor by which the bank has increased its deposits, from \$100 to \$1250.

34. (a) p^2

(b) There are two ways to do this. One way is to compute your opponent's probability of winning two in a row, which is $(1 - p)^2$. Then the probability that neither of you win the next points is:

$$1 - (\text{Probability you win next two} + \text{Probability opponent wins next two})$$

$$= 1 - (p^2 + (1 - p)^2)$$

$$= 1 - (p^2 + 1 - 2p + p^2)$$

$$= 2p^2 - 2p$$

$$= 2p(1 - p)$$

The other way to compute this is to observe either you win the first point and lose the second or vice versa. Both have probability $p(1 - p)$, so the probability you split the points is $2p(1 - p)$.

(c)

$$\text{Probability} = (\text{Probability of splitting next two}) \cdot (\text{Probability of winning two after that})$$

$$= 2p(1 - p)p^2$$

(d)

$$\text{Probability} = (\text{Probability of winning next two}) + (\text{Probability of splitting next two,}$$

winning two after that)

$$= p^2 + 2p(1 - p)p^2$$

(e)   The probability is:

w = (Probability of winning first two)
 + (Probability of splitting first two)·(Probability of winning next two)
 + (Prob. of split. first two)·(Prob. of split. next two)·(Prob. of winning next two)
 + $\cdots$
$= p^2 + 2p(1 - p)p^2 + \big(2p(1 - p)\big)^2 p^2 + \cdots$

This is an infinite geometric series with $a = p^2$ and $x = 2p(1 - p)$. Therefore the probability of winning is

$$w = \frac{p^2}{1 - 2p(1 - p)}$$

(f)   For $p = 0.5$, $w = \frac{(0.5)^2}{1 - 2(0.5)(1 - (0.5))} = 0.5$. This is what we would expect. If you and your opponent are equally likely to score the next point, you and your opponent are equally likely to win the next game.

For $p = 0.6$, $w = \frac{(0.6)^2}{1 - 2(0.6)(0.4)} = 0.69$. Here your probability of winning the next point has been magnified to a probability 0.69 of winning the game. Thus it gives the better player an advantage to have to win by two points, rather than the "sudden death" of winning by just one point. This makes sense: when you have to win by two, the stronger player always gets a second chance to overcome the weaker player's winning the first point on a "fluke."

For $p = 0.7$, $w = \frac{(0.7)^2}{1 - 2(0.7)(0.3)} = 0.84$. Again, the stronger player's probability of winning is magnified.

For $p = 0.4$, $w = \frac{(0.4)^2}{1 - 2(0.4)(0.6)} = 0.31$. We already computed that for $p = 0.6$, $w = 0.69$. Thus the value for w when $p = 0.4$, should be the same as the probability of your opponent winning for $p = 0.6$, namely $1 - 0.69 = 0.31$.

35. (a)

S = (Prob. you score first point)

   +(Prob. you lose first point, your opponent loses the next,
      you win the next)

   +(Prob. you lose a point, opponent loses, you lose,
      opponent loses, you win)

   + · · ·

= (Prob. you score first point)

   +(Prob. you lose)·(Prob. opponent loses)·(Prob. you win)

   +(Prob. you lose)·(Prob. opponent loses)·(Prob. you lose)

   ·(Prob. opponent loses)·(Prob. you win)+ · · ·

$$= p + (1-p)(1-q)p + \left((1-p)^2(1-q)\right)^2 p + \cdots$$

$$= \frac{p}{1-(1-p)(1-q)}$$

(b) Since S is your probability of winning the next point, we can use the formula computed in Problem 34 for winning two points in a row, thereby winning the game:

$$w = \frac{S^2}{1-2S(1-S)}$$

(i) When $p = 0.5$ and $q = 0.5$, $S = \dfrac{0.5}{1-(0.5)(0.5)} = 0.67$.

Therefore $w = \dfrac{S^2}{1-2S(1-S)} = \dfrac{(0.67)^2}{1-2(0.67)(1-0.67)} = 0.80$.

(ii) When $p = 0.6$ and $q = 0.5$, $S = \dfrac{0.6}{1-(0.4)(0.5)} = 0.75$ and

$w = \dfrac{(0.75)^2}{1-2(0.75)(1-0.75)} = 0.9$.

10.5 SOLUTIONS

1. (a) The Taylor polynomial of degree 0 about $t = 0$ for $f(t) = e^t$ is simply $f(0) = 1$. Since $e^t \geq 1$ on $[0, 0.5]$, the approximation is an underestimate.

   (b) Using the zero degree error bound, if $|f'(t)| \leq M$ for $0 \leq t \leq 0.5$, then

   $$|E_0| \leq M \cdot |t| \leq M(0.5).$$

   Since $|f'(t)| = |e^t| = e^t$ is increasing on $[0, 0.5]$,

   $$|f'(t)| \leq e^{0.5} < \sqrt{3} \approx 1.732.$$

Therefore

$$|E_0| \leq (1.732)(0.5) = 0.8666.$$

(Note: By looking at a graph of $f(t)$ and its 0th degree approximation, it is easy to see that the greatest error occurs when $t = 0.5$, and the error is $e^{0.5} - 1 \approx 0.65 < 0.866$. So our error bound works.)

2. (a) The second-degree Taylor polynomial for $f(t) = e^t$ is $P_2(t) = 1 + t + t^2/2$. Since the full expansion of $e^t = 1 + t + t^2/2 + t^3/6 + t^4/24 + \cdots$ is clearly larger than $P_2(t)$ for $t > 0$, $P_2(t)$ is an underestimate on $[0, 0.5]$.

    (b) Using the second-degree error bound, if $|f^{(3)}(t)| \leq M$ for $0 \leq t \leq 0.5$, then

$$|E_2| \leq \frac{M}{3!} \cdot |t|^3 \leq \frac{M(0.5)^3}{6}.$$

Since $|f^{(3)}(t)| = e^t$, and e^t is increasing on $[0, 0.5]$,

$$f^{(3)}(t) \leq e^{0.5} < \sqrt{3} \approx 1.732.$$

So

$$|E_2| \leq \frac{(1.732)(0.5)^3}{6} \approx 0.036.$$

3. (a) θ is the first degree approximation of $f(\theta) = \sin \theta$.
    $P_1(\theta) = \theta$ is an overestimate for $0 < \theta \leq 1$, and is an underestimate for $-1 \leq \theta < 0$. (This can be seen easily from a graph.)

    (b) Using the first degree error bound, if $|f^{(2)}(\theta)| \leq M$ for $-1 \leq \theta \leq 1$, then

$$|E_1| \leq \frac{M \cdot |\theta|^2}{2} \leq \frac{M}{2}.$$

For what value of M is $|f^{(2)}(\theta)| \leq M$ for $-1 \leq \theta \leq 1$? Well, $|f^{(2)}(\theta)| = |-\sin \theta| \leq 1$. So $|E_1| \leq \frac{1}{2} = 0.5$. This error estimate is very large and not particularly useful.

4. (a) $\theta - \dfrac{\theta^3}{3!}$ is the third degree Taylor approximation of $f(\theta) = \sin \theta$.
    $P_3(\theta)$ is an underestimate for $0 < \theta \leq 1$, and is an overestimate for $-1 \leq \theta < 0$. (This can be checked with a calculator.)

    (b) Using the third degree error bound, if $|f^{(4)}(\theta)| \leq M$ for $-1 \leq \theta \leq 1$, then

$$|E_3| \leq \frac{M \cdot |\theta|^4}{4!} \leq \frac{M}{24}.$$

For what value of M is $|f^{(4)}(\theta)| \leq M$ for $-1 \leq \theta \leq 1$? $f^{(4)}(\theta) = \sin \theta$. $|\sin \theta| \leq 1$. Therefore,

$$|E_3| \leq \frac{1}{24} \approx 0.042.$$

5. Let $f(x) = \tan x$. The error bound for the Taylor approximation of degree three for $f(1) = \tan 1$ about $x = 0$ is:

$$|E_3| = |f(1) - P_3(x)| \leq \frac{M \cdot |1 - 0|^4}{4!} = \frac{M}{24}$$

where $|f^{(4)}(x)| \leq M$ for $0 \leq x \leq 1$. Now, $f^{(4)}(x) = \frac{16 \sin x}{\cos^3 x} + \frac{24 \sin^3 x}{\cos^5 x}$. From a graph of $f^{(4)}(x)$, we see that $f^{(4)}(x)$ is increasing for x between 0 and 1. Thus,

$$|f^{(4)}(x)| \leq |f^{(4)}(1)| \approx 396,$$

so

$$|E_3| \leq \frac{396}{24} = 16.5.$$

This is not a very helpful error bound! The reason the error bound is so huge is that $x = 1$ is getting near the vertical asymptote of the tangent graph, and the fourth derivative is enormous there.

6. Let $f(x) = (1 - x)^{\frac{1}{3}}$, so $f(0.5) = (0.5)^{\frac{1}{3}}$. The error bound in the Taylor approximation of degree 3 for $f(0.5) = 0.5^{\frac{1}{3}}$ about $x = 0$ is:

$$|E_3| = |f(0.5) - P_3(0.5)| \leq \frac{M \cdot |0.5 - 0|^4}{4!} = \frac{M(0.5)^4}{24},$$

where $|f^{(4)}(x)| \leq M$ for $0 \leq x \leq 0.5$. Now, $f^{(4)}(x) = -\frac{80}{81}(1 - x)^{-\frac{11}{3}}$. By looking at the graph of $(1 - x)^{-\frac{11}{3}}$, we see that $|f^{(4)}(x)|$ is maximized for x between 0 and 0.5 when $x = 0.5$. Thus,

$$|f^{(4)}| \leq \frac{80}{81}\left(\frac{1}{2}\right)^{-\frac{11}{3}} = \frac{80}{81} \cdot 2^{\frac{11}{3}},$$

so

$$|E_3| \leq \frac{80 \cdot 2^{11/3} \cdot (0.5)^4}{81 \cdot 24} \approx 0.033.$$

7. Let $f(x) = \ln(1 + x)$. The error bound in the Taylor approximation of degree 3 about $x = 0$ is:

$$|E_4| = |f(0.5) - P_3(0.5)| \leq \frac{M \cdot |0.5 - 0|^4}{4!} = \frac{M(0.5)^4}{24},$$

where $|f^{(4)}(x)| \leq M$ for $0 \leq x \leq 0.5$. Since $f^{(4)}(x) = \frac{3!}{(1+x)^4}$ and the denominator attains its minimum when $x = 0$, we have $|f^{(4)}(x)| \leq 3!$, so

$$|E_4| \leq \frac{3! (0.5)^4}{24} \approx 0.016.$$

8.   Let $f(x) = (1 + x)^{-\frac{1}{2}} = \frac{1}{\sqrt{1+x}}$. The error bound for the Taylor approximation of degree three for $f(2) = \frac{1}{\sqrt{3}}$ about $x = 0$ is:

$$|E_3| = |f(2) - P_3(2)| \leq \frac{M \cdot |2 - 0|^4}{4!} = \frac{M \cdot 2^4}{24},$$

where $|f^{(4)}| \leq M$ for $0 \leq x \leq 2$. Since $f^{(4)}(x) = \frac{105}{16}(1 + x)^{-\frac{9}{2}}$, we see that if x is between 0 and 2, $|f^{(4)}x)| \leq \frac{105}{16}$. Thus,

$$|E_3| \leq \frac{105}{16} \cdot \frac{2^4}{24} = \frac{105}{24} = 4.375.$$

Again, this is not a very helpful bound on the error, but that is to be expected as the Taylor series does not converge at $x = 2$. (At $x = 2$, we are outside the interval of convergence.)

9.   The maximum possible error for the nth degree Taylor polynomial about $x = 0$ approximating $\cos x$ is $|E_n| \leq \frac{M \cdot |x-0|^{n+1}}{(n+1)!}$, where $|\cos^{(n+1)} x| \leq M$ for $0 \leq x \leq 1$. Now the derivatives of $\cos x$ are simply $\cos x, \sin x, -\cos x$, and $-\sin x$. The largest magnitude these ever take is 1, so $|\cos^{(n+1)}(x)| \leq 1$, and thus $|E_n| \leq \frac{|x|^{n+1}}{(n+1)!} \leq \frac{1}{(n+1)!}$. The same argument works for $\sin x$.

10.   By the results of Problem 9, if we approximate $\cos 1$ using the nth degree polynomial, the error is at most $\frac{1}{(n+1)!}$. For the answer to be correct to four decimal places, the error must be less than 0.00005. Thus, the first n such that $\frac{1}{(n+1)!} < 0.00005$ will work. In particular, when $n = 7$, $\frac{1}{8!} = \frac{1}{40370} < 0.00005$, so the 7th degree Taylor polynomial will give the desired result. For six decimal places, we need $\frac{1}{(n+1)!} < 0.0000005$. Since $n = 9$ works, the 9th degree Taylor polynomial is sufficient.

11.

$$\sin x = x - \frac{x^3}{3!} + \frac{x^5}{5!} - \cdots$$

Write the error in approximating $\sin x$ by the Taylor polynomial of degree $n = 2k + 1$ as E_n so that

$$\sin x = x - \frac{x^3}{3!} + \frac{x^5}{5!} - \cdots (-1)^k \frac{x^{2k+1}}{(2k + 1)!} + E_n.$$

(Notice that $(-1)^k = 1$ if k is even and $(-1)^k = -1$ if k is odd.) We want to show that if x is fixed, $E_n \to 0$ as $k \to \infty$. Since $f(x) = \sin x$, all the derivatives of $f(x)$ are $\pm \sin x$ or $\pm \cos x$, so we have for all n and all x

$$|f^{(n+1)}(x)| \leq 1.$$

Using the bound on the error given in the text on page 631, we see that

$$|E_n| \leq \frac{1}{(2k + 2)!} |x|^{2k+2}.$$

By the argument in the text on page 633, we know that for all x,

$$\frac{|x|^{2k+2}}{(2k+2)!} = \frac{|x|^{n+1}}{(n+1)!} \to 0 \quad \text{as} \quad n \to \infty.$$

Thus the Taylor series for $\sin x$ does converge to $\sin x$ for every x.

12.

$$\cos x = 1 - \frac{x^2}{2!} + \frac{x^4}{4!} - \frac{x^6}{6!} + \cdots$$

Write the error in approximating $\cos x$ by the Taylor polynomial of degree $n = 2k$ as E_n so that

$$\cos x = 1 - \frac{x^2}{2!} + \frac{x^4}{4!} - \frac{x^6}{6!} + \cdots (-1)^k \frac{x^{2k}}{(2k)!} + E_n.$$

(Notice that $(-1)^k = 1$ if k is even and $(-1)^k = -1$ if k is odd.) We want to show that if x is fixed, $E_n \to 0$ as $k \to \infty$. Since $f(x) = \cos x$, all the derivatives of $f(x)$ are $\pm \sin x$ or $\pm \cos x$, so we have for all n and all x

$$|f^{(n+1)}(x)| \le 1.$$

Using the bound on the error given in the text on page 631, we see that

$$|E_n| \le \frac{1}{(2k+1)!} |x|^{2k+1}.$$

By the argument in the text on page 633, we know that for all x,

$$\frac{|x|^{2k+1}}{(2k+1)!} = \frac{|x|^{n+1}}{(n+1)!} \to 0 \quad \text{as} \quad n \to \infty.$$

Thus the Taylor series for $\cos x$ does converge to $\cos x$ for every x.

13. (a)

TABLE 10.1 $E_1 = \sin x - x$

x	$\sin x$	E
-0.5	-0.4794	0.0206
-0.4	-0.3894	0.0106
-0.3	-0.2955	0.0045
-0.2	-0.1987	0.0013
-0.1	-0.0998	0.0002

TABLE 10.2 $E_1 = \sin x - x$

x	$\sin x$	E
0	0	0
0.1	0.0998	-0.0002
0.2	0.1987	-0.0013
0.3	0.2955	-0.0045
0.4	0.3894	-0.0106
0.5	0.4794	-0.0206

(b)   See answer to part (a) above.

(c)

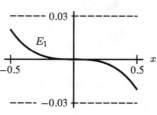

Figure 10.3

The fact that the graph of E_1 lies between the horizontal lines at ± 0.03 in Figure 10.3 shows that $|E_1| < 0.03$ for $-0.5 \leq x \leq 0.5$.

14. (a)

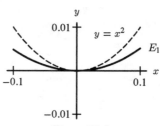

Figure 10.4

The graph of E_1 looks like a parabola. Since the graph of E_1 is sandwiched between the graph of $y = x^2$ and the x axis so

$$|E_1| \leq x^2 \quad \text{for} \quad |x| \leq 0.1.$$

(b)

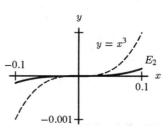

Figure 10.5

The graph of E_2 looks like a cubic, sandwiched between the graph of $y = x^3$ and the x axis,

$$|E_2| \leq x^3 \quad \text{for} \quad |x| \leq 0.1.$$

(c)   Using the Taylor expansion

$$e^x = 1 + x + \frac{x^2}{2!} + \frac{x^3}{3!} + \cdots$$

we see that

$$E_1 = e^x - (1+x) = \frac{x^2}{2!} + \frac{x^3}{3!} + \frac{x^4}{4!} + \cdots.$$

Thus for small x, the $x^2/2!$ term dominates, so

$$E_1 \approx \frac{x^2}{2!},$$

and so E_1 is approximately a quadratic.
Similarly

$$E_2 = e^x - (1 + x + \frac{x^2}{2}) = \frac{x^3}{3!} + \frac{x^4}{4!} + \cdots.$$

Thus for small x, the $x^3/3!$ term dominates, so

$$E_2 \approx \frac{x^3}{3!}$$

and so E_2 is approximately a cubic.

15.

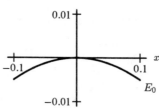

Figure 10.6

The graph of E_0 looks like a parabola, and the graph shows

$$|E_0| < 0.01 \quad \text{for} \quad |x| \leq 0.1.$$

Since

$$\cos x = 1 - \frac{x^2}{2!} + \frac{x^4}{4!} - \frac{x^6}{6!} + \cdots,$$

$$E_0 = \cos x - 1 = -\frac{x^2}{2!} + \frac{x^4}{4!} - \frac{x^6}{6!} + \cdots.$$

So, for small x,

$$E_0 \approx -\frac{x^2}{2},$$

and therefore the graph of E_0 is parabolic.

10.6 SOLUTIONS

1. Yes.

2. No. Terms should be of the form $\cos nx$ not $\cos^n x$.

3. No.

4. Yes.

5. (a) (i) The graph of $y = \sin x + \frac{1}{3}\sin 3x$ looks like

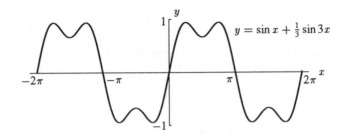

(ii) The graph of $y = \sin x + \frac{1}{3}\sin 3x + \frac{1}{5}\sin 5x$ looks like

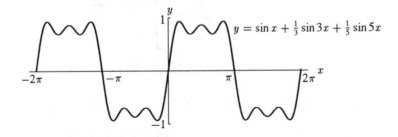

(b) Following the pattern, we add the term $\frac{1}{7}\sin 7x$.

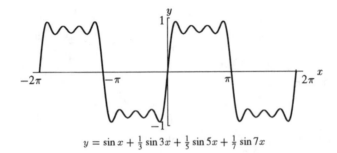

$$y = \sin x + \frac{1}{3}\sin 3x + \frac{1}{5}\sin 5x + \frac{1}{7}\sin 7x$$

(c) The equation is

$$f(x) = \begin{cases} \vdots & \vdots \\ 1 & -2\pi \le x < -\pi \\ -1 & -\pi \le x < 0 \\ 1 & 0 \le x < \pi \\ -1 & \pi \le x < 2\pi \\ \vdots & \vdots \end{cases}$$

The square wave function is not continuous at $x = 0,\ \pm\pi,\ \pm 2\pi,\ \dots$

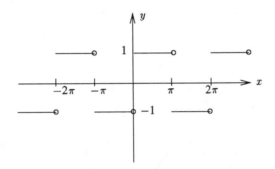

6.

$$a_0 = \frac{1}{2\pi} \int_{-\pi}^{\pi} f(x)\,dx = \frac{1}{2\pi} \left[\int_{-\pi}^{0} -1\,dx + \int_{0}^{\pi} 1\,dx \right] = 0$$

$$a_1 = \frac{1}{\pi} \int_{-\pi}^{\pi} f(x)\cos x\,dx = \frac{1}{\pi} \left[\int_{-\pi}^{0} -\cos x\,dx + \int_{0}^{\pi} \cos x\,dx \right]$$

$$= \frac{1}{\pi} \left[-\sin x \Big|_{-\pi}^{0} + \sin x \Big|_{0}^{\pi} \right] = 0.$$

Similarly, a_2 and a_3 are both 0.
(In fact, notice $f(x)\cos nx$ is an odd function, so $\int_{-\pi}^{\pi} f(x)\cos nx = 0$.)

$$b_1 = \frac{1}{\pi} \int_{-\pi}^{\pi} f(x)\sin x\,dx = \frac{1}{\pi} \left[\int_{-\pi}^{0} -\sin x\,dx + \int_{0}^{\pi} \sin x\,dx \right]$$

$$= \frac{1}{\pi} \left[\cos x \Big|_{-\pi}^{0} + (-\cos x) \Big|_{0}^{\pi} \right] = \frac{4}{\pi}.$$

$$b_2 = \frac{1}{\pi} \int_{-\pi}^{\pi} f(x)\sin 2x\,dx = \frac{1}{\pi} \left[\int_{-\pi}^{0} -\sin 2x\,dx + \int_{0}^{\pi} \sin 2x\,dx \right]$$

$$= \frac{1}{\pi}\left[\frac{1}{2}\cos 2x\Big|_{-\pi}^{0} + (-\frac{1}{2}\cos 2x)\Big|_{0}^{\pi}\right] = 0.$$

$$b_3 = \frac{1}{\pi}\int_{-\pi}^{\pi} f(x)\sin 3x\, dx = \frac{1}{\pi}\left[\int_{-\pi}^{0} -\sin 3x\, dx + \int_{0}^{\pi}\sin 3x\, dx\right]$$

$$= \frac{1}{\pi}\left[\frac{1}{3}\cos 3x\Big|_{-\pi}^{0} + (-\frac{1}{3}\cos 3x)\Big|_{0}^{\pi}\right] = \frac{4}{3\pi}.$$

Thus, $F_1(x) = F_2(x) = \frac{4}{\pi}\sin x$ and $F_3(x) = \frac{4}{\pi}\sin x + \frac{4}{3\pi}\sin 3x$.

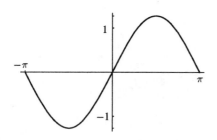

$F_1(x) = F_2(x) = \frac{4}{\pi}\sin x$

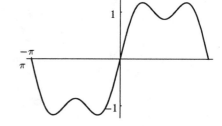

$F_3(x) = \frac{4}{\pi}\sin x + \frac{4}{3\pi}\sin 3x$

7. First,

$$a_0 = \frac{1}{2\pi}\int_{-\pi}^{\pi} f(x)\, dx = \frac{1}{2\pi}\left[\int_{-\pi}^{0} -x\, dx + \int_{0}^{\pi} x\, dx\right] = \frac{1}{2\pi}\left[-\frac{x^2}{2}\Big|_{-\pi}^{0} + \frac{x^2}{2}\Big|_{0}^{\pi}\right] = \frac{\pi}{2}.$$

To find the a_i's, we use the integral table. For $n \geq 1$,

$$a_n = \frac{1}{\pi}\int_{-\pi}^{\pi} f(x)\cos(nx)\, dx = \frac{1}{\pi}\left[\int_{-\pi}^{0} -x\cos(nx)\, dx + \int_{0}^{\pi} x\cos(nx)\, dx\right]$$

$$= \frac{1}{\pi}\left[\left(-\frac{x}{n}\sin(nx) - \frac{1}{n^2}\cos(nx)\right)\Big|_{-\pi}^{0}\right.$$

$$+ \left(\frac{x}{n} \sin(nx) + \frac{1}{n^2} \cos(nx) \right) \Big|_0^\pi \Big]$$

$$= \frac{1}{\pi} \left(-\frac{1}{n^2} + \frac{1}{n^2} \cos(-n\pi) + \frac{1}{n^2} \cos(n\pi) - \frac{1}{n^2} \right)$$

$$= \frac{2}{\pi n^2} (\cos n\pi - 1)$$

Thus, $a_1 = -\frac{4}{\pi}$, $a_2 = 0$, and $a_3 = -\frac{4}{9\pi}$.

To find the b_i's, note that $f(x)$ is even, so for $n \geq 1$, $f(x)\sin(nx)$ is odd. Thus, $\int_{-\pi}^{\pi} f(x)\sin(nx) = 0$, so all the b_i's are 0.

Thus $F_1 = F_2 = \frac{\pi}{2} - \frac{4}{\pi}\cos x$, $F_3 = \frac{\pi}{2} - \frac{4}{\pi}\cos x - \frac{4}{9\pi}\cos 3x$.

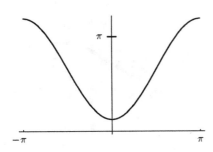 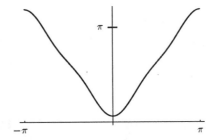

$$F_1(x) = F_2(x) = \frac{\pi}{2} - \frac{4}{\pi}\cos x \qquad\qquad F_3(x) = \frac{\pi}{2} - \frac{4}{\pi}\cos x - \frac{4}{9\pi}\cos 3x$$

8. To find the nth Fourier polynomial, we must come up with a general formula for a_n and b_n. First, we find a_0.

$$a_0 = \frac{1}{2\pi} \int_{-\pi}^{\pi} g(x)\, dx = \frac{1}{2\pi} \int_{-\pi}^{\pi} x\, dx = \frac{1}{2\pi} \left[\frac{x^2}{2} \Big|_{-\pi}^{\pi} \right] = 0.$$

Now we use the integral table (formulas III-15 and III-16) to find a_n and b_n for $n \geq 1$.

$$a_n = \frac{1}{\pi} \int_{-\pi}^{\pi} x \cos nx\, dx = \frac{1}{\pi} \left(\frac{x}{n}\sin(nx) + \frac{1}{n^2}\cos(nx) \right) \Big|_{-\pi}^{\pi}$$

$$= \frac{1}{\pi} \left(\frac{1}{n^2}\cos(n\pi) - \frac{1}{n^2}\cos(-n\pi) \right) = 0.$$

(Note that since $x \cos nx$ is odd, we could have deduced that $\int_{-\pi}^{\pi} x \cos nx = 0$.)

$$b_n = \frac{1}{\pi} \int_{-\pi}^{\pi} x \sin nx\, dx = \frac{1}{\pi} \left(-\frac{x}{n}\cos(nx) + \frac{1}{n^2}\sin(nx) \right) \Big|_{-\pi}^{\pi}$$

$$= \frac{1}{\pi}\left(-\frac{\pi}{n}\cos(n\pi) - \frac{\pi}{n}\cos(-n\pi)\right)$$

$$= -\frac{2}{n}\cos(n\pi).$$

Notice that $\cos(n\pi) = (-1)^n$ for all integers n, so $b_n = (-1)^{n+1}\left(\frac{2}{n}\right)$.
Thus the nth Fourier polynomial for g is

$$G_n(x) = \sum_{i=1}^{n}(-1)^{i+1}\frac{2}{i}\sin(ix).$$

In particular, we have the following graphs:

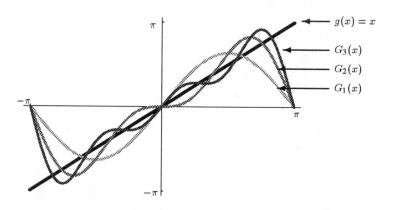

9.   First, we find a_0.

$$a_0 = \frac{1}{2\pi}\int_{-\pi}^{\pi}x^2\,dx = \frac{1}{2\pi}\left(\frac{x^3}{3}\bigg|_{-\pi}^{\pi}\right) = \frac{\pi^2}{3}.$$

To find a_n, $n \geq 1$, we use the integral table (formulas III-15 and III-16)

$$a_n = \frac{1}{\pi}\int_{-\pi}^{\pi}x^2\cos nx\,dx = \frac{1}{\pi}\left[\frac{x^2}{n}\sin(nx) + \frac{2x}{n^2}\cos(nx) - \frac{2}{n^3}\sin(nx)\right]\bigg|_{-\pi}^{\pi}$$

$$= \frac{1}{\pi}\left[\frac{2\pi}{n^2}\cos(n\pi) + \frac{2\pi}{n^2}\cos(-n\pi)\right]$$

$$= \frac{4}{n^2}\cos(n\pi).$$

Again, $\cos(n\pi) = (-1)^n$ for all integers n, so $a_n = (-1)^n \frac{4}{n^2}$. Note that

$$b_n = \frac{1}{\pi}\int_{-\pi}^{\pi} x^2 \sin nx\, dx.$$

x^2 is an even function, and $\sin nx$ is odd, so $x^2 \sin nx$ is odd. Thus $\int_{-\pi}^{\pi} x^2 \sin nx\, dx = 0$, and $b_n = 0$ for all n.

We deduce that the nth Fourier polynomial for f (where $n \geq 1$) is

$$F_n(x) = \frac{\pi^2}{3} + \sum_{i=1}^{n}(-1)^i \frac{4}{i^2}\cos(ix).$$

In particular, we have the following graphs:

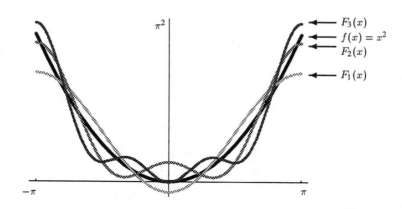

10.

$$a_0 = \frac{1}{2\pi}\int_{-\pi}^{\pi} h(x)\, dx = \frac{1}{2\pi}\int_{0}^{\pi} x\, dx = \frac{\pi}{4}.$$

As in Problem 8, we use the integral table (formulas III-15 and III-16) to find formulas for a_n and b_n.

$$a_n = \frac{1}{\pi} \int_{-\pi}^{\pi} h(x) \cos(nx)\, dx = \frac{1}{\pi} \int_{0}^{\pi} x \cos nx\, dx = \frac{1}{\pi} \left(\frac{x}{n} \sin(nx) + \frac{1}{n^2} \cos(nx) \right)\Big|_{0}^{\pi}$$

$$= \frac{1}{\pi} \left(\frac{1}{n^2} \cos(n\pi) - \frac{1}{n^2} \right)$$

$$= \frac{1}{n^2 \pi} \left(\cos(n\pi) - 1 \right).$$

Note that since $\cos(n\pi) = (-1)^n$, $a_n = 0$ if n is even and $a_n = -\frac{2}{n^2\pi}$ if n is odd.

$$b_n = \frac{1}{\pi} \int_{-\pi}^{\pi} h(x) \cos(nx)\, dx = \frac{1}{\pi} \int_{0}^{\pi} x \sin x\, dx$$

$$= \frac{1}{\pi} \left(-\frac{x}{n} \cos(nx) + \frac{1}{n^2} \sin(nx) \right)\Big|_{0}^{\pi}$$

$$= \frac{1}{\pi} \left(-\frac{\pi}{n} \cos(n\pi) \right)$$

$$= -\frac{1}{n} \cos(n\pi)$$

$$= \frac{1}{n}(-1)^{n+1} \quad \text{if } n \geq 1.$$

We have that the nth Fourier polynomial for h (for $n \geq 1$) is

$$H_n(x) = \frac{\pi}{4} + \sum_{i=1}^{n} \left(\frac{1}{i^2 \pi} \left(\cos(i\pi) - 1 \right) \cdot \cos(ix) + \frac{(-1)^{i+1} \sin(ix)}{i} \right).$$

This can also be written as

$$H_n(x) = \frac{\pi}{4} + \sum_{i=1}^{n} \frac{(-1)^{i+1} \sin(ix)}{i} + \sum_{i=1}^{\left[\frac{n}{2}\right]} \frac{-2}{(2i-1)^2 \pi} \cos((2i-1)x)$$

where $\left[\frac{n}{2}\right]$ denotes the biggest integer smaller than or equal to $\frac{n}{2}$. In particular, we have the following graphs:

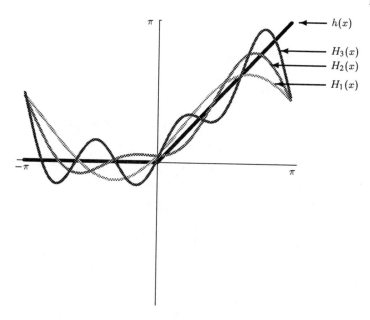

11. Let r_k and s_k be the Fourier coefficients of $Af + Bg$. Then

$$r_0 = \frac{1}{2\pi} \int_{-\pi}^{\pi} \left[Af(x) + Bg(x) \right] dx$$

$$= A\left[\frac{1}{2\pi} \int_{-\pi}^{\pi} f(x)\, dx \right] + B\left[\frac{1}{2\pi} \int_{-\pi}^{\pi} g(x)\, dx \right]$$

$$= Aa_0 + Bc_0.$$

Similarly,

$$r_k = \frac{1}{\pi} \int_{-\pi}^{\pi} \left[Af(x) + Bg(x) \right] \cos(kx)\, dx$$

$$= A\left[\frac{1}{\pi} \int_{-\pi}^{\pi} f(x) \cos(kx)\, dx \right] + B\left[\frac{1}{\pi} \int_{-\pi}^{\pi} g(x) \cos(kx)\, dx \right]$$

$$= Aa_k + Bc_k.$$

And finally,

$$s_k = \frac{1}{\pi} \int_{-\pi}^{\pi} \left[Af(x) + Bg(x) \right] \sin(kx)\, dx$$

$$= A\left[\frac{1}{\pi} \int_{-\pi}^{\pi} f(x) \sin(kx)\, dx \right] + B\left[\frac{1}{\pi} \int_{-\pi}^{\pi} g(x) \sin(kx)\, dx \right]$$

$$= Ac_k + Bd_k.$$

12. If

$$f(x) = \begin{cases} -x & -\pi < x \leq 0 \\ x & 0 < x \leq \pi \end{cases},$$

$$g(x) = x,$$

$$h(x) = \begin{cases} 0 & -\pi < x \leq 0 \\ x & 0 < x \leq \pi \end{cases},$$

then $h(x) = \frac{f(x)+g(x)}{2}$. By Problem 11, if the Fourier coefficients for f are a_k and c_k, and the Fourier coefficients for g are b_k and d_k, then the Fourier coefficients for h must be $\frac{1}{2}(a_k + b_k)$ and $\frac{1}{2}(c_k + d_k)$. Looking back at Problems 7 and 8, we have, for $k \geq 1$,

$$a_0 = \frac{\pi}{2} \qquad\qquad\qquad b_0 = 0$$
$$a_k = \frac{2}{\pi k^2}(\cos(k\pi) - 1) \text{ for } k \geq 1 \ b_k = 0$$
$$c_k = 0 \qquad\qquad\qquad d_k = -\frac{2}{k}\cos(k\pi).$$

Thus the Fourier coefficients for h, which we will denote by r_k and s_k, are, for $k \geq 1$:

$$r_0 = \frac{\pi}{4}, \quad r_k = \frac{1}{\pi k^2}(\cos(k\pi) - 1), \quad s_k = \frac{1}{k}(-1)^{k+1}.$$

Note that this matches our results from Problem 10.

13. We have $f(x) = x, 0 \leq x < 1$. Let $t = 2\pi x - \pi$. Notice that as x varies from 0 to 1, t varies from $-\pi$ to π. Thus if we rewrite the function in terms of t, we can find the Fourier series in terms of t in the usual way. To do this, let $g(t) = f(x) = x = \frac{t+\pi}{2\pi}$ on $-\pi \leq t < \pi$. We now find the fourth degree Fourier polynomial for g.

$$a_o = \frac{1}{2\pi}\int_{-\pi}^{\pi} g(t)\, dt = \frac{1}{2\pi}\int_{-\pi}^{\pi}\frac{t+\pi}{2\pi}\, dt = \frac{1}{(2\pi)^2}\left(\frac{t^2}{2} + \pi t\right)\Big|_{-\pi}^{\pi} = \frac{1}{2}$$

Notice, a_0 is the average value of both f and g. For $n \geq 1$

$$a_n = \frac{1}{\pi}\int_{-\pi}^{\pi}\frac{t+\pi}{2\pi}\cos(nt)\,dt = \frac{1}{2\pi^2}\int_{-\pi}^{\pi}(t\cos(nt) + \pi\cos(nt))dt$$

$$= \frac{1}{2\pi^2}\left[\frac{t}{n}\sin(nt) + \frac{1}{n^2}\cos(nt) + \frac{\pi}{n}\sin(nt)\right]\Big|_{-\pi}^{\pi}$$

$$= 0.$$

$$b_n = \frac{1}{\pi}\int_{-\pi}^{\pi}\frac{t+\pi}{2\pi}\sin(nt)\,dt = \frac{1}{2\pi^2}\int_{-\pi}^{\pi}(t\sin(nt) + \pi\sin(nt))\,dt$$

$$= \frac{1}{2\pi^2}\left[-\frac{t}{n}\cos(nt) + \frac{1}{n^2}\sin(nt) - \frac{\pi}{n}\cos(nt)\right]\Big|_{-\pi}^{\pi}$$

$$= \frac{1}{2\pi^2}(-\frac{4\pi}{n}\cos(\pi n)) = -\frac{2}{\pi n}\cos(\pi n) = \frac{2}{\pi n}(-1)^{n+1}.$$

We get the integrals for a_n and b_n using the integral table (formulas III-15 and III-16).

Thus, the Fourier polynomial of degree 4 for g is:

$$G_4(t) = \frac{1}{2} + \frac{2}{\pi} \sin t - \frac{1}{\pi} \sin 2t + \frac{2}{3\pi} \sin 3t - \frac{1}{2\pi} \sin 4t$$

Now, since $g(t) = f(x)$, the Fourier polynomial of degree 4 for f can be found by replacing t in terms of x again. Thus,

$$F_4(x) = \frac{1}{2} + \frac{2}{\pi} \sin(2\pi x - \pi) - \frac{1}{\pi} \sin(4\pi x - 2\pi) + \frac{2}{3\pi} \sin(6\pi x - 3\pi) - \frac{1}{2\pi} \sin(8\pi x - 4\pi).$$

Now, using the fact that $\sin(x - \pi) = -\sin x$ and $\sin(x - 2\pi) = \sin x$, etc., we have:

$$F_4(x) = \frac{1}{2} - \frac{2}{\pi} \sin(2\pi x) - \frac{1}{\pi} \sin(4\pi x) - \frac{2}{3\pi} \sin(6\pi x) - \frac{1}{2\pi} \sin(8\pi x).$$

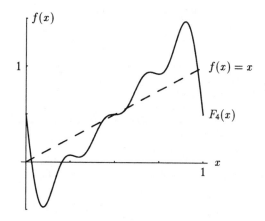

14. Since the period is 2, we make the substitution $t = \pi x - \pi$. Thus, $x = \frac{t+\pi}{\pi}$. We find the Fourier coefficients. Notice that all of the integrals are the same as in Problem 13 except for an extra factor of 2. Thus, $a_0 = 1$, $a_n = 0$, and $b_n = \frac{4}{\pi n}(-1)^{n+1}$, so:

$$G_4(t) = 1 + \frac{4}{\pi} \sin t - \frac{2}{\pi} \sin 2t + \frac{4}{3\pi} \sin 3t - \frac{1}{\pi} \sin 4t$$

Again, we substitute back in to get a Fourier polynomial in terms of x:

$$F_4(x) = 1 + \frac{4}{\pi} \sin(\pi x - \pi) - \frac{2}{\pi} \sin(2\pi x - 2\pi)$$

$$+ \frac{4}{3\pi} \sin(3\pi x - 3\pi) - \frac{1}{\pi} \sin(4\pi x - 4\pi)$$

$$= 1 - \frac{4}{\pi} \sin(\pi x) - \frac{2}{\pi} \sin(2\pi x) - \frac{4}{3\pi} \sin(3\pi x) - \frac{1}{\pi} \sin(4\pi x)$$

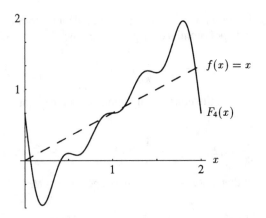

Notice in this case, the terms in our series are $\sin(n\pi x)$, not $\sin(2\pi n x)$, as in Problem 13. In general, the terms will be $\sin(n\frac{2\pi}{b}x)$, where b is the period.

15. (a) The graph of $g(x)$ is

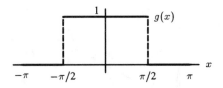

First find the Fourier coefficients: a_0 is the average value of g on $[-\pi, \pi]$ so from the graph, it is clear that

$$a_0 = \frac{1}{2\pi}(\pi \times 1) = \frac{1}{2},$$

or analytically,

$$a_0 = \frac{1}{2\pi}\int_{-\pi}^{\pi} g(x)\, dx = \frac{1}{2\pi}\int_{-\pi/2}^{\pi/2} 1\, dx = \frac{1}{2\pi} x\Big|_{-\pi/2}^{\pi/2} = \frac{1}{2\pi}\left(\frac{\pi}{2} - \left(-\frac{\pi}{2}\right)\right)$$

$$= \frac{1}{2\pi}(\pi) = \frac{1}{2}$$

$$a_k = \frac{1}{\pi}\int_{-\pi}^{\pi} g(x)\cos kx\, dx = \frac{1}{\pi}\int_{-\pi/2}^{\pi/2}\cos kx\, dx = \frac{1}{k\pi}\sin kx\Big|_{-\pi/2}^{\pi/2}$$

$$= \frac{1}{k\pi}\left(\sin\frac{k\pi}{2} - \sin\left(-\frac{k\pi}{2}\right)\right) = \frac{1}{k\pi}\left(2\sin\frac{k\pi}{2}\right)$$

$$b_k = \frac{1}{\pi} \int_{-\pi}^{\pi} g(x) \sin kx \, dx = \frac{1}{\pi} \int_{-\pi/2}^{\pi/2} \sin kx \, dx = -\frac{1}{k\pi} \cos kx \Big|_{-\pi/2}^{\pi/2}$$

$$= -\frac{1}{k\pi} \left(\cos \frac{k\pi}{2} - \cos \left(-\frac{k\pi}{2} \right) \right) = -\frac{1}{k\pi}(0) = 0$$

So,

$$a_1 = \frac{1}{\pi} \left(2 \sin \frac{\pi}{2} \right) = \frac{2}{\pi},$$

$$a_2 = \frac{1}{2\pi} \left(2 \sin \frac{2\pi}{2} \right) = 0$$

$$a_3 = \frac{1}{3\pi} \left(2 \sin \frac{3\pi}{2} \right) = -\frac{2}{3\pi},$$

which gives

$$F_3(x) = \frac{1}{2} + \frac{2}{\pi} \cos x - \frac{2}{3\pi} \cos 3x.$$

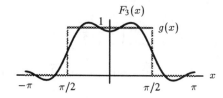

(b)   There are cosines instead sines (but the energy spectrum remains the same).

16.   The signal received on earth is in the form of a periodic function $h(t)$, which can be expanded in a Fourier series

$$h(t) = a_0 + a_1 \cos t + a_2 \cos 2t + a_3 \cos 3t + \cdots$$
$$+ b_1 \sin t + b_2 \sin 2t + b_3 \sin 3t + \cdots$$

If the periodic noise consists of *only* the second and higher harmonics of the Fourier series, then the original signal contributed the fundamental harmonic plus the constant term, i.e.

$$\underbrace{a_0}_{\text{constant term}} + \underbrace{a_1 \cos t + b_1 \sin t}_{\text{fundamental harmonic}} = \underbrace{A \cos t}_{\text{original signal}}$$

In order to find A, we need to find a_0, a_1, and b_1. Looking at the graph of $h(t)$, we see

$$a_0 = \text{average value of } h(t) = \frac{1}{2\pi}(\text{Area above the } x\text{-axis} - \text{Area below the } x\text{-axis})$$

$$= \frac{1}{2\pi} \left[80 \left(\frac{\pi}{2} \right) - \left(50 \left(\frac{\pi}{4} \right) + 30 \left(\frac{\pi}{4} \right) + 30 \left(\frac{\pi}{4} \right) + 50 \left(\frac{\pi}{4} \right) \right) \right]$$

$$= \frac{1}{2\pi} \left[80 \left(\frac{\pi}{2} \right) - 80 \left(\frac{\pi}{2} \right) \right] = \frac{1}{2\pi} \cdot 0 = 0$$

$$a_1 = \frac{1}{\pi} \int_{-\pi}^{\pi} h(t) \cos t \, dt$$

$$= \frac{1}{\pi} \left[\int_{-\pi}^{-3\pi/4} -50 \cos t \, dt + \int_{-3\pi/4}^{-\pi/2} 0 \cos t \, dt + \int_{-\pi/2}^{-\pi/4} -30 \cos t \, dt \right.$$

$$\left. + \int_{-\pi/4}^{\pi/4} 80 \cos t \, dt + \int_{\pi/4}^{\pi/2} -30 \cos t \, dt + \int_{\pi/2}^{3\pi/4} 0 \cos t \, dt + \int_{3\pi/4}^{\pi} -50 \cos t \, dt \right]$$

$$= \frac{1}{\pi} \left[-50 \sin t \Big|_{-\pi}^{-3\pi/4} - 30 \sin t \Big|_{-\pi/2}^{-\pi/4} \right.$$

$$\left. + 80 \sin t \Big|_{-\pi/4}^{\pi/4} - 30 \sin t \Big|_{\pi/4}^{\pi/2} - 50 \sin t \Big|_{3\pi/4}^{\pi} \right]$$

$$= \frac{1}{\pi} \left[-50 \left(-\frac{\sqrt{2}}{2} - 0 \right) - 30 \left(-\frac{\sqrt{2}}{2} - (-1) \right) + 80 \left(\frac{\sqrt{2}}{2} - \left(-\frac{\sqrt{2}}{2} \right) \right) \right.$$

$$\left. - 30 \left(1 - \frac{\sqrt{2}}{2} \right) - 50 \left(0 - \frac{\sqrt{2}}{2} \right) \right]$$

$$= \frac{1}{\pi} [25\sqrt{2} + 15\sqrt{2} - 30 + 40\sqrt{2} + 40\sqrt{2} - 30 + 15\sqrt{2} + 25\sqrt{2}]$$

$$= \frac{1}{\pi} [160\sqrt{2} - 60] = 52.93$$

$$b_1 = \frac{1}{\pi} \int_{-\pi}^{\pi} h(t) \sin t \, dt$$

$$= \frac{1}{\pi} \left[\int_{-\pi}^{-3\pi/4} -50 \sin t \, dt + \int_{-3\pi/4}^{-\pi/2} 0 \sin t \, dt + \int_{-\pi/2}^{-\pi/4} -30 \sin t \, dt \right.$$

$$\left. + \int_{-\pi/4}^{\pi/4} 80 \sin t \, dt + \int_{\pi/4}^{\pi/2} -30 \sin t \, dt + \int_{\pi/2}^{3\pi/4} 0 \sin t \, dt + \int_{3\pi/4}^{\pi} -50 \sin t \, dt \right]$$

$$= \frac{1}{\pi} \left[50 \cos t \Big|_{-\pi}^{-3\pi/4} + 30 \cos t \Big|_{-\pi/2}^{-\pi/4} - 80 \cos t \Big|_{-\pi/4}^{\pi/4} + 30 \cos t \Big|_{\pi/4}^{\pi/2} + 50 \cos t \Big|_{3\pi/4}^{\pi} \right]$$

$$= \frac{1}{\pi} \left[50 \left(-\frac{\sqrt{2}}{2} - (-1) \right) + 30 \left(\frac{\sqrt{2}}{2} - 0 \right) - 80 \left(\frac{\sqrt{2}}{2} - \frac{\sqrt{2}}{2} \right) \right.$$

$$\left. + 30 \left(0 - \frac{\sqrt{2}}{2} \right) + 50 \left(-1 - (-\frac{\sqrt{2}}{2}) \right) \right]$$

$$= \frac{1}{\pi}\left[-25\sqrt{2} + 50 + 15\sqrt{2} - 0 - 15\sqrt{2} - 50 + 25\sqrt{2}\right] = \frac{1}{\pi}(0) = 0$$

Also, we could have just noted that $b_1 = \frac{1}{\pi}\int_{-\pi}^{\pi} h(t)\sin t \, dt = 0$ because $h(t)\sin t$ is an odd function. Substituting in, we get

$$a_0 + a_1\cos t + b_1\sin t = 0 + 52.93\cos t + 0 = A\cos t.$$

So $A = 52.93$.

17. The energy of the function $f(x)$ is

$$E = \frac{1}{\pi}\int_{-\pi}^{\pi}(f(x))^2\,dx = \frac{1}{\pi}\int_{-\pi}^{\pi}x^2\,dx = \frac{1}{3\pi}x^3\Big|_{-\pi}^{\pi}$$

$$= \frac{1}{3\pi}(\pi^3 - (-\pi^3)) = \frac{2\pi^3}{3\pi} = \frac{2}{3}\pi^2 = 6.57974$$

From Problem 7, we know all the b_i's are 0 and $a_0 = \frac{\pi}{2}$, $a_1 = -\frac{4}{\pi}$, $a_2 = 0$, $a_3 = -\frac{4}{9\pi}$. Therefore the energy in the constant term and first three harmonics is

$$A_0^2 + A_1^2 + A_2^2 + A_3^2 = 2a_0^2 + a_1^2 + a_2^2 + a_3^2$$

$$= 2\left(\frac{\pi^2}{4}\right) + \frac{16}{\pi^2} + 0 + \frac{16}{81\pi^2} = 6.57596$$

which means that they contain $\dfrac{6.57596}{6.57974} = 0.99942 \approx 99.942\%$ of the total energy

18. Let $f(x) = a_k\cos kx + b_k\sin kx$. Then the energy of f is given by

$$\frac{1}{\pi}\int_{-\pi}^{\pi}(f(x))^2\,dx = \frac{1}{\pi}\int_{-\pi}^{\pi}(a_k\cos kx + b_k\sin kx)^2\,dx$$

$$= \frac{1}{\pi}\int_{-\pi}^{\pi}(a_k^2\cos^2 kx - 2a_kb_k\cos kx\sin kx + b_k^2\sin^2 kx)\,dx$$

$$= \frac{1}{\pi}\left[a_k^2\int_{-\pi}^{\pi}\cos^2 kx\,dx - 2a_kb_k\int_{-\pi}^{\pi}\cos kx\sin kx\,dx + b_k^2\int_{-\pi}^{\pi}\sin^2 kx\,dx\right]$$

$$= \frac{1}{\pi}\left[a_k^2\pi - 2a_kb_k\cdot 0 + b_k^2\pi\right] = a_k^2 + b_k^2$$

19. The energy spectrum of the flute shows that the first two harmonics have equal energies and contribute the most energy by far. The higher harmonics contribute relatively little energy. In contrast, the energy spectrum of the bassoon shows the comparative weakness of the first two harmonics to the third harmonic which is the strongest component.

20. (a)

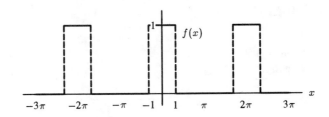

The energy of the pulse train f is

$$E = \frac{1}{\pi} \int_{-\pi}^{\pi} (f(x))^2 \, dx = \frac{1}{\pi} \int_{-1}^{1} 1^2 = \frac{1}{\pi}(1 - (-1)) = \frac{2}{\pi}.$$

Next, find the Fourier coefficients:

$$a_0 = \text{average value of } f \text{ on } [-\pi, \pi] = \frac{1}{2\pi}(\text{ Area}) = \frac{1}{2\pi}(2) = \frac{1}{\pi}$$

$$a_k = \frac{1}{\pi} \int_{-\pi}^{\pi} f(x) \cos kx \, dx = \frac{1}{\pi} \int_{-1}^{1} \cos kx \, dx = \frac{1}{k\pi} \sin kx \Big|_{-1}^{1}$$

$$= \frac{1}{k\pi}(\sin k - \sin(-k)) = \frac{1}{k\pi}(2 \sin k)$$

$$b_k = \frac{1}{\pi} \int_{-\pi}^{\pi} f(x) \sin kx \, dx = \frac{1}{\pi} \int_{-1}^{1} \sin kx \, dx = -\frac{1}{k\pi} \cos kx \Big|_{-1}^{1}$$

$$= -\frac{1}{k\pi}(\cos k - \cos(-k)) = \frac{1}{k\pi}(0) = 0$$

The energy of f contained in the constant term is

$$A_0^2 = 2a_0^2 = 2 \left(\frac{1}{\pi}\right)^2 = \frac{2}{\pi^2}$$

which is

$$\frac{A_0^2}{E} = \frac{2/\pi^2}{2/\pi} = \frac{1}{\pi} \approx 0.3183 = 31.83\% \quad \text{of the total.}$$

The fraction of energy contained in the first harmonic is

$$\frac{A_1^2}{E} = \frac{a_1^2}{E} = \frac{\left(\frac{2 \sin 1}{\pi}\right)^2}{\frac{2}{\pi}} \approx 0.4508 = 45.08\%.$$

The fraction of energy contained in both the constant term and the first harmonic together is

$$\frac{A_0^2}{E} + \frac{A_1^2}{E} \approx 0.7691 = 76.91\%.$$

(b)   The fraction of energy contained in the second harmonic is

$$\frac{A_2^2}{E} = \frac{a_2^2}{E} = \frac{\left(\frac{\sin 2}{\pi}\right)^2}{\frac{2}{\pi}} \approx 0.1316 = 13.16\%$$

so the fraction of energy contained in the constant term and first two harmonics is

$$\frac{A_0^2}{E} + \frac{A_1^2}{E} + \frac{A_2^2}{E} \approx 0.7691 + 0.1316 = 0.9007 = 90.07\%.$$

Therefore, the constant term and the first two harmonics are needed to capture 90% of the energy of f.

(c)

$$F_3(x) = \frac{1}{\pi} + \frac{2\sin 1}{\pi}\cos x + \frac{\sin 2}{\pi}\cos 2x + \frac{2\sin 3}{3\pi}\cos 3x$$

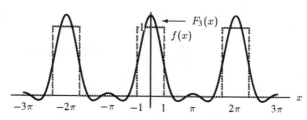

21.   (a)

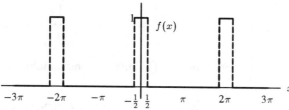

The energy of the pulse train f is

$$E = \frac{1}{\pi}\int_{-\pi}^{\pi} (f(x))^2\, dx = \frac{1}{\pi}\int_{-1/2}^{1/2} 1^2\, dx = \frac{1}{\pi}\left(\frac{1}{2} - \left(-\frac{1}{2}\right)\right) = \frac{1}{\pi}.$$

Next, find the Fourier coefficients:

$$a_0 = \text{average value of } f \text{ on } [-\pi, \pi] = \frac{1}{2\pi}(\text{ Area}) = \frac{1}{2\pi}(1) = \frac{1}{2\pi}$$

$$a_k = \frac{1}{\pi} \int_{-\pi}^{\pi} f(x) \cos kx \, dx = \frac{1}{\pi} \int_{-1/2}^{1/2} \cos kx \, dx = \frac{1}{k\pi} \sin kx \Big|_{-1/2}^{1/2}$$

$$= \frac{1}{k\pi} \left(\sin\left(\frac{k}{2}\right) - \sin\left(-\frac{k}{2}\right) \right) = \frac{1}{k\pi} \left(2\sin\left(\frac{k}{2}\right) \right)$$

$$b_k = \frac{1}{\pi} \int_{-\pi}^{\pi} f(x) \sin kx \, dx = \frac{1}{\pi} \int_{-1/2}^{1/2} \sin kx \, dx = -\frac{1}{k\pi} \cos kx \Big|_{-1/2}^{1/2}$$

$$= -\frac{1}{k\pi} \left(\cos\left(\frac{k}{2}\right) - \cos\left(-\frac{k}{2}\right) \right) = \frac{1}{k\pi}(0) = 0$$

The energy of f contained in the constant term is

$$A_0^2 = 2a_0^2 = 2\left(\frac{1}{2\pi}\right)^2 = \frac{1}{2\pi^2}$$

which is

$$\frac{A_0^2}{E} = \frac{1/2\pi^2}{1/\pi} = \frac{1}{2\pi} \approx 0.159155 = 15.9155\% \quad \text{of the total.}$$

The fraction of energy contained in the first harmonic is

$$\frac{A_1^2}{E} = \frac{a_1^2}{E} = \frac{\left(\frac{2\sin\frac{1}{2}}{\pi}\right)^2}{\frac{1}{\pi}} \approx 0.292653.$$

The fraction of energy contained in both the constant term and the first harmonic together is

$$\frac{A_0^2}{E} + \frac{A_1^2}{E} \approx 0.159155 + 0.292653 = 0.451808\%.$$

(b) The formula for the energy of the kth harmonic is

$$A_k^2 = a_k^2 + b_k^2 = \left(\frac{2\sin\frac{k}{2}}{k\pi}\right)^2 + 0^2 = \frac{4\sin^2\frac{k}{2}}{k^2\pi^2}$$

By graphing it as a continuous function for $k \geq 1$, we see its overall behavior as k gets larger. The energy spectrum for the first five terms is graphed below, as well.

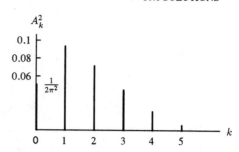

(c) The constant term and the first five harmonics are needed to capture 90% of the energy of f. This was determined by adding the fractions of energy of f contained in each harmonic until the sum reached at least 90% of the total energy of f:

$$\frac{A_0^2}{E} + \frac{A_1^2}{E} + \frac{A_2^2}{E} + \frac{A_3^2}{E} + \frac{A_4^2}{E} + \frac{A_5^2}{E} \approx 90.1995\%$$

(d) $F_5(x) = \frac{1}{2\pi} + \frac{2\sin(\frac{1}{2})}{\pi}\cos x + \frac{\sin 1}{\pi}\cos 2x + \frac{2\sin(\frac{3}{2})}{3\pi}\cos 3x + \frac{\sin 2}{2\pi}\cos 4x + \frac{2\sin(\frac{5}{2})}{5\pi}\cos 5x$

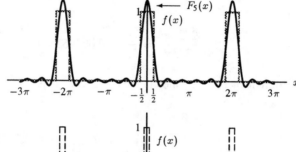

22. (a)

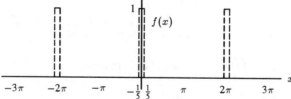

The energy of the pulse train f is

$$E = \frac{1}{\pi}\int_{-\pi}^{\pi}(f(x))^2\,dx = \frac{1}{\pi}\int_{-1/5}^{1/5}1^2\,dx = \frac{1}{\pi}\left(\frac{1}{5} - \left(-\frac{1}{5}\right)\right) = \frac{2}{5\pi}.$$

Next, find the Fourier coefficients:

$$a_0 = \text{average value of } f \text{ on } [-\pi, \pi] = \frac{1}{2\pi}(\text{ Area}) = \frac{1}{2\pi}\left(\frac{2}{5}\right) = \frac{1}{5\pi}$$

$$a_k = \frac{1}{\pi} \int_{-\pi}^{\pi} f(x) \cos kx \, dx = \frac{1}{\pi} \int_{-1/5}^{1/5} \cos kx \, dx = \frac{1}{k\pi} \sin kx \bigg|_{-1/5}^{1/5}$$

$$= \frac{1}{k\pi} \left(\sin \left(\frac{k}{5} \right) - \sin \left(-\frac{k}{5} \right) \right) = \frac{1}{k\pi} \left(2 \sin \left(\frac{k}{5} \right) \right)$$

$$b_k = \frac{1}{\pi} \int_{-\pi}^{\pi} f(x) \sin kx \, dx = \frac{1}{\pi} \int_{-1/5}^{1/5} \sin kx \, dx = -\frac{1}{k\pi} \cos kx \bigg|_{-1/5}^{1/5}$$

$$= -\frac{1}{k\pi} \left(\cos \left(\frac{k}{5} \right) - \cos \left(-\frac{k}{5} \right) \right) = \frac{1}{k\pi} (0) = 0$$

The energy of f contained in the constant term is

$$A_0^2 = 2a_0^2 = 2 \left(\frac{1}{5\pi} \right)^2 = \frac{2}{25\pi^2}$$

which is

$$\frac{A_0^2}{E} = \frac{2/25\pi^2}{2/5\pi} = \frac{1}{5\pi} \approx 0.063662 = 6.3662\% \quad \text{of the total.}$$

The fraction of energy contained in the first harmonic is

$$\frac{A_1^2}{E} = \frac{a_1^2}{E} = \frac{\left(\frac{2 \sin \frac{1}{5}}{\pi} \right)^2}{\frac{2}{5\pi}} \approx 0.12563.$$

The fraction of energy contained in both the constant term and the first harmonic together is

$$\frac{A_0^2}{E} + \frac{A_1^2}{E} \approx 0.06366 + 0.12563 = 0.18929 = 18.929\%.$$

(b) The formula for the energy of the kth harmonic is

$$A_k^2 = a_k^2 + b_k^2 = \left(\frac{2 \sin \frac{k}{5}}{k\pi} \right)^2 + 0^2 = \frac{4 \sin^2 \frac{k}{5}}{k^2 \pi^2}$$

By graphing this formula as a continuous function for $k \geq 1$, we see its overall behavior as k gets larger. The energy spectrum for the first five terms is shown as well.

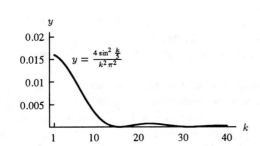

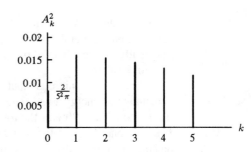

(c) The constant term and the first five harmonics contain

$$\frac{A_0^2}{E} + \frac{A_1^2}{E} + \frac{A_2^2}{E} + \frac{A_3^2}{E} + \frac{A_4^2}{E} + \frac{A_5^2}{E} \approx 61.5255\%$$

of the total energy of f.

(d) The fifth Fourier approximation to f is

$$F_5(x) = \frac{1}{5\pi} + \frac{2\sin(\frac{1}{5})}{\pi}\cos x + \frac{\sin(\frac{2}{5})}{\pi}\cos 2x + \frac{2\sin(\frac{3}{5})}{3\pi}\cos 3x + \frac{\sin(\frac{4}{5})}{2\pi}\cos 4x + \frac{2\sin 1}{5\pi}\cos 5x$$

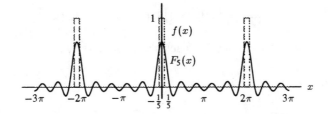

For comparison, below is the thirteenth Fourier approximation to f.

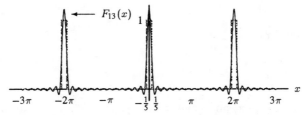

23. As c gets closer and closer to 0, the energy of the pulse train will also approach 0, since

$$E = \frac{1}{\pi}\int_{-\pi}^{\pi} (f(x))^2\,dx = \frac{1}{\pi}\int_{-c/2}^{c/2} 1^2\,dx = \frac{1}{\pi}\left(\frac{c}{2} - \left(-\frac{c}{2}\right)\right) = \frac{c}{\pi}.$$

The energy spectrum shows the *relative* distribution of the energy of f among its harmonics. The fraction of energy carried by each harmonic gets smaller as c gets closer to 0, as shown by comparing the kth terms of the Fourier series for pulse trains with $c = 2, 1, 0.4$ in Problems 20, 21, 22. For instance, notice that the *fraction* or *percentage* of energy carried by the constant term got smaller as c got smaller; notice that the *fraction* or *percentage* of energy carried by the first harmonic got smaller as c got smaller.

If each harmonic contributes less energy, then more harmonics are needed to capture a fixed percentage of energy. For example, if $c = 2$, only the constant term and the first two harmonics are needed to capture 90% of the total energy of that pulse train. If $c = 1$, the constant term and the first five harmonics are needed to get 90% of the energy of that pulse train. If $c = 0.4$, the constant term and the first thirteen harmonics are needed to get 90% of the energy of that pulse train. This means that more harmonics, or more terms in the series, are needed to get an accurate approximation. Compare the graphs of the fifth and thirteenth Fourier approximations of f in Problem 22.

24. Since each square in the graph has area $\left(\frac{\pi}{4}\right) \cdot (0.2)$,

$$
\begin{aligned}
a_0 &= \frac{1}{2\pi} \int_{-\pi}^{\pi} f(x)\,dx \\
&= \frac{1}{2\pi} \cdot \left(\frac{\pi}{4}\right) \cdot (0.2) \left[\text{Number of squares under graph above } x\text{-axis} \right. \\
&\qquad\qquad\qquad\qquad \left. - \text{ Number of squares above graph below } x \text{ axis}\right] \\
&\approx \frac{1}{2\pi} \cdot \left(\frac{\pi}{4}\right) \cdot (0.2) \cdot [13 + 11 - 14] = 0.25
\end{aligned}
$$

Approximate the Fourier coefficients using Riemann sums.

$$
\begin{aligned}
a_1 &= \frac{1}{\pi} \int_{-\pi}^{\pi} f(x) \cos x\,dx \\
&\approx \frac{1}{\pi} \left[f(-\pi)\cos(-\pi) + f\left(-\frac{\pi}{2}\right)\cos\left(-\frac{\pi}{2}\right) + f(0)\cos(0) + f\left(\frac{\pi}{2}\right)\cos\left(\frac{\pi}{2}\right) \right] \cdot \frac{\pi}{2} \\
&= \frac{1}{\pi} \left[(0.92)(-1) + (1)(0) + (-1.7)(1) + (0.7)(0) \right] \cdot \frac{\pi}{2} \\
&= -1.31
\end{aligned}
$$

Similarly for b_1:

$$
\begin{aligned}
b_1 &= \frac{1}{\pi} \int_{-\pi}^{\pi} f(x) \sin x\,dx \\
&\approx \frac{1}{\pi} \left[f(-\pi)\sin(-\pi) + f\left(-\frac{\pi}{2}\right)\sin\left(-\frac{\pi}{2}\right) + f(0)\sin(0) + f\left(\frac{\pi}{2}\right)\sin\left(\frac{\pi}{2}\right) \right] \cdot \frac{\pi}{2} \\
&= \frac{1}{\pi} \left[(0.92)(0) + (1)(-1) + (-1.7)(0) + (0.7)(1) \right] \cdot \frac{\pi}{2} \\
&= -0.15
\end{aligned}
$$

So our first Fourier approximation is

$$
F_1(x) = 0.25 - 1.31\cos x - 0.15\sin x.
$$

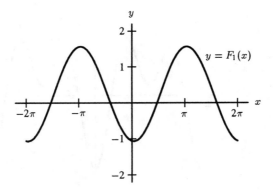

Similarly for a_2:

$$a_2 = \frac{1}{\pi} \int_{-\pi}^{\pi} f(x) \cos 2x \, dx$$

$$\approx \frac{1}{\pi} \left[f(-\pi) \cos(-2\pi) + f\left(-\frac{\pi}{2}\right) \cos(-\pi) + f(0) \cos(0) + f\left(\frac{\pi}{2}\right) \cos(-\pi) \right] \cdot \frac{\pi}{2}$$

$$= \frac{1}{\pi} \left[(0.92)(1) + (1)(-1) + (-1.7)(1) + (0.7)(-1) \right] \cdot \frac{\pi}{2}$$

$$= -1.24$$

Similarly for b_2:

$$b_2 = \frac{1}{\pi} \int_{-\pi}^{\pi} f(x) \sin 2x \, dx$$

$$\approx \frac{1}{\pi} \left[f(-\pi) \sin(-2\pi) + f\left(-\frac{\pi}{2}\right) \sin(-\pi) + f(0) \sin(0) + f\left(\frac{\pi}{2}\right) \sin(-\pi) \right] \cdot \frac{\pi}{2}$$

$$= \frac{1}{\pi} \left[(0.92)(0) + (1)(0) + (-1.7)(0) + (0.7)(0) \right] \cdot \frac{\pi}{2}$$

$$= 0$$

So our second Fourier approximation is

$$F_2(x) = 0.25 - 1.31 \cos x - 0.15 \sin x - 1.24 \cos 2x$$

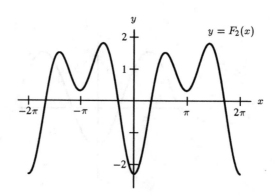

As you can see from comparing our graphs of F_1 and F_2 to the original, our estimates of the Fourier coefficients are not very accurate.

There are other methods of estimating the Fourier coefficients such as taking other Riemann sums, using Simpson's rule, and using the trapezoid rule. With each method, the greater the number of subdivisions of the interval of integration, the more accurate the numerical estimates of the Fourier coefficients.

The actual function graphed in the problem was

$$y = \frac{1}{4} - 1.3\cos x - \frac{\sin(\frac{3}{5})}{\pi}\sin x - \frac{2}{\pi}\cos 2x - \frac{\cos 1}{3\pi}\sin 2x$$

$$= 0.25 - 1.3\cos x - 0.18\sin x - 0.63\cos 2x - 0.057\sin 2x$$

25. By formula II-12 of the integral table,

$$\int_{-\pi}^{\pi} \sin kx \cos mx \, dx$$

$$= \frac{1}{m^2 - k^2}\left(m\sin(kx)\sin(mx) + k\cos(kx)\cos(mx) \right)\Big|_{-\pi}^{\pi}$$

$$= \frac{1}{m^2 - k^2}\Big[m\sin(k\pi)\sin(m\pi) + k\cos(k\pi)\cos(m\pi)$$

$$- m\sin(-k\pi)\sin(-m\pi) - k\cos(-k\pi)\cos(-m\pi)\Big]$$

Since k and m are positive integers, $\sin(k\pi) = \sin(m\pi) = \sin(-k\pi) = \sin(-m\pi) = 0$. Also, $\cos(k\pi) = \cos(-k\pi)$ since $\cos x$ is even. Thus this expression reduces to 0. [Note: since $\sin kx \cos mx$ is odd, so $\int_{-\pi}^{\pi} \sin kx \cos mx \, dx$ must be 0.]

26. By formula II-11 of the integral table,

$$\int_{-\pi}^{\pi} \cos kx \cos mx \, dx = \frac{1}{m^2 - k^2} \left(m \cos(kx) \sin(mx) - k \sin(kx) \cos(mx) \right) \Big|_{-\pi}^{\pi}$$

Again, since $\sin(n\pi) = 0$ for any integer n, it is easy to see that this expression is simply 0.

27. We make the substitution $u = mx$, $dx = \frac{1}{m} du$. Then

$$\int_{-\pi}^{\pi} \cos^2 mx \, dx = \frac{1}{m} \int_{u=-m\pi}^{u=m\pi} \cos^2 u \, du$$

By Formula IV-18 of the integral table, this equals

$$\frac{1}{m} \left[\frac{1}{2} \cos u \sin u \right] \Big|_{-m\pi}^{m\pi} + \frac{1}{m} \frac{1}{2} \int_{-m\pi}^{m\pi} 1 \, du$$

$$= 0 + \frac{1}{2m} u \Big|_{-m\pi}^{m\pi} = \frac{1}{2m} u \Big|_{-m\pi}^{m\pi}$$

$$= \frac{1}{2m} (2m\pi) = \pi.$$

28. Using formula II-10 in the integral table,

$$\int_{-\pi}^{\pi} \sin kx \sin mx \, dx = \frac{1}{m^2 - k^2} \left[k \cos(kx) \sin(mx) - m \sin(kx) \cos(mx) \right] \Big|_{-\pi}^{\pi}$$

Again, since $\sin(n\pi) = 0$ for all integers n, this expression reduces to 0.

29. The easiest way to do this is to use Problem 27.

$$\int_{-\pi}^{\pi} \sin^2 mx \, dx = \int_{-\pi}^{\pi} (1 - \cos^2 mx) \, dx = \int_{-\pi}^{\pi} dx - \int_{-\pi}^{\pi} \cos^2 mx \, dx$$

$$= 2\pi - \pi \quad \text{using Problem 27}$$

$$= \pi.$$

SOLUTIONS TO REVIEW PROBLEMS FOR CHAPTER TEN

1. Substituting $y = t^2$ in $\sin y = y - \dfrac{y^3}{3!} + \dfrac{y^5}{5!} - \dfrac{y^7}{7!} + \cdots$ gives

$$\sin t^2 = t^2 - \frac{t^6}{3!} + \frac{t^{10}}{5!} - \frac{t^{14}}{7!} + \cdots$$

2.

$$\theta^2 \cos \theta^2 = \theta^2 \left(1 - \frac{(\theta^2)^2}{2!} + \frac{(\theta^2)^4}{4!} - \frac{(\theta^2)^6}{6!} + \cdots \right)$$

$$= \theta^2 - \frac{\theta^6}{2!} + \frac{\theta^{10}}{4!} - \frac{\theta^{14}}{6!} + \cdots$$

3. Substituting $y = -4z^2$ into $\dfrac{1}{1+y} = 1 - y + y^2 - y^3 + \cdots$ gives

$$\frac{1}{1-4z^2} = 1 + 4z^2 + 16z^4 + 64z^6 + \cdots$$

4.

$$\frac{1}{\sqrt{4-x}} = \frac{1}{2\sqrt{1-\frac{x}{2}}} = \frac{1}{2}\left(1 - \frac{x}{2}\right)^{-\frac{1}{2}}$$

$$= \frac{1}{2}\left(1 - \left(-\frac{1}{2}\right)\left(\frac{x}{2}\right) + \frac{1}{2!}\left(-\frac{1}{2}\right)\left(-\frac{3}{2}\right)\left(\frac{x}{2}\right)^2 \right.$$

$$\left. - \frac{1}{3!}\left(-\frac{1}{2}\right)\left(-\frac{3}{2}\right)\left(-\frac{5}{2}\right)\left(\frac{x}{2}\right)^3 + \cdots \right)$$

$$= \frac{1}{2} + \frac{1}{8}x + \frac{3}{64}x^2 + \frac{5}{256}x^3 + \cdots$$

5.

$$\frac{a}{a+b} = \frac{a}{a\left(1+\frac{b}{a}\right)} = \left(1 + \frac{b}{a}\right)^{-1} = 1 - \frac{b}{a} + \left(\frac{b}{a}\right)^2 - \left(\frac{b}{a}\right)^3 + \cdots$$

6.

$$\sqrt{R-r} = \sqrt{R}\left(1 - \frac{r}{R}\right)^{\frac{1}{2}}$$

$$= \sqrt{R}\left(1 + \frac{1}{2}\left(-\frac{r}{R}\right) + \frac{1}{2!}\left(\frac{1}{2}\right)\left(-\frac{1}{2}\right)\left(-\frac{r}{R}\right)^2 \right.$$

$$\left. + \frac{1}{3!}\left(\frac{1}{2}\right)\left(-\frac{1}{2}\right)\left(-\frac{3}{2}\right)\left(-\frac{r}{R}\right)^3 + \cdots \right)$$

$$= \sqrt{R}\left(1 - \frac{1}{2}\frac{r}{R} - \frac{1}{8}\frac{r^2}{R^2} - \frac{1}{16}\frac{r^3}{R^3} - \cdots \right)$$

7. $\sin x \approx -\dfrac{1}{\sqrt{2}} + \dfrac{1}{\sqrt{2}}\left(x + \dfrac{\pi}{4}\right) + \dfrac{1}{2\sqrt{2}}\left(x + \dfrac{\pi}{4}\right)^2$

8. $e^x \approx 1 + e(x - 1) + \dfrac{e}{2}(x - 1)^2$

9. $\ln x \approx \ln 2 + \dfrac{1}{2}(x - 2) - \dfrac{1}{8}(x - 2)^2$

10. $f'(x) = 3x^2 + 14x - 5$, $f''(x) = 6x + 14$, $f'''(x) = 6$. The Taylor polynomial about $x = 1$ is

$$P_3(x) = 4 + \frac{12}{1!}(x - 1) + \frac{20}{2!}(x - 1)^2 + \frac{6}{3!}(x - 1)^3$$
$$= 4 + 12(x - 1) + 10(x - 1)^2 + (x - 1)^3.$$

Notice that if you multiply out and collect terms in $P_3(x)$, you will get $f(x)$ back.

11. (a) The series for $\frac{\sin 2\theta}{\theta}$ is

$$\frac{\sin 2\theta}{\theta} = \frac{1}{\theta}\left(2\theta - \frac{(2\theta)^3}{3!} + \frac{(2\theta)^5}{5!} - \cdots\right)$$
$$= 2 - \frac{4\theta^2}{3} + \frac{4\theta^4}{15} - \cdots$$

so $\lim_{\theta \to 0} \frac{\sin 2\theta}{\theta} = 2$.

(b) Near $\theta = 0$, we make the approximation

$$\frac{\sin 2\theta}{\theta} \approx 2 - \frac{4}{3}\theta^2$$

so the parabola is $y = 2 - \frac{4}{3}\theta^2$.

12. Write out series expansions about $x = 0$, and compare the first few terms:

$$\sin x = x - \frac{x^3}{3!} + \frac{x^5}{5!} + \cdots$$

$$\ln(1 + x) = x - \frac{x^2}{2} + \frac{x^3}{3} - \cdots$$

$$1 - \cos x = 1 - \left(1 - \frac{x^2}{2!} + \frac{x^4}{4!} - \cdots\right) = \frac{x^2}{2!} - \frac{x^4}{4!} + \cdots$$

$$e^x - 1 = x + \frac{x^2}{2!} + \frac{x^3}{3!} + \cdots$$

$$\arctan x = \int \frac{dx}{1 + x^2} = \int (1 - x^2 + x^4 - \cdots)\, dx$$

$$= x - \frac{x^3}{3} + \frac{x^5}{5} + \cdots \qquad \text{(note that the arbitrary constant is 0)}$$

$$x\sqrt{1-x} = x(1-x)^{1/2} = x\left(1 - \frac{1}{2}x + \frac{(1/2)(-1/2)}{2}x^2 + \cdots\right)$$

$$= x - \frac{x^2}{2} + \frac{x^3}{8} + \cdots$$

So, considering just the first term or two (since we are interested in small x)

$$1 - \cos x < x\sqrt{1-x} < \ln(1+x) < \arctan x < \sin x < x < e^x - 1.$$

13. (a) $f(t) = te^t$.

Use the Taylor expansion for e^t :

$$f(t) = t\left(1 + t + \frac{t^2}{2!} + \frac{t^3}{3!} + \cdots\right)$$

$$= t + t^2 + \frac{t^3}{2!} + \frac{t^4}{3!} + \cdots$$

(b)

$$\int_0^x f(t)\,dt = \int_0^x te^t\,dt = \int_0^x \left(t + t^2 + \frac{t^3}{2!} + \frac{t^4}{3!} + \cdots\right)dt$$

$$= \frac{t^2}{2} + \frac{t^3}{3} + \frac{t^4}{4\cdot 2!} + \frac{t^5}{5\cdot 3!} + \cdots \Big|_0^x$$

$$= \frac{x^2}{2} + \frac{x^3}{3} + \frac{x^4}{4\cdot 2!} + \frac{x^5}{5\cdot 3!} + \cdots$$

(c) Substitute $x = 1$:

$$\int_0^1 te^t\,dt = \frac{1}{2} + \frac{1}{3} + \frac{1}{4\cdot 2!} + \frac{1}{5\cdot 3!} + \cdots$$

In the integral above, to integrate by parts, let $u = t$, $dv = e^t\,dt$, so $du = dt$, $v = e^t$.

$$\int_0^1 te^t\,dt = te^t\Big|_0^1 - \int_0^1 e^t\,dt = e - (e-1) = 1$$

Hence

$$\frac{1}{2} + \frac{1}{3} + \frac{1}{4\cdot 2!} + \frac{1}{5\cdot 3!} + \cdots = 1.$$

14. (a)

$$f(x) = (1+ax)(1+bx)^{-1} = (1+ax)\left(1 - bx + (bx)^2 - (bx)^3 + \cdots\right)$$

$$= 1 + (a-b)x + (b^2 - ab)x^2 + \cdots$$

(b) $e^x = 1 + x + \frac{x^2}{2} + \cdots$

Equating coefficients:

$$a - b = 1,$$

$$b^2 - ab = \frac{1}{2}.$$

Solving gives $a = \frac{1}{2}, b = -\frac{1}{2}$.

15. **(a)** Since the expression under the square root sign, $1 - \frac{v^2}{c^2}$ must be positive in order to give a real value of m, we have

$$1 - \frac{v^2}{c^2} > 0$$

$$\frac{v^2}{c^2} < 1$$

$$v^2 < c^2,$$

so $-c < v < c$.

In other words, the object can never travel faster that the speed of light.

(b)

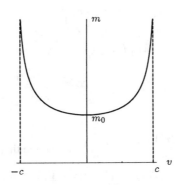

(c) Notice that $m = m_0 \left(1 - \frac{v^2}{c^2}\right)^{-1/2}$. If we substitute $u = -\frac{v^2}{c^2}$, we get $m = m_0(1+u)^{-1/2}$ and we can use the binomial expansion to get:

$$m = m_0 \left(1 - \frac{1}{2}u + \frac{(-1/2)(-3/2)}{2!}u^2 + \cdots\right)$$

$$= m_0 \left(1 + \frac{1}{2}\frac{v^2}{c^2} + \frac{3}{8}\frac{v^4}{c^4} + \cdots\right).$$

(d) We would expect this series to converge only for values of the original function that exist, namely when $|v| < c$.

16. **(a)** $F = \frac{GM}{R^2} + \frac{Gm}{(R+r)^2}$

(b) $F = \frac{GM}{R^2} + \frac{Gm}{R^2}\frac{1}{(1+\frac{r}{R})^2}$

Since $\frac{r}{R} < 1$, use the binomial expansion:

$$\frac{1}{(1+\frac{r}{R})^2} = \left(1 + \frac{r}{R}\right)^{-2} = 1 - 2\left(\frac{r}{R}\right) + (-2)(-3)\frac{(\frac{r}{R})^2}{2!} + \cdots$$

$$F = \frac{GM}{R^2} + \frac{Gm}{R^2} \left[1 - 2\left(\frac{r}{R}\right) + 3\left(\frac{r}{R}\right)^2 - \cdots \right].$$

(c)   Discarding higher power terms, we get

$$F \approx \frac{GM}{R^2} + \frac{Gm}{R^2} - \frac{2Gmr}{R^3}$$
$$= \frac{G(M+m)}{R^2} - \frac{2Gmr}{R^3}.$$

Looking at the expression, we see that the term $\frac{G(M+m)}{R^2}$ is the field strength at a distance R from a single particle of mass $M + m$. The correction term, $-\frac{2Gmr}{R^3}$ is negative because the field strength exerted by a particle of mass $(M + m)$ at a distance R would clearly be larger than the field strength at P in the question.

17.   (a)   To find when V takes on its minimum values, set $\frac{dV}{dr} = 0$. So

$$-V_0 \frac{d}{dr} \left(2\left(\frac{r_0}{r}\right)^6 - \left(\frac{r_0}{r}\right)^{12} \right) = 0$$
$$-V_0 \left(-12r_0^6 r^{-7} + 12r_0^{12} r^{-13} \right) = 0$$
$$12r_0^6 r^{-7} = 12r_0^{12} r^{-13}$$
$$r_0^6 = r^6$$
$$r = r_0$$

Rewriting $V'(r)$ as $\frac{12r_0^6 V_0}{r^7} \left(1 - \left(\frac{r_0}{r}\right)^6 \right)$, we see that $V'(r) > 0$ for $r > r_0$ and $V'(r) < 0$ for $r < r_0$. Thus, $V = -V_0(2(1)^6 - (1)^{12}) = -V_0$ is a minimum.
(Note: We discard the negative root $-r_0$ since the distance r must be positive.)

(b)

$$V(r) = -V_0 \left(2\left(\frac{r_0}{r}\right)^6 - \left(\frac{r_0}{r}\right)^{12} \right) \qquad\qquad V(r_0) = -V_0$$
$$V'(r) = -V_0(-12r_0^6 r^{-7} + 12r_0^{12} r^{-13}) \qquad\qquad V'(r_0) = 0$$
$$V''(r) = -V_0(84r_0^6 r^{-8} - 156r_0^{12} r^{-14}) \qquad\qquad V''(r_0) = 72V_0 r_0^{-2}$$

The Taylor series is thus:

$$V(r) = -V_0 + 72V_0 r_0^{-2} \cdot (r - r_0)^2 \cdot \frac{1}{2} + \cdots$$

(c)   The difference between V and its minimum value $-V_0$ is

$$V - (-V_0) = 36V_0 \frac{(r - r_0)^2}{r_0^2} + \cdots$$

which is approximately proportional to $(r - r_0)^2$ since terms containing higher powers of $(r - r_0)$ have relatively small values for r near r_0.

(d) From part (a) we know that $\frac{dV}{dr} = 0$ when $r = r_0$, hence $F = 0$ when $r = r_0$. Since, if we discard powers of $(r - r_0)$ higher than the second,

$$V(r) \approx -V_0 \left(1 - 36\frac{(r - r_0)^2}{r_0^2} \right)$$

giving

$$F = -\frac{dV}{dr} \approx 72 \cdot \frac{r - r_0}{r_0^2}(-V_0) = -72V_0\frac{r - r_0}{r_o^2}.$$

So F is approximately proportional to $(r - r_0)$.

18. We have that the second coefficient of the Taylor expansion is $\frac{g''(0)}{2} = 1$. So $g''(0) = 2$. Similarly, the third coefficient is $\frac{g'''(0)}{3!} = 0$. So $g'''(0) = 0$. And finally, the tenth coefficient is $\frac{g^{(10)}(0)}{10!} = \frac{1}{5!}$. So $g^{(10)}(0) = \frac{10!}{5!}$.

19.

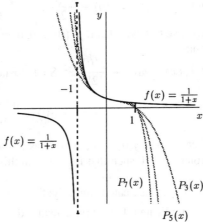

The graph suggests that the Taylor polynomials converge to $f(x) = \dfrac{1}{1 + x}$ on the interval $(-1, 1)$.

20. (a) First, we give a "local" solution which works near a specific value a.

Let $f(x) = \ln x$ and $a > 2$. We can find the Taylor polynomials for $f(x)$ about a using the old method.

$f'(x) = x^{-1}$, $f''(x) = -x^{-2}$, $f'''(x) = 2!x^{-3}$, $f^{(4)}(x) = -3!x^{-4}, \cdots$,

$f^{(k)}(x) = (-1)^{k-1}(k - 1)!x^{-k}$. Then

$$P_n(x) = \ln a + \frac{a^{-1}}{1!}(x - a) + \frac{-a^{-2}}{2!}(x - a)^2 + \frac{2!a^{-3}}{3!}(x - a)^3 + \cdots$$

$$\frac{(-1)^{n-1}(n - 1)!a^{-n}}{n!}(x - a)^n$$

$$= \ln a + \frac{1}{a}(x - a) - \frac{1}{2a^2}(x - a)^2 + \frac{1}{3a^3}(x - a)^3 + \cdots + \frac{(-1)^{n-1}}{na^n}(x - a)^n.$$

Looking at the graphs will show you that the polynomials do not converge to $f(x)$ for all x. In fact, $P_n(x)$ converges to $f(x) = \ln x$ only on the interval $(0, 2a)$. So for any Taylor expansion of $\ln x$ there are x for which that expansion will diverge.

(b)   We also give a "global" solution.

We'll use the fact that $\ln(\frac{1}{y}) = -\ln y$. Suppose that $x > 2$. Then $\frac{1}{x} < \frac{1}{2}$. Since

$$\ln(x) = -\ln\left(\frac{1}{x}\right),$$

by letting $y = \frac{1}{x}$, we have $y < \frac{1}{2}$, so we can use a Taylor approximation to approximate $\ln(y)$, and hence obtain an approximation for $\ln x$. Doing so, we get Taylor polynomials in $(\frac{1}{x} - 1)$.

21.   (a)   Since $g^{(k)}(0)$ exists for all $k \geq 0$, and $g'(0) = 0$ because g has a critical point at $x = 0$. For $n \geq 2$,

$$g(x) \approx P_n(x) = g(0) + \frac{g''(0)}{2!}x^2 + \frac{g'''(0)}{3!}x^3 + \cdots + \frac{g^{(n)}(0)}{n!}x^n.$$

(b)   The Second Derivative test says that if $g''(0) > 0$, then 0 is a local minimum and if $g''(0) < 0$, 0 is a local maximum.

(c)   Let $n = 2$. Then $P_2(x) = g(0) + \frac{g''(0)}{2!}x^2$. So, for x near 0,

$$g(x) - g(0) \approx \frac{g''(0)}{2!}x^2.$$

If $g''(0) > 0$, then $g(x) - g(0) \geq 0$, as long as x stays near 0. In other words, there exists a small interval around $x = 0$ such that for any x in this interval $g(x) \geq g(0)$. So $g(0)$ is a local minimum.

The case when $g''(0) < 0$ is treated similarly; then $g(0)$ is a local maximum.

22.   The situation is more complicated. Let's first consider the case when $g'''(0) \neq 0$. To be specific let $g'''(0) > 0$. Then

$$g(x) \approx P_3(x) = g(0) + \frac{g'''(0)}{3!}x^3.$$

So, $g(x) - g(0) \approx \frac{g'''(0)}{3!}x^3$. (Notice that $\frac{g'''(0)}{3!} > 0$ is a constant.) Now, no matter how small an open interval I around $x = 0$ is, there is always some x_1 and x_2 in I such that $x_1 < 0$ and $x_2 > 0$, which means that $\frac{g'''(0)}{3!}x_1^3 < 0$ and $\frac{g'''(0)}{3!}x_2^3 > 0$, i.e. $g(x_1) - g(0) < 0$ and $g(x_2) - g(0) > 0$. Thus, $g(0)$ is neither a local minimum nor a local maximum. (If $g'''(0) < 0$, the same conclusion still holds. Try it! The reasoning is similar.)

Now let's consider the case when $g'''(0) = 0$. If $g^{(4)}(0) > 0$, then by the fourth degree Taylor polynomial approximation to g at $x = 0$, we have

$$g(x) - g(0) \approx \frac{g^{(4)}(0)}{4!}x^4 > 0$$

for x in a small open interval around $x = 0$. So $g(0)$ is a local minimum. (If $g^{(4)}(0) < 0$, then $g(0)$ is a local maximum.)

In general, suppose that $g^{(k)}(0) \neq 0$, $k \geq 2$, and all the derivatives of g with order less than k are 0. Then $g(0)$ is neither a local minimum nor a local maximum if k is odd. For k even, $g(0)$ is a local minimum if $g^{(k)}(0) > 0$, and $g(0)$ is a local maximum if $g^{(k)}(0) < 0$.

In this case g looks like cx^k near $x = 0$, which determines its behavior there.

23. The amount of cephalexin in the body is given by $Q(t) = Q_0 e^{-kt}$, where $Q_0 = Q(0)$ and k is a constant. Since the half-life is 0.9 hours,

$$\frac{1}{2} = e^{-0.9k}, \quad k = -\frac{1}{0.9} \ln \frac{1}{2} \approx 0.8.$$

(a) After 6 hours

$$Q = Q_0 e^{-k(6)} \approx Q_0 e^{-0.8(6)} = Q_0(0.01).$$

Thus, the percentage of the cephalexin that remains after 6 hours $\approx 1\%$.

(b)

$$Q_1 = 250$$
$$Q_2 = 250 + 250(0.01)$$
$$Q_3 = 250 + 250(0.01) + 250(0.01)^2$$
$$Q_4 = 250 + 250(0.01) + 250(0.01)^2 + 250(0.01)^3$$

(c)

$$Q_3 = \frac{250(1 - (0.01)^3)}{1 - 0.01}$$
$$\approx 252.5$$
$$Q_4 = \frac{250(1 - (0.01)^4)}{1 - 0.01}$$
$$\approx 252.5$$

Thus, by the time a patient has taken three cephalexin tablets, the quantity of drug in the body has leveled off to 252.5 mg.

(d) Looking at the answers to part (b) shows that

$$Q_n = 250 + 250(0.01) + 250(0.01)^2 + \cdots + 250(0.01)^{n-1}$$
$$= \frac{250(1 - (0.01)^n)}{1 - 0.01}$$

(e) In the long run, $n \to \infty$. So,

$$Q = \lim_{n \to \infty} Q_n = \frac{250}{1 - 0.01} = 252.5.$$

24. (a) The bond is worth its present value, which is given by the finite series:

$$\text{Total present value} = \underbrace{\frac{5}{1.04} + \frac{5}{(1.04)^2} + \cdots + \frac{5}{(1.04)^{100}}}_{\text{coupons}} + \underbrace{\frac{100}{(1.04)^{100}}}_{\text{principal}}$$

$$= \frac{5}{1.04}\left(1 + \frac{1}{1.04} + \cdots + \frac{1}{(1.04)^{99}}\right) + \frac{100}{(1.04)^{100}}$$

$$= \frac{5}{1.04}\left(\frac{1 - \left(\frac{1}{1.04}\right)^{100}}{1 - \frac{1}{1.04}}\right) + \frac{100}{(1.04)^{100}}$$

$$= \$124.50.$$

(b) The present value is now given by the infinite series

$$\text{Total present value} = \frac{5}{1.04} + \frac{5}{(1.04)^2} + \frac{5}{(1.04)^3} + \cdots$$

$$= \frac{5}{1.04}\left(1 + \frac{1}{1.04} + \frac{1}{(1.04)^2} + \cdots\right)$$

$$= \frac{5}{1.04}\left(\frac{1}{1 - \frac{1}{1.04}}\right) = \$125.$$

Notice how little difference there is between the worth of the bond which pays for 100 years and the one which pays for ever.

25. We assume the interest rate is i per year. Then

$$\text{Present value of first coupon} = \frac{50}{1 + i}$$

$$\text{Present value of second coupon} = \frac{50}{(1 + i)^2}$$

Thus

$$\text{Total present value} = \underbrace{\frac{50}{1 + i} + \frac{50}{(1 + i)^2} + \cdots + \frac{50}{(1 + i)^{10}}}_{\text{coupons}} + \underbrace{\frac{1000}{(1 + i)^{10}}}_{\text{principal}}$$

$$= \frac{50}{1 + i}\left(1 + \frac{1}{1 + i} + \cdots + \frac{1}{(1 + i)^9}\right) + \frac{1000}{(1 + i)^{10}}$$

$$= \frac{50}{1 + i}\left(\frac{1 - \left(\frac{1}{1+i}\right)^{10}}{1 - \frac{1}{1+i}}\right) + \frac{1000}{(1 + i)^{10}}$$

$$= \frac{50}{1 + i}\left(\frac{1 - \left(\frac{1}{1+i}\right)^{10}}{1 - \frac{1}{1+i}}\right)\left(\frac{(1 + i)^{10}}{(1 + i)^{10}}\right) + \frac{1000}{(1 + i)^{10}}$$

$$= \frac{50}{1+i} \left(\frac{((1+i)^{10} - 1)}{(1+i)^{10}} \right) \frac{1+i}{(1+i-1)} + \frac{1000}{(1+i)^{10}}$$

$$= \frac{50((1+i)^{10} - 1)}{i(1+i)^{10}} + \frac{1000}{(1+i)^{10}}$$

Since we know the present value is \$950, we want to solve for i giving

$$\frac{50}{i} \frac{((1+i)^{10} - 1)}{(1+i)^{10}} + \frac{1000}{(1+i)^{10}} = 950$$

This equation cannot be solved analytically for i. However graphing the function

$$f(i) = \frac{50((1+i)^{10} - 1)}{i(1+i)^{10}} + \frac{1000}{(1+i)^{10}} - 950$$

and zooming on the zero shows that $f(i) = 0$ when $i \approx 0.057$, so an interest rate of about 5.7% per year gives a present value of \$950.

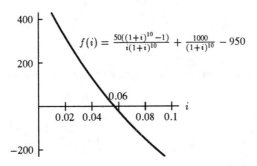

26. (a) Since the fly is traveling at 20 km/hr and the trains at 10 km/hr, each time the fly goes to meet the other train, it will cover 2/3 of the distance between them, while the train covers 1/3 of the distance.

Thus, the first time the fly turns around, it will have covered a distance of

$$d_1 = 30 \left(\frac{2}{3} \right) = 20 \text{ km.}$$

By this time each train has gone 10 km, so the distance between the trains is now reduced to one-third of what it was originally, namely $30(1/3) = 10$ km. Thus, by the next turn around the fly has gone an additional $10(2/3) = 30(1/3)(2/3)$ km. By the second turn-around, the fly has covered a total distance of

$$d_2 = 30 \left(\frac{2}{3} \right) + 30 \left(\frac{1}{3} \right) \left(\frac{2}{3} \right) \text{ km.}$$

At the time of the second turn-around the distance between the trains has been reduced to one third of what it was the time before, or $10(1/3) = 30(1/3)^2$ km. The third turn around adds a distance of $30(1/3)^2(2/3)$:

$$d_3 = 30 \left(\frac{2}{3}\right) + 30 \left(\frac{1}{3}\right) \left(\frac{2}{3}\right) + 30 \left(\frac{1}{3}\right)^2 \left(\frac{2}{3}\right) \text{ km.}$$

By the third turn-around, the distance between the trains is $30(1/3)^3$ km, so, at the fourth turn-around

$$d_4 = 30 \left(\frac{2}{3}\right) + 30 \left(\frac{1}{3}\right) \left(\frac{2}{3}\right) + 30 \left(\frac{1}{3}\right)^2 \left(\frac{2}{3}\right) + 30 \left(\frac{1}{3}\right)^3 \left(\frac{2}{3}\right) \text{ km.}$$

(b) Generalizing of the answers to part (a) gives

$$d_n = 30 \left(\frac{2}{3}\right) + 30 \left(\frac{1}{3}\right) \left(\frac{2}{3}\right) + 30 \left(\frac{1}{3}\right)^2 \left(\frac{2}{3}\right) + \cdots + 30 \left(\frac{1}{3}\right)^{n-1} \left(\frac{2}{3}\right)$$

$$= 30 \left(\frac{2}{3}\right) \left(1 + \left(\frac{1}{3}\right) + \left(\frac{1}{3}\right)^2 + \cdots + \left(\frac{1}{3}\right)^{n-1} \right)$$

$$= \frac{20 \left(1 - \left(\frac{1}{3}\right)^n \right)}{1 - \frac{1}{3}}.$$

(c) By the time the trains meet and squash the fly, the poor thing will have flown

$$d = \lim_{n \to \infty} d_n$$

$$= \lim_{n \to \infty} \frac{20 \left(1 - \left(\frac{1}{3}\right)^n \right)}{1 - \frac{1}{3}}$$

$$= \frac{20}{1 - \frac{1}{3}}$$

$$= 30 \text{ km.}$$

(d) It will take $30/20 = 3/2$ hours for the trains to meet, since they are 30 km apart and the distance between them is decreasing at a speed of 20 km/hr. So the fly will have traveled $20(3/2) = 30$ km by the time trains meet.

There is a joke that accompanies this problem. The mathematician, John von Neumann (called the father of the computer) was asked this question, and instantaneously gave the correct answer. The person who had posed the problem complimented him on seeing the trick. Von Neumann responded "What trick? I just summed the geometric series."

27. Let $f(x) = \sqrt{1 + x}$. We will use a Taylor polynomial with $x = 1$ to approximate $\sqrt{2}$. The error bound for the Taylor approximation of degree three for $f(x) = \sqrt{2}$ about $x = 0$ is:

$$|E_3| = |f(1) - P_3(1)| \leq \frac{M \cdot |1 - 0|^4}{4!} = \frac{M}{24},$$

where $|f^{(4)}(x)| \le M$ for $0 \le x \le 1$. Now, $f^{(4)}(x) = -\frac{15}{16}(1+x)^{-\frac{7}{2}} = \frac{-15}{16(1+x)^{\frac{7}{2}}}$. Since $1 \le$ $(1+x)^{\frac{7}{2}}$ for x between 0 and 1, $|f^{(4)}(x)| = \frac{15}{16(1+x)^{\frac{7}{2}}} \le \frac{15}{16}$ for x between 0 and 1. Thus,

$$|E_3| \le \frac{15}{16 \cdot 24} < 0.039$$

28. (a) Since $4 \arctan 1 = \pi$, we approximate π by approximating $4 \arctan x$ by Taylor polynomials with $x = 1$. Let $f(x) = 4 \arctan x$. We find the Taylor polynomial of f about $x = 0$.

$$\begin{aligned} f(0) &= 0 \\ f'(x) &= \frac{4}{1+x^2} & f'(0) &= 4 \\ f''(x) &= -\frac{8x}{(1+x^2)^2} & f''(0) &= 0 \\ f'''(x) &= -\frac{8}{(1+x^2)^2} + \frac{32x^2}{(1+x^2)^3} & f'''(0) &= -8 \end{aligned}$$

Thus, the third degree Taylor polynomial for f is $F_3(x) = \frac{4x}{1!} - \frac{8}{3!}x^3 = 4x - \frac{4}{3}x^3$. In particular, $F_3(1) = 4 - \frac{4}{3} = \frac{8}{3} \approx 2.67$.

Note: If you already have the Taylor series for $1/(1+x^2)$, the Taylor polynomial for $\arctan x$ can also be found by integration.

   (b) We now approximate π by looking at $g(x) = 2 \arcsin x$ about $x = 0$ and substituting $x = 1$.

$$\begin{aligned} g(0) &= 0 \\ g'(x) &= \frac{2}{\sqrt{1-x^2}} & g'(0) &= 2 \\ g''(x) &= \frac{2x}{(1-x^2)^{\frac{3}{2}}} & g''(0) &= 0 \\ g'''(x) &= \frac{2}{(1-x^2)^{\frac{3}{2}}} + \frac{6x^2}{(1-x^2)^{\frac{5}{2}}} & g'''(0) &= 2 \end{aligned}$$

Thus, the third degree Taylor polynomial for g is

$$G_3(x) = \frac{2x}{1!} + \frac{2x^3}{3!} = 2x + \frac{1}{3}x^3.$$

In particular, $G_3(1) = \frac{7}{3} \approx 2.33$.

Note: If you already have the Taylor series for $1/\sqrt{1-x^2}$, the Taylor polynomial for $\arcsin x$ can also be found by integration.

   (c) To estimate the maximum possible error, $|E_3|$, in the approximation using the arctangent, we need a bound on the fourth derivative of $f(x) = \arctan x$ on $0 \le x \le 1$. Since

$$f^{(4)}(x) = -\frac{192x^3}{(1+x^2)^4} + \frac{96x}{(1+x^2)^3},$$

now use a graphing calculator to see that the maximum value of $|f^{(4)}(x)|$, on $0 \le x \le 1$ is about 18.6. Thus,

$$|E_3| \le \frac{18.6}{4!} \approx 0.78.$$

(Notice that $\pi \approx 3.14$ is within 0.78 of 2.67.)

(d)   To estimate the maximum possible error, $|E_n|$, in an approximation using the arcsine, we need a bound on the derivatives of $g(x) = \arcsin x$ on $0 \le x \le 1$. Notice that the derivatives of arcsin x contain terms of the form $(1 - x^2)^{-a}$, for some positive a. In fact, the more derivatives you take, the bigger a gets. The problem is that $(1 - x^2)^{-a}$ is unbounded for $0 \le x < 1$. That is, as x gets close to 1, $(1 - x^2)^{-a}$ approaches ∞. Thus, we cannot get a bound on the derivatives of arcsin x which means that we cannot get a bound on $|E_n|$. Thus, using arctan x seems like a better idea, because we can get a bound on the error of the approximation.

29.   Let $t = 2\pi x - \pi$. Then, $g(t) = f(x) = e^{2\pi x} = e^{t+\pi}$. Notice that as x varies from 0 to 1, t varies from $-\pi$ to π. Thus, we can find the Fourier coefficients for $g(t)$:

$$a_o = \frac{1}{2\pi} \int_{-\pi}^{\pi} g(t)dt = \frac{1}{2\pi} \int_{-\pi}^{\pi} e^{t+\pi} dt = \frac{1}{2\pi} e^{t+\pi} \Big|_{-\pi}^{\pi} = \frac{e^{2\pi} - 1}{2\pi}$$

$$a_n = \frac{1}{\pi} \int_{-\pi}^{\pi} e^{t+\pi} \cos(nt)dt = \frac{e^{\pi}}{\pi} \int_{-\pi}^{\pi} e^t \cos(nt)dt$$

Using the integral table, Formula II-8, yields:

$$= \frac{e^{\pi}}{\pi} \frac{1}{n^2 + 1} e^t (\cos(nt) + n \sin(nt)) \Big|_{-\pi}^{\pi}$$

$$= \frac{e^{\pi}}{\pi} \frac{1}{n^2 + 1} (e^{\pi} - e^{-\pi})(\cos(n\pi))$$

$$= \frac{(e^{2\pi} - 1)}{\pi} \frac{(-1)^n}{n^2 + 1}$$

$$b_n = \frac{1}{\pi} \int_{-\pi}^{\pi} e^{t+\pi} \sin(nt)dt = \frac{e^{\pi}}{\pi} \int_{-\pi}^{\pi} e^t \sin(nt)dt$$

Again, using the integral table, Formula II-9, yields:

$$= \frac{e^{\pi}}{\pi} \frac{1}{n^2 + 1} e^t (\sin(nt) - n \cos(nt)) \Big|_{-\pi}^{\pi}$$

$$= -\frac{e^{\pi}}{\pi} \frac{n}{n^2 + 1} (e^{\pi} - e^{-\pi}) \cos(n\pi)$$

$$= \frac{(e^{2\pi} - 1)}{\pi} \frac{(-1)^{n+1} n}{n^2 + 1}$$

Thus, after factoring a bit, we get:

$$G_3(t) = \frac{e^{2\pi} - 1}{\pi} \left(\frac{1}{2} - \frac{1}{2} \cos t + \frac{1}{2} \sin t + \frac{1}{5} \cos 2t - \frac{2}{5} \sin 2t - \frac{1}{10} \cos 3t + \frac{3}{10} \sin 3t \right)$$

Now, we substitute x back in for t:

$$F_3(x) = \frac{e^{2\pi} - 1}{\pi}(\frac{1}{2} - \frac{1}{2} \cos(2\pi x - \pi) + \frac{1}{2} \sin(2\pi x - \pi) + \frac{1}{5} \cos(4\pi x - 2\pi)$$
$$- \frac{2}{5} \sin(4\pi x - 2\pi) - \frac{1}{10} \cos(6\pi x - 3\pi) + \frac{3}{10} \sin(6\pi x - 3\pi))$$

Recalling that $\cos(x - \pi) = -\cos x, \sin(x - \pi) = -\sin x, \cos(x - 2\pi) = \cos x,$ and $\sin(x - 2\pi) = \sin x$, we have:

$$F_3(x) = \frac{e^{2\pi} - 1}{\pi} \left(\frac{1}{2} + \frac{1}{2} \cos 2\pi x - \frac{1}{2} \sin 2\pi x + \frac{1}{5} \cos 4\pi x - \frac{2}{5} \sin 4\pi x \right.$$
$$\left. + \frac{1}{10} \cos 6\pi x - \frac{3}{10} \sin 6\pi x \right)$$

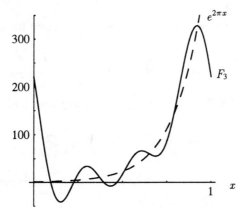

30. Let us begin by finding the Fourier coefficients for $f(x)$. Since f is odd, $\int_{-\pi}^{\pi} f(x)\, dx = 0$ and $\int_{-\pi}^{\pi} f(x) \cos nx\, dx = 0$. Thus $a_i = 0$ for all $i \geq 0$. On the other hand,

$$b_i = \frac{1}{\pi} \int_{-\pi}^{\pi} f(x) \sin nx\, dx = \frac{1}{\pi} \left[\int_{-\pi}^{0} -\sin(nx)\, dx + \int_{0}^{\pi} \sin(nx)\, dx \right]$$
$$= \frac{1}{\pi} \left[\frac{1}{n} \cos(nx) \Big|_{-\pi}^{0} - \frac{1}{n} \cos(nx) \Big|_{0}^{\pi} \right]$$
$$= \frac{1}{n\pi} \left[\cos 0 - \cos(-n\pi) - \cos(n\pi) + \cos 0 \right]$$
$$= \frac{2}{n\pi} \left(1 - \cos(n\pi) \right).$$

Since $\cos(n\pi) = (-1)^n$, this is 0 if n is even, and $\frac{4}{n\pi}$ if n is odd. Thus the nth Fourier polynomial (where n is odd) is

$$F_n(x) = \frac{4}{\pi}\sin x + \frac{4}{3\pi}\sin 3x + \cdots + \frac{4}{n\pi}\sin(nx).$$

As $n \to \infty$, the nth Fourier polynomial must approach $f(x)$ on the interval $(-\pi, \pi)$, except at the point $x = 0$ (where f is not continuous). In particular, if $x = \frac{\pi}{2}$,

$$F_n(1) = \frac{4}{\pi}\sin\frac{\pi}{2} + \frac{4}{3\pi}\sin\frac{3\pi}{2} + \frac{4}{5\pi}\sin\frac{5\pi}{2} + \frac{4}{7\pi}\sin\frac{7\pi}{2} + \cdots + \frac{4}{n\pi}\sin\frac{n\pi}{2}$$

$$= \frac{4}{\pi}\left(1 - \frac{1}{3} + \frac{1}{5} - \frac{1}{7} + \cdots + (-1)^{2n+1}\frac{1}{2n+1}\right).$$

But $F_n(1)$ approaches $f(\frac{\pi}{2}) = 1$ as $n \to \infty$, so

$$\frac{\pi}{4}F_n(1) = 1 - \frac{1}{3} + \frac{1}{5} - \frac{1}{7} + \cdots + (-1)^{2n+1}\frac{1}{2n+1} \to \frac{\pi}{4} \cdot 1 = \frac{\pi}{4}.$$

31. The triangular wave has period 2 and can be described over the interval $[-1, 1]$ by

$$f(x) = \begin{cases} -x & -1 \le x < 0 \\ x & 0 \le x < 1 \end{cases}$$

Since f has period $b = 2$, we let $x = bt/2\pi = t/\pi$ and we define a new function g by the formula

$$g(t) = f(x) = f\left(\frac{t}{\pi}\right) = \begin{cases} -t/\pi & -\pi \le t < 0 \\ t/\pi & 0 \le t < \pi \end{cases}$$

which has period 2π, and first find the third Fourier approximation for $g(t)$.

$$a_0 = \frac{1}{2\pi}\int_{-\pi}^{\pi} g(t)\,dt = \frac{1}{2\pi}\left[\int_{-\pi}^{0} -\frac{t}{\pi}\,dt + \int_{0}^{\pi}\frac{t}{\pi}\,dt\right]$$

$$= \frac{1}{2\pi}\left[-\frac{t^2}{2\pi}\Big|_{-\pi}^{0} + \frac{t^2}{2\pi}\Big|_{0}^{\pi}\right] = \frac{1}{2\pi}\left[-\left(-\frac{\pi^2}{2\pi}\right) + \frac{\pi^2}{2\pi}\right] = \frac{1}{2}$$

From an integral table, we know that $\int x\cos kx\,dx = \frac{x\sin kx}{k} + \frac{\cos kx}{k^2} + C$. So,

$$a_k = \frac{1}{\pi}\int_{-\pi}^{\pi} g(t)\cos kt\,dt = \frac{1}{\pi}\left[\int_{-\pi}^{0} -\frac{t}{\pi}\cos kt\,dt + \int_{0}^{\pi}\frac{t}{\pi}\cos kt\,dt\right]$$

$$= \frac{1}{\pi^2}\left[\int_{-\pi}^{0} -t\cos kt\,dt + \int_{0}^{\pi} t\cos kt\,dt\right]$$

$$= \frac{1}{\pi^2} \left[\left(-\frac{t \sin kt}{k} - \frac{\cos kt}{k^2} \right) \Big|_{-\pi}^{0} + \left(\frac{t \sin kt}{k} + \frac{\cos kt}{k^2} \right) \Big|_{0}^{\pi} \right]$$

$$= \frac{1}{\pi^2} \left[-\frac{1}{k^2} + \frac{\cos k\pi}{k^2} + \frac{\cos k\pi}{k^2} - \frac{1}{k^2} \right]$$

$$= \frac{1}{\pi^2} \left[-\frac{1}{k^2} + \frac{1}{k^2} + \frac{1}{k^2} - \frac{1}{k^2} \right] = 0 \quad \text{if } k \text{ even}$$

$$= \frac{1}{\pi^2} \left[-\frac{1}{k^2} - \frac{1}{k^2} - \frac{1}{k^2} - \frac{1}{k^2} \right] = -\frac{4}{k^2 \pi^2} \quad \text{if } k \text{ odd.}$$

From an integral table, we know that $\int x \sin kx \, dx = -\frac{x \cos kx}{k} + \frac{\sin kx}{k^2} + C$. So,

$$b_k = \frac{1}{\pi} \int_{-\pi}^{\pi} g(t) \sin kt \, dt = \frac{1}{\pi} \left[\int_{-\pi}^{0} -\frac{t}{\pi} \sin kt \, dt + \int_{0}^{\pi} \frac{t}{\pi} \sin kt \, dt \right]$$

$$= \frac{1}{\pi^2} \left[\int_{-\pi}^{0} -t \sin kt \, dt + \int_{0}^{\pi} t \sin kt \, dt \right]$$

$$= \frac{1}{\pi^2} \left[\left(\frac{t \cos kt}{k} - \frac{\sin kt}{k^2} \right) \Big|_{-\pi}^{0} + \left(-\frac{t \cos kt}{k} + \frac{\sin kt}{k^2} \right) \Big|_{0}^{\pi} \right]$$

$$= \frac{1}{\pi^2} \left[-\frac{-\pi \cos(-k\pi)}{k} + \frac{-\pi \cos(k\pi)}{k} \right] = \frac{1}{\pi^2} [0] = 0$$

Thus, $a_1 = -\frac{4}{\pi^2}$, $a_2 = 0$, $a_3 = -\frac{4}{9\pi^2}$, and all b_k's are zero. The third Fourier approximation of $g(t)$ is

$$g(t) \approx \frac{1}{2} - \frac{4}{\pi^2} \cos t - \frac{4}{9\pi^2} \cos 3t,$$

so we have

$$f(x) = g(t) = g(\pi x) \approx \frac{1}{2} - \frac{4}{\pi^2} \cos \pi x - \frac{4}{9\pi^2} \cos 3\pi x$$

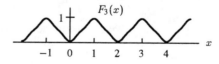

32. **(a)** Expand $f(x)$ into its Fourier series:

$$f(x) = a_0 + a_1 \cos x + a_2 \cos 2x + a_3 \cos 3x + \cdots + a_k \cos kx + \cdots$$
$$+ b_1 \sin x + b_2 \sin 2x + b_3 \sin 3x + \cdots + b_k \sin kx + \cdots$$

Then differentiate term-by-term:

$$f'(x) = -a_1 \sin x - 2a_2 \sin 2x - 3a_3 \sin 3x - \cdots - ka_k \sin kx - \cdots$$
$$+ b_1 \cos x + 2b_2 \cos 2x + 3b_3 \cos 3x + \cdots + kb_k \cos kx + \cdots$$

Regroup terms:

$$f'(x) = + b_1 \cos x + 2b_2 \cos 2x + 3b_3 \cos 3x + \cdots + kb_k \cos kx + \cdots$$
$$- a_1 \sin x - 2a_2 \sin 2x - 3a_3 \sin 3x - \cdots - ka_k \sin kx - \cdots$$

which forms a Fourier series for the derivative $f'(x)$. The Fourier coefficients of $\cos kx$ is kb_k and the Fourier coefficients of $\sin kx$ is $-ka_k$. Note that there is no constant term as you would expect from the formula ka_k with $k = 0$. Note also that if the kth harmonic f is absent, so is that of f'.

(b) If the amplitude of the kth harmonic of f is

$$A_k = \sqrt{a_k^2 + b_k^2}, \quad k \geq 1,$$

then the amplitude of the kth harmonic of f' is

$$\sqrt{(kb_k)^2 + (-ka_k)^2} = \sqrt{k^2(b_k^2 + a_k^2)} = k\sqrt{a_k^2 + b_k^2} = kA_k.$$

(c) The energy of the kth harmonic of f' is k^2 times the energy of the kth harmonic of f.

33. Since $g(x) = f(x + c)$, we have that $[g(x)]^2 = [f(x + c)]^2$, so g^2 is f^2 shifted horizontally by c. Since f has period 2π, so does f^2 and g^2. If you think of the definite integral as an area, then because of the periodicity, integrals of f^2 over any interval of length 2π have the same value. So

$$\int_{-\pi}^{\pi} (f(x))^2 \, dx = \int_{-\pi+c}^{\pi+c} (f(x))^2 \, dx$$

Now we know that

$$\text{Energy of } g = \frac{1}{\pi} \int_{-\pi}^{\pi} (g(x))^2 \, dx$$

$$= \frac{1}{\pi} \int_{-\pi}^{\pi} (f(x + c))^2 \, dx.$$

Using the substitution $t = x + c$, we transform the integral on the right, obtaining

$$= \frac{1}{\pi} \int_{-\pi+c}^{\pi+c} (f(t))^2 \, dt$$

$$= \frac{1}{\pi} \int_{-\pi}^{\pi} (f(t))^2 \, dt \quad \text{from above equation}$$

$$= \text{Energy of } f$$

APPENDIX

A   SOLUTIONS

1.   The graph is

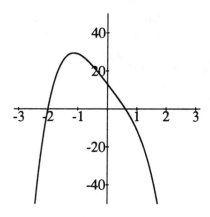

   (a)   The range appears to be $y \leq 30$.
   (b)   The function has two zeros.

2.   (a)   The root is between 0.3 and 0.4, at about 0.35.
   (b)   The root is between 1.5 and 1.6, at about 1.55.
   (c)   The root is between -1.8 and -1.9, at about -1.85.

3.   The root occurs at about -1.05

4.   The root is between -1.7 and -1.8, at about -1.75.

5.   The largest root is at about 2.5.

6.   There is one root at $x = -1$ and another at about $x = 1.35$.

7.   There is one real root at about $x = 1.05$.

8.   The root occurs at about 0.9, since the function changes sign between 0.8 and 1.

9.   The root occurs between 1.1 and 1.2, at about 1.15.

10.   The root occurs between 0.6 and 0.7, at about 0.65.

11.   The root occurs between 1.2 and 1.4, at about 1.3.

12.   Zoom in on graph: $t = \pm 0.824$. [Note: t must be in radians; one must zoom in two or three times.]

13.   (a)   Only one real zero, at about $x = -1.15$.
   (b)   Three real zeros: at $x = 1$, and at about $x = 1.41$ and $x = -1.41$.

14.   First, notice that $f(3) \approx 0.5 > 0$ and that $f(4) \approx -0.25 < 0$.
   1st iteration: $f(3.5) > 0$, so a zero is between 3.5 and 4.
   2nd iteration: $f(3.75) < 0$, so a zero is between 3.5 and 3.75.

3rd iteration: $f(3.625) < 0$, so a zero is between 3.5 and 3.625.
4th iteration: $f(3.588) < 0$, so a zero is between 3.5 and 3.588.
5th iteration: $f(3.545) > 0$, so a zero is between 3.545 and 3.588.
6th iteration: $f(3.578) < 0$, so a zero is between 3.567 and 3.578.
7th iteration: $f(3.572) > 0$, so a zero is between 3.572 and 3.578.
8th iteration: $f(3.575) > 0$, so a zero is between 3.575 and 3.578.

Thus we know that, rounded to two places, the value of the zero must be 3.58. We know that this is the largest zero of $f(x)$ since $f(x)$ approaches -1 for larger values of x.

15. (a) Let $F(x) = \sin x - 2^{-x}$. Then $F(x) = 0$ will have a root where $f(x)$ and $g(x)$ cross. The first positive value of x for which the functions intersect is $x \approx 0.7$.
     (b) The functions intersect for $x \approx 0.4$.

16. The graph is

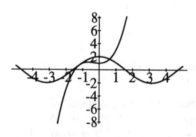

We find one zero at about 0.6. It looks like there might be another one at about -1.2, but zoom in close...closer...closer, and you'll see that though the graphs are very close together, they do not touch, and so there is no zero near -1.2. Thus the zero at about 0.6 is the only one. (How do you know there are no other zeros off the screen?)

17. (a) Since f is continuous, there must be one zero between $\theta = 1.4$ and $\theta = 1.6$, and another between $\theta = 1.6$ and $\theta = 1.8$. These are the only clear cases. We might also want to investigate the interval $0.6 \le \theta \le 0.8$ since $f(\theta)$ takes on values close to zero on at least part of this interval. Now, $\theta = 0.7$ is in this interval, and $f(0.7) = -0.01 < 0$, so f changes sign twice between $\theta = 0.6$ and $\theta = 0.8$ and hence has two zeros on this interval (assuming f is not *really* wiggly here, which it's not). There are a total of 4 zeros.
     (b) As an example, we find the zero of f between $\theta = 0.6$ and $\theta = 0.7$. $f(0.65)$ is positive; $f(0.66)$ is negative. So this zero is contained in $[0.65, 0.66]$. The other zeros are contained in the intervals $[0.72, 0.73]$, $[1.43, 1.44]$, and $[1.7, 1.71]$.
     (c) You've found all the zeros. A picture will confirm this; see Figure A.1.

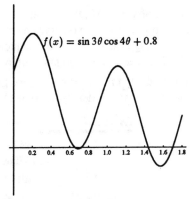

$f(x) = \sin 3\theta \cos 4\theta + 0.8$

0.2 0.4 0.6 0.8 1.0 1.2 1.4 1.6 1.8

Figure A.1:

18. (a) There appear to be two solutions: one on the interval from 1.13 to 1.14 and one on the interval from 1.08 to 1.09. From 1.13 to 1.14, $\frac{x^3}{\pi^3}$ increases from 0.0465 to 0.0478 while $(\sin 3x)(\cos 4x)$ decreases from 0.0470 to 0.0417, so they must cross in between. Similarly, going from 1.08 to 1.09, $\frac{x^3}{\pi^3}$ increases from 0.0406 to 0.0418 while $(\sin 3x)(\cos 4x)$ increases from 0.0376 to 0.0442. Thus the difference between the two changes sign over that interval, so their difference must be zero somewhere in between.

    (b) Reasonable estimates are $x = 1.085$ and $x = 1.131$.

19. (a) The first ten results are:

TABLE A.1

n	0	1	2	3	4	5	6	7	8
1	3.14159	5.05050	5.50129	5.56393	5.57186	5.57285	5.57297	5.57299	5.57299

   (b) The solution is $x \approx 5.573$. We started with an initial guess of 1, and kept repeating the given procedure until our values converged to a limit at around 5.573. For each number on the table, the procedure was in essence asking the question "Does this number equal 4 times the arctangent of itself?" and then correcting the number by repeating the question for 4 times the arctangent of the number.

   (c) P_0 represents our initial guess of $x = 1$ (on the line $y = x$). P_1 is 4 times the arctangent of 1. If we now use take this value for P_1 and slide it horizontally back to the line $y = x$, we can now use this as a new guess, and call it P_2. P_3, of course, represents 4 times the arctangent of P_2, and so on. Another way to make sense of this diagram is to consider the function $F(x) = 4\arctan x - x$. On the diagram, this difference is represented by the vertical lines connecting P_0 and P_1, P_2 and P_3 and so on. Notice how these lines (and hence the difference between $\arctan x$ and x) get smaller as we approach the intersection point, where $F(x) = 0$.

   (d) For an initial guess of $x = 10$, the procedure gives a decreasing sequence which converges (more quickly) to the same value of about 5.573. Graphically, our initial guess of P_0 will lie to the right of the intersection on the line $y = x$. The iteration procedure gives us a sequence of $P_1, P_2, \ldots$ that zigzags to the left, toward the intersection point.

For an initial guess of $x = -10$, the procedure gives an increasing sequence converging to the other intersection point of these two curves at $x \approx -5.573$. Graphically, we get a sequence which is a reflection through the origin of the sequence we got for an initial guess of $x = 10$. This is so because both $y = x$ and $y = \arctan x$ are odd functions.

20. Starting with $x = 0$, and repeatedly taking the cosine, we get the numbers below. Continuing until the first three decimal places remain fixed under iteration, we have this list:

TABLE A.2

x	$\cos x$
0	0.735069
1	0.7401473
0.5403023	0.7356047
0.8575532	0.7414251
0.6542898	0.7375069
0.7934804	0.7401473
0.7013688	0.7383692
0.7639597	0.7395672
0.7221024	0.7387603
0.7504178	0.7393039
0.7314043	0.7389378
0.7442374	etc.

and this diagram:

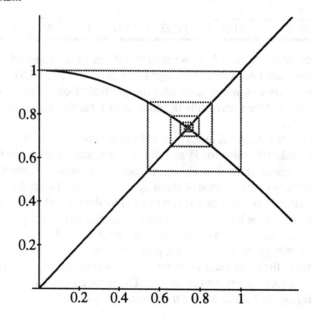

B   SOLUTIONS

1. Yes, there is no break in the graph of $f(x)$ although it does have a 'corner' at $x = 0$.

2. The graph of $g(x)$ is in Figure B.2. It has a break at $x = 0$, so $g(x)$ is not continuous on $[-1, 1]$.

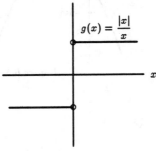

Figure B.2

3. The graph has no breaks.

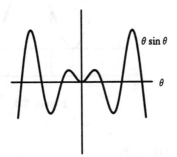

Figure B.3

4. The graph appears to have a vertical asymptote at $t = 0$, so $f(t)$ is not continuous on $[-1, 1]$.

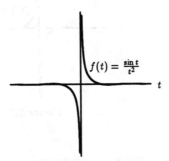

Figure B.4

5.

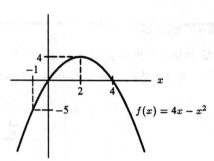

Figure B.5

Bounded and $-5 \leq f(x) \leq 4$.

6.

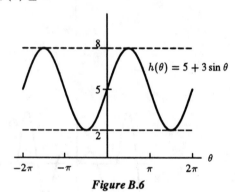

Figure B.6

Bounded and $2 \leq h(\theta) \leq 8$.

7.

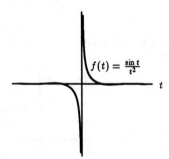

Figure B.7

Not bounded because $f(t)$ goes to infinity as t goes to 0.

8.

a

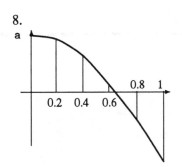

b

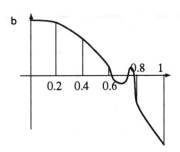

c

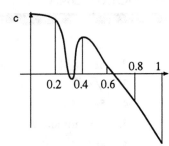

C SOLUTIONS

1. $(1,0)$

2. $(0,0)$

3. $(-2,0)$

4. $(-1,-1)$

5. $(\frac{5\sqrt{3}}{2}, -\frac{5}{2})$

6. $(0,3)$

7. $(\cos 1, \sin 1)$

8. $r = \sqrt{1^2 + 0^2} = 1, \quad \theta = 0.$

9. $r = \sqrt{0^2 + 2^2} = 2, \quad \theta = \pi/2.$

10. $r = \sqrt{1^2 + 1^2} = \sqrt{2}.$
    $\tan \theta = 1/1 = 1.$ Since the point is in the first quadrant, $\theta = \pi/4.$

11. $r = \sqrt{(-1)^2 + 1^2} = \sqrt{2}.$
    $\tan \theta = (-1)/1 = -1.$ Since the point is in the second quadrant, $\theta = 3\pi/4.$

12. $r = \sqrt{(-3)^2 + (-3)^2} = 4.2.$
    $\tan \theta = (-3/-3) = 1.$ Since the point is in the third quadrant, $\theta = 5\pi/4.$

13. $r = \sqrt{(0.2)^2 + (-0.2)^2} = 0.28.$
    $\tan \theta = 0.2/(-0.2) = -1.$ Since the point is in the fourth quadrant, $\theta = 7\pi/4.$ (Alternatively $\theta = -\pi/4.$)

14. $r = \sqrt{3^2 + 4^2} = 5, \quad \tan \theta = 4/3.$ The point is in the first quadrant, so $\theta = 0.92.$

15. $r = \sqrt{(-3)^2 + 1^2} = 3.16, \quad \tan \theta = 1/(-3).$ Since the point is in the second quadrant $\theta = 2.82.$

16. For each pair of Cartesian coordinates, there is more than one pair of polar coordinates for that point. For example, if $(x, y) = (1, 0)$ then $(r, \theta) = (1, 0), (r, \theta) = (1, 2\pi),$ and $(r, \theta) = (1, 4\pi)$ all represent the same point.

D   SOLUTIONS

1. $2e^{i\frac{\pi}{2}}$

2. $5e^{i\pi}$

3. $\sqrt{2}e^{i\frac{\pi}{4}}$

4. $5e^{i4.069}$

5. $0e^{i\theta}$, for any θ.

6. $e^{i\frac{3\pi}{2}}$

7. $\sqrt{10}e^{i\theta}$, where $\theta = \arctan(-3) \approx -1.249 + \pi = 1.893$ is an angle in the second quadrant.

8. $13e^{i\theta}$, where $\theta = \arctan(-\frac{12}{5}) \approx -1.176$ is an angle in the fourth quadrant.

9. $-3 - 4i$

10. $-11 + 29i$

11. $-5 + 12i$

12. $1 + 3i$

13. $\frac{1}{4} - \frac{9i}{8}$

14. $3 - 6i$

15. $\cos\frac{2\pi}{3} + i\sin\frac{2\pi}{3} = -\frac{1}{2} + i\frac{\sqrt{3}}{2}$

16. $\cos\frac{\pi}{6} + i\sin\frac{\pi}{6} = \frac{\sqrt{3}}{2} + \frac{i}{2}$ is one solution.

17. $5^3(\cos\frac{3\pi}{2} + i\sin\frac{3\pi}{2}) = -125i$

18. $\sqrt[4]{10}\cos\frac{\pi}{8} + i\sqrt[4]{10}\sin\frac{\pi}{8}$ is one solution.

19. One value of $\sqrt{i}$ is $\sqrt{e^{i\frac{\pi}{2}}} = (e^{i\frac{\pi}{2}})^{\frac{1}{2}} = e^{i\frac{\pi}{4}} = \cos\frac{\pi}{4} + i\sin\frac{\pi}{4} = \frac{\sqrt{2}}{2} + i\frac{\sqrt{2}}{2}$

20. One value of $\sqrt{-i}$ is $\sqrt{e^{i\frac{3\pi}{2}}} = (e^{i\frac{3\pi}{2}})^{\frac{1}{2}} = e^{i\frac{3\pi}{4}} = \cos\frac{3\pi}{4} + i\sin\frac{3\pi}{4} = -\frac{\sqrt{2}}{2} + i\frac{\sqrt{2}}{2}$

21. One value of $\sqrt[3]{i}$ is $\sqrt[3]{e^{i\frac{\pi}{2}}} = (e^{i\frac{\pi}{2}})^{\frac{1}{3}} = e^{i\frac{\pi}{6}} = \cos\frac{\pi}{6} + i\sin\frac{\pi}{6} = \frac{\sqrt{3}}{2} + \frac{i}{2}$

22. One value of $\sqrt{7i}$ is $\sqrt{7e^{i\frac{\pi}{2}}} = (7e^{i\frac{\pi}{2}})^{\frac{1}{2}} = \sqrt{7}e^{i\frac{\pi}{4}} = \sqrt{7}\cos\frac{\pi}{4} + i\sqrt{7}\sin\frac{\pi}{4} = \frac{\sqrt{14}}{2} + i\frac{\sqrt{14}}{2}$

23. $(1 + i)^{100} = (\sqrt{2}e^{i\frac{\pi}{4}})^{100} = (2^{\frac{1}{2}})^{100}(e^{i\frac{\pi}{4}})^{100} = 2^{50} \cdot e^{i\cdot25\pi} = 2^{50}\cos 25\pi + i2^{50}\sin 25\pi = -2^{50}$

24. One value of $(1 + i)^{2/3}$ is $(\sqrt{2}e^{i\frac{\pi}{4}})^{2/3} = (2^{\frac{1}{2}}e^{i\frac{\pi}{4}})^{\frac{2}{3}} = \sqrt[3]{2}e^{i\frac{\pi}{6}} = \sqrt[3]{2}\cos\frac{\pi}{6} + i\sqrt[3]{2}\sin\frac{\pi}{6} = \sqrt[3]{2}\cdot\frac{\sqrt{3}}{2} + i\sqrt[3]{2}\cdot\frac{1}{2}$

25. One value of $(-4 + 4i)^{2/3}$ is $[\sqrt{32}e^{i\frac{3\pi}{4}}]^{2/3} = (\sqrt{32})^{2/3}e^{i\frac{\pi}{2}} = 2^{\frac{10}{3}}\cos\frac{\pi}{2} + i2^{\frac{10}{3}}\sin\frac{\pi}{2} = 8i\sqrt[3]{2}$

26. One value of $(\sqrt{3} + i)^{1/2}$ is
    $(2e^{i\frac{\pi}{6}})^{1/2} = \sqrt{2}e^{i\frac{\pi}{12}} = \sqrt{2}\cos\frac{\pi}{12} + i\sqrt{2}\sin\frac{\pi}{12} \approx 1.366 + 0.366i$

27. One value of $(\sqrt{3} + i)^{-1/2}$ is
    $(2e^{i\frac{\pi}{6}})^{-1/2} = \frac{1}{\sqrt{2}}e^{i(-\frac{\pi}{12})} = \frac{1}{\sqrt{2}}\cos(-\frac{\pi}{12}) + i\frac{1}{\sqrt{2}}\sin(-\frac{\pi}{12}) \approx 0.683 - 0.183i$

28. Since $\sqrt{5} + 2i = 3e^{i\theta}$, where $\theta = \arctan\frac{2}{\sqrt{5}} \approx 0.730$, one value of $(\sqrt{5} + 2i)^{\sqrt{2}}$ is $(3e^{i\theta})^{\sqrt{2}} = 3^{\sqrt{2}}e^{i\sqrt{2}\theta} = 3^{\sqrt{2}}\cos\sqrt{2}\theta + i3^{\sqrt{2}}\sin\sqrt{2}\theta \approx 3^{\sqrt{2}}(0.513) + i3^{\sqrt{2}}(0.859) \approx 2.426 + 4.062i$

29. Substituting $A_1 = 2 - A_2$ into the second equation gives

$$(1 - i)(2 - A_2) + (1 + i)A_2 = 0$$

so

$$2iA_2 = -2(1 - i)$$
$$A_2 = \frac{-(1 - i)}{i} = \frac{-i(1 - i)}{i^2} = i(1 - i) = 1 + i$$

Therefore $A_1 = 2 - (1 + i) = 1 - i$.

30. Substituting $A_2 = i - A_1$ into the second equation gives

$$iA_1 - (i - A_1) = 3,$$

so

$$iA_1 + A_1 = 3 + i$$
$$A_1 = \frac{3 + i}{1 + i} = \frac{3 + i}{1 + i} \times \frac{1 - i}{1 - i} = \frac{3 - 3i + i - i^2}{2}$$
$$= 2 - i$$

Therefore $A_2 = i - (2 - i) = -2 + 2i$.

31. (a) $z_1 z_2 = (-3 - i\sqrt{3})(-1 + i\sqrt{3}) = 3 + (\sqrt{3})^2 + i(\sqrt{3} - 3\sqrt{3}) = 6 - i2\sqrt{3}$.
    $\frac{z_1}{z_2} = \frac{-3 - i\sqrt{3}}{-1 + i\sqrt{3}} \cdot \frac{-1 - i\sqrt{3}}{-1 - i\sqrt{3}} = \frac{3 - (\sqrt{3})^2 + i(\sqrt{3} + 3\sqrt{3})}{(-1)^2 + (\sqrt{3})^2} = \frac{i \cdot 4\sqrt{3}}{4} = i\sqrt{3}$.

    (b) We find (r_1, θ_1) corresponding to $z_1 = -3 - i\sqrt{3}$.
    $r_1 = \sqrt{(-3)^2 + (\sqrt{3})^2} = \sqrt{12} = 2\sqrt{3}$.
    $\tan\theta_1 = \frac{-\sqrt{3}}{-3} = \frac{\sqrt{3}}{3}$, so $\theta_1 = \frac{7\pi}{6}$.
    Thus $-3 - i\sqrt{3} = r_1 e^{i\theta_1} = 2\sqrt{3}\, e^{i\frac{7\pi}{6}}$.

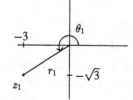

We find (r_2, θ_2) corresponding to $z_2 = -1 + i\sqrt{3}$.

$r_2 = \sqrt{(-1)^2 + (\sqrt{3})^2} = 2$;

$\tan \theta_2 = \dfrac{\sqrt{3}}{-1} = -\sqrt{3}$, so $\theta_2 = \dfrac{2\pi}{3}$.

Thus, $-1 + i\sqrt{3} = r_2 e^{i\theta_2} = 2e^{i\frac{2\pi}{3}}$.

We now calculate $z_1 z_2$ and $\dfrac{z_1}{z_2}$.

$$z_1 z_2 = \left(2\sqrt{3}e^{i\frac{7\pi}{6}}\right)\left(2e^{i\frac{2\pi}{3}}\right) = 4\sqrt{3}e^{i\left(\frac{7\pi}{6} + \frac{2\pi}{3}\right)} = 4\sqrt{3}e^{i\frac{11\pi}{6}}$$

$$= 4\sqrt{3}\left[\cos\frac{11\pi}{6} + i\sin\frac{11\pi}{6}\right] = 4\sqrt{3}\left[\frac{\sqrt{3}}{2} - i\frac{1}{2}\right] = 6 - i2\sqrt{3}.$$

$$\frac{z_1}{z_2} = \frac{2\sqrt{3}e^{i\frac{7\pi}{6}}}{2e^{i\frac{2\pi}{3}}} = \sqrt{3}e^{i\left(\frac{7\pi}{6} - \frac{2\pi}{3}\right)} = \sqrt{3}e^{i\frac{\pi}{2}}$$

$$= \sqrt{3}\left(\cos\frac{\pi}{2} + i\sin\frac{\pi}{2}\right) = i\sqrt{3}.$$

These agrees with the values found in (a).

32. If the roots are complex numbers, we must have $(2b)^2 - 4c < 0$ so $b^2 - c < 0$. Then the roots are

$$x = \frac{-2b \pm \sqrt{(2b)^2 - 4c}}{2} = -b \pm \sqrt{b^2 - c}$$

$$= -b \pm \sqrt{-1(c - b^2)}$$

$$= -b \pm i\sqrt{c - b^2}.$$

Thus, $p = -b$ and $q = \sqrt{c - b^2}$.

33. True, since $\sqrt{a}$ is real for all $a \geq 0$.

34. True, since $(x - iy)(x + iy) = x^2 + y^2$ is real.

35. False, since $(1 + i)^2 = 2i$ is not real.

36. False. Let $f(x) = x$. Then $f(i) = i$ but $f(\bar{i}) = \bar{i} = -i$.

37. True. We can write any nonzero complex number z as $re^{i\beta}$, where r and β are real numbers with $r > 0$. Since $r > 0$, we can write $r = e^c$ for some real number c. Therefore, $z = re^{i\beta} = e^c e^{i\beta} = e^{c + i\beta} = e^w$ where $w = c + i\beta$ is a complex number.

38. False, since $(1 + 2i)^2 = -3 + 4i$.

39.

$$1 = e^0 = e^{i(\theta-\theta)} = e^{i\theta}e^{i(-\theta)}$$
$$= (\cos\theta + i\sin\theta)(\cos(-\theta) + i\sin(-\theta))$$
$$= (\cos\theta + i\sin\theta)(\cos\theta - i\sin\theta)$$
$$= \cos^2\theta + \sin^2\theta$$

40. Using Euler's formula, we have:

$$e^{i(2\theta)} = \cos 2\theta + i\sin 2\theta$$

On the other hand,

$$e^{i(2\theta)} = (e^{i\theta})^2 = (\cos\theta + i\sin\theta)^2 = (\cos^2\theta - \sin^2\theta) + i(2\cos\theta\sin\theta)$$

Equating imaginary parts, we find

$$\sin 2\theta = 2\sin\theta\cos\theta.$$

41. Using Euler's formula, we have:

$$e^{i(2\theta)} = \cos 2\theta + i\sin 2\theta$$

On the other hand,

$$e^{i(2\theta)} = (e^{i\theta})^2 = (\cos\theta + i\sin\theta)^2 = (\cos^2\theta - \sin^2\theta) + i(2\cos\theta\sin\theta)$$

Equating real parts, we find
$$\cos 2\theta = \cos^2\theta - \sin^2\theta.$$

42. $\frac{d}{d\theta}(e^{i\theta}) = ie^{i\theta} = i(\cos\theta + i\sin\theta) = -\sin\theta + i\cos\theta$

Since in addition $\frac{d}{d\theta}(e^{i\theta}) = \frac{d}{d\theta}(\cos\theta + i\sin\theta) = \frac{d}{d\theta}(\cos\theta) + i\frac{d}{d\theta}(\sin\theta)$, by equating imaginary parts, we conclude that $\frac{d}{d\theta}\sin\theta = \cos\theta$.

43. $\frac{d^2}{d\theta^2}(e^{i\theta}) = \frac{d^2}{d\theta^2}(\cos\theta + i\sin\theta) = \frac{d^2}{d\theta^2}(\cos\theta) + i\frac{d^2}{d\theta^2}(\sin\theta)$

But $\frac{d^2}{d\theta^2}(e^{i\theta}) = i^2 e^{i\theta} = -e^{i\theta} = -\cos\theta - i\sin\theta$

Equating real parts, we find $\frac{d^2}{d\theta^2}(\cos\theta) = -\cos\theta.$